POLYMER CHEMISTRY

AN INTRODUCTION

UNDERGRADUATE CHEMISTRY

A Series of Textbooks

edited by
J. J. Lagowski
Department of Chemistry
The University of Texas at Austin

POLYMER CHEMISTRY

AN INTRODUCTION

Raymond B. Seymour
Charles E. Carraher, Jr.

MARCEL DEKKER, INC. New York and Basel

Library of Congress Cataloging in Publication Data

Seymour, Raymond Benedict, [Date]
Polymer chemistry.

Includes bibliographies and index.
1. Polymers and polymerization. I. Carraher, Charles E., joint author. II. Title.
QD381.S483 547.8'4 80-29631
ISBN 0-8247-6979-1

MARCEL DEKKER, INC.
270 Madison Avenue, New York, New York 10016

Current printing (last digit):
10 9 8 7 6 5 4 3 2

PRINTED IN THE UNITED STATES OF AMERICA

Foreword

During the last few years about fifty American universities have initiated some kind of organized teaching in polymer science and technology, and many more have started to present a few special courses in this field. As a result, the number of students who need tutorial assistance is much larger than it was only a few years ago. There exist already several good textbooks on polymers: some of them emphasize more the organic chemical aspects—synthesis of monomers and polymers, others place emphasis on physical chemical methods for characterization and structure determination, and still others focus their interest on processing and application. In addition, some of the older texts are not quite as up to date in the registration of recent progress.

Professors R. B. Seymour and C. E. Carraher's new textbook on polymer chemistry offers, in my mind, several important advantages to the user.

It is recent and includes all significant modern methods and aspects.

It is well balanced in respect to the existing subdisciplines of the polymer field.

It is relatively short, very clearly written, brings home all significant points, and still avoids unnecessary complications.

On the basis of this brief evaluation and in view of the necessity to supply our students with a variety of texts depending on their later specialization, Professors Seymour and Carraher's new text is a very welcomed addition to the literature.

Herman F. Mark
Professor Emeritus
Polytechnic Institute of New York

Preface

While the eminent Professor Mark, who wrote the foreword, offered graduate courses in general polymer chemistry at the Polytechnic Institute in Brooklyn in 1940, the senior author of this new book offered his first undergraduate course in polymer chemistry at the University of Chattanooga in 1945. The only undergraduate textbook available at that time was Synthetic Resins and Rubbers by Dr. Paul Powers.

This pioneering book was acceptable in the early days of polymer chemistry, but it was no longer acceptable when the senior author joined the Los Angeles Trade Tech College as an Adjunct Professor and Sul Ross State University as a Professor less than 15 years later. Hence, Introduction to Polymer Chemistry was written using classroom notes from lectures at Trade Tech and Sul Ross.

Introduction to Polymer Chemistry was published by McGraw-Hill and translated into several foreign languages. Then it was published as an international edition by McGraw-Hill Kogakusha (Tokyo) and reprinted by Krieger Publishing Co. However, that book is no longer acceptable as an undergraduate text and does not meet the newer ACS guidelines nor the syllabus suggested by the polymer education committees of that society. The latter is shown below with appropriate chapters from our new book and points assigned from 127 replies received from 97 schools in answer to a survey by members of the American Chemical Society. (The full results of this survey are given in the Journal of Chemical Education, 57(6), 436 (1980), Core curriculum in introductory courses of polymer chemistry.)

As shown by the chapters cited in the table, Polymer Chemistry includes all the major and optional topics recommended in the syllabus adopted by the joint polymer education committee of the American Chemical Society. (A fuller discussion of the suggested syllabus is found in Appendix D—Syllabus.) We have emphasized the topics given high points in the national survey. A similar viewpoint was taken in the development of the ACS

Standard Examination of Polymer Chemistry. This book also includes relevant chapters on inorganic polymers (11) and the synthesis of reactants (15) and some emphasis on history and additives, in the attempt to make this a complete textbook on polymer chemistry.

While no specific chapter is devoted to commercial polymers, these important products, as well as emerging and projected future areas of research activity, are discussed throughout the text.

Information already presented in traditional undergraduate courses of organic chemistry, physical chemistry, etc., is interrelated with information presented that focuses on polymer topics. This assists the students in integrating his or her chemical knowledge and illustrates the interrelationship between theoretical and applied chemical knowledge. Further, industrial practices and testing procedures are integrated with the theoretical treatment of the various topics allowing the reader to bridge the gap between industrial practice and the classroom. Also incorporated into the text are uses and amounts of uses of particular polymers and procedures allowing the reader to better judge the importance and potential applications of the presented material.

Suggested Syllabus

Major topics	Suggested percentage of course time	Corresponding chapter in polymer chemistry	Survey[a] points
1. Introduction	5	1	—
2. Polymer Structure	10	2	104
(Morphology)			86
3. Molecular Weights	10	3, 4	104
4. Step Reaction Polymers	10	7	100
5. Chain Reaction Polymers	10		
Ionic and Complex Coord.		8	83
Free Radical		9	100
6. Copolymerization	10	10	86
7. Testing and characterization	10	5	51
Optional topics			
8. Rheology	5	3	85
9. Solubility	5	3	85
10. Natural and Biomedical Polymers	5	6	11
11. Additives	5	12, 13	4
12. Reactions of Polymers	5	14	61
13. Synthesis of Reactant	5	15	—
14. Polymer Technology	5	16	28

[a] From 127 replies from 97 schools, based on +1, topic to be included in introductory courses; 0, no strong feeling; -1, topic should be omitted from introductory courses.

A section relating to the topics of condensation, stepwise kinetics, vinyl polymers, and chainwise kinetics is added, since these topics are critical to an understanding of polymer chemistry but are often items of confusion to students.

The first chapter is shorter than the others in order to provide time for student orientation. However, the other 15 chapters should not require more than a week's time each and hence should fit in well with the time allotted for a one semester course. Some of the topics listed as optional in the suggested syllabus may be omitted when the course is taught on the quarter system, or expanded if taught over a two-quarter period.

Each chapter in this book is essentially self-contained, but each relates to preceding chapters. Whenever possible, difficult concepts are distributed over several chapters. A glossary, suggested questions, and a list of references are included at the end of each chapter. Some relevant trade names may be found in the glossaries and many tradenames are listed in a separate section at the end of the book. The toxicity of monomers and reactants is discussed throughout the book.

In addition to serving as a one semester or one- or two-quarter undergraduate textbook, this book should also be of considerable value to biologists, environmental scientists, engineers, and technologists who are concerned with plastics, fibers, elastomers (rubbers), coatings (paints), adhesives, biopolymers, or other macromolecules.

Raymond B. Seymour
Charles E. Carraher, Jr.

Acknowledgment

The authors gratefully acknowledge the contributions of Herman Mark of the Polytechnic Institute of New York; Charles L. McCormick, University of Southern Mississippi; William Feld, Wright State University; Eli Pearce, Polytechnic Institute of New York; Fredinard Rodriguez, Cornell University and Otto Vogl, University of Massachusetts for their reviewing, advising and counciling efforts; and to Charles Carraher III and Shawn Carraher for their help in proofing and indexing. A further special thanks to Maurits Dekker, for his encouragement and many contributions to the polymer literature.

The authors also thank the following for their special contributions to the book: Charles Gebelein, Les Sperling, Angelo Volpe, Stan Israel, Rita Blumstein, Eckhard Hellmuth, Frank Millich, Norman Miller, Rudy Deanin, Guy Donaruma, Leo Mandelkern, R. V. Subramanian, Charles Pittman, Brian Currell, C. Bamford, Roger Epton, Paul Flory, Charles Overberger, William Bailey, Jim O'Donnell, Rob Burford, Edgar Hardy, John H. Coates, Don Napper, Rick Richards, Frank Harris, D.H. Richards, G. Allan Stahl, John Westerman, William A. Field, and Nan-Loh Yang.

This book could not have been written without the long-time efforts of Professor Herman Mark who is one of the fathers of Polymer Science.

Contents

A Note on the Nomenclature

As with most areas of science, names associated with reactions, particular chemical and physical tests, etc., were historically derived with few overall guiding principles. Further, the wide diversity of polymer science permitted a wide diversity in naming polymers. Even though the International Union of Pure and Applied Chemistry, IUPAC, has a long-standing commission associated with the nomenclature of polymers [reports include "Report on nomenclature in the field of macromolecules," Journal of Polymer Science, 8, 257 (1952); "Report on nomenclature dealing with steric regularity in high polymers," Pure and Applied Chemistry, 12, 645 (1966); "Basic definitions of terms relating to polymers," IUPAC Information Bull. App., 13, 1 (1971); and "Nomenclature of regular single-strand organic polymers," Macromolecules, 6(2), 149(1973)], the acceptance of most of these suggestions relative to the naming of simple polymers have not yet been accepted by many in the polymer science community.

While there exists a wide diversity in the practice of naming polymers we will concentrate on three which represent the most utilized systems. The accompanying table gives the names of some common polymers illustrating the three systems. The only formal system is the IUPAC system which conforms to the Definitive Rules for the Nomenclature of Organic Chemistry ["Nomenclature of Organic Chemistry", Butterworths, London, 1971 and "Tentative Rules for the Nomenclature of Organic Chemistry. Section E. Fundamental Stereochemistry," IUPAC Information Bulletin, 35, 36(1969), and Journal of Organic Chemistry, 35, 2849(1970)], and which enables one to name both simple and complex polymers. The second system is referred to as simply the Industrial System since it is utilized by a number of industrial societies within their publications. The third system is referred to as the Common System because of past historical use. The latter two systems are informal (semisystematic) and are only useful for the more common, simple polymers and typically differ from one another only through the absence or presence of paraphrases.

It is interesting that the majority of undergraduate texts utilize the industrial system and that few of the polymer texts have adopted the IUPAC system for common polymers. [(It must be noted that the IUPAC report appearing in Macromolecules, 6(2), 149 (1973) includes . . . "The Commission recognized that a number of common polymers have semisystematic or trivial names that are well established by usage; it is not intended that they be immediately supplanted by the structure-based names. Nonetheless, it is hoped that for scientific communication the use of semisystematic or trivial names for polymers will be kept to a minimum.")] In fact, the trend is towards usage of the industrial system.

Comparison of Polymer Names

Common	Industrial	IUPAC
Polyacrylonitrile	Polyacrylonitrile	Poly(1-cyanoethylene)
Poly(ethylene oxide)	Polyethylene oxide	Poly(oxyethylene)
Poly(ethylene terephthalate)	Polyethylene terephthalate	Poly(oxyethylene-oxyterephthaloyl)
Polyisobutylene	Polyisobutylene	Poly(1,1-dimethylethylene)
Poly(methyl methacrylate)	Polymethyl methacrylate	Poly[1-methoxycarbonyl)-1-methylethylene]
Polypropylene	Polypropylene	Poly(propylene)
Polystyrene	Polystyrene	Poly(1-phenylethylene)
Poly(tetrafluoroethylene)	Polytetrafluoroethylene	Poly(difluoromethylene)
Poly(vinyl acetate)	Polyvinyl acetate	Poly(1-acetoxyethylene)
Poly(vinyl alcohol)	Polyvinyl alcohol	Poly(1-hydroxyethylene)
Poly(vinyl chloride)	Polyvinyl chloride	Poly(1-chloroethylene)
Poly(vinyl butyral)	Polyvinyl butyral	Poly[(2-propyl-1,3-dioxane-4,6-diyl)-methylene]

POLYMER CHEMISTRY

AN INTRODUCTION

1

Introduction to Polymer Science

1.1 HISTORY OF POLYMERS

Since most chemists and chemical engineers are now involved in some phase of polymer science or technology, some have called this the polymer age. Actually, we have always lived in a polymer age.

The ancient Greeks classified all matter as animal, vegetable, and mineral. The last was emphasized by the alchemists and medieval artisans; animal and vegetable matter, which are largely polymers, have, for the most part, always been more important than minerals.

Polymer is derived from the Greek poly and meros, meaning many and parts, respectively. Some scientists prefer to use the word macromolecule, or large molecule, instead of polymer. Others maintain that naturally occurring polymers, or biopolymers, and synthetic polymers should be studied in different courses. However, the same principles apply to all polymers. If one discounts the end uses, the differences between all polymers, including plastics, fibers, and elastomers or rubbers, are determined primarily by the intermolecular and intramolecular forces between the molecules and within the individual molecule, respectively, and by the functional groups present.

In addition to being the basis of life itself, protein, which was the first polymer, was (and is) used as a source of amino acids and energy. The ancients degraded or depolymerized the protein in tough meat by aging and cooking and denatured egg albumin by heating or adding vinegar to the eggs.

Early humans learned how to process, dye, and weave the natural proteinaceous fibers of wool and silk and the carbohydrate fibers of flax and cotton. Early South American civilizations such as the Aztec used natural rubber (Hevea braziliensis) for making elastic articles and for waterproofing of fabrics.

There has always been an abundance of natural fibers and elastomers but few plastics. Of course, early humans employed a crude plastic art in tanning the protein in animal skins to make leather and in heat forming tortoise shells. They also used naturally occurring tars as caulking materials and extracted shellac from the excrement of small coccid insects (*Coccus lacca*).

Until Wöhler synthesized urea from inorganic compounds in 1828, there had been little progress in organic chemistry since the alchemists emphasized the transmutation of base metals to gold and believed in a vital force theory. Despite this essential breakthrough, little progress was made in understanding organic chemistry until the 1850s, when Kekule developed the presently accepted technique for writing structural formulas.

However, polymer scientists have always displayed a talent for making empirical discoveries before the science was developed. Thus, Charles and Nelson Goodyear transformed hevea rubber from a sticky thermoplastic to a useful elastomer (vulcanized rubber) and a hard thermoset plastic (ebonite), respectively, by heating it with small and large amounts of sulfur long before Kekule had developed his formula-writing techniques.

Likewise, Schonbein reacted cellulose with nitric acid and Menard, in 1846, made collodion by dissolving the cellulose nitrate product of that reaction in a mixture of ethanol and ethyl ether. Collodion, which was used as a liquid court plaster, also served in the 1860s as Parkes and Hyatt's reactant for making celluloid, which was the first synthetic thermoplastic, and Chardonnet's reactant for making artificial silk.

While most of these early discoveries were empirical, they may be used to explain some terminology and theory in modern polymer science. It is important to note that all these inventors, like ancient humans, converted a naturally occurring polymer to a more useful product. Thus, Charles Goodyear transformed the heat-softenable thermoplastic hevea rubber to a less heat-sensitive product by using sulfur to form a relatively small number of connecting links or cross links between the long individual polyisoprene chainlike molecules.

Nelson Goodyear used sulfur to produce many cross links between the polyisoprene chains so that the product was no longer thermoplastic but was a thermoset plastic. *Thermoplastics* are two-dimensional molecules which may be softened by heat and returned to their original state by cooling, while *thermosetting plastics* are three-dimensional network polymers that cannot be reshaped by heating.

Both cellulose and cellulose nitrate are linear, or two-dimensional, polymers, but the former cannot be softened because of the presence of multitudinous hydrogen bonds between the chainlike molecules. When used as an explosive, the cellulose nitrate is completely nitrated and is essentially a trinitrate of cellulose. In contrast, Parkes and Hyatt used a dinitrate, or secondary cellulose nitrate, which contained many residual hydrogen bonds and in addition was highly flammable.

Parkes added castor oil in order to plasticize—to reduce the effect of—the intermolecular hydrogen bonds. Hyatt used camphor for the same purpose. Count Hilaire de Chardonnet forced Menard's collodion through very small holes called spinnerets and obtained filaments by evaporating the mixture of solvents. The flammability of these cellulosic filaments was reduced by denitrification using sodium bisulfite.

It is of interest to note that the Goodyears converted a thermoplastic elastomer to a thermoset elastomer and a hard thermoset plastic by the addition of small and large amounts of sulfur cross links. Schonbein reduced the number of intermolecular hydrogen bonds present in cellulose by reacting it with nitric acid, and while neither cellulose nor cellulose dinitrate was soluble in ethanol or ethyl ether, Menard dissolved the latter in an equimolar solution of these two solvents.

Hyatt softened the flammable cellulose dinitrate by adding camphor, which reduced the effectiveness of the intermolecular hydrogen bonds. Chardonnet regenerated cellulose in the form of continuous filaments. After denitrification and stretching, these filaments possessed all the chemical and physical properties of the original cellulose.

However, since no one at that time knew what a polymer was, they had no idea of the complex changes that had taken place in the pioneer production of useful rubber, plastics, and fibers. Even today, some organic chemists find it difficult to visualize these large, or macro, molecules. Over a century ago, Graham coined the term colloid for aggregates with dimensions in the range of 10^{-9} to 10^{-7} m. Unfortunately, the size of many polymer molecules is in this range, but it is important to note that unlike colloids, polymers are individual molecules whose size cannot be reduced without breaking the covalent bonds which hold the atoms together in these chainlike molecules.

An oligomer, a very low molecular weight polymer of ethylene glycol was prepared and the correct structure of [$HO(OCH_2CH_2)_8OH$] was assigned in 1860. Nevertheless, Fittig and Engelhorn incorrectly assigned a cyclic structure to polymethacrylic acid [$—CH_2\overset{|}{C}(CH_3)COOH$] which they prepared in 1880. By use of the Raoult and van't Hoff concepts, several chemists obtained high molecular weight values for these and other linear polymers, but since they were unable to visualize such things as macromolecules, they concluded that the Raoult technique was not applicable to the determination of the molecular weight of these molecules.

It was generally recognized by the leading organic chemists of the nineteenth century that phenol would condense with formaldehyde. Since they did not recognize the concept of functionality, Baeyer, Michael, and Kleeberg produced useless cross-linked goos, gunks, and messes and then returned to their research on reactions of monofunctional reactants. However, by use of a large excess of phenol, Smith, Luft, and Blumer were able to obtain thermoplastic condensation products.

While there is no evidence that Baekeland recognized the existence of macromolecules, he did understand functionality, and by the use of controlled amounts of phenol and formaldehyde, he produced thermoplastic resins which could be converted to thermosetting plastics. He coined the term A-stage resole resin to describe the thermoplastic Bakelite produced by the condensation of an excess of formaldehyde and phenol under alkaline conditions. This A-stage resole resin was converted to a thermoset (infusible) cross-linked C-stage Bakelite by additional heating or advancement of the resin. Baekeland also prepared thermoplastic resins called novolacs by the condensation of phenol with a small amount of formaldehyde in acidic solutions. The novolacs were converted to thermosets by the addition of formaldehyde from hexamethylenetetramine. While other polymers had been synthesized in the laboratory before 1910, Bakelite was the first synthetic plastic. The fact that the recipes used today are essentially the same as those revealed in the original patents demonstrates Baekeland's ingenuity and knowledge of the chemistry of the condensation of trifunctional phenol with difunctional formaldehyde.

Prior to World War I, celluloid, shellac, Galalith (casein), Bakelite, and cellulose acetate plastics; hevea rubber, cotton, wool, silk and rayon fibers; Glyptal polyester coatings, bitumen or asphalt, and coumarone-indene and petroleum resins were all commercially available. However, as evidenced by the chronological data shown in Table 1.1, there was little additional development in polymer technology prior to World War II because of the lack of knowledge of polymer science.

Nobel laureate Hermann Staudinger laid the groundwork for modern polymer science in the 1920s when he demonstrated that natural and synthetic polymers were not aggregates like colloids or cyclic compounds like cyclohexane but were long chainlike molecules with characteristic end groups. The advice given to Dr. Staudinger by his colleagues was "Dear Colleague, Leave the concept of large molecules well alone . . . There can be no such thing as a macromolecule." Unfortunately, some nonpolymer scientists who no longer believe in the vital force concept, like Staudinger's colleagues, still question the existence or importance of macromolecules.

In 1928, Meyer and Mark used X-ray techniques to determine the dimensions of crystallites in cellulose and natural rubber. During the following year, Carothers synthesized and characterized linear aliphatic polyesters. Since these were not suitable for fibers, he synthesized the polyamides which are known by the generic name of nylon. It is of interest to note that naturally occurring wool and silk protein fibers are also polyamides.

The leading polymer scientists of the 1930s agreed that polymers were chainlike molecules and that the viscosities of solution of these macromolecules were dependent on the size and shape of the molecules in the solution. While it is true that the large-scale production of many polymers was accelerated by World War II, it must be recognized that the production of these essential products was dependent on the concepts developed by Staudinger, Carothers, Mark, and other leading polymer scientists.

TABLE 1.1 Chronological Development of Commercial Polymers

Date	Material
Before 1800	Cotton, flax, wool, and silk fibers; bitumen caulking materials; glass and hydraulic cements; leather and cellulose sheet (paper); natural rubber (*Hevea braziliensis*), gutta-percha, balata, and shellac.
1839	Vulcanization of rubber (Charles Goodyear)
1846	Nitration of cellulose (Schönbein)
1851	Ebonite (hard rubber; Nelson Goodyear)
1860	Molding of shellac and gutta-percha
1868	Celluloid (plasticized cellulose nitrate; Hyatt)
1889	Regenerated cellulosic fibers (Chardonnet)
1889	Cellulose nitrate photographic films (Reichenbach)
1890	Cuprammonia rayon fibers (Despeisses)
1892	Viscose rayon fibers (Cross, Bevan and Beadle)
1907	Phenol-formaldehyde resins (Bakelite; Baekeland)
1907	Cellulose acetate solutions (dope; Doerfinger)
1908	Cellulose acetate photographic fibers
1912	Regenerated cellulose sheet (cellophane)
1923	Cellulose nitrate automobile lacquers
1924	Cellulose acetate fibers
1926	Alkyd polyester (Kienle)
1927	Poly(vinyl chloride) (PVC) wall covering
1927	Cellulose acetate sheet and rods
1929	Polysulfide synthetic elastomer (Thiokol; Patrick)
1929	Urea-formaldehyde resins
1931	Polymethyl methacrylate plastics (PMMA)
1931	Polychloroprene elastomer (Neoprene)
1935	Ethylcellulose
1936	Polyvinyl acetate
1936	Polyvinyl butyral safety glass

(continued)

TABLE 1.1 (continued)

Date	Material
1937	Polystyrene
1937	Styrene-butadiene (Buna-S) and styrene-acrylonitrile (Buna-N) copolymer elastomers
1938	Nylon-66 fibers (Carothers)
1939	Melamine-formaldehyde resins
1940	Isobutylene-isoprene elastomer (butyl rubber; Sparks and Thomas)
1941	Low-density polyethylene
1942	Unsaturated polyesters
1943	Fluorocarbon resins (Teflon; Plunkett)
1943	Silicones
1943	Polyurethanes (Baeyer)
1947	Epoxy resins
1948	Copolymers of acrylonitrile, butadiene and styrene (ABS)
1950	Polyester fibers
1950	Polyacrylonitrile fibers
1956	Polyoxymethylene (acetals)
1957	High-density (linear) polyethylene
1957	Polypropylene
1957	Polycarbonate
1959	cis-Polybutadiene and polyisoprene elastomers
1960	Ethylene-propylene copolymer elastomers
1962	Polyimide resins
1964	Polyphenylene oxide
1965	Polysulfone
1965	Styrene-butadiene block copolymers
1970	Polybutylene terephthalate
1971	Polyphenylene sulfide

The development of polymer technology since the 1940s has been extremely rapid. In some instances, such as polymerization in aqueous emulsion systems, the art has preceded the science, but much theory was developed so that polymer science today is relevant and no longer largely empirical.

As shown in Tables 1.2, 1.3, and 1.4, almost 20 million metric tons of synthetic polymers are produced annually in the USA and the growth of the industry is continuing at a faster rate than any other industry. There is every reason to believe that this polymer age will continue as long as petroleum and other feedstocks are available and as long as consumers continue to enjoy the comfort provided by elastomers, fibers, plastics, adhesives, and coatings.

TABLE 1.2 U.S. Production of Plastics

Material	1000 metric tons		
	1975	1976	1978
Polyethylenes			
LDPE and copolymers	2188	2641	3186
HDPE	1116	1416	1852
Vinyls			
PVC and copolymers	1635	2134	2617
Polyvinyl acetate	231	250	260
Polyvinyl alcohol	54	120	130
Other vinyl and vinylidene resins	92	100	110
Styrenes			
ABS	304	459	508
SAN	55		
Polystyrene and copolymers	1399	1686	1741
Polypropylene and copolymers	864	1167	1341
Phenolics	578	708	700
Polyesters, unsaturated	364	400	524
Polyesters, saturated (PETP, etc.)	35	60	280
Aminoplastics (UF and MF)	480[b]	550	575

(continued)

TABLE 1.2 (continued)

Material	1000 metric tons		
	1975	1976	1978
Acrylics	350	420	449
Alkyd resins	306	420	515
Coumarone and petroleum resins	163	190	
Cellulosics	71	67	74
Epoxies	86	140	141
Polyamides, nylon type (excluding fibers)	54	95	123
Polyamides, nonnylon type	11	15	17
Polyurethanes (excluding foams)	82[c]	100	120
Engineering plastics[a]	123	200	261
Miscellaneous	87[d]	—	100
Total	10,728	13,500	15,424

[a] Acetal, polycarbonate, polyimide, polysulfone, and polyphenylene oxide and sulfide resins. ABS and polyamides are reported separately.
[b] About 86% is urea-formaldehyde.
[c] Includes polyurethane elastomers.
[d] Includes resin modifications, silicone resins, polytetrafluoroethylene, miscellaneous thermosets, and miscellaneous thermoplastics.
Source: Data from U.S. International Trade Commission.

TABLE 1.3 U.S. Production of Fibers (thousands of metric tons)

Fiber	1976	1977	1979
Rayon	206	272	275
Acetate rayon	135	132	147
Polyester	1519	1655	1900
Nylon	943	1057	1236
Acrylic	282	322	346
Olefinic	262	288	345
Total	3655	4084	4717
Cotton	2000	2100	—

TABLE 1.4 Consumption of Elastomers in U.S.A. and Canada (thousands of metric tons)

Elastomer	1975	1976	1978
SBR	1288	1485	1526
Natural rubber	735	780	857
Polydienes	395	470	520
Butyl rubber	115	130	146
Polychloroprene	100	115	126
Ethylene-propylene copolymer	90	110	151
Nitrilic rubber	55	70	79
Total	2778	3160	3470

SUMMARY

After reading this chapter, you should understand the following concepts.

1. Polymers or macromolecules are giant molecules with molecular weights at least 100 times greater than those of smaller molecules like water or methanol.

2. If we disregard metals and inorganic compounds, we observe that practically everything else in this world is polymeric. This includes the protein and nucleic acid in our bodies, the fibers we use for clothing, the protein and starch we eat, the elastomers in our automobile tires, the paint, plastic wall and floor coverings, foam insulation, dishes, furniture, pipes, and so forth, in our homes.

3. In spite of the many varieties of fibers, elastomers, and plastics, they all have a similar structure and are governed by the same theories. Linear polymers, such as high-density polyethylene (HDPE), consist of long chains made up of thousands of covalently bonded carbon atoms. The repeating unit for HDPE is represented as $[CH_2CH_2]_n$ where n is the number of repeating units.

4. Most linear polymers such as HDPE are thermoplastic, that is, they may be softened by heat and hardened by cooling in a reversible physical process. However, linear polymers, like cellulose which have very strong intermolecular forces (hydrogen bonds), cannot be softened by heating below the decomposition temperature.

5. Thermoset polymers are cross-linked and cannot be softened by heating. Thermoplastics such as natural rubber and A-stage resole Bakelite resins can be transformed to thermosetting polymers by the introduction of crosslinks between the polymer chains.

6. Early developments in polymer technology were empirical because of a lack of knowledge of polymer science. Advancements in polymer technology were rapid in the 1930s and 1940s because of the theories developed by Staudinger, Carothers, Mark, and other polymer scientists.

7. Thermoplastic resole resins that may be thermoset by heating are obtained by heating phenol and formaldehyde on the alkaline side. Novolacs are obtained when an insufficient amount of formaldehyde is reacted in acid solution. Novolacs are converted to infusible plastics by heating with hexamethylenetetramine.

GLOSSARY

ABS: A polymer produced by the copolymerization of acrylonitrile, butadiene, and styrene.

acetal: A polymer produced by the polymerization of formaldehyde.

alkyd: A polyester produced by the condensation of a dihydric alcohol, such as ethylene glycol, and a dicarboxylic acid, such as phthalic acid, in the presence of controlled amounts of an unsaturated monofunctional organic acid, such as oleic acid.

A-stage: A linear resole resin.

Bakelite: A polymer produced by the condensation of phenol and formaldehyde.

biopolymer: A naturally occurring polymer, such as protein.

buna: Copolymer of butadiene and styrene or acrylonitrile.

butyl rubber: A copolymer of isobutylene and isoprene.

cellulose: A naturally occurring carbohydrate polymer consisting of repeating glucose units.

cellulose acetate: The ester of cellulose and acetic acid.

cellulose nitrate: The product obtained by the reaction of nitric acid and sulfuric acid with cellulose; erroneously called nitrocellulose. The product is classified as primary, secondary, or tertiary according to how many groups in each repeating anhydroglucose unit in cellulose are nitrated.

cis: A geometric isomer with both groups on the same side of the ethylenic double bond.

collodion: A solution of cellulose nitrate in an equimolar mixture of ethanol and ethyl ether.

colloid: An aggregate 10^{-9} to 10^{-7} m long made up of smaller particles.

coumarone-indene resins: Polymers produced by the polymerization of distillation residues.

covalent bond: Chemical bonds formed by the sharing of electrons of the bonded atoms as the carbon atoms in graphite or diamonds.

cross links: Covalent bonds between two or more linear polymeric chains.

crystallites: Aggregates of polymers in crystalline form.

C-stage: A cross-linked resole resin.

cuprammonia rayon: Rayon produced from a solution of cellulose in a copper ammonia hydroxide solution.

denaturation: The change in properties of a protein resulting from the application of heat or the addition of a foreign agent, such as ethanol.

Ebonite: Hard rubber, highly cross-linked NR.

elastomer: A rubber.

filament: The individual extrudate emerging from the holes in a spinneret.

functionality: The number of reactive groups in a molecule.

Galalith: A plastic produced by molding casein.

glyptal: A polyester produced by the condensation of glycerol and phthalic anhydride.

hydrogen bonds: Very strong forces resulting from the attraction of hydrogen atoms in one molecule with an oxygen or nitrogen atom in another molecule. These forces may also be present as intramolecular forces in macromolecules.

intermolecular forces: Secondary valence forces between molecules.

intramolecular forces: Secondary valence forces within a molecule.

linear: A continuous chain, such as HDPE.

macromolecule: A polymer.

natural rubber: NR (Hevea braziliensis), polyisoprene obtained from rubber plants.

novolac: A thermoplastic phenol-formaldehyde resin prepared by the condensation of phenol and a small amount of formaldehyde on the acid side. Novolacs may be advanced to thermoset by heating with formaldehyde, which is usually obtained by the thermal decomposition of hexamethylenetetramine.

NR: natural rubber.

Nylon-66: A polyamide produced by the condensation of adipic acid [$HOOC(CH_2)_4COOH$] and hexamethylenediamine [$H_2N(CH_2)_6NH_2$].

oligomer: A very low molecular weight polymer in which the number of repeating units (n) equals 2 to 10 (oligos is the Greek term for few).

plasticizer: An additive which reduces intermolecular forces in polymers.

polymer: A giant or macromolecule made up of multiple repeating units, such as polyethylene, in which at least 1000 ethylene units $-\!\!(CH_2CH_2)\!\!-$ are joined together by covalent bonds. The word is derived from the Greek words meaning many parts.

polymer age: An age when the use of polymers is emphasized, as in the twentieth century.

protein: A polymer made up of many amino acid repeating units, i.e., a polyamide.

Raoult's law: A law which states that colligative properties of solutions, such as osmotic pressure and changes in vapor pressure, are related to the number of solute molecules present.

rayon: Regenerated cellulose in the form of filaments.

resole: A condensation product produced by the reaction of phenol and formaldehyde under alkaline conditions.

shellac: A resin secreted by small coccid insects.

spinneret: Small holes through which a solution or molten polymer is extruded in order to form filaments for fibers.

tanning: cross linking of proteins by the reaction with cross-linking agents such as tannic acid.

thermoplastic: A linear polymer which may be softened by heat and cooled in a reversible physical process.

thermoset plastic: A network polymer usually obtained by cross linking a linear polymer.

Thiokol: A polyethylene sulfide elastomer.

viscose: A solution of cellulose xanthate. The latter is produced by the reaction of alkali cellulose and carbon disulfide.

viscosity: The resistance to flow as applied to a solution or a molten solid.

vital force concept: A hypothesis that stated that organic compounds could be produced only by natural processes and not in the laboratory.

vulcanization: The process in which NR is cross linked by heating with sulfur.

EXERCISES

1. Name six polymers that you encounter daily.
2. Which would be more likely to be softened by heat?
   A. (1) unvulcanized rubber, or (2) ebonite
   B. (1) A-stage, or (2) C-stage resole
   C. (1) cellulose, or (2) cellulose acetate
3. Name a polymer having the following repeating units:
   A. ethylene $\text{+}CH_2CH_2\text{+}$
   B. phenol and formaldehyde residual units
   C. amino acid residual units
4. In which of the following polymers will hydrogen bonding predominate?
   (a) natural rubber (NR)
   (b) linear polyethylene (HDPE)
   (c) cellulose
   (d) cellulose nitrate
5. Which of the following products are polymeric?
   (a) water
   (b) wood
   (c) meat
   (d) cotton
   (e) rubber tires
   (f) paint
6. Which of the following is a thermoset or crosslinked polymer?
   (a) cellulose
   (b) unvulcanized rubber
   (c) A-stage resole
   (d) cellulose nitrate
   (e) molded Bakelite
   (f) ebonite
7. Which of the items in question 6 are thermoplastic?
8. If you were Staudinger, how would you answer your critical colleagues?
9. Why are so many outstanding polymer scientists alive today?
10. What percentage of polymer science students receive job offers after graduation?
11. What is the molecular weight of $H(CH_2CH_2)_{1000}H$?
12. What is the principal difference between rayon and cellophane?
13. Which is the more heat stable, a resole or a novolac phenolic (Bakelite) resin?

BIBLIOGRAPHY

Allen, P. W. (1972): Natural Rubber and Synthetics, Halsted, New York.

—— (1974): Palmerton, New York.

Anderson, J. C., Leaver, K. D., Alexander, J. M., Rawlins, R. D. (1975): Material Science, Halsted, New York.

Baun, C. E. H. (1972): Macromolecular Science, John Wiley, New York.

Billmeyer, F. W. (1971): Textbook of Polymer Science, Chap. 1, Wiley Interscience, New York.

Bolker, H. I. (1974): Natural and Synthetic Polymers, Dekker, New York.

Briston, J. H. (1974): Plastic Fibers, Halsted, New York.

Brydson, J. A. (1966): Plastic Materials, Chap. 1, Van Nostrand, Princeton.

—— (1975): Plastic Materials, 3rd ed., Newmes-Butterworths, Kent, England.

Collinan, T. D., Navitz, A. E. (1972): Fundamentals of Polymer Chemistry, Hayden, New York.

Cowie, J. M. G. (1974): Polymers: Chemistry and Physics of Modern Materials, Intext Educational Publishers, New York.

Cross, J. A. (1974): Plastics: Resource and Environmental Profile Analysis, Manufacturing Chemists Assoc., Washington, D.C.

Dubois, J. H. (1972): Plastics History U.S.A., Cahners Books, Boston.

Dubois, J. H., John, F. W. (1974): Plastics, Van Nostrand-Reinhold, New York.

Flory, P. J. (1953): Principles of Polymer Chemistry, Chap. 1, Cornell University Press, Ithaca, N.Y.

Garvey, B. S. (1959): History and Summary of Rubber Technology, in Chap. 1 (M. Morton, ed.), Reinhold, New York.

Glanville, A. B. (1973): The Plastics Engineers Data Book, Industrial Press, New York.

Golding, B. (1959): Polymers and Resins, Van Nostrand, Princeton.

Harper, C. A. (1975): Handbook of Plastics and Elastomers, McGraw-Hill, New York.

Heinisch, K. F. (1974): Dictionary of Rubber, Halsted, New York.

Huggins, M. A. (1976): Annual Review of Material Science, Annual Reviews, Inc., Palo Alto, California.

Jenkins, A. D. (1972): Polymer Science, American Elsevier, New York.

Kaufman, M. (1963): The First Century of Plastics-Celluloid and Its Sequel, The Plastics Institute, London.

Korshak, V. V. (1970): The Chemical Structure and Thermal Characterization of Polymers, Halsted, New York.

Kirshenbaum, G. S. (1973): Polymer Science Study Guide, Gordon and Breach, New York.

Lynch, C. T. (1976): Handbook of Material Science, CRC Press, Cleveland, Ohio.

Mandelkern, L. L. (1972): An Introduction to Macromolecules, Springer-Verlag, New York.

Mark, H. F. (1975): Applied Polymer Science, in Chap. 3 (J. K. Craver and R. W. Tess, eds.), Organic Coatings and Plastics Chemistry Division of ACS, Washington, D.C.

Matijevic, E. (1976): Surface and Colloidal Science, John Wiley, New York.

Milby, R. V. (1973): Plastics Technology, Chap. 1, McGraw-Hill, New York.

Moncreif, R. W. (1975): Manmade Fibers, Halsted, New York.

Morrell, R. S. (1951): Synthetic Resins and Allied Plastics, 3rd ed., Chap. 1, Oxford University Press, London.

Morton, M. (1973): Rubber Technology, Van Nostrand-Reinhold, New York.

Ott, E., Spurlin, H. M., Graffin, M. W. (1954): Cellulose and Its Derivatives, Part 1, Wiley Interscience, New York.

Parker, D. B. V. (1975): Polymer Chemistry, Applied Science, Essex, England.

Patterson, G. J. (1975): Plastics Book List, Technomic Publishing, Westport, Connecticut.

Powers, P. O. (1943): Synthetic Resins and Rubbers, Chap. 1, John Wiley, New York.

Raave, A. (1967): Organic Chemistry of Macromolecules, Chap. 1, Dekker, New York.

Rodriguez, F. (1971): Principles of Polymer Systems, McGraw-Hill, New York.

Saunders, K. J. (1973): Organic Polymer Chemistry, Halsted, New York.

Schlenker, B. R. (1975): Introduction to Material Science, John Wiley, New York.

Seymour, R. B. (1971): Introduction to Polymer Chemistry, Chap. 1, McGraw-Hill, New York.

—— (1975): Modern Plastics Technology, Reston Publishing, Reston, Virginia.

Shalaby, S. W., Pearce, E. M. (1976): Polymer Science and Technology, American Chemical Society, Washington, D.C.

Spaak, A. (1977): Polymer Science and Engineering Programs, Plastics Institute of America, Hoboken, New Jersey.

Staudinger, H. (1932): Die Hochmolekularen, Springer-Verlag, Berlin.

Stevens, M. P. (1975): Polymer Chemistry, Addison-Wesley, Reading, Massachusetts.

Treloar, L. R. G. (1975): Introduction to Polymer Science, Wykeham, England.

Williams, H. T. (1975): Polymer Engineering, Elsevier Scientific, New York.

Van Krevelen, D. W. (1972): Properties of Polymers, American Elsevier, New York.

Vold, M. J., Vold, R. D. (1964): Colloid Chemistry, Reinhold, New York.

2

Polymer Structure (Morphology)

2.1 STEREOCHEMISTRY OF POLYMERS

High-density polyethylene (HDPE), formerly called low-pressure polyethylene $[H(CH_2CH_2)_nH]$, like other alkanes $[H(CH_2)_nH]$, may be used to illustrate polymer structure. As in introductory organic chemistry, we can comprehend almost all the complex organic compounds if we understand the simplest chemistry, i.e., alkane chemistry.

High-density polyethylene, like decane $[H(CH_2)_{10}H]$ or paraffin $[H(CH_2)_{\sim 50}H]$, is a linear chainlike molecule consisting of catenated carbon atoms bonded by covalent bonds. The carbon atoms in all alkanes, including HDPE, are joined at characteristic tetrahedral bond angles of approximately 109.5°. While decane consists of 10 methylene groups (CH_2), HDPE may contain more than 1000 of these groups. While we use the term normal straight chain or linear for alkanes, we know that, because of the characteristic bond angles, the chains are zigzag-shaped.

The distance between the carbon atoms is 1.54 angstroms (Å) or 0.154 nanometers (nm). The apparent zigzag distance between carbon atoms in a chain of many carbon atoms is 1.26 Å, or 0.126 nm. Therefore, the length of an extended decane chain would be 8 (1.26 Å), or 10.08 Å, or 1.008 nm. Likewise, the length of an extended chain of HDPE having 1000 repeating ethylene units or structural elements $[H(CH_2CH_2)_{1000}H$ or $H(CH_2)_{2000}H]$ would be 2517.5 Å or 251.75 nm. However, as shown by the magnified simulated structure in the diagram for HDPE (Fig. 2.1, right) because of rotation of the carbon-carbon bonds, these chains are seldom extended to their full contour length but are present in many different shapes, or conformations. Since the size of the hydrogen atoms and bond angles are less significant in giant molecules, they are not usually shown in HDPE and other polymers.

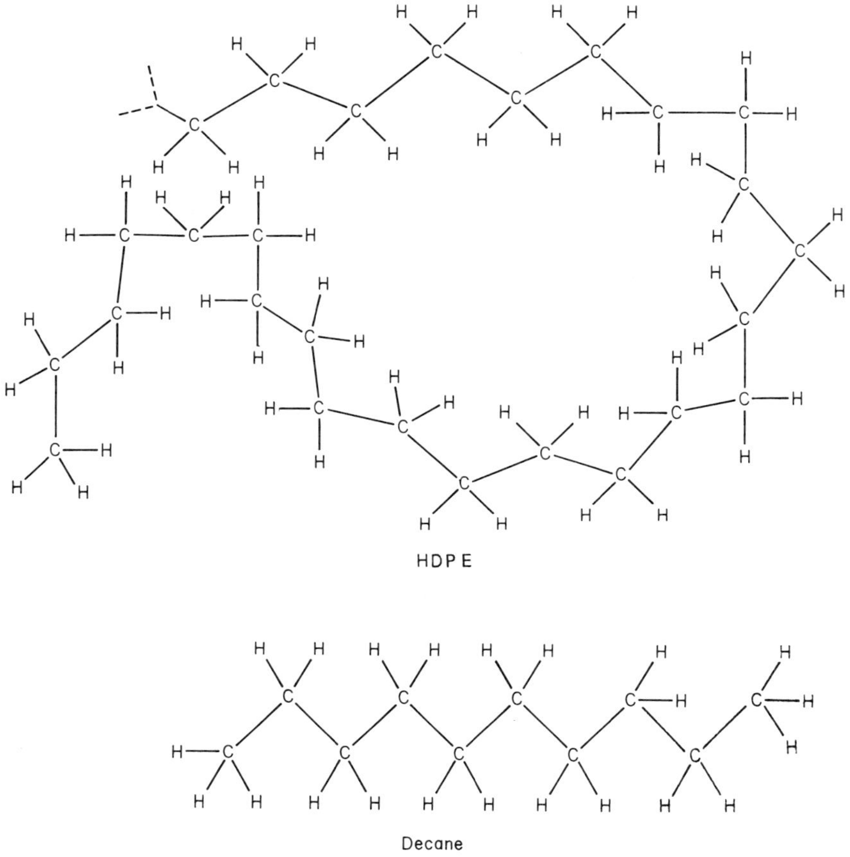

HDPE

Decane

FIGURE 2.1 Magnified simulated structure of high-density polyethylene (HDPE), contrasted with the structural formula of decane.

Each specific protein molecule has a specific molecular weight, like the classic small molecules, and is said to be monodisperse. However, commercial synthetic polymers, such as HDPE, are made up of molecules of different molecular weights. Thus, the numerical value for n, or the degree of polymerization (DP), should be considered as an average DP and designated with an overbar, i.e., $\overline{DP}$. Accordingly, the average molecular weight ($\overline{M}$) of a polydisperse polymer will equal the product of $\overline{DP}$ and the molecular weight of the repeating unit or mer.

In classic organic chemistry, it is customary to call a nonlinear molecule, like isobutane, a branched chain. However, the polymer chemist uses the term pendant group to label any group present on the repeating units. Thus, polypropylene

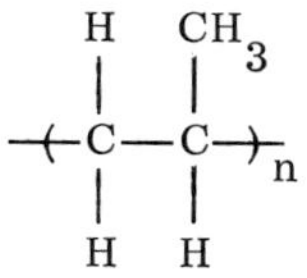

$$\left(\begin{array}{cc} \text{H} & \text{CH}_3 \\ | & | \\ \text{C} - & \text{C} \\ | & | \\ \text{H} & \text{H} \end{array}\right)_n$$

has a pendant methyl group but is designated as a linear polymer. In contrast, low-density polyethylene (LDPE), which was formerly called high-pressure polyethylene, is a branched polymer because chain extensions or branches of polyethylene sequences are present on branch points, irregularly spaced along the polymer chain, as shown in Fig. 2.2. The number of branches in nonlinear polyethylene (LDPE) may vary from 1 per 20 methylene groups to 1 per 100 methylene groups. This branching, like branching in simple alkanes like isobutane, increases the volume and thus reduces the density of the polymer.

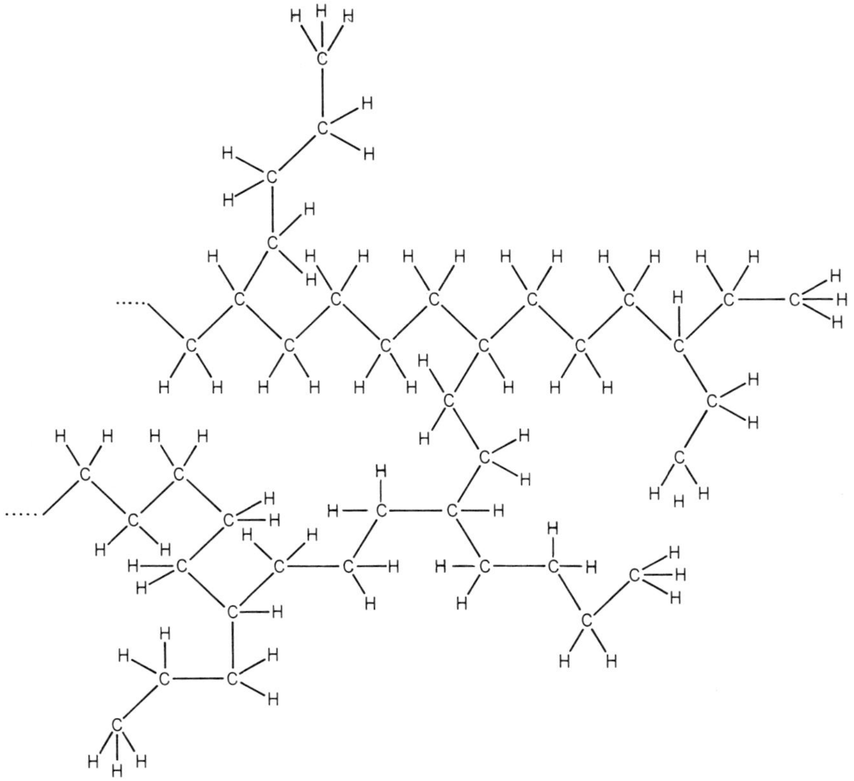

FIGURE 2.2 Simulated structural formula of branched low density polyethylene (LDPE; compare to Fig. 2.1, HDPE).

Both linear and branched polymers are thermoplastic. However, cross-linked three-dimensional, or network polymers are thermoset polymers. As shown in Fig. 2.3, the cross-linked density may vary from the low cross-linked density in vulcanized rubber to the high cross-linked density observed in ebonite.

While there is only one possible arrangement for the repeating units in HDPE, these units in polypropylene (PP) and many other polymers may be arranged in a head-to-tail or a head-to-head configuration, as shown in Figs. 2.4 and 2.5. Fortunately, the usual arrangement is head to tail, so that the pendant groups are usually on every other carbon atom in the chain.

Proteins are polyamides in which the building units consist of the l (levo) optical isomers of amino acids. In contrast, the building units in starch and cellulose are d (dextro)-glucose which are joined by α and β acetal groups. All d and l enantiomers are structurally related to the d and l glyceraldehyde structures shown in Fig. 2.6.

In the early 1950s, Nobel laureate Giulio Natta used stereospecific coordination catalysts to produce stereospecific isomers of polypropylene. Natta used the term tacticity to describe the different possible structures.

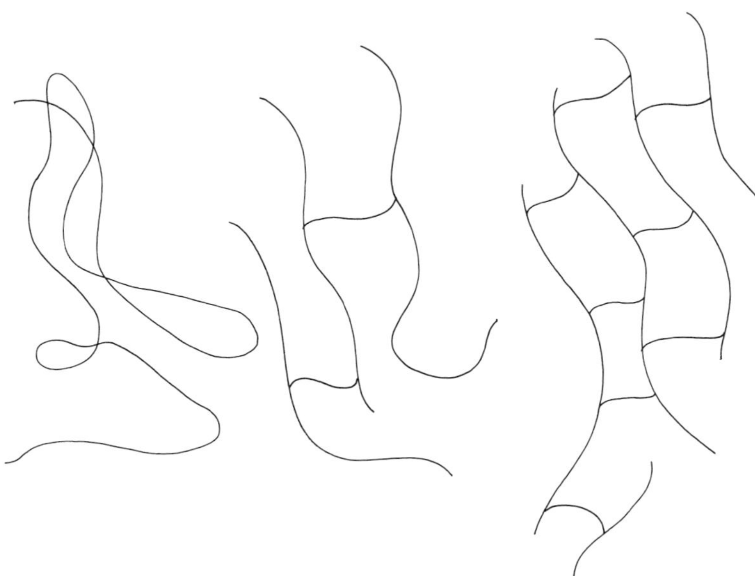

FIGURE 2.3 Simulated skeletal structural formulas of a linear polymer (left) and network polymers with low (middle) and high (right) cross-linked density.

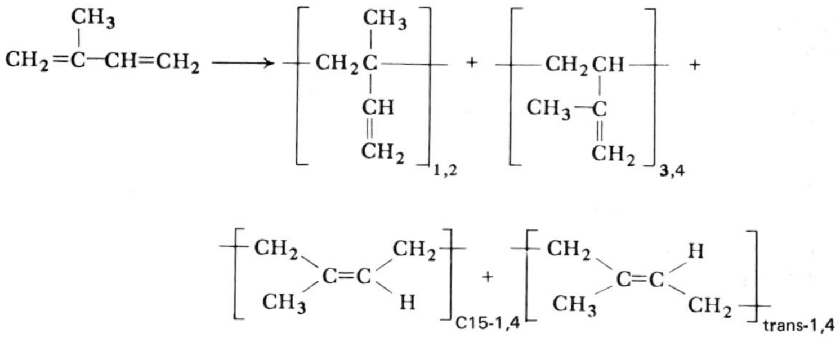

$$CH_2{=}C(CH_3){-}CH{=}CH_2 \longrightarrow \left[{-}CH_2C(CH_3)(CH{=}CH_2){-}\right]_{1,2} + \left[{-}CH_2CH(C(CH_3){=}CH_2){-}\right]_{3,4} +$$

$$\left[{-}CH_2(CH_3)C{=}C(H)CH_2{-}\right]_{C15\text{-}1,4} + \left[{-}CH_2(CH_3)C{=}C(H)CH_2{-}\right]_{trans\text{-}1,4}$$

FIGURE 2.4 Simulated structures of polyisoprenes.

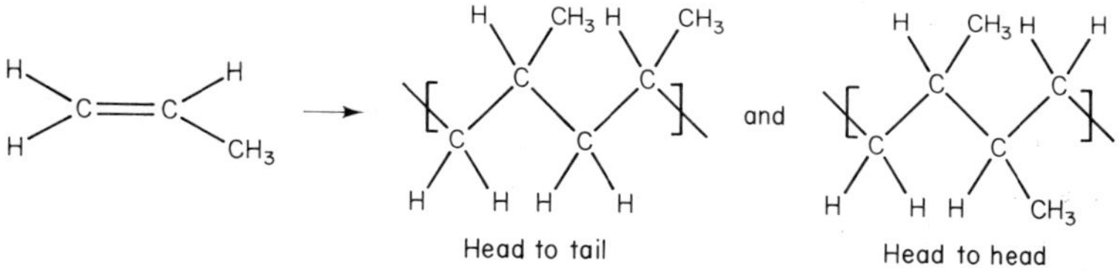

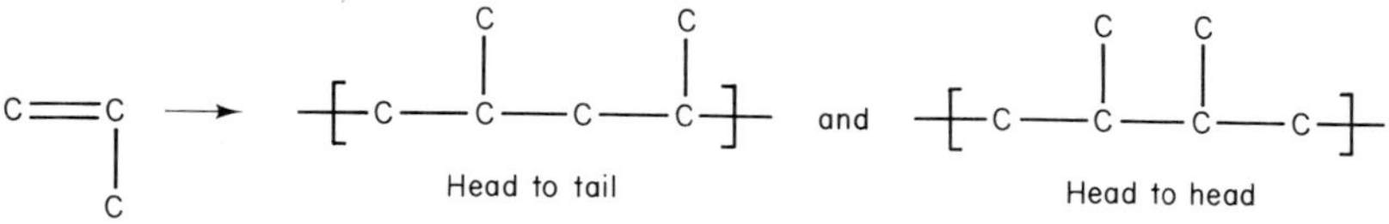

$$H_2C{=}CH(CH_3) \longrightarrow \left[{-}CH_2{-}CH(CH_3){-}CH_2{-}CH(CH_3){-}\right] \text{ and } \left[{-}CH_2{-}CH(CH_3){-}CH(CH_3){-}CH_2{-}\right] \qquad (2.1)$$

Head to tail   Head to head

$$C{=}C(C) \longrightarrow \left[{-}C{-}C(C){-}C{-}C(C){-}\right] \text{ and } \left[{-}C{-}C(C){-}C(C){-}C{-}\right] \qquad (2.2)$$

Head to tail   Head to head

FIGURE 2.5 Simulated structural (2.1) and skeletal (2.2) formulas showing the usual head-to-tail and the less usual head-to-head configurations of polypropylene (PP).

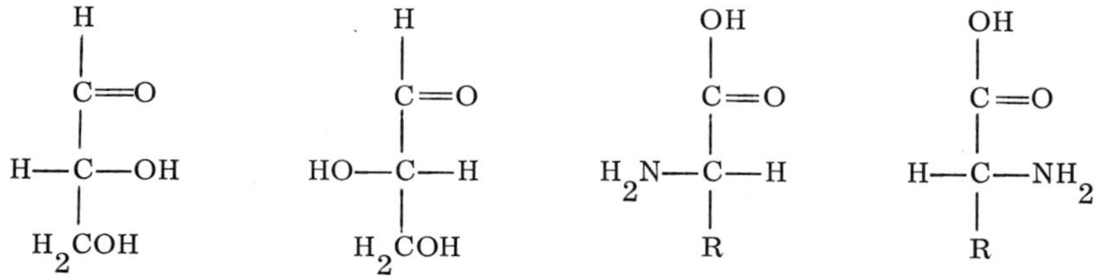

H	H	OH	OH
C=O	C=O	C=O	C=O
H—C—OH	HO—C—H	H_2N—C—H	H—C—NH_2
H_2COH	H_2COH	R	R
d-Glyceraldehyde	l-Glyceraldehyde	l-Amino acids	d-Amino acids

FIGURE 2.6 Optical isomers of glyceraldehyde and amino acids.

As shown in Fig. 2.7, the isomer corresponding to the arrangement dddd or llll is called isotactic PP. The isomer corresponding to the arrangement dldl is called syndiotactic PP, and polypropylene having a random arrangement of building units corresponding to ddlddld, and so forth, is called atactic PP. Isotactic PP, which is available commercially, is a highly crystalline polymer with a melting point of 160°C, while the atactic isomer is an amorphous (noncrystalline) soft polymer with a melting point of 75°C. The term eutactic is used to describe either an isotactic polymer, a syndiotactic polymer, or a mixture of both.

While most polymers contain only one chiral or asymmetric center in the repeating units, it is possible to have diisotacticity when two different substituents (R and R') are present at the chiral centers. These isomers are labeled erythro and threodiisotactic and erythro and threosyndiotactic isomers as shown in Fig. 2.8.

The many different conformers resulting from rotation about the carbon-carbon bond in a simple molecule like n-butane [$H(CH_2)_4H$] may be shown by Newman projections. As shown in Fig. 2.9, the most stable form is the anti or trans (t) conformer in which the two methyl groups (Me) are as far apart as possible. The difference in energy between the anti and eclipsed conformer is at least 3 kcal and, of course, there are numerous conformations between these two extremes. Among these are the two mirror-image gauche (g) conformers in which the methyl groups are 60° apart.

In a polymer such as HDPE, the methyl groups shown in Fig. 2.9 would be replaced by methylene groups in the chain. The flexibility in a polymer

```
       C     C     C                            C
       |     |     |                            |
  —C—C—C—C—C—C—                —C—C—C—C—C—C—
                                       |           |
                                       C           C

    Isotactic PP                   Syndiotactic PP


          C     C           C     C
          |     |           |     |
     —C—C—C—C—C—C—C—C—C—C—
                      |
                      C

                 Atactic PP
```

FIGURE 2.7 Skeletal formulas of isotactic, syndiotactic, and atactic polypropylene (PP).

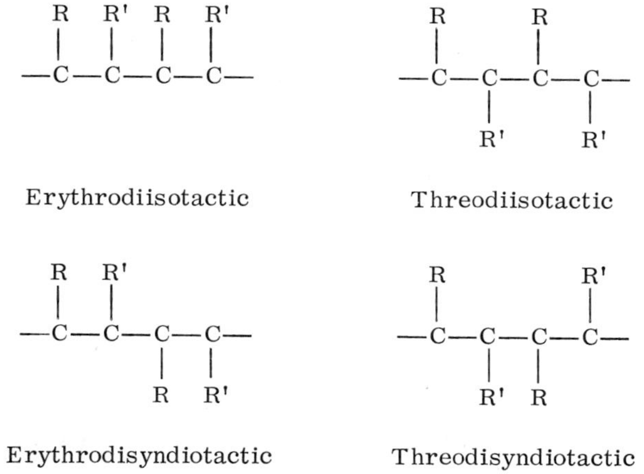

Erythrodiisotactic

Threodiisotactic

Erythrodisyndiotactic

Threodisyndiotactic

FIGURE 2.8 Skeletal formulas of ditactic isomers.

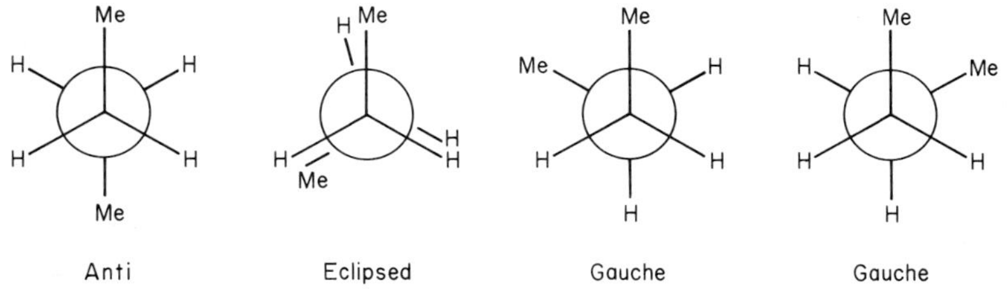

Anti

Eclipsed

Gauche

Gauche

FIGURE 2.9 Newman projections of designated conformers of n-butane.

would be related to the ease of conversion from t to g. The latter is dependent on the lack of hindering groups or increased temperature. Thus, polymethyl methacrylate (PMMA) is hard at room temperature because of the polar ester groups which restrict rotation. In contrast, polyisobutylene is flexible at room temperature. The flexibility of both polymers will be increased as the temperature is increased.

2.2 MOLECULAR INTERACTIONS

The forces present in nature are often divided into primary forces (typically greater than 50 kcal/mol of interactions) and secondary forces (typically less than 10 kcal/mol of interactions). Primary bonding forces can be further subdivided into ionic (characterized by a lack of directional bonding; between atoms of largely differing electronegativities; not typically present within polymer backbones), metallic (the number of outer, valence electrons is too small to provide complete outer shells; often considered as charged atoms surrounded by a potentially fluid sea of electrons; lack of bonding direction; not typically found in polymers), and covalent (including coordinate and dative) bonding (which are the major means of bonding within polymers; directional). The bonding lengths of primary bonds are usually about 0.90 to 2.0 Å, with the carbon-carbon bond length being about 1.5 to 1.6 Å.

Secondary forces, frequently called van der Waals forces, since they are the forces responsible for the van der Waals correction to the ideal gas relationships, are of longer distance in interaction generally having significant interaction between 2.5 and 5 Å. The force of these interactions is inversely proportional to some power of r, generally 2 or greater [force $\propto 1/(\text{distance})^r$] and thus are quite dependent on the distance between the interacting molecules. Thus, many physical properties of polymers are indeed quite dependent on both the conformation (arrangements related to rotation about single bonds) and configuration (arrangements related to the actual chemical bonding about a given atom) since both affect the proximity one chain can have relative to another. Thus, amorphous polypropylene is more flexible than crystalline polypropylene (compare a and b of Fig. 2.10).

Atoms in individual polymer molecules are thus joined to each other by relatively strong covalent bonds. The bond energies of the carbon-carbon bonds are on the order of 80 to 90 kcal/mol. Further polymer molecules, like all other molecules, are attracted to each other (and for long-chain polymer chains even between segments of the same chain) by intermolecular, secondary forces.

These intermolecular forces are also responsible for the increase in boiling points within a homologous series such as the alkanes, for the higher than expected boiling points of polar organic molecules such as alkyl chlorides, and for the abnormally high boiling points of alcohols, amines, and amides. While the forces responsible for these increases in boiling points are all called van der Waals forces, these forces are subclassified in accordance with their source and intensity. Secondary, intermolecular forces include London dispersion forces, induced permanent forces, and dipolar forces, including hydrogen bonding.

Nonpolar molecules such as ethane [$H(CH_2)_2H$] and polyethylene are attracted to each other by weak London or dispersion forces resulting from induced dipole-dipole interaction. The temporary or transient dipoles in ethane or along the polyethylene chain are due to instantaneous fluctuations in the density of the electron clouds. The energy range of these forces is about 2 kcal per unit in nonpolar and polar polymers alike, and this force is independent of temperature. These London forces are typically the major forces present between chains in largely nonpolar polymers present in elastomers and soft plastics.

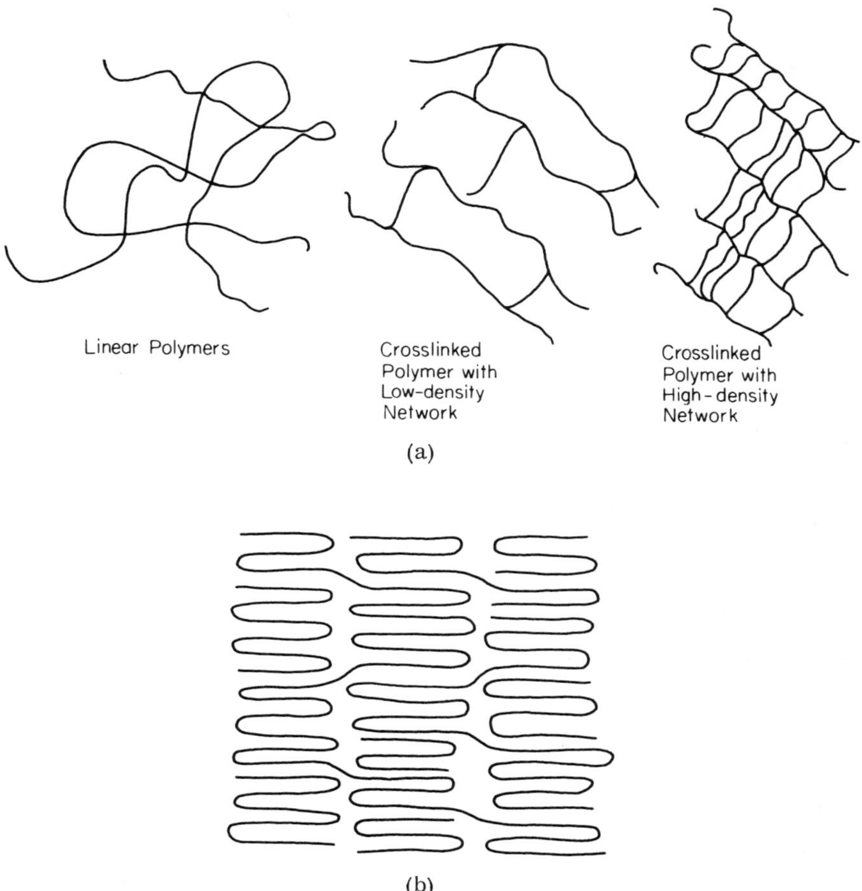

FIGURE 2.10 Representation of an amorphous polymer and representation of folded polymer chains in polymer crystals. (From Modern Plastics Technology by R. Seymour, 1975, Reston Publishing Company, Reston, Virginia. Used with permission of Reston Publishing Company.)

It is of interest to note that methane, ethane, and ethene are all gases; hexane, octane, and nonane are all liquids (at room conditions); while polyethylene is a waxy solid. This trend is primarily due to both an increase in mass per molecule and to an increase in the London forces per molecule as the chain length increases. Assuming that the attraction between methylene or methyl units is 2 kcal/mol we calculate an interaction between methane of 2 kcal/mol, hexane of 12 kcal/mol, and for a polyethylene chain of 1000 units, 2000 kcal/mol.

Polar molecules such as ethyl chloride ($H_3C—CH_2Cl$) and polyvinyl chloride [$—(—CH_2—CHCl—)—_n$, PVC, see Fig. 2.11] are attracted to each other by dipole-dipole interactions resulting from the electrostatic attraction of a chlorine atom in one molecule to a hydrogen atom in another molecule. Since this dipole-dipole interaction, which ranges from 2 to 6 kcal per mol repeating unit in the molecule, is temperature dependent, these forces are reduced as the temperature is increased in the processing of polymers. While the London forces are typically weaker than the dipole-dipole forces, they are also present in polar compounds, such as ethyl chloride and PVC. These dipole-dipole forces are characteristic of many plastics.

Strong polar molecules such as ethanol, polyvinyl alcohol, and cellulose are attracted to each other by a special type of dipole-dipole interaction called hydrogen bonding in which the oxygen atoms in one molecule are attracted to the hydrogen atoms in another molecule. These are the strongest of the intermolecular forces and may have energies as high as 10 kcal per mol repeating unit. Intermolecular hydrogen bonds are usually present in fibers, such as cotton, wool, silk, nylon, Acrylan, polyesters, and polyurethanes. Intramolecular hydrogen bonds are responsible for the helices observed in starch and globular proteins.

It is important to note that the high melting point of nylon-66 (265°C, Fig. 2.12) is the result of a combination of London, dipole-dipole, and hydrogen bonding forces between the polyamide chains. The hydrogen bonds are decreased when the hydrogen atoms in the amide groups in nylon are

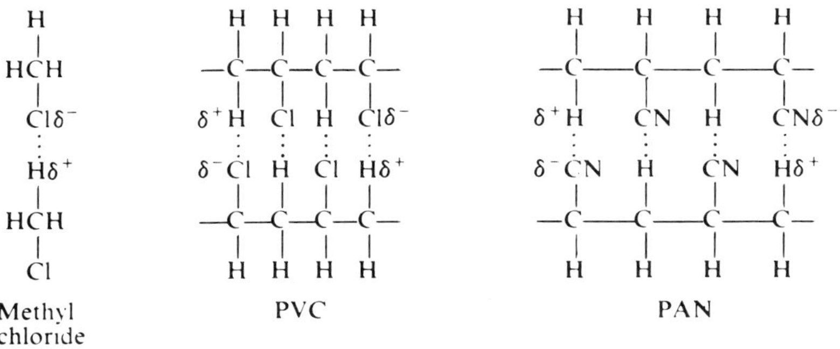

FIGURE 2.11 Typical dipole-dipole interaction between molecules of methyl chloride and segments of chains of polyvinyl chloride and polyacrylonitrile. (From Modern Plastics Technology by R. Seymour, 1975, Reston Publishing Company, Reston, Virginia. Used with permission of Reston Publishing Company.)

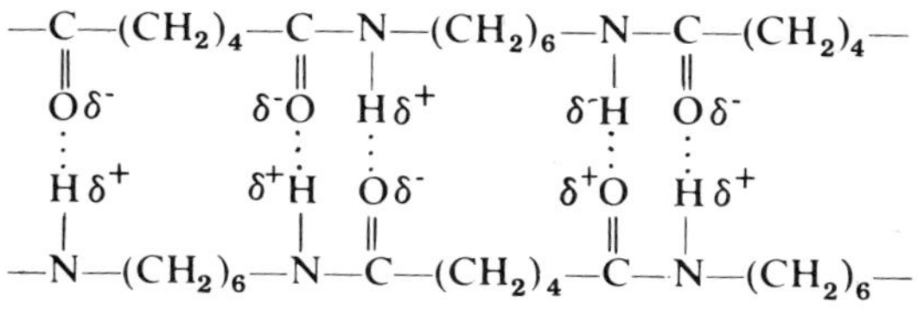

```
—C—(CH2)4—C—N—(CH2)6—N—C—(CH2)4—
 ‖         ‖  |         |  ‖
 Oδ-      δ-O  Hδ+     δ-H  Oδ-
 :         :  :         :  :
 Hδ+      δ+H  Oδ-     δ+O  Hδ+
 |         |  ‖         ‖  |
—N—(CH2)6—N—C—(CH2)4—C—N—(CH2)6—
```

FIGURE 2.12 Typical hydrogen bonding between hydrogen and oxygen or nitrogen atoms in nylon-66. (From Modern Plastics Technology, by R. Seymour, 1975, Reston Publishing Company, Reston, Virginia. Used with permission of Reston Publishing Company.)

replaced by methyl groups and when the hydroxyl groups in cellulose are esterified.

In addition to the contribution of intermolecular forces, chain entanglement is also an important contributory factor to the physical properties of polymers. While paraffin wax and HDPE are homologs with relatively high molecular weights, the chain length of paraffin is too short to permit entanglement and hence it lacks the strength and other characteristic properties of HDPE.

The critical chain length (z) required for the onset of entanglement is dependent on the polarity and shape of the polymer. Thus, the number of atoms in the critical chain lengths of polymethyl methacrylate (PMMA), polystyrene (PS), and polyisobutylene are 208, 730, and 610, respectively. The melt viscosity (η) of a polymer is often found to be proportional to the 3.4 power of the chain length above the critical chain length as related in (2.3), regardless of the structure of the polymer. The constant K is temperature dependent.

$$\log \eta = 3.4 \log z + \log K \tag{2.3}$$

Viscosity is a measure of the resistance to flow. The latter, which is the result of cooperative movement of the polymer segments from hole to hole in a melt, is impeded by chain entanglement, intermolecular forces, the presence of reinforcing agents, and by cross-links.

The flexibility of amorphous polymers above the glassy state, which is governed by the same forces as melt viscosity, is dependent on a wriggling type of segment motion in the polymer chains. This flexibility is increased when many methylene groups (CH_2) are present between stiffening groups in the chain and when oxygen atoms are present in the chain. Thus, the flexibility of aliphatic polyesters usually increases as either m is increased.

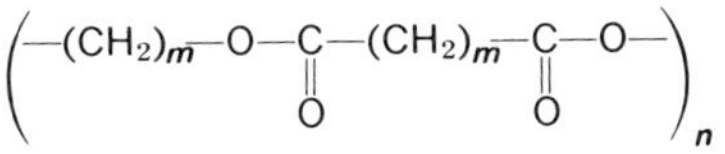

$$\left(-(CH_2)_m-O-\underset{\underset{O}{\|}}{C}-(CH_2)_m-\underset{\underset{O}{\|}}{C}-O- \right)_n$$

Aliphatic polyester

In contrast, the flexibility of amorphous polymers above the glassy state is decreased when stiffening groups such as

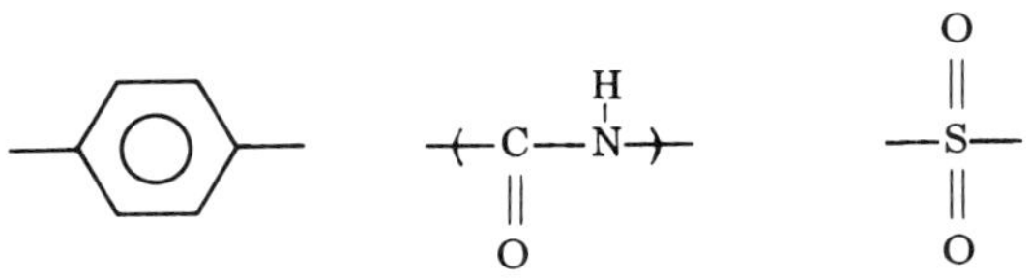

p-phenylene amide sulfone

are present in the polymer backbone. Thus, polyethylene terephthalate is stiffer and higher melting than polyethylene adipate and the former is stiffer than polybutylene terephthalate because of the presence of fewer methylene groups between the stiffening groups.

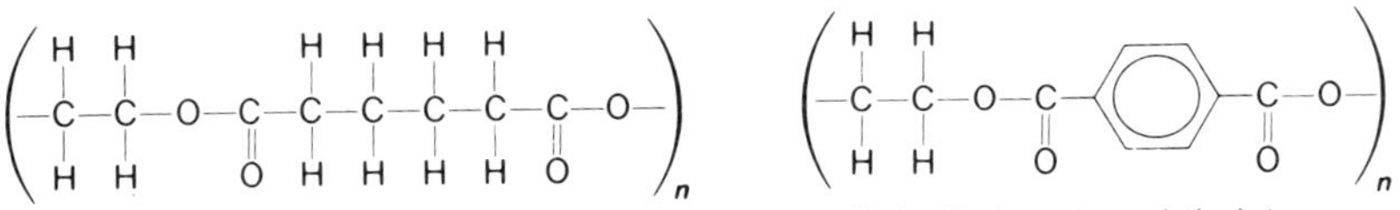

Polyethylene adipate

Polyethylene terephthalate

The flexibility of amorphous polymers is reduced drastically when they are cooled below a characteristic transition temperature called the glass transition temperature (T_g). At temperatures below T_g, there is no segmental motion and any dimensional changes in the polymer chain are the result of temporary distortions of the primary valence bonds. Amorphous plastics perform best below T_g, but elastomers must be used above the brittle point, or T_g.

The melting point (T_m) is called the first-order transition temperature, and T_g is sometimes called the second-order transition temperature. The values for T_m are usually 33 to 100% greater than T_g, and symmetrical polymers like HDPE exhibit the greatest difference between T_m and T_g. As shown by the data in Table 2.1, the T_g values are low for elastomers and flexible polymers and relatively high for hard amorphous plastics.

As shown in Table 2.1, the T_g value of polypropylene (PP) is 373°K or 100°C, yet because of its high degree of crystallinity it does not flow to any great extent below its melting point of 438°K (165°C). In contrast, the highly amorphous polyisobutylene, which has a Tg value of 203°K (-70°C), flows at room temperature. Also, as shown in Table 2.1, T_g decreases as the size of the ester groups increase in polyacrylates and polymethacrylates. The effect of the phenylene stiffening group is also demonstrated by the Tg of polyethylene terephthalate, which is 119 K° higher than that of polyethylene adipate.

TABLE 2.1 Approximate Glass Transition Temperatures (T_g) for Selected Polymers

Polymer	T_g (degrees Kelvin)
Cellulose acetate butyrate	323
Cellulose triacetate	430
Polyethylene (LDPE)	148
Polypropylene (atactic)	253
Polypropylene (isotactic)	373
Polytetrafluoroethylene	160, 400[a]
Polyethyl acrylate	249
Polymethyl acrylate	279
Polybutyl methacrylate (atactic)	339
Polymethyl methacrylate (atactic)	378
Polyacrylonitrile	378
Polypropylene (isotactic)	263
Polyvinyl acetate	301
Polyvinyl alcohol	358
Polyvinyl chloride	354
Cis-poly-1,3-butadiene	165
Trans-poly-1,3-butadiene	255
Polyhexamethylene adipamide (nylon-66)	330
Polyethylene adipate	223
Polyethylene terephthalate	342
Polydimethyl siloxane (silicone)	150
Polystyrene	373

[a] Two major transitions observed.

Since the specific volume of polymers increases at T_g in order to accommodate the increased segmental chain motion, T_g values may be estimated from plots of the change in specific volume with temperature. Other properties, such as stiffness (modulus), refractive index, dielectric properties, gas permeability, X-ray adsorption, and heat capacity all change at T_g. Thus, T_g may be estimated by noting the change in any of these values, such as the increase in gas permeability. Since the change in the slope of the specific volume-temperature or index of refraction-temperature curves are not always obvious, it is best to extrapolate the curves linearly and designate the intersection of these curves as T_g, as shown in Fig. 2.13.

As shown in Fig. 2.14, values for both T_g and T_m are observed as endothermic transitions in calorimetric measurements, such as differential thermal analysis (DTA) or differential scanning calorimetry (DSC). It is

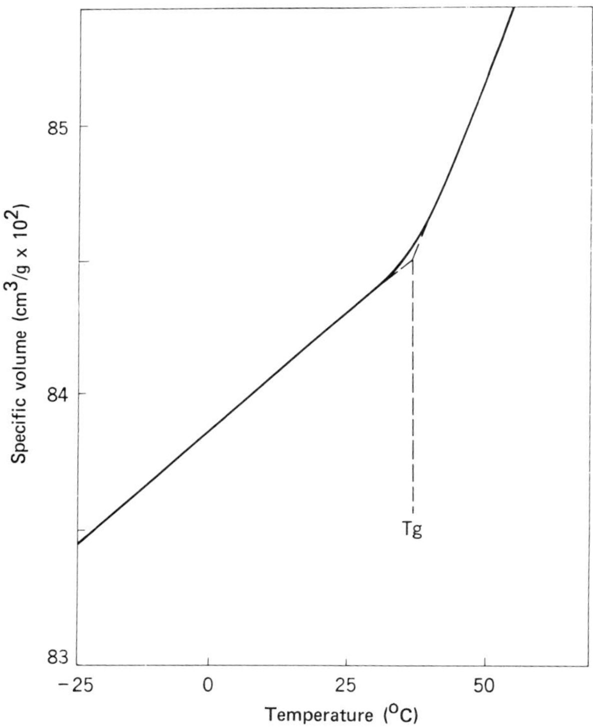

FIGURE 2.13 Determination of T_g by noting abrupt change in specific volume. (From Introduction to Polymer Chemistry by R. Seymour, 1971, McGraw-Hill, New York. Used with permission of McGraw-Hill Book Company.)

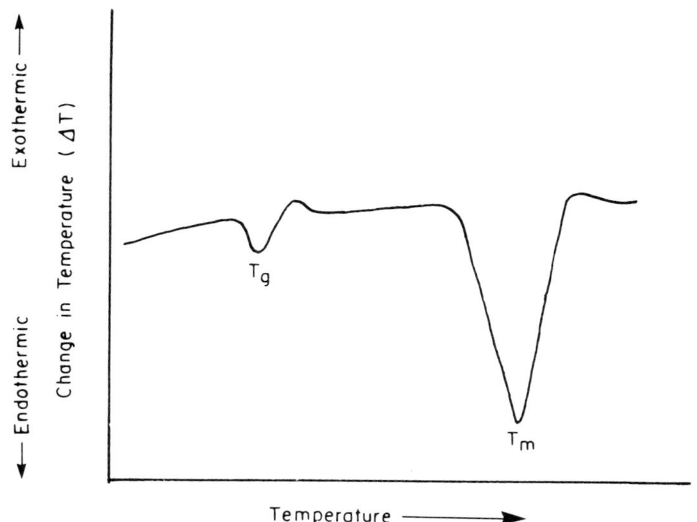

FIGURE 2.14 A typical DTA thermogram of a polymer.

important to note that since the values observed for T_g are dependent on the test method and on time, the values obtained by different techniques may vary by a few degrees. While the T_g value reported in the literature is related to the onset of segmental motion in the principal chain of polymer backbone, separate values, called α, β, etc., T_g, or secondary, tertiary, may be observed for the onset of motion of large pendant groups or branches on the polymer chain.

While no motion exists, except the stretching or distortion of covalent bonds, at temperatures below T_g the onset of segmental motion leads to many different conformations. Thus, the full contour length (nl) of a polymer chain obtained by multiplying the length of each mer, or repeating unit (l), by the number of units in the chain (n) provides a value of the length of only one of the many possible conformers present.

It is not possible or generally useful to calculate the length of other conformers, but it is important to know the average end-to-end distance of polymer chains. The statistical method for this determination, called the random flight technique, was developed by Lord Raleigh in 1919. This classic statistical approach may be used to show the distance traveled by a blindfolded person taking n number of steps of length l in a random walk or the distance flown by a confused moth or bird.

The distance traveled from start to finish is not the straight-line path measured as nl but the root mean square distance $\left(\sqrt{\bar{r}^2}\right)$ which is equal to

$l\sqrt{n}$. Nobel laureate Paul Flory and others have introduced several corrections so that this random flight technique could be applied to polymer chains having a full contour length of ln.

When we calculate the distance values for HDPE $[H(CH_2CH_2)_nH]$, where DP or n equals 1000 using a C—C bond length of 1.26 Å or 0.126 nm, we will find approximate values of ln of 252 nm, i.e., [0.126(2)(1000)] and of $l\sqrt{n}$ of 6.9 nm, i.e., $(0.126\sqrt{2000})$. Thus, the calculated root mean square distance $\sqrt{\bar{r}^2}$, where r is the vector distance from end to end, is less than 3% of the full contour end-to-end distance.

Since there are restrictions in polymer chain motions that do not apply to the blindfolded walker, corrections must be made which increase the value found by the Raleigh technique. Thus, the value of $\sqrt{\bar{r}^2}$ increases from 6.9 to 9.8 nm when one corrects for the fixed tetrahedral angles in the polymer chain.

A still higher value of 12.2 nm is obtained for the root mean square end-to-end distance when one corrects for the hindrance to motion caused by the hydrogen atoms. Since the hydrogen atoms of the first and fifth carbon atom overlap when the methylene groups assume a cyclopentane-like shape, another correction must be made for this so-called pentane interference. The corrected value for $\sqrt{\bar{r}^2}$ is 18.0 nm.

While corrections should also be made for the excluded volume, the approximate value of 18.0 nm will be used for the root mean square end-to-end distance. The excluded volume results from the fact that in contrast to the blindfolded walker who may backtrack without interference, only one atom of a three-dimensional carbon-carbon chain may occupy any specific volume at any specified time, and thus all other atoms must be excluded.

The number of possible conformers increases with chain length and can be shown statistically to equal 2^{2n}. Thus, when n = 1000, the number of possible conformers of HDPE is 2^{2000}, or 10^{300}. As shown in Fig. 2.15, the end-to-end distance (r) of a linear molecule such as HDPE may be readily visualized and must be viewed as an (statistically) average value.

However, since there are many ends in a branched polymer, it is customary to use the radius of gyration (S) instead of r for such polymers. The radius of gyration is actually the root mean square distance of a chain end from the polymer's center of gravity. S is less than the end-to-end distance (r) and for linear polymers, $\bar{r}^2$ is equal to $6\bar{S}^2$

In addition to the restrictions to free rotation noted for HDPE, free rotation of polymer chains will be hindered when the hydrogen atoms in polyethylene are replaced by bulky groups. Because the energy barrier (E) restricting the rotation from trans to gauche conformers is low (3 kcal per mer) in HDPE, these polymers are flexible, and this flexibility increases with temperature (T) in accordance with the Arrhenius equation shown in (2.4). The flexibility is related to the orientation time (τ_m), which is a

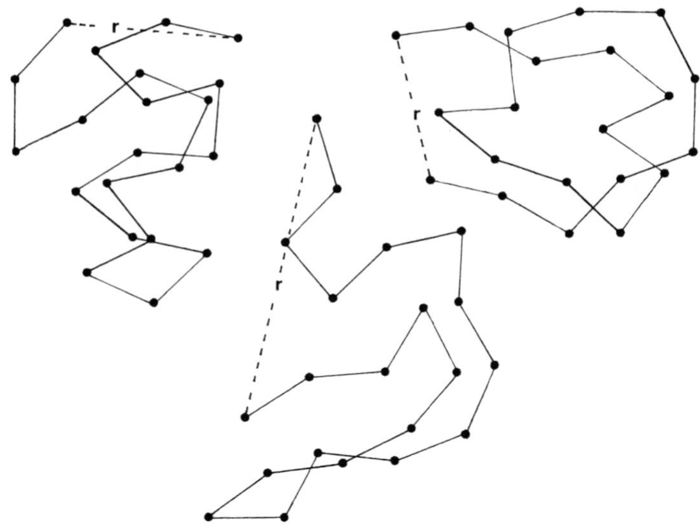

FIGURE 2.15 End-to-end distances (r) of linear polymer chains containing the same number of units.

measure of the ease of uncoiling of polymer coils. The constant A is related to the polymer structure, and R is the ideal gas constant.

$$\tau_m = A\,e^{E/RT} \quad \text{or} \quad \log \tau_m = \log A + \frac{E}{2.3RT} \tag{2.4}$$

The bulky phenyl group in polystyrene (PS) restricts rotation and hence its T_g and τ_m are higher than the values for HDPE. When substituents such as chlorine atoms are present in polystyrene, the T_g and τ_m values are even higher. Likewise, aromatic nylons, called aramides, have greater heat resistance than aliphatic nylons.

The intermolecular bonds in these polyamides and other fibers, including β-keratin, produce strong pleated sheets. Hair, fingernails and toenails, feathers, and horns have a β-keratin structure. Polyurethanes, polyacrylonitrile, and polyesters are characterized by the presence of strong hydrogen bonds. In contrast, isotactic polypropylene, which has no hydrogen bonds, is also a strong fiber as a result of the good fit of the regularly spaced methyl pendant groups on the chain. Since this molecular geometry is not present in atactic polypropylene, the latter is not a fiber.

α-Keratin and other globular proteins are characterized by intramolecular bonds. These and many other polymers, including nucleic acids, may form helices. Ribonucleic acid (RNA) exists as a single helix, while deoxyribonucleic acid (DNA) may exist as a double helix.

2.3 POLYMER CRYSTALS

Prior to 1920, leading chemistry researchers not only stated that macromolecules were nonexistent, but they also believed that the products called macromolecules, i.e., proteins, hevea elastomer, and cellulose could not exist in the crystalline form. However, in the early 1920s, Haworth used X-ray diffraction techniques to show that elongated cellulose was a crystalline polymer consisting of repeating units of cellobiose. In 1925, Katz jokingly placed a stretched natural rubber band in an X-ray spectrometer and to his surprise observed an interference pattern typical of a crystalline substance.

This phenomenon may also be shown qualitatively by the development of opacity when a rubber band is stretched and by the abnormal stiffening and whitening of unvulcanized rubber when it is stored for several days at 0°C. The opacity noted in stretched rubber and cold rubber is the result of the formation of crystallites, or regions of crystallinity. The latter were first explained by a fringed micelle model which is now outmoded because single crystals of stereoregular polymers have been observed.

In contrast to the transparent films of amorphous polymers, relatively thick films of LDPE are translucent because of the presence of crystals. This opacity is readily eliminated when the film is heated above 100°C. It is of interest to note that Sauter produced single crystals of polymers in 1932, and Bunn produced single crystals of LDPE in 1939, but the existence of single crystals was not generally recognized until the 1950s, when three experimenters, namely, Fischer, Keller, and Till, reproduced Bunn's work independently.

It is now recognized that ordered polymers may form lamellar crystals with a thickness of 10 to 20 nm in which the polymer chains are folded back upon themselves to produce parallel chains perpendicular to the face of the crystals, as shown in Fig. 2.16.

Amorphous polymers with irregular bulky groups are seldom crystallizable, and unless special techniques are used, ordered polymers are seldom 100% crystalline. The rate of crystallization may be monitored by X-ray diffraction techniques or by dilatometry (measurement of change in volume).

The crystallites in polymers are small and usually organized into larger, shallow pyramidlike structures called spherulites which may be seen by the naked eye and viewed as Maltese cross-like structures with polarized light and crossed Nicol prisms in a microscope, as shown in Fig. 2.17.

As in most crystallization processes, in the absence of nucleation, there is an induction period during which disentanglement of chains takes place. This step is followed by a slow rate of crystal growth. However,

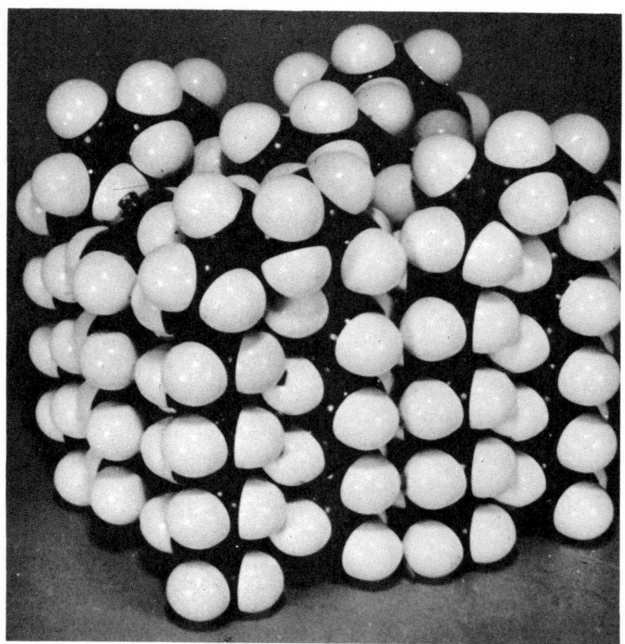

FIGURE 2.16 Model representation of a folded-chain lamellar crystal for polyethylene at the surface of a single crystal. [P. Geil and D. Reneker, J. Appl. Physics, 31:1921 (1960). With permission from the American Institute of Physics.]

FIGURE 2.17 Maltese cross-like pattern for spherulites viewed under a polarizing microscope with crossed Nichol prisms in a siliconelike polymer. The large and small spherulites are the result of crystallization occurring at different temperatures. (F. Price, in Growth and perfection of crystals (R. Doremus, B. Roberts, and D. Turnbull, eds.). John Wiley, New York, 1958, p. 466. With permission from John Wiley and Sons, Publishers.)

the rate of crystallization increases and then slows down towards the end of the crystallization process. The rate of crystalline growth may be followed by dilatometry using the Avrami equation which was developed to follow the rate of crystallization of metals.

As shown by (2.5), the quotient of the difference between the specific volume V_t at time t and the final volume V_f, divided by the difference between the original specific volume V_o and the final volume is equal to an experimental expression in which K is a kinetic constant related to the rate of nucleation and growth and n is an integer related to nucleation and growth of crystals. The value of n may be from 1 to 4 and is equal to 4 for three-dimensional crystal growth.

$$\frac{V_t - V_f}{V_o - V_f} = e^{-Kt^n} \tag{2.5}$$

It is now believed that the crystalline and amorphous domains may be represented by the switchboard model shown in Fig. 2.18 or the related fringed micelle model shown in Fig. 2.19.

The crystalline regions may be disrupted by processing techniques such as thermoforming and extrusion of plastics and biaxial orientation and cold drawing of fibers. In the last process, which is descriptive of the others, the crystallites are ordered in the direction of the stress, the filament shrinks in diameter (necks down), and heat is evolved and reabsorbed as a result of additional orientation and crystallization.

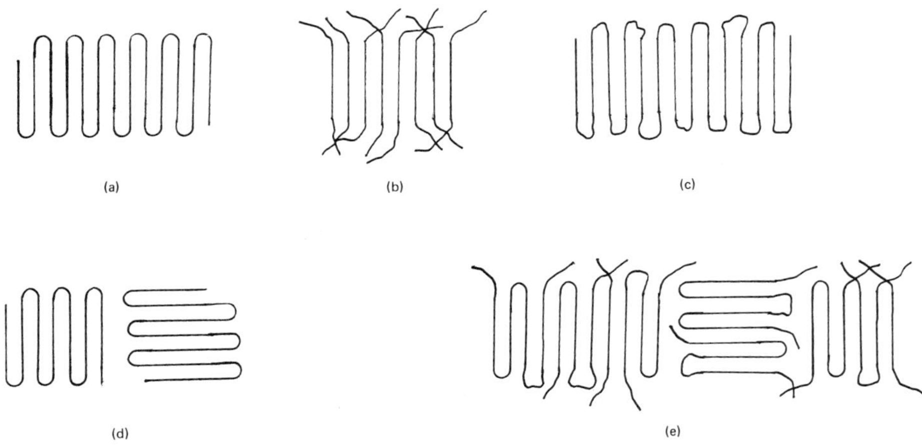

FIGURE 2.18 Schematic two-dimensional representations of models of the fold surface in polymer lamellae: (a) sharp folds, (b) switchboard model, (c) loops with loose folds, (d) buttressed loops, and (e) a combination of these features.

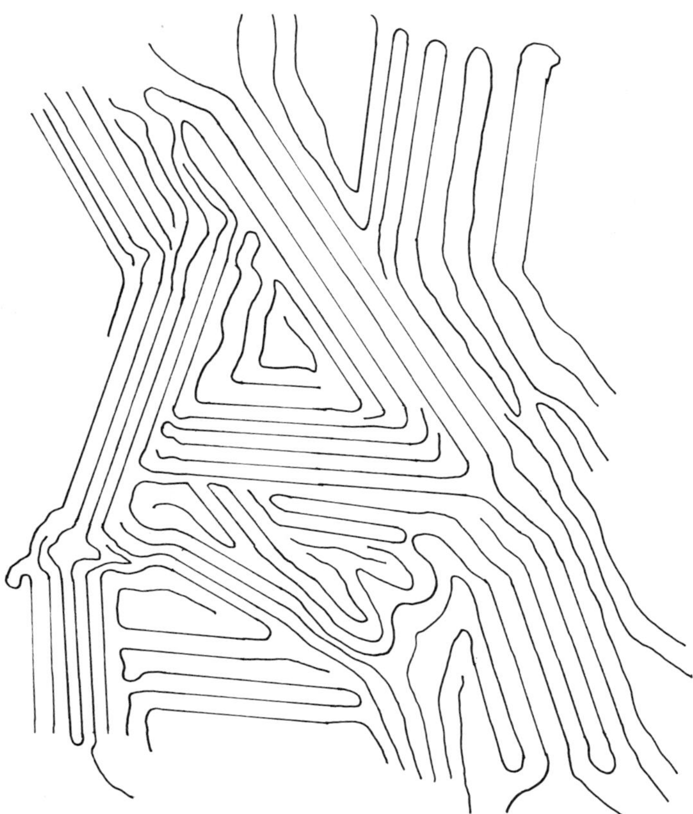

FIGURE 2.19 Schematic two-dimensional representation of a modified micelle model of the crystalline-amorphous structure of polymers incorporating features from Fig. 2.18.

In addition to crystallization of the backbone of polymers, crystallization may also occur in regularly spaced bulky groups even when an amorphous structure is maintained in the backbone. In general, the pendant group must contain at least 10 carbon atoms in order for this side-chain crystallization to occur. Rapid crystallization to produce films with good transparency may be brought about by the addition of a crystalline nucleating agent, such as benzoic acid, and by cooling rapidly.

Ordered polymers with small pendant groups crystallize more readily than those with bulky groups, such as polyvinyl acetate, $+CH_2\overset{|}{C}HOOCCH_3$. However, the hydrolytic product of the latter [polyvinyl alcohol, $-CH_2-\overset{|}{C}HOH$] crystallizes readily. Crystallization also occurs when different groups with similar size, like CH , CHOH, CF , and C=O, are present (see Fig. 2.20).

While polymeric hydrocarbons have been used as illustrations for simplicity, it is important to note that the principles discussed apply to all polymers, organic as well as inorganic and natural as well as synthetic, and to elastomers, plastics, and fibers. The principal differences among the last are related to T_g, which is governed by the groups present in the chain and as pendant groups and the relative strength of the intermolecular bonds.

2.4 POLYMER STRUCTURE-PROPERTY RELATIONSHIPS

Throughout the text we will relate polymer structure with the properties of the polymer. Polymer properties are related not only to the chemical nature of the polymer but also to such factors as extent and distribution of crystallinity, distribution of polymer chain lengths, nature and amount of additives, such as fillers, reinforcers, and plasticizers, to mention only a few. These factors influence essentially all the polymeric properties to some extent, properties like hardness, tear strength, flammability, weatherability, chemical resistance, biologic responses, comfort, appearance, dyeability, softening point, electrical properties, stiffness, flex life, moisture retention, and so forth. Chapters 1 through 11 concentrate on the chemical nature of the polymer itself, whereas Chaps. 12 and 13 deal with the nature and effect on polymer properties by addition of plasticizers, fillers, stabilizers, and so on. Chapter 16 deals with the application of both the polymers themselves and suitable additives aimed at deriving polymers exhibiting desired properties.

Here we will briefly deal with only the chemical and physical nature of polymeric materials that permit their division into three broad divisions—elastomers or rubbers, fibers, and plastics.

Elastomers are high polymers possessing chemical and/or physical cross linking. For industrial application the "use" temperature must be above the T_g (to allow for "chain" mobility), and its normal state (unextended) must be amorphous. The restoring force, after elongation, is largely due to entropy. As the material is elongated, the random chains are forced to occupy more ordered positions. On release of the applied force the chains tend to return to a more random state. Gross, actual mobility of chains must be low. The cohesive energy forces between chains should be low to permit rapid, easy expansion. In its extended state a chain should exhibit a high tensile strength, whereas at low extensions it should have a low tensile strength. Cross-linked vinyl polymers most often meet the desired property requirements. The material after deformation should return to its original shape because of the cross linking. This property is often referred to as a rubber's "memory." Figure 2.21 illustrates some of these properties of elastomers.

Fiber properties include high tensile strength and high modulus (high stress for small strains). These can be obtained from high molecular

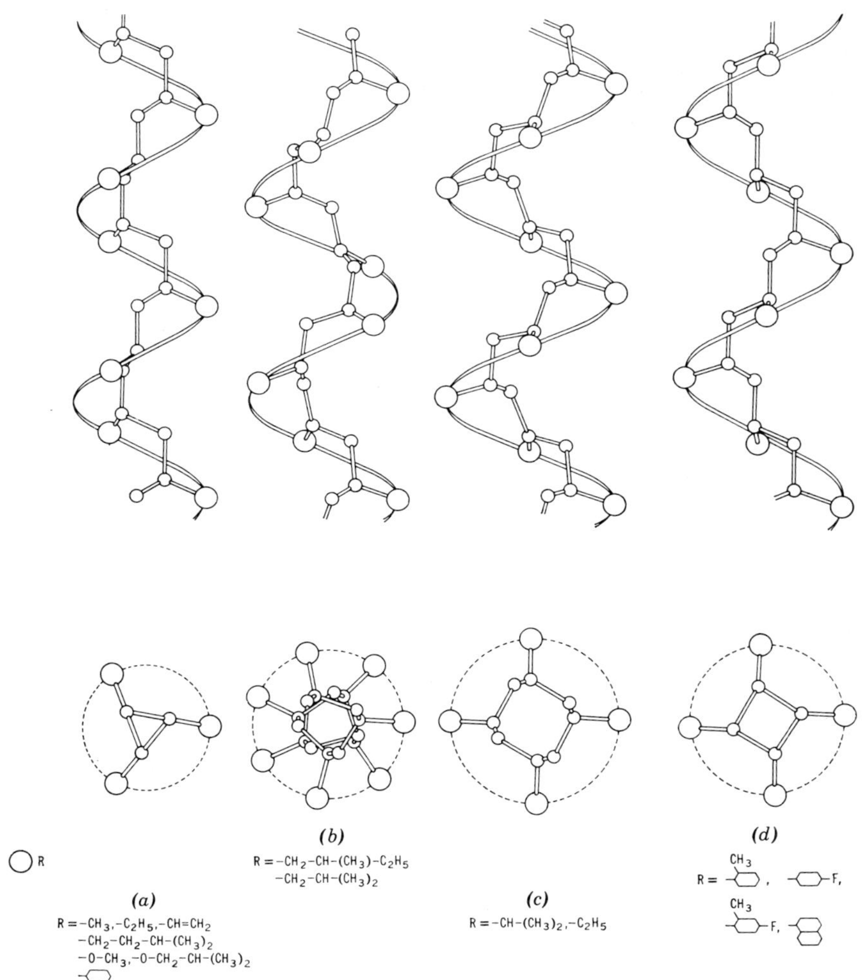

FIGURE 2.20 Helical conformations of isotactic vinyl polymers. [N. Gaylord, in <u>Linear and Stereoregular Addition Polymers</u> (N. Gaylord and H. Mark, eds.).] Wiley Interscience, New York, 1959. With permission from the Interscience Division of John Wiley and Sons, Publishers).

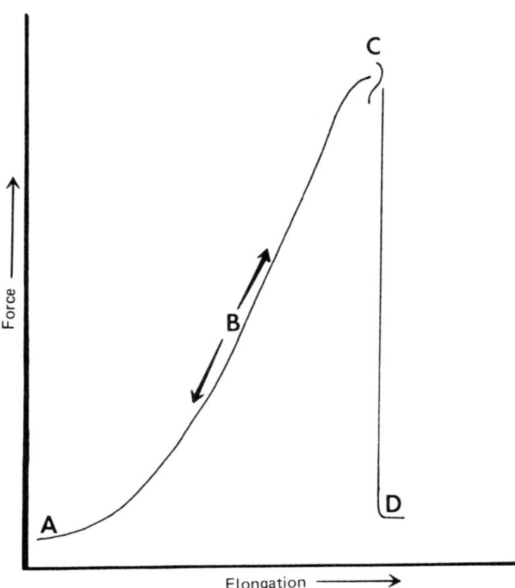

FIGURE 2.21 Elongation of an elastomer as a function of applied force.

symmetry and high cohesive energies between chains, both requiring a fairly high degree of polymer crystallinity. Fibers are normally linear and drawn (oriented) in one direction, producing high mechanical properties in that direction. Typical condensation polymers, such as polyester and nylon, often exhibit these properties. If the fiber is to be ironed, its T_g should be above 200°C, and if it is to be drawn from the melt its T_g should be below 300°C. Branching and cross linking are undesirable since they disrupt crystalline formation even though a small amount of cross linking may increase some physical properties if effected after the material is suitably drawn and processed.

Products with properties intermediate between elastomers and fibers are grouped together under the heading "plastics."

Some polymers can be classified within two categories, with properties being greatly varied by varying molecular weight, end groups, processing, cross linking, plasticizer, and so on. Nylon in its more crystalline form behaves as a fiber, whereas less crystalline forms are generally classified as plastics.

SUMMARY

1. Polymers, or macromolecules, are high molecular weight compounds with chain lengths greater than the critical length required for the

entanglement of these chains. There is an abrupt change in melt viscosity and other physical properties of high molecular weight compounds when the chain length exceeds the critical chain length.

2. While some naturally occurring polymers, such as proteins, are monodisperse, i.e., all have the same molecular weight, other natural and synthetic polymers, such as cellulose and polyethylene, are polydisperse, i.e., they consist of a mixture of polymer chains with different molecular weights. Hence, one uses the term $\overline{DP}$ to indicate an average degree of polymerization, where $\overline{DP}$ is equal to the number of mers (repeating units) in the polymer chain.

3. Many polymers, such as cellulose and HDPE, are linear polymers consisting of long, continuous, covalently bonded atoms. Others such as amylodextrin and LDPE have branches or chain extensions from the polymer backbone and hence have greater volume and lower density than linear polymers. Both linear polymers and those with branches are thermoplastics. In contrast, network polymers such as ebonite, in which individual chains are joined to each other by covalently bonded cross-links, are infusible thermoset polymers.

4. Functional groups in the polymer backbone, such as the methyl group in polypropylene and hevea rubber, are called pendant groups.

5. Many rubberlike polymers are flexible because the free rotation of carbon-carbon single bonds allows the formation of many different shapes, or conformations. This segmental motion is restricted by bulky pendant groups, by stiffening groups in the polymer chains, and by strong intermolecular forces. Hydrogen bonding which is the strongest of these intermolecular forces is essential for most strong fibers.

6. Free rotation of covalently bonded atoms is also prevented by the presence of double bonds. Thus, stable trans and cis configurations are possible for polymers such as polyisoprene. The cis and trans isomeric forms of the latter are known as flexible hevea rubber and hard plastic gutta percha, respectively.

7. When a chiral center is present in a polymer such as polypropylene, many different configurations or optical isomers are possible. The principal configurations with ordered arrangements of the pendant groups are high-melting, strong molecules known as isotactic and syndiotactic isomers. Lower-melting isomers in which the pendant groups are randomly oriented in space are known as atactic polymers.

8. The temperature at which segmental motion occurs because of free rotation of the covalent bonds is a characteristic temperature called the glass transition temperature. To be useful as plastics and elastomers, the polymers must be at a temperature below and above the glass transition temperature (T_g), respectively.

9. Since the specific volume, index of refraction, gas permeability, and heat capacity increase because of the onset of segmental motion at T_g, abrupt changes in these properties may be used to determine T_g.

10. The first-order transition, or melting point (T_m), is 33 to 100% greater than T_g, which is sometimes called the second-order transition. The greatest difference between T_m and T_g is demonstrated by symmetrical polymers like HDPE.

11. A polymer chain stretched out to its full contour length represents only one of the myriad of conformations present in a polymer at temperatures above T_g. Hence, the chain length is expressed statistically as the root mean square distance $\sqrt{\bar{r}^2}$, which is about 7% of the full contour length of the polymer chain.

12. Since branched chains like LDPE have many chain ends it is customary to use the radius of gyration (S), which is the distance of a chain end from the polymer's center of gravity, instead of r.

13. The flexibility, which is related inversely to the orientation time (τ_m) increases as the temperature increases and may be calculated from the Arrhenius equation:

$$\tau_m = A\, e^{E/RT}$$

14. Fibers and stretched elastomers are translucent because of the presence of spherulites consisting of organized crystallites or regions of crystallinity.

15. Since single-lamella crystals consisting of folded chains of symmetrical polymers can be prepared, it is now assumed that crystalline polymers may be represented by a switchboard model consisting of crystalline and amorphous domains.

16. Additional orientation of crystalline polymers occurs and physical properties are improved when films are biaxially oriented or when fibers are stretched.

17. The principal differences between elastomers, plastics, and fibers are the presence and absence of stiffening groups in the chain, the size of the pendant groups on the chain, and the strength of the intermolecular forces. Elastomers are usually characterized by the absence of stiffening groups in the polymer backbone, the presence of bulky pendant groups, and the absence of strong intermolecular forces. In contrast, fibers are characterized by the presence of stiffening groups in the polymer backbone and of intermolecular hydrogen bonds and the absence of branching or irregularly spaced pendant groups. The structure and properties of plastics are between these two extremes.

GLOSSARY

amorphous: Noncrystalline polymer or noncrystalline areas in a polymer.

anti form: Trans (t) or low-energy conformer.

aramids: Aromatic nylons.

Arrhenius equation: An equation showing the exponential effect of temperature on a process.

atactic: A polymer in which there is a random arrangement of pendant groups on each side of the chain, as in atactic PP:

```
    C   C               C
    |   |               |
(—C—C—C—C—C—C—C—C—C—C—C—C—C—C—)
            |   |   |       |
            C   C   C       C
```

Avrami equation: An equation used to describe the crystallization rate.

backbone: The principal chain in a polymer molecule.

biaxially oriented film: A strong film prepared by stretching in two directions at right angles to each other. This strong film will shrink to its original dimensions when heated.

branched polymer: A polymer having extensions of the polymer chain attached to the polymer backbone, such as LDPE. Polymers having pendant groups, such as the methyl groups in polypropylene, are not considered to be branched polymers.

bulky groups: Large pendant groups on a polymer chain.

cellulose: A polymer in which cellobiose is the repeating unit.

chiral center: An asymmetric center such as a carbon atom with four different groups.

cold drawing: The stretching of a fiber or fibers to obtain products with high tensile strength.

configurations: Related chemical structures produced by the breaking and making of primary valence bonds.

conformations: Various shapes of polymers resulting from the rotation of single bonds in the polymer chain.

conformer: A shape produced by a change in the conformation of a polymer.

contour length: The fully extended length of a polymer chain, equal to the product of the length of each repeating unit (l) times the number of units, or mers (n), i.e., nl is the full contour length.

critical chain length (z): The minimum chain length required for entanglement of the polymer chains.

cross-linked density: A measure of the relative degree of cross linking in a network polymer.

crystalline polymer: A polymer with ordered structure which has been allowed to disentangle and form crystals such as HDPE. Thus, isotactic polypropylene, cellulose, and stretched rubber are crystalline polymers.

crystallites: Regions of crystallinity.

differential scanning calorimetry (DSC): An instrumental thermal analytical technique in which the difference in the amount of heat absorbed by a polymer sample and a standard is measured by the power consumed as the temperature is increased.

differential thermal analysis (DTA): A thermal instrumental analytical technique in which the rate of absorption of heat by a polymer is compared with that of a standard such as glass or alumina.

dilatometry: A technique in which changes in specific volume are measured.

dipole-dipole interactions: Moderate secondary valence forces between polar groups in different molecules or in different locations in the same molecule.

dispersion forces: Same as London forces.

DNA: Deoxyribonucleic acid.

DP: Degree of polymerization or the number of repeating units (mers) in a polymer chain.

$\overline{DP}$: Average degree of polymerization in a polydisperse polymer.

η: Viscosity or coefficient of viscosity.

end-to-end distance (r): The shortest distance between chain ends in a polymer.

endothermic: A process in which energy is absorbed.

eutactic: An isotactic or syndiotactic polymer.

excluded volume: The volume which must be disregarded because only one atom of a chain may occupy any specific space at any specified time.

fiber: A polymer with strong intermolecular hydrogen bonding.

flexibilizing groups: Those groups in the polymer backbone that increase the segmental motion of polymers, e.g., oxygen atoms or multiple methylene groups.

fringed micelle model: An outmoded model showing amorphous and crystalline domains in a polymer.

gauche forms (g): Conformers in which the methylene groups in the polymer chain are 60° apart relative to rotation about a C—C bond.

glass transition temperature (T_g): A characteristic temperature at which glassy amorphous polymers become flexible or rubberlike because of the onset of segmental motion.

glassy state: Hard, brittle state.

gutta percha: Naturally occurring trans isomer of polyisoprene.

head-to-tail configuration: The normal sequence of mers in which the pendant groups are regularly spaced like the methyl groups in polypropylene, i.e.,

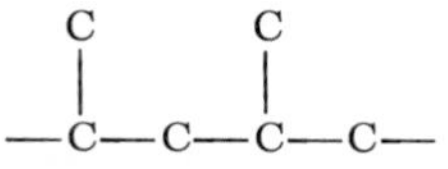

```
   C     C                      C  C
   |     |                      |  |
 —C—C—C—C—     and not     —C—C—C—C—
```

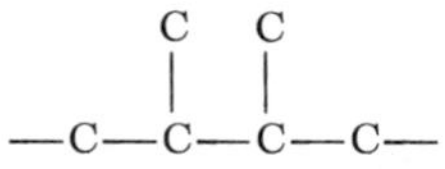

high-density polyethylene (HDPE): Formerly called low-pressure polyethylene, it is a linear polymer produced by the polymerization of ethylene in the presence of Ziegler-Natta catalysts.

hydrogen bonding: Strong secondary valence forces between a hydrogen atom in one molecule and an oxygen, nitrogen, or fluorine atom in another molecule. These forces may also exist between hydrogen atoms in one location and oxygen, nitrogen, or fluorine atoms in another location in the same molecule. Intermolecular hydrogen bonds are responsible for the high strength of fibers. Helices are the result of intramolecular hydrogen bonds.

intermolecular forces: Secondary valence, or van der Waals, forces between different molecules.

intramolecular forces: Secondary valence, or van der Waals, forces within the same molecule.

isotactic: A polymer in which the pendant groups are all on the same side of the polymer backbone, as in isotactic PP:

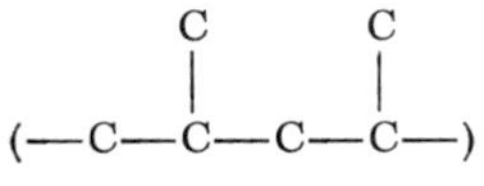

```
      C     C
      |     |
(—C—C—C—C—)
```

lamella: Platelike in shape.

linear polymer: A polymer like HDPE which consists of a linear chain without chain-extending branches.

London forces: Weak transitory dispersion forces resulting from induced dipole-induced dipole interaction.

low-density polyethylene (LDPE): Formerly called high-pressure polyethylene, this is a branched polymer produced by the free radical-initiated polymerization of ethylene at high pressure.

Maltese cross: A cross with arms like arrowheads pointing inward.

melting point (T_m): The first-order transition when the solid and liquid phases are in equilibrium.

mer: The repeating unit in a polymer chain.

methylene: $-CH_2-$.

modulus: The ratio of stress to strain, as of strength to elongation, which is a measure of stiffness of a polymer.

monodisperse: A polymer made up of molecules of one specific molecular weight, such as a protein.

n: Symbol for the number of mers (repeating units) in a polymer.

nanometer (nm): 10^{-9} m.

nylon: A synthetic polyamide.

pendant groups: Groups attached to the main polymer chain or backbone, like the methyl groups in polypropylene.

pentane interference: The interference to free motion caused by the overlap of the hydrogen atoms on the terminal carbon atoms in pentane.

polydisperse: A polymer consisting of molecules of many different molecular weights, such as commercial HDPE.

r: symbol for end-to-end distance.

radius of gyration (S): The root mean square distance of a chain end to a polymer's center of gravity.

random flight technique: A statistical approach used to measure the shortest distance between the start and finish of a random flight.

RNA: Ribonucleic acid.

root mean square distance: $\sqrt{\bar{r}^2} = l\sqrt{n}$, the average end-to-end distance of polymer chains.

S: The radius of gyration.

side-chain crystallization: Crystallization related to that of regularly spaced long pendant groups.

single polymer crystals: A lamellar structure consisting of folded chains of a linear polymer, such as polyethylene.

spherulites: Aggregates of polymer crystallites.

stiffening groups: Those groups in the polymer backbone that decrease the segmental motion of polymers, e.g., phenylene, amide, and sulfonyl groups.

switchboard model: A model resembling a switchboard used to depict crystalline and amorphous domains in a polymer.

syndiotactic: A polymer in which the pendant groups are arranged alternately on each side of the polymer backbone, as in syndiotactic PP:

```
        C
        |
(—C—C—C—C—)
            |
            C
```

τ_m: The orientation time, a measure of the ease of uncoiling.

tacticity: The arrangement of the pendant groups in space such as isotactic or syndiotactic.

van der Waals forces: Forces based on attractions between groups in different molecules or in different locations in the same molecule.

viscosity: A measure of the resistance of a polymer to flow, either as a melt or as a solution.

EXERCISES

1. Make crude sketches or diagrams showing (a) a linear polymer, (b) polymer with pendant groups, (c) a polymer with short branches, (d) a polymer with long branches, and crosslinked polymers with (e) low and (f) high cross-linked density.
2. Which has the (a) greater volume and (b) the lower softening point: HDPE or LDPE?
3. What is the approximate bond angle of the carbon atoms in (a) a linear and (b) cross-linked polymer?
4. What is the approximate length of an HDPE chain when n equals 2000? Of a PVC chain of the same number of repeating units?
5. Which of the following is a monodisperse polymer? (a) hevea rubber, (b) corn starch, (c) cellulose from cotton, (d) casein from milk, (e) HDPE, (f) PVC, (g) β-keratin, (h) nylon-66, (i) DNA.
6. What is the degree of polymerization ($\overline{DP}$) of LDPE having an average molecular weight ($\overline{M}$) of 27,974?

7. What is the structure of the repeating unit (mer) in (a) polypropylene, (b) polyvinyl chloride, (c) hevea rubber?

8. Which of the following is a branched chain polymer? (a) HDPE, (b) isotactic PP, (c) LDPE, (d) amylose starch

9. Which of the following is a thermoplastic? (a) ebonite, (b) Bakelite, (c) vulcanized rubber, (d) HDPE, (e) celluloid, (f) PVC, (g) LDPE

10. Which has the higher cross-linked density, (a) ebonite or (b) soft vulcanized rubber?

11. Do HDPE and LDPE differ in (a) configuration, or (b) conformation?

12. Which is a trans isomer: (a) gutta percha, or (b) hevea rubber?

13. Which will have the higher softening point: (a) gutta percha or (b) hevea rubber?

14. Show (a) a head-to-tail and (b) a head-to-head configuration for polyvinyl alcohol (PVA).

15. Show the structure of a typical portion of the chain of (a) syndiotactic PVC, (b) isotactic PVC.

16. Show Newman projections of the gauche forms of HDPE.

17. Name polymers whose intermolecular forces are principally (a) London forces, (b) dipole-dipole forces, (c) hydrogen bonding.

18. Which will be more flexible (a) polyethylene terephthalate or (b) polybutylene terephthalate?

19. Which will have the higher glass transition temperature (T_g): (a) poly(methyl methacylate) or (b) poly(butyl methacylate)?

20. Which will have the higher T_g: (a) isotactic polypropylene or (b) atactic polypropylene?

21. Which will be more permeable to a gas at room temperature: (a) isotactic polypropylene or (b) atactic polypropylene?

22. Which will have the greater difference between T_m and T_g values: (a) HDPE or (b) LDPE?

23. What is the full contour length of a molecule of HDPE with a DP of 1500?

24. Which would be more flexible: (a) polymethyl acrylate or (b) polymethyl methacrylate?

25. Would you expect the orientation time of HDPE to increase by approximately 5 or 50% when it is cooled from 90 to 80°C?

26. Which would have the higher melting point: (a) nylon-66 or (b) an aramide?

27. What type of hydrogen bonds are present in a globular protein?

28. Which would have the greater tendency to cold flow at room temperature: (a) polyvinyl acetate (T_g = 301°K) or (b) polystyrene (T_g = 375°K)?

29. Which would be more transparent: (a) polystyrene or (b) isotactic polypropylene?

30. Which would be more apt to produce crystallites: (a) HDPE or (b) polybutyl methacylate?

31. How would you cast a nearly transparent film of LDPE?

32. Which would tend to be more crystalline when stretched: (a) unvulcanized rubber or (b) ebonite?

33. Which would be more apt to exhibit side-chain crystallization (a) polymethyl methacrylate or (b) polydodecyl methacylate?

BIBLIOGRAPHY

Alfrey, T. (1948): Mechanical Behavior of High Polymer, Wiley Interscience, New York.

Alfrey, T., Gurnee, E. F. (1956): Dynamics of viscoelastic behavior, in Rheology-Theory and Applications (F. R. Eirich, ed.), Academic, New York.

——. (1967): Organic Polymers, Prentice Hall, Englewood Cliffs, New Jersey.

Bartenov, G. M., Zelenov, Y. V. (1974): Relaxation Phenomena in Polymers, Halsted, New York.

Bassett, D. C. (1964): Preferential attack on folds on single crystals, Polymer 5:457.

Battista, O. A. (1975): Microcrystal Polymer Science, McGraw-Hill, New York.

Billmeyer, F. W. (1957): Lattice energy of crystalline polyethylene, J. Appl. Phys. 28:1114.

——. (1971): Textbook of Polymer Science, Chap. 5, John Wiley, New York.

Blackadder, D. A. (1967): Ten years of polymer single crystals, J. Macromal. Sci. Rev. Makromol. Chem. 1:297.

Boenig, H. V. (1973): Structure and Properties of Polymers, Halsted, New York.

Brandrup, J., Immergut, E. H. (1975): Polymer Handbook, 2nd ed., John Wiley, New York.

Briston, J. H. (1974): Plastic Fibers, Halsted, New York.

Bueche, F. (1962): Physical Properties of Polymers, Chap. 13, Wiley Interscience, New York.

Bunn, C. W. (1953): in Fibers from Synthetic Polymers (R. Hill, ed.), Chap. 11, American Elsevier, New York.

——. (1961): Chemical Crystallography, Oxford University Press, London.

Chargaff, E., Davidson, J. N. (1955): The Nucleic Acids, Academic, New York.

Chompff, A. J., Newman, S. (1973): Polymer Networks, Plenum, New York.

Corradini, P. (1968): in The Stereochemistry of Macromolecules (A. D. Ketley, ed.), Chaps. 1 and 3, Dekker, New York.

Cowie, J. M. G. (1974): Polymers: Chemistry and Physics of Modern Materials, Chap. 6, Intext Educational Publishers, New York.

Deanin, R. D. (1972): Polymer Structure, Properties and Applications, Cahners Books, Boston.

Di Benedetto, A. T. (1967): The Structure and Properties of Materials, Chap. 8, McGraw-Hill, New York.

Dimarzio, E. A., Gibbs, J. H. (1959): Glass transition temperatures of copolymers, J. Polymer Sci., 40:121.

Eisenberg, A., Shen, M. (1970): Recent advances in glass transitions in polymers, Rubber Chem. Technol., 43:156.

Ferry, J. D. (1970): Viscoelastic Properties of Polymers, John Wiley, New York.

Fischer, E. W. (1957): Step and spiral growth of high polymers, Z. Naturforsch. 12a:753.

Fitch, R. M. (1973): Polymer Colloids, Plenum, New York.

Flory, P. J. (1953): Principles of Polymer Chemistry, Cornell University Press, Ithaca, New York.

——. (1962): On the morphology of the crystalline state of polymers, J. Am. Chem. Soc., 84:2857.

Geil, P. H. (1963): Polymer Single Crystals, Wiley Interscience, New York.

Goodman, M., Schulman, J. S. (1966): Stereochemistry of polymers, J. Polymer Sci., Part C, 12:23.

Harward, R. N. (1973): The Physics of Glassy Polymers, Halsted, New York.

Hopfinger, H. J. (1974): Conformational Properties of Macromolecules, Academic, New York.

Katz, J. R. (1925): Crystalline structure of rubber, Kolloid, 36:300.

Keller, A. (1962): Polymer single crystals, Polymer, 3:393.

Lindenmeyer, P. H. (1963): Single crystals, J. Polymer Sci., Part C, 1:5.

Lenz, R. W. (1967): Organic Chemistry of High Polymers, Wiley Interterscience, New York.

Lenz, R. W., Stein, R. S. (1972): Structure and Properties of Polymer Films, Plenum, New York.

Mandelkern, L. (1964): Crystallization of Polymers, McGraw-Hill, New York.

——. (1972): An Introduction to Macromolecules, Chap. 3, Springer-Verlag, Berlin.

—— . (1972): An Introduction to Macromolecules, Chap. 5, Springer-Verlag, New York.

Margerison, D., East, G. C. (1967): An Introduction to Polymer Chemistry, Chap. 1, Pergamon, New York.

Mark, H. F. (1967): Giant molecules, Sci. Am., 197:80.

Marvel, C. S. (1959): An Introduction to the Organic Chemistry of High Polymers, John Wiley, New York.

Matijevic, E. (1976): Surface and Colloidal Science, John Wiley, New York.

McGregor, R. (1975): Diffusion and Sorption in Fibers and Films, Academic, New York.

McGrew, F. C. (1938): Structure of synthetic high polymers, J. Chem. Ed., 35:178.

Meares, P. (1964): Polymers—Structure and Bulk Properties, Chap. 4, Van Nostrand, Princeton.

——. (1964): Polymers—Structure and Bulk Properties, Chap. 7, Van Nostrand, Princeton.

Mendelson, R. A. (1968): Melt viscosity, in Encyclopedia of Polymer Science and Technology, Vol. 8, p. 587 (H. F. Mark, N. G. Gaylord, N. M. Bihalis, eds.), Wiley Interscience, New York.

Miller, M. L. (1964): The Structure of Polymers, Reinhold, New York.

———. (1966): The Structure of Polymers, Chaps. 4, 6, and 10, Reinhold, New York.

Natta, G. (1955): Stereospecific macromolecules, J. Polymer Sci., 16:143.

Newman, B. A., Kay, H. F. (1967): Chain folding in polyethylene and cyclic paraffins, J. Appl. Phys., 38:4105.

Nielson, L. E. (1963): Mechanical Properties of Polymers, Reinhold, New York.

O'Driscoll, K. F. (1964): The Nature and Chemistry of High Polymers, Chap. 5, Reinhold, New York.

Oswin, C. R. (1975): Plastic Films and Packaging, Halsted, New York.

Pauling, L., Corey, R. B., Branson, H. R. (1951): The structure of proteins, Proc. Natl. Acad. Sci. USA, 37:205.

Plastics and Rubber Institute. (1976): Polypropylene Fibers in Textiles, London.

Price, F. P. (1969): Nucleation in polymer crystallization, Nucleation, 405.

Raave, A. (1967): Organic Chemistry of Macromolecules, Chap. 2, Dekker, New York.

Raleigh, Lord. (1929): Random flight problem, Phil. Mag., 37:321.

Rochow, T. G. (ed.). (1963): Morphology of Polymers, Wiley Interscience, New York.

Rodriguez, F. (1970): Principles of Polymer Systems, Chap. 2, McGraw-Hill, New York.

Schlesinger, W., Leeper, H. M. (1953): Gutta I. Single crystals of alpha-Gutta, J. Polymer Sci., 11:203.

Schönhorn, H., Luongo, J. P. (1969): Fold structure of polyethylene single crystals, Macromolecules, 2:366.

Seymour, R. B. (1971): Introduction to Polymer Chemistry, Chap. 1, McGraw-Hill, New York.

———. (1975): Modern Plastics Technology, Chap. 1, Reston, Reston, Virginia.

Sharpler, A. (1966): Introduction to Polymer Crystallization, St. Martin's, New York.

Small, P. A. (1975): Long Chain Branching in Polymers, Springer-Verlag, New York.

Stevens, M. P. (1975): Polymer Chemistry, An Introduction, Chap. 3, Addison-Wesley, Reading, Massachusetts.

Stille, J. K. (1962): Introduction to Polymer Chemistry, Chap. 3, John Wiley, New York.

Till, P. H. (1975): The growth of single crystals of linear polyethylene, J. Polymer Sci., 24:301.

Treloar, L. R. G. (1970): Introduction to Polymer Science, Chap. 1, Wykeham Publications, London.

Van Kevelen, D. W. (1972): Properties of Polymers, Chap. 1, American Elsevier, New York.

Wall, F. T., Erkenbeck, J. J. (1959): Computer calculations of root mean square distance, J. Chem. Phys., 30:634.

Ward, I. M. (1975): Structure and Properties of Oriented Polymers, Wiley, New York.

Watson, J. D., Crick, F. H. C. (1953): A structure for DNA, Nature, 171:737.

Williams, H. L. (1975): Polymer Engineering, Chap. 1, American Elsevier, New York.

Wunderlich, B. (1969): Crystalline High Polymers, American Chemical Society, Washington, D.C.

——. (1976): Macromolecular Physics, Academic, New York.

3

Rheology and Solubility

3.1 RHEOLOGY

The branch of science related to the study of deformation and flow of materials was given the name rheology by Bingham, who some have called the father of modern rheology. The prefix rheo is derived from the Greek term rheos, meaning current or flow. The study of rheology includes two vastly different branches of mechanics called fluid and solid mechanics. The polymer chemist is usually concerned with viscoelastic materials that act as both solids and fluids.

The elastic component is dominant in solids, hence their mechanical properties may be described by Hooke's law (3.1) which states that the applied stress (S) is proportional to the resultant strain (γ) but is independent of the rate of this strain ($d\gamma/dt$).

$$S = E\gamma \qquad (3.1)$$

Stress is equal to force per unit area, and strain or elongation is the extension per unit length. For an isotropic solid, i.e., one having the same properties regardless of direction, the strain is defined by Poisson's ratio, $V = \gamma_l/\gamma_w$, the percentage change in longitudinal strain, γ_l, to the percentage change in lateral strain, γ_w.

When there is no volume change, as when an elastomer is stretched, Poisson's ratio is 0.5. This value decreases as T_g of the substance increases and approaches 0.3 for rigid PVC and ebonite. For simplicity, the polymers will be considered to be isotropic viscoelastic solids with a Poisson's ratio of 0.5, and only deformations in tension and shear will be considered. Thus, a shear modulus (G) will usually be used in place of Young's modulus of elasticity (E) [refer to (3.2), Hooke's law for shear], where

$E \simeq 2.6G$ at temperatures below T_g. The moduli (G) for steel, HDPE, and hevea rubber (NR) are 86, 0.087, and 0.00067 m^{-2}, respectively.

$$S = G\gamma \tag{3.2}$$

The viscous component is dominant in liquids, hence their flow properties may be described by Newton's law (3.3) which states that the applied stress S is proportional to the rate of strain $d\gamma/dt$, but is independent of the strain γ or applied velocity gradient. The symbol $\dot{\gamma}$ is sometimes used for strain rate.

$$S = \eta \frac{d\gamma}{dt} \tag{3.3}$$

Both Hooke's and Newton's laws are valid for small changes in strain or rate of strain, and both are useful in studying the effect of stress on viscoelastic materials. The initial elóngation of a stressed polymer below T_g is the reversible elongation due to a stretching of covalent bonds and distortion of the bond angles. Some of the very early stages of elongation by disentanglement may also be reversible.

However, the rate of flow, which is related to slow disentanglement and slippage of polymer chains past each other, is irreversible and increases (and η decreases) as the temperature increases in accordance with the following Arrhenius equation (3.4) in which E is the activation energy for viscous flow.

$$\eta = Ae^{E/RT} \tag{3.4}$$

It is convenient to use a simple weightless Hookean, or ideal, elastic spring with a modulus of G and a simple Newtonian (fluid) dash pot or shock absorber having a liquid with a viscosity of η as models to demonstrate the deformation of an elastic solid and an ideal liquid. The stress-strain curves for these models are shown in Fig. 3.1.

Since polymers are viscoelastic solids, combinations of these models are used to demonstrate the deformation resulting from the application of stress to an isotropic solid polymer. As shown in Fig. 3.2, Maxwell joined the two models in series to explain the mechanical properties of pitch and tar. He assumed that the contribution of both the spring and dash pot to strain were additive and that the application of stress would cause an instantaneous elongation of the spring followed by a slow response of the piston in the dash pot. Thus, the relaxation time (τ), when the stress and elongation have reached equilibrium, is equal to η/G.

In the Maxwell model for viscoelastic deformation, it is assumed that $\gamma_{total} = \gamma_{elastic} + \gamma_{viscous}$. This may be expressed in the form of the following differential equation:

$$\frac{d\gamma}{dt} = \frac{s}{\eta} + \frac{ds}{dt}\frac{1}{G} \tag{3.5}$$

The rate of strain $d\gamma/dt$ is equal to zero under conditions of constant stress (s), i.e.,

$$\frac{s}{\eta} + \frac{ds}{dt}\frac{1}{G} = 0 \tag{3.6}$$

Then, assuming that $s = s_o$ at zero time, gives

$$s = s_o e^{-tG/\eta} \tag{3.7}$$

And, since the relaxation time $\tau = \eta/G$, then

$$s = s_o e^{-t/\tau} \tag{3.8}$$

Thus, according to (3.8) for the Maxwell model or element, under conditions of constant strain, the stress or stresses will decrease exponentially with time and at the relaxation time τ will be equal to $1/e = 1/2.7$, or 0.37 of its original value (s_o).

As shown in Fig. 3.3, the spring and dash pot are parallel in the Voigt-Kelvin model. In this model or element, the applied stress (or stresses) is

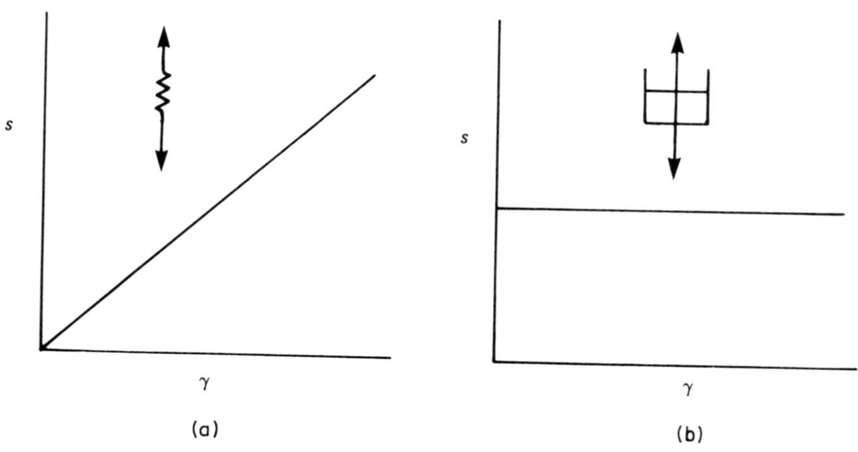

FIGURE 3.1 Stress-strain plots for (a) a Hookean spring, and (b) a Newtonian dash pot.

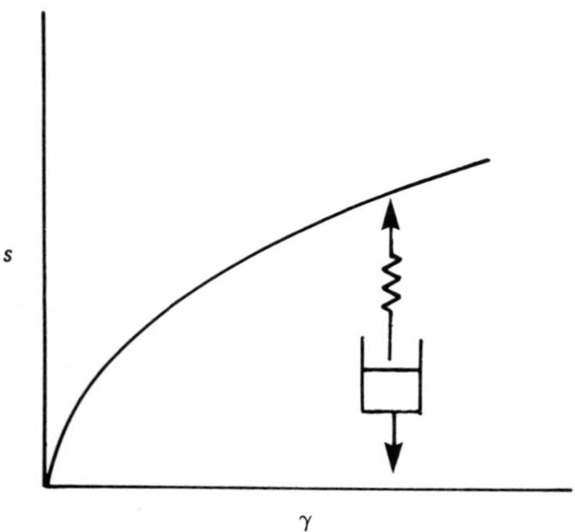

FIGURE 3.2 Stress-strain plot for stress relaxation in the Maxwell model.

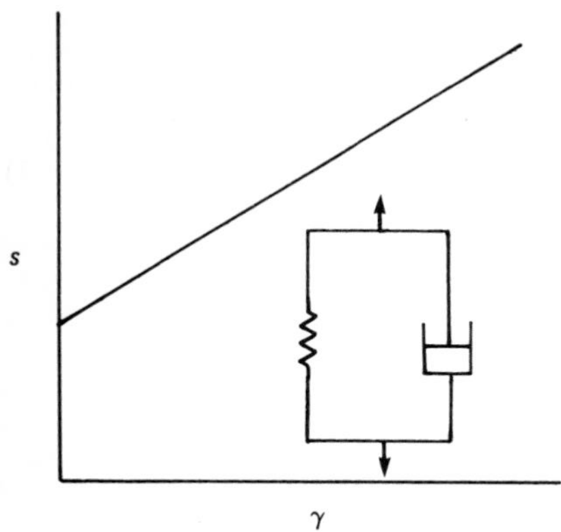

FIGURE 3.3 Stress-strain plot for a Voigt-Kelvin Model.

shared between the spring and thus dash pot, and the elastic response is thus retarded by the viscous resistance of the liquid in the dash pot. In this model, the vertical movement of the spring is essentially equal to that of the piston in the dash pot. Thus, if G is much larger than η, the retardation time (η/G) or τ is small, and the latter is large if η is larger than G.

In the Voigt-Kelvin model for viscoelastic deformation, it is assumed that the total stress is equal to the sum of the viscous and elastic stress, as shown in (3.9).

$$s = \eta \frac{d\gamma}{dt} + G\gamma \tag{3.9}$$

On integration one obtains (3.10),

$$\gamma = \frac{s}{G}(1 - e^{-tG/\eta}) = \frac{s}{G}(1 - e^{-t/\tau}) \tag{3.10}$$

The retardation time τ is the time for the model to decrease to 1 - (1/e) or 1 - (1/2.7) = 0.63 of the original value. The viscoelastic flow of polymers is explained by appropriate combinations of the Maxwell and Voigt-Kelvin models.

While polymer melts and elastomers flow readily when stress is applied, structural plastics must resist irreversible deformation and behave as elastic solids when relatively small stresses are applied. These plastics are called ideal or Bingham plastics as described by (3.11).

$$s - s_o = \eta \frac{d\gamma}{dt} \tag{3.11}$$

As shown in Fig. 3.4, a Bingham plastic exhibits Newtonian flow above the stress yield value (s_o). The curves for shear thickening (dilatant) and shear thinning (pseudoplastic) materials are also shown in Fig. 3.4.

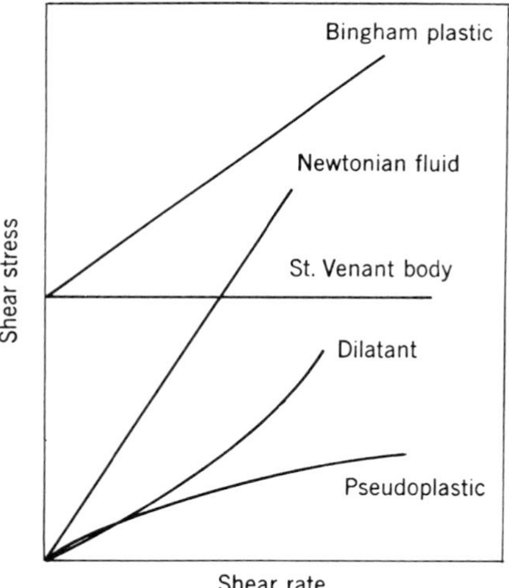

FIGURE 3.4 Various types of polymer flow. (From Introduction to Polymer Chemistry by R. Seymour, McGraw-Hill, New York, 1971. Used with permission of McGraw-Hill Book Company.)

Liquids which undergo a decrease in viscosity with time are called thixotropic, or false-bodied. Those that undergo an increase in viscosity with time are called rheopectic (shear thickening). The term creep is used to describe the slow slippage of polymer chains over a long period of time. The Herschel-Buckley equation (3.12) is a general equation which reduces to the Bingham equation when $\eta = 1$ and to the Newtonian equation when $\eta = 1$ and $s_o = 0$.

$$(s - s_o)\eta = \phi \frac{d\gamma}{dt} \qquad (3.12)$$

Eyring has explained liquid flow using a random hole filling model in which the holes account for about 15% of the volume at room temperature. The size of these holes is similar to that of small molecules, and hole filling is restrained by an energy barrier which is about one-third the value of the heat of evaporation. The number of holes increases as the temperature increases, and thus flow or hole filling is temperature dependent.

Small molecules jump into the holes and leave them empty when their energy exceeds the activation energy (E_a). This last value is smaller for linear polymers which fill the holes by successive correlated jumps of chain segments along the polymer chain. The jump frequency ϕ is governed by a segmental factor (f_0) and both ϕ and f_0 are related to molecular structure and temperature.

For convenience and simplicity, polymers have been considered to be isotropic in which the principal force is a shear stress. While such assumptions are acceptable for polymers at low shear rates, they fail to account for stresses perpendicular to the plane of the shear stress, which are encountered at high shear rates. Thus, an extrudate such as a pipe or filament expands when it emerges from the die in what is called the Barus or Weissenberg effect, or die swell.

As illustrated later in Figure 5.2 viscoelasticity can be subclassified into five types: (1) viscous glass, Hookean elastic, or Hookean glass region, where chain segmental motion is quite restricted and involves mainly only bond bending and bond angle deformation; the material behaves as a glass like a glass window; while flow occurs it is detectable only with delicate, exacting instruments; stained-glass windows in the old churches in Europe are typically thicker at the bottom of each segment due to the slow flow; (2) glassy transition and (3) the rubbery flow region are both related to what is often referred to as the viscoelastic region where polymer deformation is reversible but time dependent and associated with both side-chain and main-chain rotation; (4) rubbery, highly elastic rubbery, or rubberlike elasticity, where local segmental mobility occurs but total chain flow is restricted by physical and/or chemical network matrix structure; and (5) rubbery flow or viscous flow region where irreversible bulk deformation and slippage of chains past one another occur. Each of these viscoelastic types are time dependent. Thus, given a short interaction time, window glass acts as a Hookean glass or like a solid, yet observation of glass over many years would permit the visual observation of flow, with the window glass giving a viscous flow response and thus acting as a fluid. In fact, most polymers give a response as noted in Fig. 3.5 if a rubber ball were dropped onto the material either as the temperature of the sample were increased or as the interaction time decreased. Commercial Silly Putty or Nutty Putty easily illustrates three of these regions. When struck rapidly it shatters as a solid, when dropped at a moderate rate it acts as a rubber, and when allowed to reside in its container it will flow to occupy the container contour, acting as a liquid. The exact response (illustrated in Fig. 3.5) varies from material to material.

The study of these types of viscoelasticity may be simplified by application of the Boltzman time-temperature superposition principle which provides master curves. This transposition for amorphous polymers is readily accomplished by use of a shift factor a_T calculated relative to a reference temperature T_R, which may be equal to T_g.

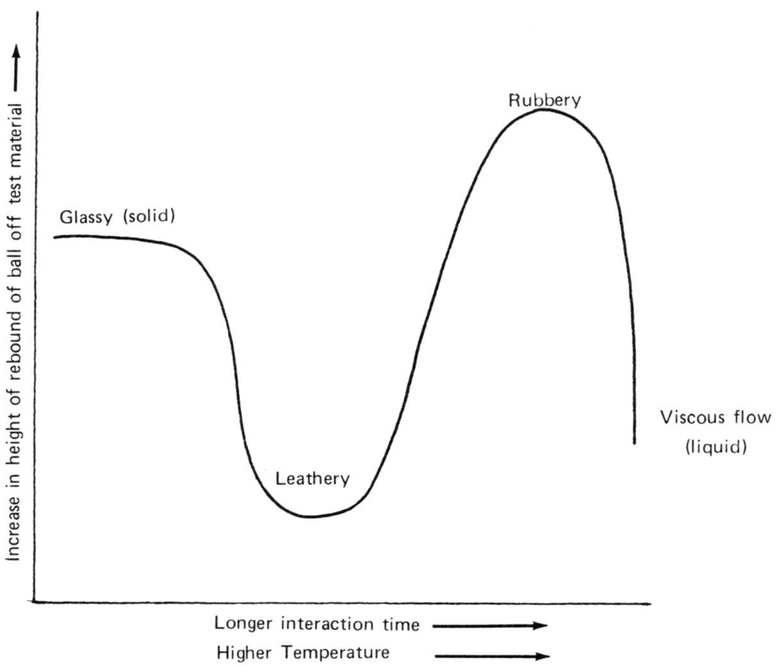

FIGURE 3.5 Regions of material response as a function of interaction (reaction) time and temperature.

The relationship of the shift factor a_T to the reference temperature T_R and some other temperature T, which is less than T_g + 100 K, may be approximated by the Arrhenius equation shown in (2.4).

$$\log a_T = -\frac{b}{2.3TT_g}(T - T_g) \tag{3.13}$$

According to the more widely used empirical Williams, Landel, and Ferry (WLF) equation, all polymers have similar viscoelastic properties at T_g and at specified temperatures above T_g such as T_g + 25°C; log a_T in the WLF equation (3.14) is equal to log (η_T/η_{T_g}), and the constants C_1 and C_2 are related to holes or free volume. When T_g is the reference temperature, C_1 = 17.44 and C_2 = 51.6.

$$\log a_T = -\frac{C_1(T - T_g)}{C_2 + (T - T_g)} \tag{3.14}$$

3.2 SOLUBILITY

The physical properties of polymers, including T_g values, are related to the strength of the covalent bonds, the stiffness of the segments in the polymer backbone, and the strength of the intermolecular forces between the polymer molecules. The strength of the intermolecular forces is equal to the cohesive energy density (CED), which is the molar energy of vaporization per unit volume. Since intermolecular attractions of solvent and solute must be overcome when a solute dissolves, CED values may be used to predict solubility.

When a polymer dissolves, the first step is a slow swelling process called solvation in which the polymer molecule swells by a factor δ which is related to CED. Linear and branched polymers dissolve in a second step, but network polymers remain in a swollen condition.

In order for solution to take place, it is essential that the free energy G, which is the driving force in the solution process, decrease as shown in the Gibbs free energy equation for constant temperature (3.15). ΔH and ΔS are equal to the change in enthalpy and the change in entropy in this equation.

$$\Delta G = \Delta H - T\,\Delta S \tag{3.15}$$

Assuming that the sizes of polymer segments were similar to those of solvent molecules, Flory and Huggins obtained an expression for the partial molar Gibbs free energy of dilution which included the dimensionless Flory-Huggins interaction parameter, $\chi_1 = Z\,\Delta e/RT$ in which Z = a lattice coordination number. It is now recognized that χ_1 is composed of enthalpic and entropic considerations.

While the Flory-Huggins theory has its limitations, it may be used to predict the equilibrium behavior between liquid phases containing an amorphous polymer. The theory may also be used to predict a cloud point which is just below the critical solution temperature T_c at which the two phases coalesce. The Flory-Huggins interaction parameter may be used as a measure of solvent power. The value of χ_1 for poor solvents is 0.5 and decreases for good solvents.

The limitations of the Flory-Huggins lattice theory were overcome by Flory and Krigbaum, who assumed the presence of an excluded volume from which long-range interactions originate. The latter are described in terms of free energy by introducing the enthalpy and entropy terms K_1 and ψ_1. These terms are equal when ΔG equals zero. The temperature at which these conditions prevail is the θ temperature at which the effects of the excluded volume are eliminated and the polymer molecule assumes an unperturbed conformation in dilute solutions. The θ temperature is the lowest temperature at which a polymer of infinite molecular weight is completely miscible with a specific solvent. The coil expands above the θ temperature and contracts at lower temperatures.

As early as 1926, Hildebrand showed a relationship between solubility and the internal pressure of the solvent, and in 1931 Scatchard incorporated the CED concept into Hildebrand's equation. This led to the concept of a solubility parameter which is the square root of CED. Thus, as shown below, the solubility parameter δ for nonpolar solvents is equal to the square root of the heat of vaporization per unit volume:

$$\delta = \left(\frac{\Delta E}{V}\right)^{1/2} \tag{3.16}$$

According to Hildebrand, the heat of mixing of a solute and solvent is proportional to the square of the difference in solubility parameters, as shown by the following equation in which ϕ is the partial volume of each component, namely, solvent ϕ_1 and solute ϕ_2. Since typically the entropy term favors solution and the enthalpy term acts counter to solution, the general objective is to match solvent and solute so that the difference between their δ values is small.

$$\Delta H_m = \phi_1 \phi_2 (\delta_1 - \delta_2)^2 \tag{3.17}$$

The solubility parameter concept predicts the heat of mixing of liquids and amorphous polymers. Hence, any nonpolar amorphous polymer will dissolve in a liquid or a mixture of liquids having a solubility parameter that does not differ by more than ± 1.8 (cal cm^{-3})$^{0.5}$. The Hildebrand (H) is preferred over these complex units.

The solubility parameters concept, like Flory's θ temperature, is based on Gibbs free energy. Thus, as the term ΔH in the expression ($\Delta G = \Delta H - T\,\Delta S$) approaches zero, ΔG will have the negative value required for solution to occur. The entropy (ΔS) increases in the solution process and hence the emphasis is on negative or low values of ΔH_m.

For nonpolar solvents which have been called regular solvents by Hildebrand, the solubility parameter δ is equal to the square root of the difference between the enthalpy of evaporation (ΔH_V) and the product of the ideal gas constant (R) and the Kelvin temperature (T) divided by the molar volume (V), as shown below:

$$\delta = \left(\frac{\Delta E}{V}\right)^{1/2} = \left(\frac{\Delta H_V - RT}{V}\right)^{1/2} \qquad (3.18)$$

Since it is difficult to measure the molar volume, its equivalent, namely, the molecular weight M divided by density D, is substituted for V as shown below:

$$\delta = \left[D\,\frac{(\Delta H_V - RT)}{M}\right]^{1/2} \qquad (3.19)$$

As shown by the following illustration, this expression may be used to calculate the solubility parameter δ for any nonpolar solvent such as n-heptane at 298°K. n-Heptane has a molar heat of vaporization of 8700 cal, a density of 0.68 g cm^{-3}, and a molecular weight of 100.

$$\delta = \left\{\frac{0.68[8700 - 2(298)]}{100}\right\}^{1/2} = (55.1 \text{ cal cm}^{-3})^{1/2} = 7.4\text{H} \qquad (3.20)$$

The solubility parameter $(CED)^{1/2}$ is also related to the intrinsic viscosity of solutions ($[\eta]$) as shown by the following expression:

$$[\eta] = \eta_o e^{-V(\delta-\delta_o)^2} \qquad (3.21)$$

The term intrinsic viscosity or limiting viscosity number is defined later in this chapter.

Since the heat of vaporization of solid polymers is not readily obtained, Small has supplied values for molar attraction constants (G) which are additive and can be used in the following equation for the estimation of the solubility parameter of nonpolar polymers:

$$\delta = \frac{D\Sigma G}{M} \qquad (3.22)$$

Typical values for G at 25°C are shown in Table 3.1.

TABLE 3.1 Small's Molar Attraction Constants (at 25°C)

Group	$G[(\text{cal cm}^3)^{1/2}\ \text{mol}^{-1}]$
$-CH_3$	214
$>CH_2$	133
$>CH-$	28
$-\overset{\vert}{\underset{\vert}{C}}-$	-93
$=CH_2$	190
$=CH-$	111
$=C<$	19
$HC\equiv C-$	285
Phenyl	735
Phenylene	658
$-H$	80-100
$-C\equiv N$	410
F or Cl	250-270
Br	340
$>CF_2$	150
$-S-$	225

The use of Small's equation may be illustrated by calculating the solubility parameter of amorphous polypropylene (D = 0.905) which consists of the units CH, CH_2, and CH_3 in each mer. Polypropylene has a mer weight of 42.

$$\delta = \frac{0.905(28 + 133 + 214)}{42} = 8.1\ \text{H} \tag{3.23}$$

Since CED is related to intermolecular attractions and chain stiffness, Hayes has derived an expression relating δ, T_g, and a chain stiffness constant as shown below:

$$\delta = [M(T_g - 25)]^{1/2} \tag{3.24}$$

Since the polarity of most solvents except the hydrocarbons decreases as the molecular weight increases in a homologous series, δ values also decrease, as shown in Fig. 3.6.

Since "like dissolves like" is not a quantitative expression, paint technologists attempted to develop more quantitative empirical parameters before the Hildebrand solubility parameter had been developed. The Kauri-Butanol and aniline points are still in use and are considered standard tests by the American Society for Testing and Materials (ASTM).

The Kauri-Butanol value is equal to the minimum volume of test solvent which produces turbidity when added to a standard solution of Kauri-Copal

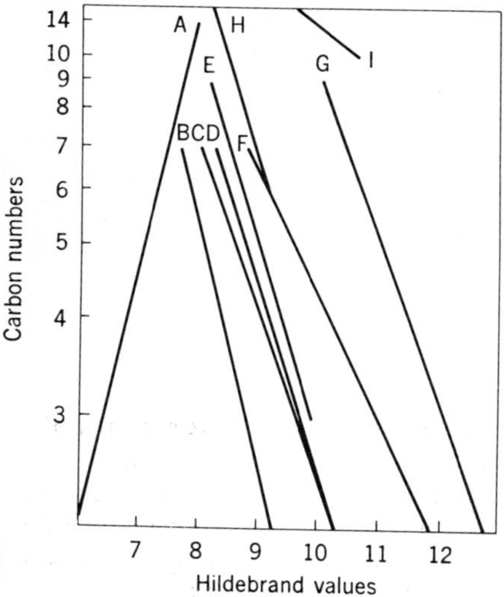

A = Normal alkanes, B = Normal chloroalkanes, C = Methyl esters, D = Other alkyl formates and acetates, E = Methyl ketones, F = Alkyl nitriles, G = Normal alkanols, H = Alkyl benzenes, I = Dialkyl phthalates.

FIGURE 3.6 Spectrum of solubility-parameter values for polymers (δ = 6.2 to 15.4). (From Introduction to Polymer Chemistry by R. Seymour, McGraw-Hill, New York, 1971. Used with permission of McGraw-Hill Book Company.)

resin in 1-butanol. The aniline point is the lowest temperature at which equal volumes of aniline and the test solvent are completely miscible. Both tests are measurements of the relative aromaticity of the test solvent, and their values may be converted to δ values.

Since the law of mixtures applies to the solubility parameter, it is possible to blend nonsolvents to form a mixture which will serve as a good solvent. For example, an equimolar mixture of n-pentane ($\delta = 7.1$ H) and n-octane ($\delta = 7.6$ H) will have a solubility parameter value of 7.35 H.

The solubility parameter of a polymer may be readily determined by noting the extent of swelling or actual solution of small amounts of polymer in a series of solvents having different δ values. Providing the polymer is in solution, its δ value may be determined by turbidimetric titration using two different nonsolvents, one which is more polar and one that is less polar than the solvent present in the solution.

Since dipole-dipole forces are present in polar solvents and polar molecules, these must be taken into account when estimating solubilities with "nonregular solvents." A third factor must be considered for hydrogen-bonded solvents or polymers. Domains of solubility for nonregular solvents or solutes may be shown on three-dimensional plots.

Plasticizers are typically nonvolatile solvents with $\Delta\delta$ values between the polymer and the plasticizer of less than 1.8 H. Plasticizers reduce the intermolecular attractions (CED and δ) of polymers such as cellulose nitrate (CN) and PVC and make processing less difficult. While camphor and tricresyl phosphate, which are plasticizers for CN and PVC, were discovered empirically, it is now possible to use δ values to screen potential plasticizers.

Complete data for solubility parameters may be found in the Polymer Handbook (see the Bibliography). Typical data are tabulated in Tables 3.2 and 3.3.

3.3 VISCOMETRY

Viscometry is the most widely utilized method for the characterization of polymer molecular weight since it provides the easiest and most rapid means of obtaining molecular weight-related data and requires a minimum amount of instrumentation. A most obvious characteristic of polymer solutions is their high viscosity, even when the amount of added polymer is small.

The ratio of the viscosity of a polymer solution to that of the solvent is called relative viscosity (η_r). This value less 1 is called the specific viscosity (η_{sp}) and the reduced viscosity (η_{red}), or viscosity number, is obtained by dividing η_{sp} by the concentration of the solution (c). The intrinsic viscosity, or limiting viscosity number, is obtained by extrapolating η_{red} to zero concentration. These relationships are given in Table 3.4 and a typical plot of η_{sp}/c and ln η_r/c as a function of concentration is given in Fig. 3.7.

TABLE 3.2 Solubility Parameters (δ) for Typical Solven[+]

Poorly hydrogen-bonded solvents (δ_p)		Moderately hydrogen-bonded solvents (δ_m)		Strongly hydrogen-bonded solvents (δ_s)	
Hydrogen	3.0	Diisopropyl ether	6.9	Diethylamine	8.0
Dimethylsiloxane	5.5	Diethyl ether	7.4	n-Amylamine	8.7
Difluorodichloromethane	5.5	Isoamyl acetate	7.8	2-Ethylhexanol	9.5
Ethane	6.0	Diisobutyl ketone	7.8	Isoamyl alcohol	10.0
Neopentane	6.3	Di-n-propyl ether	7.8	Acetic acid	10.1
Amylene	6.9	sec-Butyl acetate	8.2	Meta-cresol	10.2
Nitro-n-octane	7.0	Isopropyl acetate	8.4	Aniline	10.3
n-Pentane	7.0	Methyl amyl ketone	8.5	n-Octyl alcohol	10.3
n-Octane	7.6	Butyraldehyde	9.0	tert-Butyl alcohol	10.6
Turpentine	8.1	Ethyl acetate	9.0	n-Amyl alcohol	10.9
Cyclohexane	8.2	Methyl ethyl ketone	9.3	n-Butyl alcohol	11.4
Cymene	8.2	Butyl cellosolve	9.5	Isopropyl alcohol	11.5
Monofluorodichloromethane	8.3	Methyl acetate	9.6	Diethylene glycol	12.1
Dipentene	8.5	Dichloroethyl ether	9.8	Furfuryl alcohol	12.5
Carbon tetrachloride	8.6	Acetone	9.9	Ethyl alcohol	12.7
n-Propylbenzene	8.6	Dioxane	10.0	N-ethylformamide	13.9
p-Chlorotoluene	8.8	Cyclopentanone	10.4	Methanol	14.5
Decalin	8.8	Cellosolve	10.5	Ethylene glycol	14.6
Xylene	8.8	N,N-dimethylacetamide	10.8	Glycerol	16.5
Benzene	9.2	Furfural	11.2	Water	23.4
Styrene	9.3	N,N-dimethylformamide	12.1		
Tetralin	9.4	1,2-Propylene carbonate	13.3		
Chlorobenzene	9.5	Ethylene carbonate	14.7		
Ethylene dichloride	9.8				
p-Dichlorobenzene	10.0				
Nitroethane	11.1				
Acetonitrile	11.9				
Nitroethane	12.7				

TABLE 3.3 Approximate Solubility-Parameter Values for Polymers

Polymer	δ_p	δ_m	δ_s
Polytetrafluorocarbons	5.8-6.4		
Ester gum	7.0-10.6	7.4-10.8	9.5-10.9
Alkyd 45% soy oil	7.0-11.1	7.4-10.8	9.5-11.8
Silicone DC-1107	7.0-9.5	9.3-10.8	9.5-11.5
Polyvinyl ethyl ether	7.0-11.0	7.4-10.8	9.5-14.0
Polybutyl acrylate	7.0-12.5	7.4-11.5	
Polybutyl methacrylate	7.4-11.0	7.4-10.0	9.5-11.2
Silicone DC-23	7.5-8.5	7.5-8.0	9.5-10.0
Polyisobutylene	7.5-8.0	—	—
Polyethylene	7.7-8.2	—	—
Gilsonite	7.9-9.5	7.8-8.5	—
Polyvinyl butyl ether	7.8-10.6	7.5-10.0	9.5-11.2
Natural rubber	8.1-8.5	—	—
Hypalon 20	8.1-9.8	8.4-8.8	—
Ethyl cellulose N-22	8.1-11.1	7.4-10.8	9.5-14.5
Chlorinated rubber	8.5-10.6	7.8-10.8	—
Dammar gum	8.5-10.6	7.8-10.0	9.5-10.9
Versamid 100	8.5-10.6	8.5-8.9	9.5-11.4
Polystyrene	8.5-10.6	9.1-9.4	—
Polyvinyl acetate	8.5-9.5	—	—
Polyvinyl chloride	8.5-11.0	7.8-10.5	—
Phenolic resins	8.5-11.5	7.8-13.2	9.5-13.6
Buna N (butadiene-acrylonitrile copolymer)	8.7-9.3	—	—
Polymethyl methacrylate	8.9-12.7	8.5-13.3	—
Carbowax 4000 (polyethylene oxide)	8.9-12.7	8.5-14.5	9.5-14.5
Thiokol (polyethylene sulfide)	9.0-10.0	—	—
Polycarbonate	9.5-10.6	9.5-10.0	—
Pliolite P-1230	9.5-10.6	—	—
Mylar (polyethylene phthalate)	9.5-10.8	9.3-9.9	—
Vinyl chloride-acetate copolymer	9.5-11.0	7.8-13.0	—
Polyurethane	9.8-10.3	—	—
Styrene acrylonitrile copolymer	10.6-11.1	9.4-9.8	—
Vinsol (rosin derivative)	10.6-11.8	7.7-13.0	9.5-12.5
Epon 1001 (epoxy)	10.6-11.1	8.5-13.3	—
Shellac	—	10.0-11.0	9.5-14.0
Polymethacrylonitrile	—	10.6-11.0	—
Cellulose acetate	11.1-12.5	10.0-14.5	—
Nitrocellulose	11.1-12.5	8.0-14.5	12.5-14.5
Polyacrylonitrile	—	12.0-14.0	—
Poly(vinyl alcohol)	—	—	12.0-13.0
Nylon-66 (polyhexamethylene adipamide)	—	—	13.5-15.0
Cellulose	—	—	14.5-16.5

TABLE 3.4 Commonly Used Viscometry Terms

Common name	Recommended name (IUPAC)	Definition	Symbol
Relative viscosity	Viscosity ratio	η/η_o	η_{rel}
Specific viscosity	—	$\eta/\eta_o - 1$ or $\eta - \eta_o/\eta_o$ or $\eta_r - 1$	η_{sp}
Reduced viscosity	Viscosity number	η_{sp}/c	η_{red} or η_{sp}/c
Inherent viscosity	Logarithmic viscosity number	$\ln \eta_r/c$	η_{inh} or $\ln \eta_r/c$
Intrinsic viscosity	Limiting viscosity number	$\lim(\eta_{sp}/c)_{c\to o}$ or $\lim(\ln \eta_r/c)_{c\to o}$	$[\eta]$ or LVN

Staudinger showed that the intrinsic viscosity of a solution ($[\eta]$), like the viscosity of a melt (η), was related to the average molecular weight of the polymer (M). The present form of this relationship is expressed by the Mark-Houwink equation (3.25), in which the proportionality constant K is characteristic of the polymer and solvent and the exponential a is a function of the shape of the polymer coil in a solution. In a θ solvent, the a value

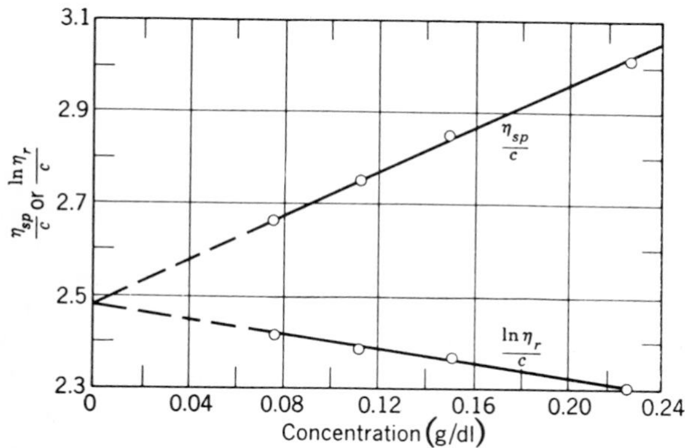

FIGURE 3.7 Reduced and inherent viscosity-concentration curves for a polystyrene in benzene. (R. Ewart, in Advances in Colloid Science, Vol. II (H. Mark and G. Whitby, eds.). Wiley Interscience, New York, 1946. With permission from the Interscience Division of John Wiley and Sons, Publishers.)

for the ideal statistical coil is 0.5. This value, which is actually a measure of the interaction of the solvent and polymer, increases as the coil expands in good solvents, and the value is found to be between 1.8 and 2.0 for a rigid polymer chain extended to its full contour length and 0 for spheres. When a equals 1.0, the Mark-Houwink equation becomes the Staudinger viscosity equation. However, the value of a is usually 0.5 to 0.8 in polymer solutions. K generally has values in the range of 10^{-2} to 10^{-4} ml/g. Sample values are given in Table 3.5. A more complete collection of K and a values can be found in the Polymer Handbook (see the Bibliography).

Since the relative viscosity η_{rel} is a ratio of viscosities, it is dimensionless, as is the specific viscosity. However, since the value for reduced viscosity is obtained by dividing η_{sp} by the concentration, η_{red} is expressed in reciprocal concentration units, such as milliliters per gram. The intrinsic viscosity will have the same units.

$$[\eta] = K\overline{M}^{a} \tag{3.25}$$

Unlike most of the methods dealt with in the following chapter, viscometry does not lead to obtaining absolute molecular weight values, but rather is only a relative measure of a polymer's molecular weight. The reason may be stated in several ways. First, an exact theory of polymer solution viscosity as related to chain size is still in the formulation stage. Second, an expression such as (3.25) cannot be directly used to relate (absolutely) polymer viscosity and polymer molecular weight using only viscometry measurements since there are two additional unknowns, K and a, which must be determined.

Thus, viscometry measurements must be correlated with an "absolute molecular weight method" such as light scattering. Taking the log of (3.25) yields (3.26):

$$\log [\eta] = a \log \overline{M} + \log K \tag{3.26}$$

This predicts a linear relationship between log $[\eta]$ and log $\overline{M}$ with a slope of a and intercept log K. Experimentally the viscosity is determined for several polymer samples varying in only molecular weight. Then the molecular weight of each sample is determined using an absolute method. A plot of log $[\eta]$ versus log $\overline{M}$ is constructed enabling the determination of a and K. Often K is determined by inserting a known $[\eta]$ and $\overline{M}$ value along with the calculated a value and solving for K. It is customary to distinguish the type of a and K value determined. For instance, if light scattering were employed to determine molecular weights then the a and K values, and subsequent $\overline{M}$ values are designated as weight-average values.

After calculation of an a and a K value for a given polymer-solvent pair, $\overline{M}$ can be easily calculated using a determined $[\eta]$ and (3.25).

TABLE 3.5 Typical K Values for the Mark-Houwink Equation

Polymer	Solvent	Temp. (°K)	$K \times 10^5$ dl g^{-1}
LDPE (low-density polyethylene)	Decalin	343	39
HDPE (high-density polyethylene)	Decalin	408	68
Polypropylene (isotactic)	Decalin	408	11
Polystyrene	Decalin	373	16
Polyvinyl chloride	Chlorobenzene	303	71
Polyvinyl acetate	Acetone	298	11
Polymethyl acrylate	Acetone	298	6
Polyacrylonitrile	Dimethylformamide	298	17
Polymethyl methacrylate	Acetone	298	10
Polyethylene terephthalate	m-Cresol	298	1
Nylon-66	90% aqueous formic acid	298	110

Flory, Debye, and Kirkwood have shown that $[\eta]$ is directly proportional to the effective hydrodynamic volume of the polymer in solution and inversely proportional to the molecular weight (M). The effective hydrodynamic volume is the cube of the root mean square end-to-end distance $(\sqrt{\bar{r}^2})^3$. The proportionality constant (ϕ) in the Flory equation for hydrodynamic volume (3.27) has been considered a universal constant independent of solvent, polymer, temperature, and molecular weight. The value of ϕ is 2.5×10^{23} mol^{-1}.

$$[\eta] = \phi(\bar{r}^2)^{3/2}M^{-1} \tag{3.27}$$

The θ temperature corresponds to the Boyle point in an imperfect gas and is the range in which the virial coefficient B in the expanded gas law becomes zero. This same concept applies to the modification of the gas law (PV = nRT) used to determine the osmotic pressure (π) of a polymer solution as shown below:

$$\pi = \frac{RT}{\overline{\overline{M}}} C + BC^2 + \cdots \tag{3.28}$$

where R is the universal gas constant, T is the temperature in degrees Kelvin, $\overline{M}$ is the number-average molecular weight, and C is the concentration of polymer in solution.

For linear chains at their θ temperature, i.e., the temperature at which the chain attains its unperturbed dimensions, the Flory equation resembles the Mark-Houwink equation in which a is equal to 1.0, as shown below:

$$[\eta] = KM^{1/2}a^3 \tag{3.29}$$

The intrinsic viscosity of a solution, like the melt viscosity, is temperature dependent and will decrease as the temperature increases as shown by the following Arrhenius equation:

$$[\eta] = Ae^{E/RT} \tag{3.30}$$

However, if the original temperature is below the θ temperature, the viscosity will increase when the mixture of polymer and solvent is heated to a temperature slightly above the θ temperature.

Provided the temperature is held constant, the viscosity of a solution may be measured in any simple viscometer such as an Ubbelohde viscometer, a falling ball viscometer, or a rotational viscometer, such as the Brookfield viscometer. It is customary to describe the viscosity of a solid plastic in terms of the melt index, which is the weight in grams of a polymer extruded through an orifice.

Viscosity measurements of polymer solutions are carried out using a viscometer such as those pictured in Fig. 3.8, placed in a constant temperature bath with temperature controlled to greater than 0.1°C.

The most commonly used viscometers are the Ubbelohde viscometers which, because of the side arm, give flow times independent of the volume of liquid in the reservoir bulb.

The following relationship exists for a given viscometer

$$\frac{\eta}{\eta_o} = \frac{\rho t}{\rho_o t_o} \tag{3.31}$$

where t and t_o are the flow times for the polymer solution and solvent respectively, and ρ is the density of the polymer solution.

Viscometry measurements are generally made on solutions which contain 0.01 to 0.001 g of polymer per milliliter of solution. For such dilute solutions, $\rho = \rho_o$, giving

$$\frac{\eta}{\eta_o} = \frac{t}{t_o} = \eta_r \tag{3.32}$$

Thus, η_r is simply a ratio of flow times for equal volumes of polymer solution and solvent. Reduced viscosity is related to $[\eta]$ by a virial equation as follows:

$$\eta_{sp}/c = [\eta] + k_1 [\eta]^2 c + k' [\eta]^3 c^2 + \cdots \tag{3.33}$$

For most systems, (3.33) reduces to the Huggins viscosity relationship

$$\eta_{sp}/c = [\eta] + k_1 [\eta]^2 c \tag{3.34}$$

which allows $[\eta]$ to be determined from the intercept of a plot of η_{sp}/c versus c and is the basis for the top plot given in Fig. 3.7.

Another relationship often used in determining $[\eta]$ is called the inherent viscosity equation and is as follows.

$$\frac{\ln \eta_r}{c} = [\eta] - k_2 [\eta]^2 c \tag{3.35}$$

Again, in a plot of $\ln \eta_r/c$ versus c an extrapolation to c equals zero allows the calculation of $[\eta]$. Plotting using (3.34) is more common than

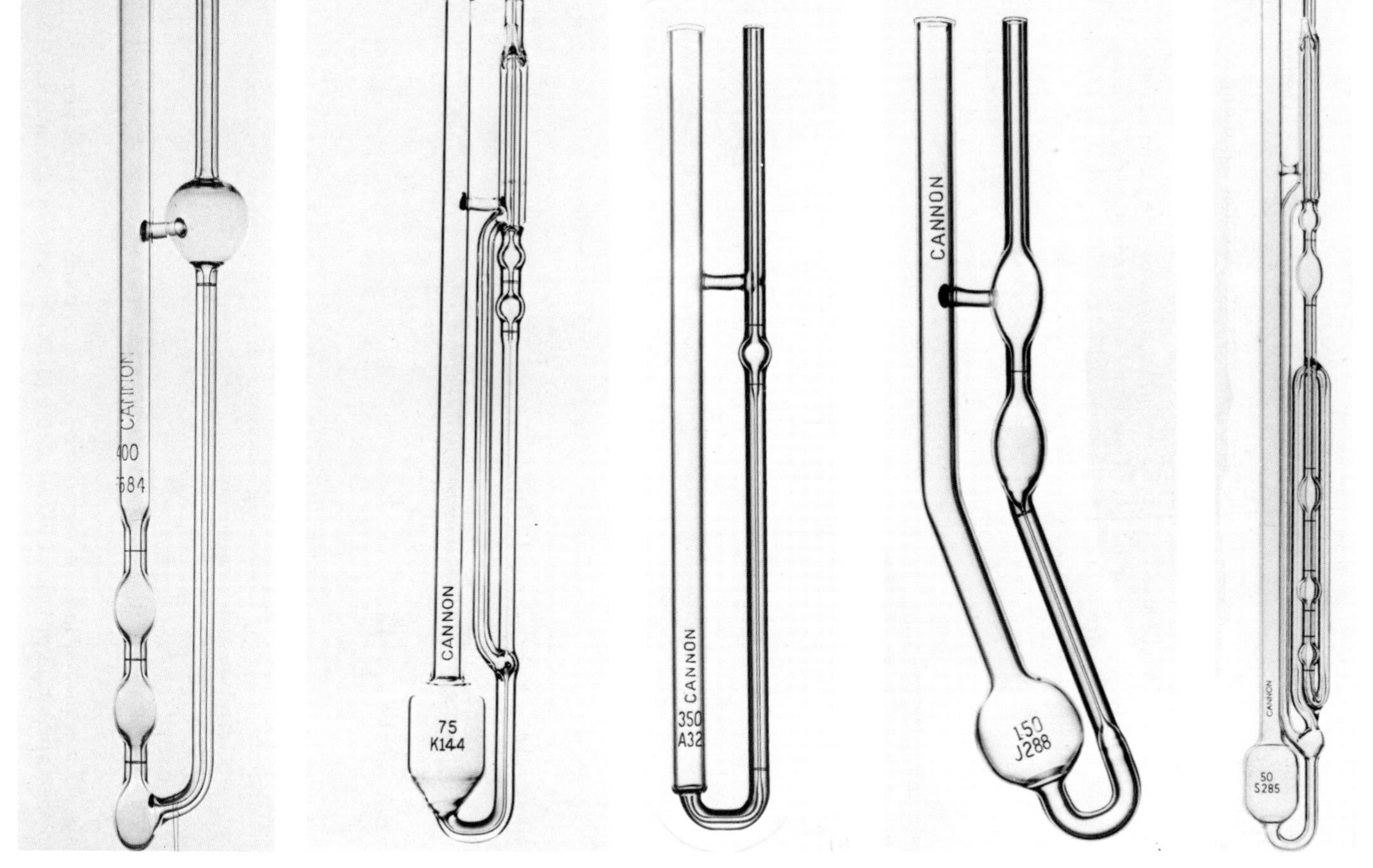

FIGURE 3.8 Common solution viscometers: (1) Cannon–Fenske Opaque, (2) Cannon–Ubbelohde Semi–Micro Dilution, (3) Cannon–Manning Semi–Micro, (4) Cannon–Fenske Routine, (5) Cannon–Ubbelohde Shear Dilution. (With permission from Cannon Instrument Co.)

plotting using Eq. (3.35), even though (3.35) probably yields more precise values of η since k_1 is generally larger than k_2.

While k_1 and k_2 are mathematically related by

$$k_1 + k_2 = 0.5 \tag{3.36}$$

many systems appear not to follow this relationship.

SUMMARY

1. Since polymers have properties of both solids and fluids they are called viscoelastic materials. Both Hooke's law for elastic solids ($S = E\gamma$) and Newton's law for ideal liquids [$S = \eta(d\gamma/dt)$] are used with modifications to describe polymers.

2. If there is no change in volume when an isotropic solid is stretched it has a Poisson's ratio of 0.5, but this value decreases as motion is restricted by cross-linking or by increased cohesive energy density (CED). The latter is a measure of intermolecular forces. An isotropic solid is one having similar properties in all directions. The viscosity [η] decreases as the temperature is increased.

3. The behavior of viscoelastic materials may be described using combinations of Maxwell and Voigt-Kelvin models or elements. In the Maxwell element, which consists of a Hookean spring and a Newtonian dash pot in series, the application of stress causes an instantaneous elongation of the spring followed by a slow response of the piston in the cylinder or dash pot. The term relaxation time (τ), which is equal to η/G, is used to describe the time when the stress and elongation have reached equilibrium or when the stress is equal to 1/e of its original value.

4. In the Voigt-Kelvin model or element, which consists of a Hookean spring and Newtonian dash pot or shock absorber in parallel, the elastic response to the application of stress is retarded by the resistance of the liquid in the dash pot. The term retardation time (τ), which is equal to η/G, is used to describe the time for the model to decrease to 1 - (1/e), or 0.63 of its original value.

5. A Bingham plastic is one which does not flow until the applied stress exceeds a threshold stress value (s_o). In non-Newtonian fluids, the viscosity may increase with time (rheopetic) or decrease with time (thixotropic). If the shear rate does not increase as rapidly as the applied stress, the system is dilatant, and if it increases more rapidly, the system is pseudoplastic.

6. Eyring has described polymer flow as a random hole-filling process in which the chain segments overcome an energy barrier and fill the holes by successive correlated jumps of segments along the polymer chain.

7. Since the viscoelastic properties of polymers are similar at their glass transition temperatures, these properties are also similar at temperatures

up to 100 K° above T_g. The shift factor for a reference temperature such as T_g may be calculated from the WLF equation which includes constants for the free volume.

8. A polymer dissolves by a swelling process followed by a dispersion process or disintegration of the swollen particles. This process may occur if there is a decrease in free energy. Since the second step in the solution process involves an increase in entropy, it is essential that the change in enthalpy be negligible or negative to assure a negative value for the change in free energy.

9. Flory and Huggins developed an interaction parameter (χ_1) which may be used as a measure of the solvent power of solvents for amorphous polymers. Flory and Krigbaum introduced the term θ temperature at which a polymer of infinite molecular weight exists as a statistical coil in a solvent.

10. Hildebrand used solubility parameters which are the square root of CED to predict the solubility of nonpolar polymers in nonpolar solvents. This concept is also applicable to mixtures of solvents. For polar solvents it is also necessary to consider dipole-dipole interactions and hydrogen bonding in predicting solubility.

11. The molecular weight of a polymer is proportional to the intrinsic viscosity of its solution ($[\eta]$) when the polymer chain is extended to its full contour length. The value $[\eta]$, or limiting viscosity number, is proportional to the square root of the molecular weight M when the polymer is in a θ solvent. In general, $[\eta] = K\overline{M}^a$ where a, which is a measure of the shape of the polymer chain, is usually 0.5 to 0.8. The constant K is dependent on the polymer and solvent studied.

12. The intrinsic viscosity is the limiting reduced viscosity (η_{red}) at zero concentration. The reduced viscosity or viscosity number is equal to the specific viscosity (η_{sp}) divided by concentration. The value η_{sp} is obtained by subtracting 1 from the relative viscosity (η_r), which is the ratio of the viscosities of the solution and the solvent. Plasticizers are nonvolatile good solvents which reduce the CED and T_g of a polymer.

GLOSSARY

a: Constant in the WLF equation related to holes or free volume of a polymer.

a: Symbol for exponent in Mark-Houwink equation; a measure of solvent polymer interaction.

a_T: Shift factor relative to a reference temperature.

alpha (α): The linear expansion ratio of a polymer molecule in a Flory θ solvent.

aniline point: A measure of the aromaticity of a solvent.

Arrhenius equation for viscosity: $\eta = A\ e^{E/RT}$

biaxially stretching: Stretching of a film in two directions perpendicular to each other.

Bingham, E. C.: The father of rheology.

Bingham equation: $s - s_o = \eta \frac{d\gamma}{dt}$

Bingham plastic: A plastic that does not flow until the external stress exceeds a critical threshold value (s_o).

chi (χ): Flory-Huggins interaction parameter.

cloud point: The temperature at which a polymer starts to precipitate when the temperature is lowered.

CN: Symbol for cellulose nitrate.

cohesive energy density (CED): The heat of vaporization per unit volume $\Delta E(V^{-1})$.

creep: Cold flow of a polymer.

critical solution temperature (T_c): The temperature at which the two liquid phases, containing an amorphous polymer, coalesce.

dash pot: A model for Newtonian fluids consisting of a piston and a cylinder containing a viscous liquid.

delta (δ): Symbol for solubility parameter.

dilatant: Shear thickening.

e: Symbol for base of naperian logarithms (e = 2.718).

E: Energy of activation.

E: Symbol for Young's modulus of elasticity.

effective hydrodynamic volume: $(\sqrt{\bar{r}^2})^3$, the cube of the root mean square end-to-end distance of a polymer chain.

eta (η): Symbol for viscosity.

Flory-Huggins theory: A theory used to predict the equilibrium behavior between liquid phases containing an amorphous polymer.

G: Symbol for shear modulus.

G: Symbol for Small's molar attraction constants.

gamma (γ): Symbol for strain.

Gibbs equation: The relationship between free energy (ΔG), enthalpy (ΔH), and entropy (ΔS); $\Delta G = \Delta H - T\,\Delta S$ at constant T.

H: Symbol for enthalpy or heat content.

Herschel-Buckley equation: $(s - s_0)^n = \phi(d\gamma/dt)$.

Hildebrand (H): Unit used in place of $(\text{cal cm}^{-3})^{0.5}$ for solubility parameter values.

Hookean: Obeys Hooke's law.

Hooke's law: $s = E\gamma$.

isotropic: Having similar properties in all directions.

K: Symbol for Kelvin or absolute temperature scale.

Kauri-Butanol values: A measure of the aromaticity of a solvent.

log: Common logarithm based on the number 10

M: Symbol for Hayes chain stiffening constant.

M: Symbol for molecular weight.

$\overline{M}$: Symbol for average molecular weight.

Mark-Houwink equation: $[\eta] = K\overline{M}^a$, where a is 0.5 for a statistical coil in a θ solvent and 2.0 for a rigid rod.

Maxwell element or model: A model in which an ideal spring and dash pot are connected in series, used to study the stress relaxation of polymers.

melt index: A measure of flow related inversely to melt viscosity, the time for 10 g of a polymer, such as a polyolefin, to pass through a standard orifice at a specified time and temperature.

modulus: stress per unit strain. A high modulus plastic is stiff and has very low elongation.

Newtonian fluid: A fluid whose viscosity (η) is proportional to the applied viscosity gradient $d\gamma/dt$.

Newton's law: Stress is proportional to flow; $s = \eta(d\gamma/dt)$.

osmotic pressure (π): The pressure exerted by a solvent when it is separated from a solution by a membrane.

phi (ϕ): Proportionality constant in Flory equation $= 2.5 \times 10^{23}\ \text{mol}^{-1}$.

plasticizer: A nonvolatile solvent which is compatible with a hard plastic and reduces its T_g.

Poisson's ratio: The ratio of the percentage change in length of a specimen under tension to its percentage change in width.

pseudoplastic: shear thinning.

relaxation time (τ): Time for stress of a polymer under constant strain to decrease to 1/e or 0.37 of its original value.

retardation time (τ): Time for the stress in a deformed polymer to decrease to 63% of the original value.

rheology: The science of flow.

rheopectic: A rheopectic liquid is one whose viscosity increases with time.

s: Symbol for applied stress.

S: Symbol for entropy or measure of disorder.

shear: Stress caused by planes sliding by each other, as in a pair of shears or the greasing or polishing of a flat surface.

solubility parameter (δ): A numerical value equal to $\sqrt{CED}$ which can be used to predict solubility.

stress (s): Force per unit area.

stress relaxation: The relaxation of a stressed specimen with time after the load is removed.

theta (θ) solvent: A solvent in which the polymer exists as a statistical coil and where the second virial constant B equals zero at the θ temperature.

theta temperature: The temperature at which a polymer of infinite molecular weight starts to precipitate from a solution.

thixotropic: A thixotropic liquid is one whose viscosity increases with time.

turbidimetric titration: A technique in which a poor solvent is added slowly to a solution of a polymer and the point of incipient turbidity is observed.

V: Symbol for molar volume.

velocity gradient: $d\gamma/dt$, $\dot{\gamma}$, or flow rate.

viscoelastic: Having the properties of a liquid and a solid.

viscosity: Resistance to flow.

viscosity, intrinsic $[\eta]$: The limiting viscosity number obtained by extrapolation of the reduced viscosity to zero concentration.

viscosity, reduced: The specific viscosity divided by the concentration.

viscosity, relative: The ratio of the viscosities of a solution and its solvent.

viscosity, specific: The difference between the relative viscosity and 1.

Voigt-Kelvin element or model: A model consisting of an ideal spring and dash pot in parallel in which the elastic response is retarded by viscous resistance of the fluid in the cylinder.

WLF: Williams, Landel, and Ferry equation for predicting viscoelastic properties at temperatures above T_g when these properties are known for one specific temperature such as T_g.

EXERCISES

1. What is the difference between morphology and rheology?
2. Which of the following is viscoelastic: (a) steel, (b) polystyrene, (c) diamond, or (d) neoprene?
3. Define G in Hooke's law.
4. Which would be isotropic: (a) a nylon filament, (b) an extruded pipe, or (c) ebonite?
5. Would Poisson's ratio increase or decrease when (a) a plasticizer is added to rigid PVC and (b) the amount of sulfur used in the vulcanization of rubber is increased?
6. How would the slopes in Fig. 3.1a differ for polyisobutylene and polystyrene?
7. Which will have the higher relaxation time (τ): (a) unvulcanized rubber or (b) ebonite?
8. Which would be more readily extruded through a die: (a) a pseudoplastic or (b) a dilatant substance?
9. Which would increase in volume when stretched: (a) plasticized PVC or (b) rigid PVC.
10. According to the Eyring theory, which would have the higher percentage of holes: (a) polystyrene at its T_g or (b) hevea rubber at its T_g?
11. In designing a die for a pipe with an outside diameter of 5 cm, would you choose inside dimensions of (a) less than 5 cm, (b) 5 cm, or (c) greater than 5 cm for the die?
12. At what temperature would the properties of polystyrene resemble those of hevea rubber at 35 K° above its T_g?
13. What is the significance of the constants in the WLF equation?
14. Define the proportionality constant in Newton's law.
15. What term is used to describe the decrease of stress at constant length with time?

16. In which element or model for a viscoelastic body, (a) Maxwell or (b) Voigt-Kelvin, will the elastic response be retarded by viscous resistance?

17. According to Hildebrand, what is a regular solvent?

18. Which of the two steps that occur in the solution process, (a) swelling and (b) dispersion of the polymer particles, can be accelerated by agitation?

19. Define CED.

20. For solution to occur ΔG must be: (a) 0, (b) < 0, or (c) > 0.

21. Will a polymer swollen by a solvent have higher or lower entropy than the solid polymer?

22. Define the change in entropy in the Gibbs free energy equation.

23. Is a liquid that has a value of 0.3 for its interaction parameter (χ_1), a good or a poor solvent?

24. What is the value of ΔG at the θ temperature?

25. What term is used to describe the temperature at which a polymer of infinite molecular weight precipitates from a dilute solution?

26. At which temperature will the polymer coil be larger in a poor solvent? (a) at the θ temperature, (b) above the θ temperature, or (c) below the θ temperature.

27. If δ for water is equal to 23.4 H, what is the CED for water?

28. What is the heat of mixing of two solvents having identical δ values?

29. If the density (D) is 0.85 g/cm^3 and the molar volume (V) is 1,176,470 cm^3, what is the molecular weight?

30. Use Small's molar attraction constants to calculate δ for polystyrene

```
   H   H
   |   |
(—C—C—)
   |   |
   H   C6H5
```

31. Calculate M for a polymer having a δ value of 10 H and a T_g value of 325°K (M = chain stiffness).

32. Why do δ values decrease as the molecular weight increases in a homologous series of aliphatic polar solvents?

33. Which would be the better solvent for polystyrene: (a) n-pentane, (b) benzene, or (c) acetonitrile?

34. Which will have the higher slope when its reduced viscosity or viscosity number is plotted against concentration: (a) a solution of polystyrene in benzene, or (b) in n-octane?

35. What is the value of the virial constant B in (3.28) at the θ temperature?

36. When is the Flory equation (3.27) similar to the Mark-Houwink equation?

37. What is the term used for the cube root of the hydrodynamic volume?

38. Explain why the viscosity of a polymer solution decreases as the temperature increases.

39. Which sample of LDPE has the higher average molecular weight: (a) one with a melt index of 10, or (b) one with a melt index of 8?

BIBLIOGRAPHY

Aklonis, J. J., MacKnight, W. J., Shen, M. (1972): Introduction to Polymer Viscoelasticity, Wiley Interscience, New York.

Alfrey, T. (1948): Mechanical Behavior of High Polymers, Interscience, New York.

Alfrey, T., Gurnee, E. F. (1956): Dynamics of viscoelastic behavior, Chap. 11, in Rheology—Theory and Applications (F. R. Eirich, ed.), Academic, New York.

Allan, W. B. (1973): Fiber Optics, Plenum, New York.

Allen, P. W. (1959): Solubility and choice of solvents, in Techniques of Polymer Characterization (P. W. Allen, ed.), Butterworths, London.

Arridge, P. G. C. (1975): Mechanics of Polymers, Oxford University Press, New York.

Bagley, E. B. (1975): Theories of solvency and solution, Chap. 43, in Applied Polymer Science (J. K. Craves, R. W. Tess, eds.), Organic Coatings and Plastics Chemistry Division ACS.

Bartenov, G. M., Zelenev, Y. V. (1974): Relaxation Phenomenon in Polymers, Halsted, New York.

Battista, O. A. (1967): Summative fractionation, Chaps. 1 to 4, in Polymer Fractionation (M. J. R. Cantow, ed.), Academic, New York.

Billmeyer, F. W. (1971): Textbook of Polymer Science, Chap. 6, John Wiley, New York.

Bingham, E. C. (1922): Fluidity and Plasticity, McGraw-Hill, New York.

Boenig, H. V. (1973): Structure and Properties of Polymers, Halsted, New York.

Boger, R. F. (1963): The relationship of transition temperatures to chemical structures in high polymers, Rubber Chem. Technol., 36:1303.

Bristow, G. M., Watson, W. F. (1958): Cohesive energy densities of polymers, Trans. Faraday Soc., 54:1731, 1942.

Brydson, J. A. (1970): Flow Properties of Polymer Melts, Iliffe, London.

Bueche, F. (1959): Physical Properties of Polymers, Interscience, New York.

Burrell, H. (1968): Solubility parameter concept, ACS Div. Org. Coatings and Plastics Chem. Preprints, 28:682.

——. (1974): Solubility parameter values, in Polymer Handbook (J. Brandrup and E. H. Immergut, eds.), John Wiley, New York.

Carraher, C. E. (1970): Polymer models, J. Chem. Ed., 47:58.

Christensen, R. M. (1971): Theory of Viscoelasticity, an Introduction, Academic, New York.

Cowie, J. M. G. (1973): Polymers: Chemistry and Physics of Modern Materials, Chaps. 11, 12, Intext Educational Publishers, New York.

——. (1974): Polymers: Chemistry and Physics of Modern Materials, Intext Educational Publishers, New York.

Crowley, J. D., Teague, D. S. (1966): J. Paint Technol., 38:269.

Dack, M. R. J. (1975): Solutions and Solubilities Techniques of Chemistry, John Wiley, New York.

DiMarzio, E. A., Gibbs, J. H. (1958): Chain stiffness and lattice theory of polymer phases, J. Chem. Phys., 28:807.

——. (1959): Glass transition temperature of copolymers, J. Polymer Sci., 40:121.

Doolittle, A. K. (1954): The Technology of Solvents and Plasticizers, John Wiley, New York.

——. (1969): Polymer solution thermodynamics, state of the art survey, J. Paint Technol., 41:483.

Eirich, F. R. (1956): Rheology—Theory and Applications, Academic, New York.

Elias, H. G. (1975): Macromolecules, Structure and Properties, Plenum, New York.

Ferry, J. D. (1970): Viscoelastic Properties of Polymers, Wiley Interscience, New York.

Fitch, R. M. (1973): Polymer Colloids, Plenum, New York.

Flory, P. J. (1953): Principles of Polymer Chemistry, Cornell University Press, Ithaca, New York.

Flory, P. J., Ellenson, J. L., Echinger, B. E. (1968): Thermodynamics of mixing n-alkanes with polyisobutylene, Macromolecules, 1:294.

Frederickson, A. G. (1964): Principles and Applications of Rheology, Prentice-Hall, Englewood Cliffs, New Jersey.

Gardon, J. L. (1965): Cohesive energy density, in Encyclopedia of Polymer Science and Technology (H. F. Mark, N. G. Gaylord, N. M. Bihales, eds.), Vol. 3, p. 833, Wiley Interscience, New York.

Giesekus, H. (1967): Turbidimetric titrations, Chap. C1, in Polymer Fractionation (M. J. R. Cantow, ed.), Academic, New York.

Gittus, J. (1975): Creep, Viscoelasticity, and Creep Fracture in Solids, Halsted, New York.

Han, C. D. (1976): Rheology in Polymer Processing, Academic, New York.

Hancock, J. R. (1975): Fatigue of Composite Materials, American Society of Testing Materials, Philadelphia.

Harris, F., Seymour, R. B. (1977): Solubility Property Relationships in Polymer, Academic, New York.

Harvard, R. N. (1973): The Physics of Glassy Polymers, Halsted, New York.

Hayes, R. A. (1961): Relationship of CED to T_g, J. Appl. Polymer Sci., 5:318.

Hildebrand, J. H., Scott, R. L. (1950): The Solubilities of Nonelectrolytes, Reinhold, New York.

———. (1962): Regular Solutions, Prentice-Hall, Inc., Englewood Cliffs, New Jersey.

Hildebrand, J. H., Prausnetz, J. M., Scott, R. L. (1970): Regular and Related Solutions, Van Nostrand-Reinhold, New York.

Hoy, K. L. (1970): New values of solubility parameters from vapor pressure data, J. Paint Technol., 42:76.

Huggins, M. L. (1942): Some properties of solutions of long chain compounds, J. Phys. Chem., 46:151.

———. (1958): Physical Chemistry of High Polymers, John Wiley, New York.

———. (1968): Evaluation of important parameters, ACS Div. Polymer Chem. Polymer Preprints, 9:558

Ledwith, A., North, A. M. (1975): Molecular Behavior and Development of Polymeric Materials, Halsted, New York.

Lenk, R. S. (1968): Plastics Rheology, Mechanical Behavior of Solid and Liquid Polymers, Interscience, New York.

McKelvey, J. M. (1962): Polymer Processing, John Wiley, New York.

Meares, P. (1965): Polymers: Structure and Bulk Properties, Van Nostrand, Princeton.

Mendelson, R. A. (1968): Melt viscosity, in Encyclopedia of Polymer Science and Technology (H. F. Mark, N. G. Gaylord, N. M. Bikales, eds.), Vol. 8, p. 587, Wiley Interscience, New York.

Middleman, S. (1968): The Flow of High Polymers, Wiley Interscience, New York.

Morawetz, H. (1975): Macromolecules in Solution, Wiley Interscience, New York.

Nielsen, L. E. (1974): Mechanical Properties of Polymers, Dekker, New York.

Ogorkiewiz, R. M. (1974): Thermoplastic Properties and Design, John Wiley, New York.

Parkman, N. (1965): in Physic of Plastics (P. D. Richie, ed.), p. 285, Van Nostrand, Princeton.

Passaglia, E., Know, J. R. (1962): Viscoelastic behavior and time-temperature relationships, Chap. 3, in Engineering Design for Plastics (E. Baer, ed.), Reinhold, New York.

Schultz, J. M. (1973): Polymer Materials Science, Prentice-Hall, Englewood Cliffs, New Jersey.

Severs, E. T. (1962): Rheology of Polymers, Reinhold, New York.

Seymour, R. B. (1972): Introduction to Polymer Chemistry, Chap. 2, McGraw-Hill, New York.

——. (1975): Modern Plastics Technology, Chap. 1, Reston, Virginia.

——. (1975): Solubility parameters of organic compounds, in Handbook of Chemistry and Physics, C-720, 56th ed., CRC Press, Cleveland.

Shen, M. C., Eisenberg, A. (1970): Glass transitions in polymers, Rubber Chem. Technol., 43:95.

Small, P. A. (1953): Some factors affecting the solubility of polymers, J. Appl. Chem., 3:71.

Sylvester, N. D. (1973): Drag Reduction in Polymer Solutions, American Institute of Chemical Engineers, New York.

———. (1973): Solvents Theory and Practice, Advances in Chemistry Series No. 129, American Chemical Society, Washington, D.C.

———. (1975): Chemistry and technology of solvents, Chap. 44, in Applied Polymer Science (J. K. Craver, R. W. Tess, eds.), Organic Coatings and Plastics Chemistry Division of ACS, Washington, D.C.

Tobolsky, A. V. (1960): Properties and Structure of Polymers, John Wiley, New York.

Tompa, H. (1956): Polymer Solutions, Academic, New York.

Van Krevelen, D. W. (1972): Properties of Polymers, American Elsevier, New York.

Van Krevelen, D. W., Hoftyzer, P. J. (1972): Properties of Polymers, Chap. 6, American Elsevier, New York.

Van Wazer, J. R., Lyons, J. W., Kim, K. Y., Colwell, R. E. (1963): Viscosity and Flow Measurement, a Laboratory Handbook of Rheology, Wiley Interscience, New York.

Vollmert, B. (1975): Polymer Chemistry, Chap. 3, Springer-Verlag, New York.

Walters, K. (1975): Rheometry, Halsted, New York.

Ward, I. M. (1972): Mechanical Properties of Solid Polymers, John Wiley, New York.

———. (1975): Structure and Properties of Oriented Polymers, John Wiley, New York.

Williams, A. (1973): Stress Analysis of Plastics, Halsted, New York.

Williams, H. L. (1975): Polymer Engineering, Chap. 6, American Elsevier, New York.

Williams, J. G. (1972): Stress Analysis of Polymers, Halsted, New York.

Williams, M. L., Landel, R. R., Ferry, J. D. (1955): The temperature dependence of relaxation mechanisms in amorphous polymers, J. Am. Chem. Soc., 77:3701.

4

Molecular Weight of Polymers

4.1 INTRODUCTION

The average molecular weight ($\overline{M}$) of a polymer is the product of the average number of repeating units or mers expressed as $\overline{n}$ or $\overline{DP}$ times the molecular weight of these repeating units. M for $(CH_2CH_2)_{1000}$ is 1000(28) = 28,000.

Polymerization reactions, both synthetic and natural, lead to polymers with a heterogeneous molecular weight, i.e., polymer chains with a different number of units. Molecular weight distributions may be relatively broad as is the case for most synthetic polymers and many naturally occurring polymers. It may be relatively narrow for certain natural polymers (because of the imposed steric and electronic constraints), or may be mono-, bi-, tri-, or polymodal. A bimodal curve is often characteristic of a polymerization occurring under two distinct pathways or environments. Thus, most synthetic polymers and many naturally occurring polymers consist of molecules with different molecular weights and are said to be polydisperse. In contrast, specific proteins and nucleic acids, like typical small molecules, consist of molecules with a specific molecular weight (M) and are said to be monodisperse.

Since typical small molecules and large molecules with molecular weights less than a critical value (Z) required for chain entanglement are weak and are readily attacked by appropriate reactants, it is apparent that these properties are related to molecular weight. Thus, melt viscosity, tensile strength, modulus, impact strength or toughness, and resistance to heat and corrosives are dependent on the molecular weight of amorphous polymers and the molecular weight distribution (MWD). In contrast, density, specific heat capacity, and refractive index are essentially independent of the molecular weight at molecular weight values above the critical molecular weight.

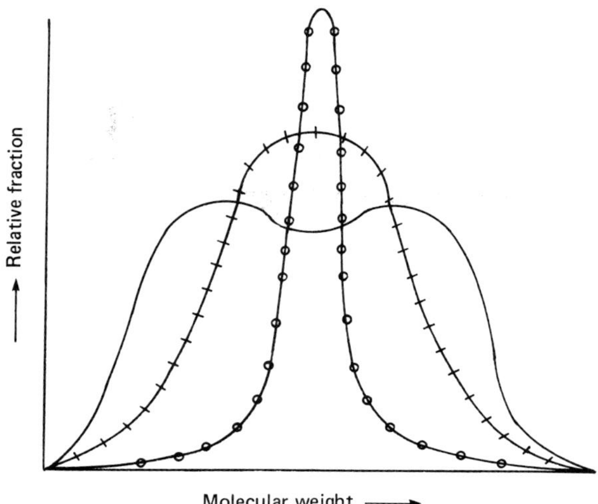

FIGURE 4.1 Representative differential weight distribution curves; (-+-+-+-+-) relatively broad distribution curve; (-o-o-o-o-) relatively narrow distribution curve; (———) bimodal distribution curve.

The melt viscosity is usually proportional to the 3.4 power of the average molecular weight at values above the critical molecular weight required for chain entanglement, i.e., $\eta = \overline{M}^{3.4}$. Thus, the melt viscosity increases rapidly as the molecular weight increases and more energy is required for the processing and fabrication of these large molecules. However, as shown in Fig. 4.2, the strength of polymers increases as the molecular weight increases and then tends to level off.

Thus, while a value above the threshold molecular weight value (TMWV) is essential for most practical applications, the additional cost of energy required for processing extremely high molecular weight polymers is seldom justified. Accordingly, it is customary to establish a commercial polymer range above the TMWV but below the extremely high molecular weight range. However, it should be noted that since toughness increases with molecular weight, extremely high molecular weight polymers, such as ultrahigh molecular weight polyethylene (UHMPE), are used for the production of tough articles such as trash barrels.

Oligomers and other low molecular weight polymers are not useful for applications where high strength is required. The word oligomer is derived from the Greek word oligos, meaning few. The value for TMWV will be dependent on T_g, the cohesive energy density (CED) of amorphous polymers, the extent of crystallinity in crystalline polymers, and the effect of reinforcements in polymeric composites. Thus, while a low molecular weight

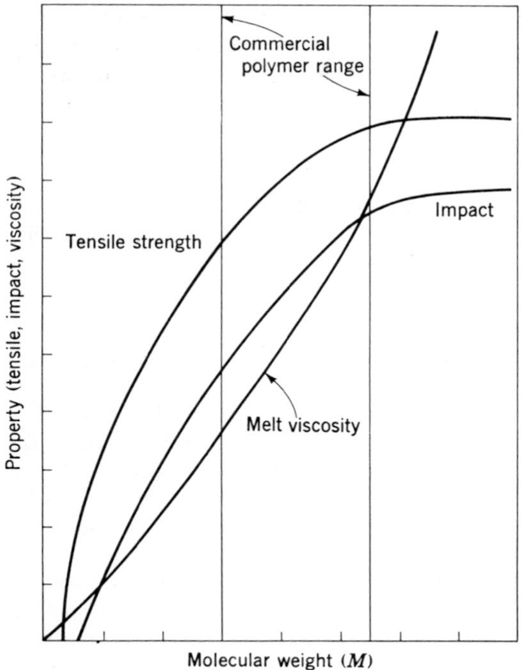

FIGURE 4.2 Relationship of polymer properties to molecular weight. (From Introduction to Polymer Chemistry by R. Seymour, McGraw-Hill, New York, 1971. Used with permission of McGraw-Hill Book Company.)

amorphous polymer may be satisfactory for use as a coating or adhesive, a $\overline{\mathrm{DP}}$ value of at least 1000 may be required if the polymer is used as an elastomer or plastic. With the exception of polymers with highly regular structures, such as isotactic polypropylene, strong hydrogen intermolecular bonds are required for fibers. Because of their higher CED values, lower $\overline{\mathrm{DP}}$ values are satisfactory for polar polymers used as fibers.

4.2 AVERAGE MOLECULAR WEIGHT VALUES

Several mathematical moments can be described using the differential or frequency distribution curve, and can be described by equations. The first moment is called the number-average molecular weight, $\overline{M}_n$. Any measurement that leads to the number of molecules, functional groups, or particles, that are present in a given weight of sample, allows the calculation of $\overline{M}_n$. The number-average molecular weight $\overline{M}_n$ is calculated like any other numerical average by dividing the sum of the individual molecular weight values by the number of molecules. Thus, $\overline{M}_n$ for three molecules having molecular weights of 1.00×10^5, 2.00×10^5, and 3.00×10^5 would be $(6.00 \times 10^5)/3 = 2.00 \times 10^5$. This solution is shown mathematically:

$$\overline{M}_n = \frac{\text{total weight of sample}}{\text{no. of molecules of } N_i} = \frac{W}{\sum_{i=1}^{\infty} N_i} = \frac{\sum_{i=1}^{\infty} M_i N_i}{\sum_{i=1}^{\infty} N_i} \tag{4.1}$$

Most thermodynamic properties are related to the number of particles present and thus are dependent on $\overline{M}_n$.

Colligative properties dependent on the number of particles present are obviously related to $\overline{M}_n$. $\overline{M}_n$ values are independent of molecular size and are highly sensitive to small molecules present in the mixture. Values for $\overline{M}_n$ are determined by Raoult's techniques that are dependent on colligative properties such as ebulliometry (boiling point elevation), cryometry (freezing point depression), osmometry, and end-group analysis.

Weight-average molecular weight, $\overline{M}_w$, is determined from experiments in which each molecule or chain makes a contribution to the measured result. This average is more dependent on the number of heavier molecules than is the number-average molecule weight, which is dependent simply on the total number of particles.

The weight average molecular weight $\overline{M}_w$ is the second moment or second power average and is shown mathematically as :

$$\overline{M}_w = \frac{\sum_{i=1}^{\infty} M_i^2 N_i}{\sum_{i=1}^{\infty} M_i N_i} \tag{4.2}$$

Thus, the weight average molecular weight, for the example used in calculating $\overline{M}_n$, would be 2.33×10^5,

$$\frac{(1.00 \times 10^{10}) + (4.00 \times 10^{10}) + (9 \times 10^{10})}{6.00 \times 10^5} = 2.33 \times 10^5$$

Bulk properties associated with large deformations, such as viscosity and toughness, are particularly affected by $\overline{M}_w$ values. $\overline{M}_w$ values are determined by light scattering and ultracentrifugation techniques.

However, melt elasticity is more closely dependent on $\overline{M}_z$—the z-average molecular weight can also be obtained by ultracentrifugation techniques. M_z is the third moment or third power average and is shown mathematically as:

$$\overline{M}_z = \frac{\sum_{i=1}^{\infty} M_i^3 N_i}{\sum_{i=1}^{\infty} M_i^2 N_i} \tag{4.3}$$

Thus, the $\overline{M}_z$ average molecular weight for the example used in calculating $\overline{M}_n$ and $\overline{M}_w$ would be 2.57×10^5:

$$\frac{(1 \times 10^{15}) + (8 \times 10^{15}) + (27 \times 10^{15})}{(1 \times 10^{10}) + (4 \times 10^{10}) + (9 \times 10^{10})} = 2.57 \times 10^5$$

While z + 1 and higher average molecular weights may be calculated, the major interests are in $\overline{M}_n$, $\overline{M}_v$, $\overline{M}_w$, and $\overline{M}_z$, which as shown in Fig. 4.3 are listed in order of increasing size. Since $\overline{M}_w$ is always greater than $\overline{M}_n$ except in monodisperse systems the ratio $\overline{M}_w/\overline{M}_n$ is a measure of polydispersity and is called the polydispersity index. The most probable

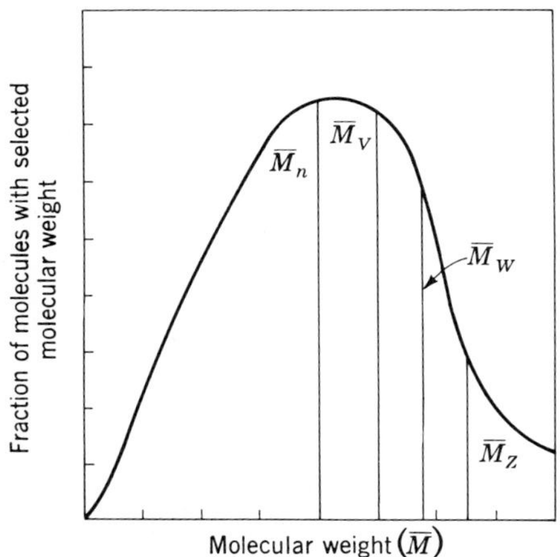

FIGURE 4.3 Molecular weight distributions. (From Introduction to Polymer Chemistry by R. Seymour, McGraw-Hill, New York, 1971. Used with permission of McGraw-Hill Book Company.)

TABLE 4.1 Typical Molecular Weight Determination Methods[a]

Method	Type of mol. wt. average	Applicable wt. range	Other information
Light scattering	$\overline{M}_w$	to ∞	Can also give shape
Membrane osmometry	$\overline{M}_n$	2×10^4 to 2×10^6	
Vapor phase osmometry	$\overline{M}_n$	to 40,000	
Electron and X-ray microscopy	$\overline{M}_{n,w,z}$	10^2 to ∞	Shape, distribution
Isopiestic method (isothermal distillation)	$\overline{M}_n$	to 20,000	
Ebullionmetry (boiling elevation)	$\overline{M}_n$	to 40,000	
Cryoscopy (melting point depression)	$\overline{M}_n$	to 50,000	
End-group analysis	$\overline{M}_n$	to 20,000	
Osmodialysis	$\overline{M}_n$	500-25,000	
Centrifugation			
Sedimentation equilibrium	$\overline{M}_z$	to ∞	
Archibald modification	$\overline{M}_{z,w}$	to ∞	
Trautman's method	$\overline{M}_w$	to ∞	
Sedimentation velocity	Gives a real mol. wt. only for monodisperse systems	to ∞	

[a]"To ∞" means that the molecular weight of the largest particles soluble in a suitable solvent can be determined in theory.

distribution for polydisperse polymers produced by condensation techniques is a polydispersity index of 2.0. Thus, for a polymer mixture which is heterogeneous with respect to molecular weight, $\overline{M}_z > \overline{M}_w > \overline{M}_n$. As the heterogeneity decreases the various molecular weight values converge until for homogeneous mixtures $\overline{M}_z = \overline{M}_w = \overline{M}_n$. The ratios of such molecular weight values are often used to describe the molecular weight heterogeneity of polymer samples.

Typical techniques for molecular weight determination are given in Table 4.1. Comprehensive discussion of any of these techniques is beyond the scope of this text. The most popular techniques will be considered briefly.

All classic molecular weight determination methods require the polymer to be in solution. To minimize polymer-polymer interactions, solutions equal to and less than 1 g of polymer to 100 ml of solution are utilized. To further minimize solute interactions, extrapolation of the measurements to infinite dilution is normally practiced.

When the exponent a in the Mark-Houwink equation is equal to 1, the average molecular weight obtained by viscosity measurements ($\overline{M}_v$) is equal to $\overline{M}_w$. However, since typical values of a are 0.5 to 0.8, the value $\overline{M}_w$ is usually greater than $\overline{M}_v$. Since viscometry does not yield absolute values of $\overline{M}$ as is the case with other techniques, one must plot $[\eta]$ against known values of $\overline{M}$ and determine the constants K and a in the Mark-Houwink equation. Some of these values are available in the Polymer Handbook (see the Bibliography), and simple comparative effluent times or melt indices are often sufficient for comparative purposes and quality control where k and a are known.

4.3 FRACTIONATION OF POLYDISPERSE SYSTEMS

The data plotted in Fig. 4.3 were obtained by the fractionation of a polydisperse polymer. Prior to the introduction of gel permeation chromatography (GPC), polydisperse polymers were fractionated by the addition of a nonsolvent to a polymer solution, by cooling a solution of polymer, solvent evaporation, zone melting, extraction, diffusion, or centrifugation. The molecular weight of the fractions may be determined by any of the classic techniques previously mentioned and discussed subsequently in this chapter.

The least sophisticated but most convenient technique is fractional precipitation, which is dependent on the slight change in the solubility parameter with molecular weight. Thus, when a small amount of miscible nonsolvent is added to a polymer solution at a constant temperature, the product with the highest molecular weight precipitates. This procedure may be repeated after the precipitate is removed. These fractions may also be redissolved and fractionally precipitated.

For example, isopropyl alcohol or methanol may be added dropwise to a solution of polystyrene in benzene until the solution becomes turbid. It is preferable to heat this solution and allow it to cool before removing the first and subsequent fractions. Extraction of a polymer in a Soxhlet-type apparatus in which fractions are removed at specific time intervals may also be used as a fractionation procedure.

4.4 GEL PERMEATION CHROMATOGRAPHY (GPC)

Gel permeation chromatography (GPC), which has been called gel filtration, is a type of liquid-solid elution chromatography that separates polydisperse polymers into fractions by means of the sieving action of a cross-linked polystyrene gel or other sievelike packing. The polystyrene gel, which serves as the stationary phase, is commercially available with a wide distribution of pore sizes (1 to 10^6 nm). Since the smaller molecules permeate the gel particles preferentially, the highest molecular weight fractions are eluted first. Thus, the fractions are separated on the basis of size.

As shown in Fig. 4.4, a solution in a solvent such as tetrahydrofuran (THF) and the solvent (THF) are pumped through separate columns at a rate of about 1 ml/min. The differences in refractive index between the solvent

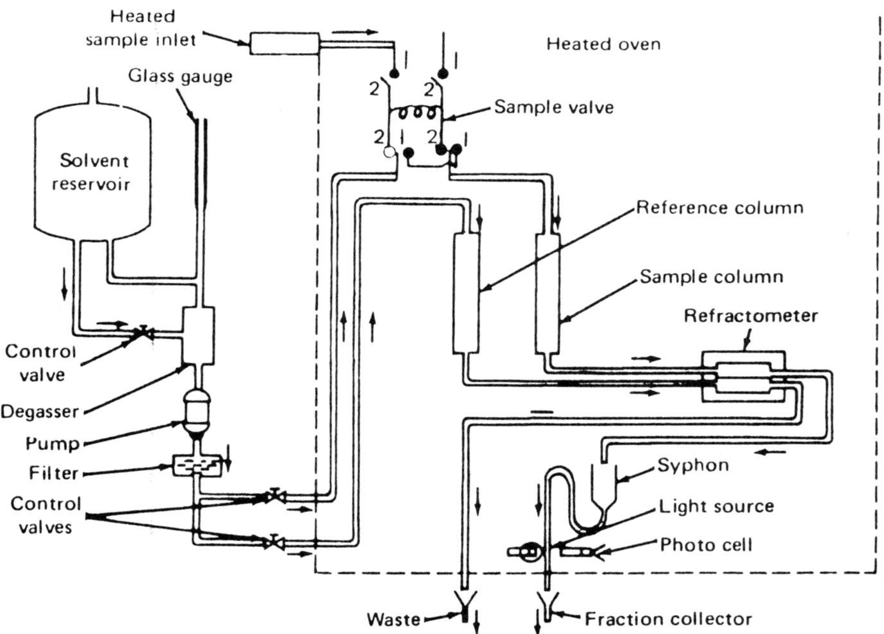

FIGURE 4.4 Sketch showing flow of solution and solvent in gel permeation chromatograph (GPC). (With permission of Waters Associates.)

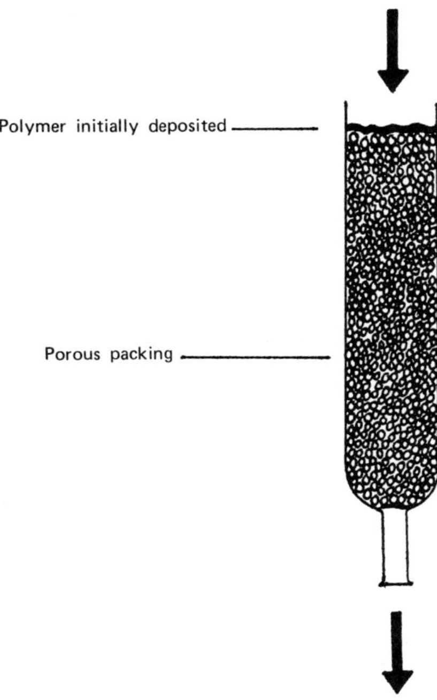

FIGURE 4.5 Sketch showing solvent-swollen cross-linked polymer packing in GPC column.

and solution are determined by a differential refractometer and recorded automatically. Each column unit must be calibrated using polymers of known molecular weights. The details of the packed column are shown in Fig. 4.5.

The unautomated procedure was used first to separate protein oligomers (polypeptides) by use of Sephadex gels. Silica gels are also used as the sieves. The efficiency of these packed columns may be determined by calculating the height in feet equivalent to a theoretical plate (HETP) which is the reciprocal of the plate count per foot (P). As shown by the expression in (4.4), P is directly proportional to the square of the elution volume (V_e) and inversely proportional to the height of the column in feet (f) and the square of the baseline (d). As shown in Fig. 4.6, the latter is the width of the baseline of an idealized peak obtained by drawing lines tangent to the sides of the actual GPC bell-shaped peak of a pure substance such as THF.

$$P = \frac{16}{f}\left(\frac{V_e}{d}\right)^2 \tag{4.4}$$

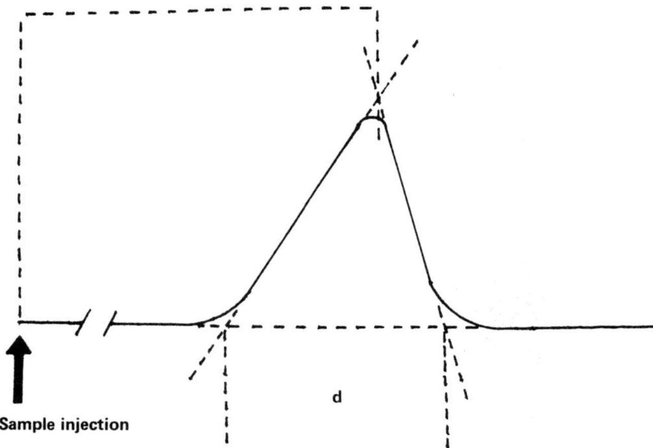

FIGURE 4.6 Sketch showing the width (d) of a peak in GPC.

The molecular weight of a polymer is related to the effective size occupied by the polymer chain in solution or its hydrodynamic volume (V). For example, V for polystyrene in THF at 25°C is equal to $1.5 \times 10^{-2}\ M_w^{1.70}$. In addition to fractionating polydisperse polymers and providing information on polymer size, GPC may be coupled with other instruments, such as an ultraviolet spectrophotometer, for analysis of the eluted fractions.

4.5 END GROUP ANALYSIS

While early experimenters were unable to detect the end groups present in polymers, appropriate techniques are now available for detecting and analyzing quantitatively functional end groups of linear polymers, such as those in nylon. The amino end groups of nylon dissolved in m-cresol are readily determined by titration with a methanolic perchloric acid solution. The sensitivity of this method decreases as the molecular weight increases. Thus, this technique is limited to the determination of polymers with a molecular weight of less than about 20,000. Other titratable end groups are the hydroxyl and carboxyl groups in polyesters and the epoxy end groups in epoxy resins.

4.6 EBULLIOMETRY AND CRYOMETRY

These techniques, based on Raoult's law, are similar to those used for classic low molecular weight compounds and are dependent on the sensitivity of the thermometry available. The number-average molecular weight $\overline{M}_n$

in both cases is based on the Clausius-Clapeyron equation using boiling point elevation and freezing point depression (ΔT), as shown:

$$\overline{M}_n = \frac{RT^2V}{\Delta H}\left(\frac{C}{\Delta T}\right)_{C \to 0} \tag{4.5}$$

Results obtained using the Clausius-Clapeyron equation, in which T is the Kelvin temperature and ΔH is the heat of transition, must be extrapolated to zero concentration. This technique, like end group analysis, is limited to low molecular weight polymers. By use of thermistors sensitive to 1×10^{-4} °C, it is possible to measure molecular weight values up to 40,000 to 50,000, although more typical limits are about 5000.

4.7 OSMOMETRY

A measurement of any of the colligative properties of a polymer solution leads to a counting of solute (polymer) molecules in a given amount of solvent giving a number-average result. The only colligative property that is conveniently measured for high polymers is osmotic pressure. This is based on the use of a semipermeable membrane through which solvent molecules pass freely, but through which polymer molecules are unable to pass. Existing membranes only approximate ideal semipermeability, the chief limitation being the passage of low molecular weight chains through the membrane.

There is a thermodynamic drive toward dilution of the polymer-containing solution with a net flow of solvent toward the cell containing the polymer, resulting in an increase in liquid in that cell developing a rise in the liquid level in the corresponding measuring tube. The rise in liquid level is opposed and finally balanced by a hydrostatic pressure resulting in a difference in the liquid levels of the two measuring tubes—the difference directly related to the osmotic pressure of the polymer-containing solution. Thus, solvent molecules tend to pass through a semipermeable membrane toward reaching a "static" equilibrium, as illustrated in Fig. 4.7.

Since osmotic pressure is dependent on colligative properties, i.e., the number of particles present, the measurement of this pressure (osmometry) may be applied to the determination of the osmotic pressure of solvents versus polymer solutions. The difference in height (Δh) of the liquids in the columns may be converted to osmotic pressure (π) by multiplying by gravity (g) and the density of the solution (ρ), i.e., $\pi = \Delta h\, \rho g$.

In an automatic membrane osmometer, such as the one shown in Fig. 4.8, the unrestricted capillary rise in a dilute solution is measured in accordance with the modified van't Hoff equation shown in (4.6).

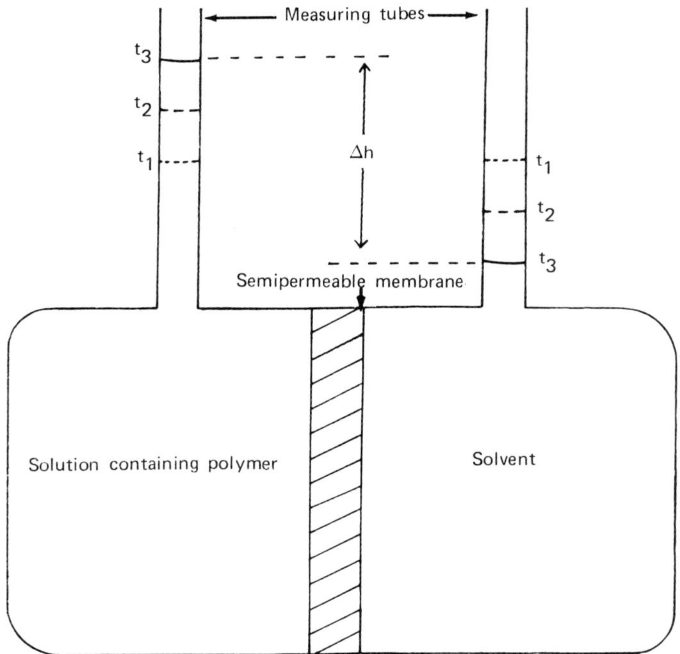

FIGURE 4.7 Schematic diagram showing the effect of pressure exerted by a solvent separated by a semipermeable membrane from a solution containing a nontransportable material (polymer) as a function of time, where t_1 represents the initial measuring tube levels, t_2 the levels after an elapsed time, and t_3 the levels when the "static" equilibrium occurs.

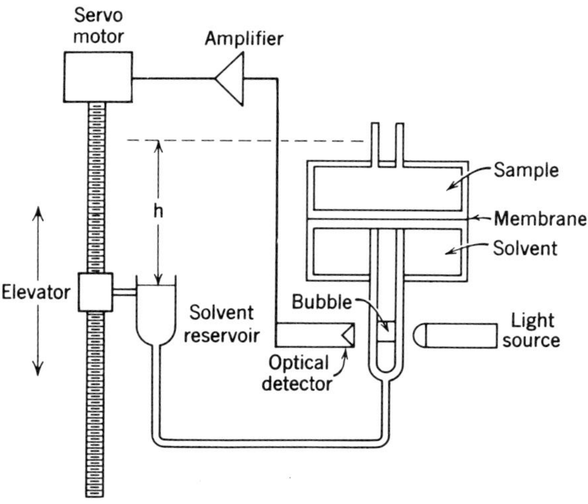

FIGURE 4.8 Automatic membrane osmometer. (Courtesy of Hewlett-Packard Company.)

$$\pi = \frac{RT}{\overline{M}_n} C + BC^2 \tag{4.6}$$

As shown in Fig. 4.9, the reciprocal of the number average molecular weight ($\overline{M}_n^{-1}$) is the intercept when data for π/RTC versus C are extrapolated to zero concentration.

The slope of the line in Fig. 4.9, the virial constant B, is related to CED. The value for B would be 0 at the θ temperature. Since this slope increases as the solvency increases, it is advantageous to use a dilute solution consisting of a polymer and a poor solvent. Semipermeable membranes may be constructed from hevea rubber, polyvinyl alcohol, or cellulose nitrate.

The static head (Δh) developed in the static equilibrium method is eliminated in the dynamic equilibrium method in which a counterpressure is applied to prevent the rise of solvent in the measuring tubes, as shown in Fig. 4.8. Since osmotic pressure is large (1 atm for a 1 M solution), osmometry is useful for the determination of the molecular weight of large molecules.

Static osmotic pressure measurements generally require several days to weeks before a suitable equilibrium is established to permit a meaningful measurement of osmotic pressure. The time required to achieve equilibrium is shortened to several minutes to an hour in most commercial instruments utilizing dynamic techniques.

Classic osmometry is useful and widely used for the determination of a range of $\overline{M}_n$ values from 5×10^4 to 2×10^6. New dynamic osmometers allow this range to lower to 2×10^4 to 2×10^6. The molecular weight of polymers with lower molecular weights which may pass through a membrane

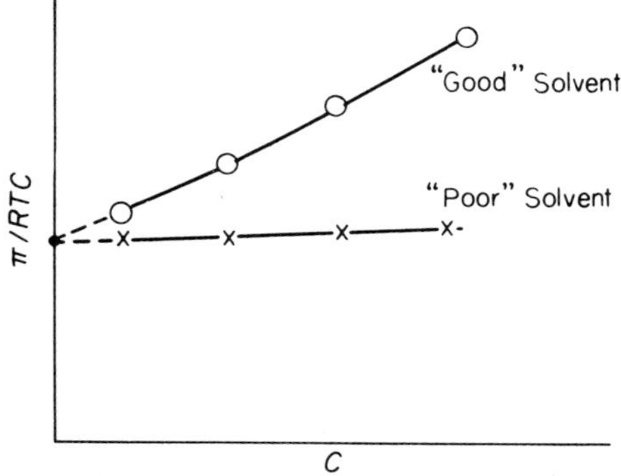

FIGURE 4.9 Plot of π/RTC versus C used to determine $1/\overline{M}_n$ in osmometry. (From Modern Plastics Technology by R. Seymour, Reston Publishing, Reston, Virginia, 1975. Used with permission of Reston Publishing Co.)

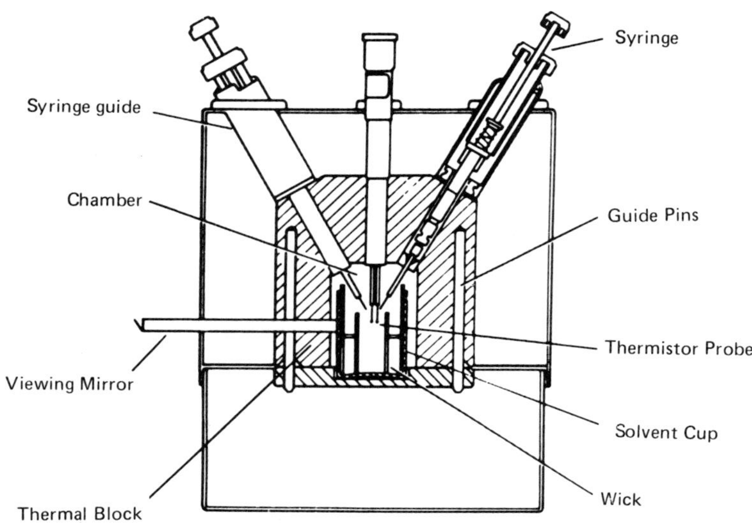

FIGURE 4.10 A sketch of a vapor pressure osmometer. (Courtesy of Hewlett-Packard Company.)

may be determined by vapor pressure osmometry (VPO) or isothermal distillation. Both techniques provide absolute values for $\overline{M}_n$.

In the VPO technique, drops of solvent and solution are placed in an insulated chamber in proximity to thermistor probes. Since the solvent molecules evaporate more rapidly from the solvent than from the solution, a difference in temperature (ΔT) is recorded. Thus, the molality ($\underline{M}$) may be determined by use of (4.7) if the heat of vaporization per gram of solvent (λ) is known.

$$\Delta T = \left(\frac{RT^2}{\lambda 100}\right) M \qquad (4.7)$$

A sketch of a vapor pressure osmometer is shown in Fig. 4.10.

4.8 REFRACTOMETRY

The index of refraction decreases slightly as the molecular weight increases, and as demonstrated by the techniques used in GPC, this change has been used for the determination of molecular weight after calibration using samples of known molecular weight distribution.

4.9 LIGHT-SCATTERING MEASUREMENTS

Ever watch a dog or young child chase "moon beams"? The illumination of dust particles is an illustration of light scattering, not of reflection. Reflection is the deviation of incident light through one particular angle such that the angle of incidence is equal to the angle of reflection. Scattering is the radiation of light in all directions. Thus, in observing the "moon beam," the dust particle directs a beam toward you regardless of the angle you are with relation to the scattering particle. The energy scattered per second (scattered flux) is related to the size and shape of the scattering particle and to the scattering angle.

The measurement of light scattering by polymer molecules in solution is a widely used technique for the determination of absolute values of $\overline{M}_w$. This technique, which is based on the optical heterogeneity of polymer solutions, was developed by Nobel laureate Peter Debye in 1944.

Raleigh showed in 1871 that induced oscillatory dipoles were developed when light passed through gases and that the amount of scattered light (τ) was inversely proportional to the fourth power of the wavelength of light. This investigation was extended to liquids by Einstein and Smoluchowski in 1908. These oscillations reradiate the light energy to produce turbidity, or the Tyndall effect. Other sources of energy, such as X-rays or laser beams, may be used in place of light waves.

For light-scattering measurements the total amount of the scattered light is deduced from the decrease in intensity of the incident beam, I_o, as it passes through a polymer sample. This can be described in terms of Beer's law for the absorption of light as follows

$$\frac{I}{I_o} = e^{-\tau l} \tag{4.8}$$

where τ is the measure of the decrease of the incident-beam intensity per unit length l of a given solution and is called the turbidity.

The intensity of scattered light or turbidity (τ) is proportional to the square of the difference between the index of refraction (n) of the polymer solution and the solvent, to the molecular weight of the polymer ($\overline{M}$), and to the inverse fourth power of the wavelength of light used (λ). Thus,

$$\frac{Hc}{\tau} = \frac{1}{\overline{M}_w P_o} (1 + 2Bc + Cc^2 + \cdots) \tag{4.9}$$

where the expression for the constant H is as follows:

$$H = \frac{32\pi^3}{3} \frac{n_o^2 (dn/dc)^2}{\lambda^4 N} \tag{4.10}$$

where n_o = index of refraction of the solvent, n = index of refraction of the solution, c = concentration, the virial constants B, C, etc., are related to the interaction of the solvent, P_θ is the particle scattering factor, and N is Avogadro's number. The expression dn/dc is the specific refractive increment and is determined by taking the slope of the refractive index readings as a function of polymer concentration.

In the determination of the weight-average molecular weight of polymer molecules in dust-free solutions, one measures the intensity of scattered light from a mercury arc lamp or laser at different concentrations and at different angles (θ), typically 0, 90, 45, and 135° (Fig. 4.11). The incident light sends out a scattering envelope which has four equivalent quadrants. The ratio of scattering at 45° compared with that for 135° is called the dissymmetry factor or dissymmetry ratio Z. The reduced dissymmetry factor Z_0 is the intercept of the plot of Z as a function of concentration extrapolated to zero concentration. For polymer solutions containing polymers of moderate to low molecular weight, P_θ is 1 and (4.9) reduces to

$$\frac{Hc}{\tau} = \frac{1}{\overline{M}_w} (1 + 2Bc + Cc^2 + \cdots) \tag{4.11}$$

At low concentrations of polymer in solution, (4.11) reduces to an equation of a straight line, (4.12):

$$\begin{aligned} \frac{Hc}{\tau} &= \frac{1}{\overline{M}_w} + \frac{2Bc}{\overline{M}_w} \\ y &= b + mx \end{aligned} \tag{4.12}$$

When the ratio of the concentration c to the turbidity τ (related to the intensity of scattering at 0 and 90°) multiplied by the constant H is plotted against concentration, the intercept of the extrapolated curve is the reciprocal of $\overline{M}_w$ and the slope is the virial constant B, as shown in Fig. 4.12. Z_0 is directly related to P_θ, and both are related to both the size and shape of the scattering particle. As the size of the polymer chain approaches about one-twentieth the wavelength of incident light, scattering interference occurs giving a scattering envelope which is no longer symmetrical. Here the scattering dependency on molecular weight reverts back to the relationship given in (4.9), thus, a plot of Hc/T versus C extrapolated to zero polymer concentration gives as the intercept $1/\overline{M}_w P_\theta$, not $1/\overline{M}_w$. The molecular weight for such situations is typically found using one of two techniques.

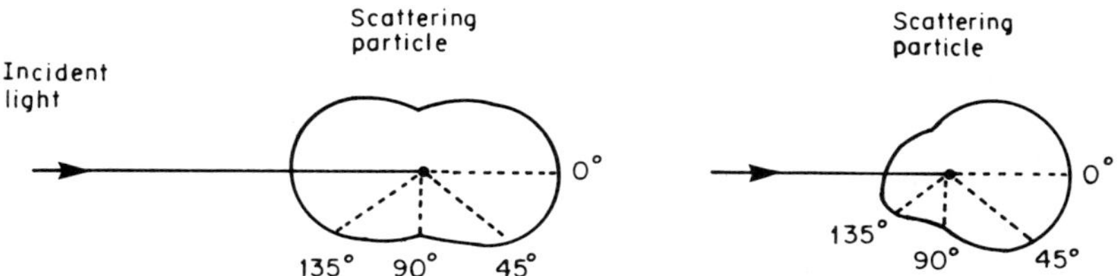

FIGURE 4.11 Light-scattering envelopes. Distance from the scattering particle to the boundaries of the envelope represents the magnitude of scattered light as a function of angle.

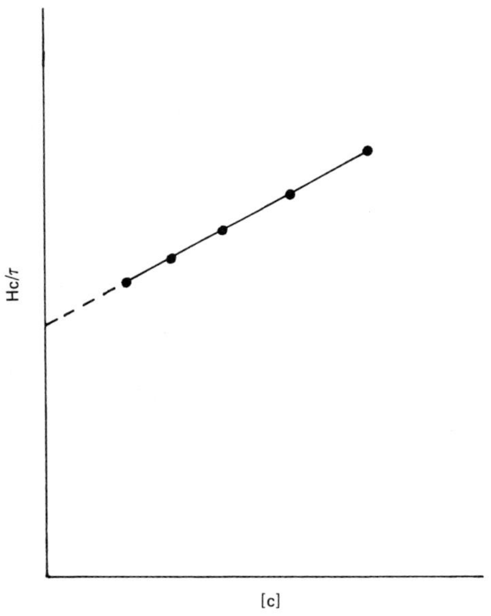

FIGURE 4.12 Typical plot used to determine $\overline{M}_W^{-1}$ from light-scattering data.

The first of the techniques is called the dissymmetric method or approach because it utilizes the determination of Z_0 versus P_θ as a function of polymer shape. $\overline{M}_W$ is determined from the intercept $\overline{1}/\overline{M}_W P_\theta$ through substitution of the determined P_θ. The weak point of this approach is the necessity of having to assume a shape for the polymer in that particular solution. For small Z_0 values, a mistake in choosing the correct polymer shape results in a small error, but for larger Z_0 values, the error may become significant, greater than 30%. The positive feature is that the dissymmetric approach is simple compared to the second approach, the Zimm method, where no assumption of polymer shape is necessary.

The Zimm method utilizes the Zimm plot, which is a double extrapolation of the light-scattering data to zero concentration and zero scattering angle. The plot utilizes a redistribution of the Hc/T factors designating this combination as Kc/R. Figure 4.13 contains a representative Zimm plot. Figures 4.14 and 4.15 contain illustrations of a typical light-scattering photometer suitable for determination of weight-average polymer molecular weights. L contains the light source, typically a mercury lamp, F contains a series of filters, C contains the cell containing the polymer solution, and PT is the detection phototube which can freely rotate to the desired angles.

Recently new light-scattering photometers have become available utilizing low scattering angles employing laser lamps as the incident light.

A major error involved in the determination of weight-average molecular weight using light-scattering photometry involves determination of dn/dc, since any error in its determination is magnified because it appears as the squared value in the equation relating light scattering and molecular weight, such as (4.10).

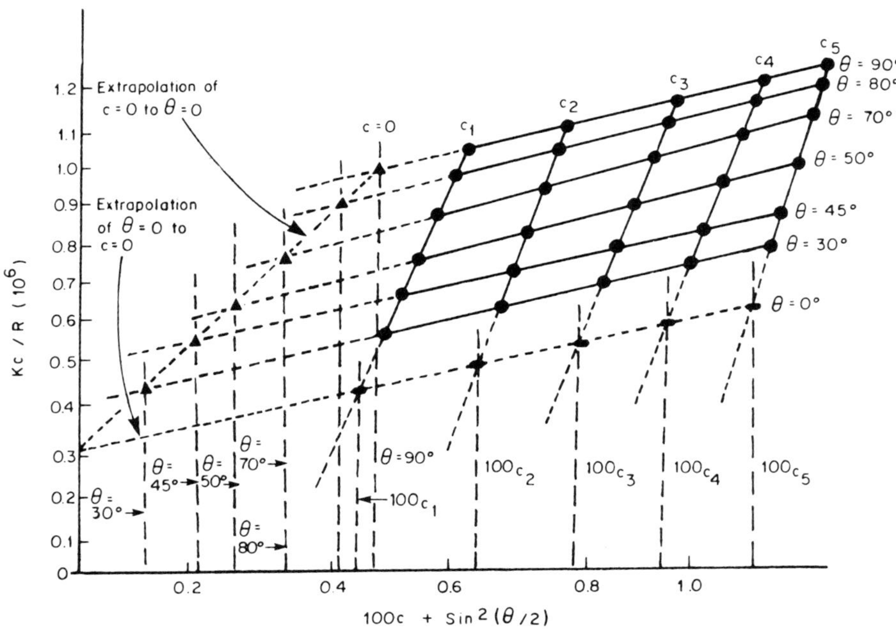

FIGURE 4.13 Representative Zimm light-scattering plot.

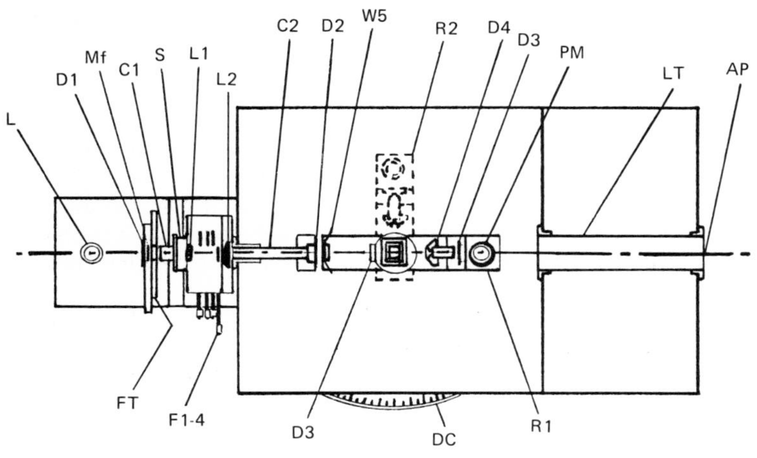

L	Lamp	D3	Diaphragm detector
D1	Diaphragm limiting	CT	Cell table
MF	Monochromatic filter	D4	Detector entrance slit
C1	Shutter collimating tube	AP	Alignment port
S	Shutter/Iris diaphragm	PM	Photomultiplier tube
L1	Achromatic lens	FT	Filter turret
F1-4	Neutral filters F1, F2, F3, F4	DC	Disc
		LT	Light trap tube
L2	Plano cylindrical lens	R1	Detector housing
C2	Collimating tube	R2	Detector housing (dual only)
D2	Diaphragm collimating		
WS	Working standard		

FIGURE 4.14 Diagram of the essential components of the Brice-Phoenix light-scattering photometer. (Courtesy of Virtis Co., Inc.)

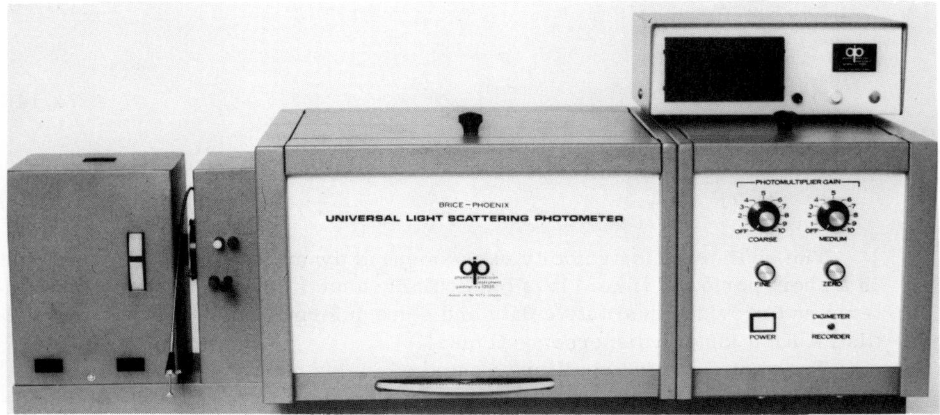

FIGURE 4.15 Exterior view of the Brice-Phoenix light-scattering photometer. (Courtesy of Virtis Co., Inc.)

4.10 ULTRACENTRIFUGATION

Since the kinetic energy of solvent molecules is much greater than the sedimentation force of gravity, polymer molecules remain suspended in solution. However, this traditional gravitation field, which permits Brownian motion, may be overcome by increasing its force by use of high centrifugal forces, such as the ultracentrifugal forces developed by Nobel laureate The Svedberg in 1925.

Both $\overline{M}_W$ and $\overline{M}_Z$ may be determined by subjecting dilute solutions of polymers in appropriate solvents to ultracentrifugal forces at high speeds. Solvents with densities and indices of refraction different from the polymers are chosen to ensure polymer motion and optical detection of this motion.

In the sedimentation velocity experiments, the ultracentrifuge is operated at extremely high speeds up to 70,000 rpm in order to transport the polymer molecules through the less dense solvent to the cell bottom or to the top if the density of the solvent is greater than that of the polymer. The boundary movement during ultracentrifugation can be followed by using optical measurements to monitor the sharp change in index of refraction (n) between solvent and solution.

The rate of sedimentation is defined by the sedimentation constant s which is directly proportional to the mass m, solution density ρ, and specific volume of the polymer $\overline{V}$, and inversely proportional to the angular velocity of rotation ω, the distance from the center of rotation to the point of observation in the cell r, and the frictional coefficient f. The latter is inversely related to the diffusion coefficient D extrapolated to infinite dilution. These relationships are shown in the following equations in which $(1 - \overline{V}\rho)$ is called the buoyancy factor since it determines the direction of macromolecular transport in the cell.

$$s = \frac{1}{\omega^2 r} \frac{dr}{dt} = \frac{m(1 - \overline{V}\rho)}{f} \tag{4.13}$$

$$D = \frac{kT}{f} \tag{4.14}$$

$$\frac{D}{s} = \frac{RT}{\overline{M}_{\omega}(1 - \overline{V}\rho)} \tag{4.15}$$

The sedimentation velocity experiment is dynamic and can be completed in a short period of time. It is particularly useful for monodisperse systems and provides qualitative data and some information on molecular weight distribution for polydisperse systems.

The sedimentation equilibrium method yields quantitative results, but long periods of time are required for centrifugation at relatively low velocities to establish equilibrium between sedimentation and diffusion.

As shown in the following equation, the weight-average molecular weight $\overline{M}_w$ is directly proportional to the temperature T and the ln of the ratio of concentration c_2/c_1 at distances r_1 and r_2 from the center of rotation and the point of observation in the cell and inversely proportional to the buoyancy factor, the square of the angular velocity of rotation and the difference between the squares of the distances r_1 and r_2.

$$\overline{M}_w = \frac{2RT \ln c_2/c_1}{(1 - \overline{V}\rho)\omega^2(r_2^2 - r_1^2)} \tag{4.16}$$

SUMMARY

1. Some naturally occurring polymers such as proteins consist of molecules with a specific molecular weight and are called monodisperse. However, cellulose, natural rubber, and most synthetic polymers consist of molecules with different molecular weights and are called polydisperse. Many properties of polymers are dependent on their molecular weight above that required for entanglement. Since the melt viscosity increases exponentially with molecular weight, the high energy costs of processing high molecular weight polymers are not usually justified.

2. The distribution of molecular weights in a polydisperse system may be represented on a typical probability curve. The number-average molecular weight $\overline{M}_n$, which is smallest in magnitude, and a simple arithmetic mean may be determined by techniques based on colligative properties, such as osmotic pressure, boiling point increase, and freezing point depression. The weight-average molecular weight ($\overline{M}_w$), which is larger than $\overline{M}_n$ for polydisperse systems, is the second-power average. This value may be determined by light-scattering which, like techniques based on colligative properties, yields absolute values for molecular weights.

3. Since $\overline{M}_w = \overline{M}_n$ for a monodisperse system, the polydispersity index $\overline{M}_w/\overline{M}_n$ is a measure of polydispersity. The most probable value for this index for polymers synthesized by condensation techniques is 2.0. The viscosity average $\overline{M}_v$, which is not an absolute value, is usually between $\overline{M}_n$ and $\overline{M}_w$, but when the exponent a in the Mark-Houwink equation is equal to 1, $\overline{M}_w = \overline{M}_v$.

4. Various molecular weight distributions may be obtained by special analytical techniques—centrifugation, gel permeation chromatography, and solvent fractionation. In the last technique one adds a small amount of nonsolvent to precipitate the highest molecular weight polymer from solution. In gel permeation chromatography, smaller cross-linked polymers in a column act as a sieve and allow the larger molecules to elute first. After calibration, the molecular weight of the eluted polymer is determined automatically by measuring the difference in index of refraction of the solution and solvent.

5. The use of boiling point increase and freezing point lowering is limited to the determination of the molecular weights of relatively small polymers. However, since the osmotic pressure of a 1 m solution is large (1 atm), osmometry is readily used for characterizing large molecules. The possibility of oligomers and other small polymers passing through the semipermeable membrane is avoided by use of vapor pressure osmometry for characterization of polymers having molecular weights less than 40,000. This technique utilizes the difference in temperatures noted during the evaporation of a solvent from a solution and the pure solvent.

6. Absolute molecular weight values reported as weight-average molecular weights are obtained by light-scattering techniques. $\overline{M}_w$ values for nonpolar polymers with molecular weights less than 100,000 are determined by extrapolating the plot of the product of the ratio of the concentration and the turbidity and a constant H versus concentration, the intercept is $\overline{M}_w{}^{-1}$.

7. Since the gravitational force present in the ultracentrifuge is sufficient to precipitate polymer molecules in accordance with their size, ultracentrifugation is used as a technique for the determination of molecular weight, especially for monodisperse systems such as proteins.

GLOSSARY

a: Exponent in Mark-Houwink equation, usually 0.6 to 0.8.

B: Symbol for the second virial constant.

Brownian motion: Movement of large particles in a liquid as a result of bombardment by smaller molecules. This phenomenon was named after the botanist Robert Brown who observed it in 1827.

buoyancy factor: $(1 - \overline{V}\rho)$ or 1 - the specific volume × density of a polymer. This term, used in ultracentrifugal experiments, determines the direction of polymer transport under the effect of centrifugal forces in the cell.

CED: Cohesive energy density.

Clausius-Clapeyron equation: For small changes in pressure, the unintegrated expression $dT/dp = RT^2/Lp$ may be used where L is the molar heat of vaporization. The form used for molecular weight determination is as follows:

$$\overline{M}_n = \frac{RT^2V}{\Delta H}\left(\frac{C}{\Delta T}\right)_{C \to 0}$$

colligative properties: Properties of a solution which are dependent on the number of solute molecules present and are usually related to the effect of these molecules on vapor pressure lowering.

commercial polymer range: A molecular weight range high enough to have good physical properties but not too high for economical processing.

critical molecular weight: The threshold value of molecular weight required for chain entanglement.

cryometry: Measurement of $\overline{M}_n$ from freezing point depression.

d: The width of the baseline of idealized peaks in a gel permeation chromatogram.

ebulliometry: Measurement of $\overline{M}_n$ from boiling point elevation of a solution.

end group analysis: The determination of molecular weight by counting the number of end groups.

end groups: The functional groups at chain ends such as the carboxyl groups (COOH) in polyesters.

f: Symbol for frictional coefficient in ultracentrifugal experiments.

fractional precipitation: Fractionation of polydisperse systems by adding small amounts of a nonsolvent to a solution of the polymer and separating the precipitate.

fractionation of polymers: Separation of a polydisperse polymer into fractions of similar molecular weights.

gel permeation chromatography: A type of liquid-solid elution chromatography which automatically separates solutions of polydisperse polymers into fractions by means of the sieving action of a swollen cross-linked polymeric gel.

GPC: Gel permeation chromatography.

H: Symbol for the proportionality constant in a light-scattering equation.

HETP: Height equivalent to a theoretical plate (in feet).

isothermal distillation: Same as vapor pressure osmometry.

lambda (λ): Symbol for the wavelength of light.

ln: Symbol for natural or naperian logarithm.

$\overline{M}_n$: Number-average molecular weight.

monodisperse: A system consisting of molecules of one molecular weight only

$\overline{M}_w$: Weight-average molecular weight.

$\overline{M}_z$: z-Average molecular weight.

MWD: Molecular weight distribution.

n: Index of refraction.

N: Symbol for Avogadro's number, 6.23×10^{23}.

number average molecular weight: The arithmetical mean value obtained by dividing the sum of the molecular weights by the number of molecules.

oligomer: Very low molecular weight polymer usually with DP less than 10 (the Greek oligos means few).

omega (ω): Symbol for the angular velocity of rotation.

osmometry: The determination of molecular weight $\overline{M}_n$ from measurement of osmotic pressure.

osmotic pressure: The pressure a solute would exert in solution if it were an ideal gas at the same volume.

P: Symbol for plate count in GPC.

pi (π): Symbol for osmotic pressure.

plate count (P): The reciprocal of HETP.

polydisperse: A mixture containing polymer molecules of different molecular weights.

polydispersity index: $\overline{M}_w/\overline{M}_n$.

polypeptides: A term used to describe oligomers of proteins, which of course are also polypeptides or polyamino acids.

Raoult's law: The vapor pressure of a solvent in equilibrium with a solution is equal to the product of the mole fraction of the solvent and the vapor pressure of the pure solvent at any specified temperature. Osmotic pressure, boiling point elevation, and freezing point depression are related to this decrease in vapor pressure.

rho (ρ): Symbol for density.

sedimentation equilibrium experiment: An ultracentrifugal technique which provides quantitative information on molecular weights. Long times are required for the attainment of equilibrium in this method.

sedimentation velocity experiment: A dynamic experiment with the ultracentrifuge which provides qualitative information on molecular weight in a short period of time.

semipermeable membranes: Those membranes which will permit the diffusion of solvent molecules but not large molecules such as polymers.

tau (τ): Symbol for turbidity.

theta (θ): Symbol for the angle of the incident beam in light-scattering experiments.

ultracentrifuge: A centrifuge which by increasing the force of gravity by as much as 100,000 times causes solutes to settle from solutions in accordance with their molecular weights.

$\bar{V}$: Symbol for specific volume.

V: Hydrodynamic volume in GPC.

V_e: Elution volume in GPC.

van't Hoff's law: Osmotic pressure

$$\pi = \frac{C}{M}\frac{RT}{V} = \frac{RTC}{M}$$

vapor pressure osmometry: A technique for determining the molecular weight of relatively small polymeric molecules by measuring the relative heats of evaporation of a solvent from a solution and pure solvent.

weight average molecular weight: The second-power average of molecular weights in a polydisperse polymer.

z-average molecular weight: The third-power average of molecular weights in a polydisperse polymer.

Zimm plot: A type of double extrapolation used to determine M_w in light-scattering experiments. Both the concentration of the solution and the angle of the incident beam of light are extrapolated to zero on one plot.

zone melting: The fractionation of polydisperse systems by heating over long periods of time.

EXERCISES

1. Which of the following is polydisperse: (a) casein, (b) commercial polystyrene, (c) paraffin wax, (d) cellulose, or (e) Hevea braziliensis?
2. If $\overline{M}_n$ for LDPE is 1,400,000, what is the value of $\overline{DP}$?
3. What are the $\overline{M}_n$ and $\overline{M}_w$ values for a mixture of five molecules each having the following molecular weights: 1.25×10^6, 1.35×10^6, 1.50×10^6, 1.75×10^6, 2.00×10^6?
4. What is the most probable value for the polydispersity index for (a) a monodisperse polymer, (b) a polydisperse polymer synthesized by condensation techniques?
5. List in order of increasing values: $\overline{M}_z$, $\overline{M}_n$, $\overline{M}_w$, and $\overline{M}_v$.
6. Which of the following provides an absolute measure of the molecular weight of polymers: (a) viscometry, (b) cryometry, (c) osmometry, (d) light scattering, (e) GPC?

7. What is the relationship between the intrinsic viscosity or limiting viscosity number $[\eta]$ and average molecular weight $\overline{M}$?

8. What molecular weight determination techniques can be used to fractionate polydisperse polymers?

9. Which of the following techniques yields a number-average molecular $\overline{M}_n$: (a) viscometry, (b) light scattering, (c) ultracentrifugation, (d) osmometry, (e) ebulliometry, (f) cryometry?

10. What is the relationship of HETP and plate count per foot in GPC?

11. What is the value of the exponent a in the Mark-Houwink equation for polymers in θ solvents?

12. How many amino groups are present in each molecule of nylon-66 made with an excess of hexamethylenediamine?

13. What is the value of the exponent a in the Mark-Houwink equation for a rigid rod?

14. If the value of K and a in the Mark-Houwink equation are 1×10^{-2} cm^3 g^{-1} and 0.5, respectively. what is the average molecular weight of a polymer whose solution has an intrinsic viscosity of 150 cm^3 g^{-1}?

15. Which polymer of ethylene will have the highest molecular weight: (a) a trimer, (b) an oligomer, or (c) UHMWPE?

16. What is a Zimm plot?

17. What type of molecular weight average, $\overline{M}_w$ or $\overline{M}_n$, is based on colligative properties?

18. What principle is used in the determination of molecular weight by vapor pressure osmometry?

19. Why does the melt viscosity increase faster with molecular weight increase than other properties such as tensile strength?

20. In spite of the high costs of processing, ultrahigh molecular weight polyethylene is used for making trash cans and other durable goods. Why?

21. Under what conditions are $\overline{M}_v$ and $\overline{M}_w$ equal for a polydisperse system?

22. What nonsolvent would you use to fractionate a polydisperse polymer in a solution?

23. Which colligative property technique would you use to determine the molecular weight of a polymer having a molecular weight of (a) 40,000, (b) 80,000?

24. What is the advantage of vapor pressure osmometry when measuring relatively low molecular weight polymers?

25. Which will yield the higher apparent molecular weight values in the light-scattering method: (a) a dust-free system, or (b) one in which dust particles are present?

26. Which is the more rapid ultracentrifugation technique for the determination of molecular weight of polymers: (a) sedimentation velocity method, or (b) sedimentation equilibrium method?

27. Which ultracentrifugation technique is more accurate: (a) sedimentation velocity, or (b) sedimentation equilibrium method?

28. What is the significance of the virial constant B in osmometry and light-scattering equations?

BIBLIOGRAPHY

Adams, Jr., E. T. (1968): Molecular weights and molecular-weight distribution from sedimentation-equilibrium experiments, pp. 84-142 in Characterization of Macromolecular Structure (D. McIntyre, ed.), National Academy of Science Publication No. 1573, Washington, D.C.

Allen, P. W. (1959): Techniques of Polymer Characterization, Butterworths, London.

Altgelt, K. H., Moore, J. C. (1967): Gel permeation chromatography, Chap. 4 in Polymer Fractionation (M. J. R. Cantow, ed.), Academic, New York.

Armstrong, J. L. (1968): Critical evaluation of commercially available hi-speed membrane osmometers, pp. 51-55 in Characterization of Macromolecular Structure (D. McIntyre, ed.), National Academy of Sciences Publication No. 1573, Washington, D.C.

Armstrong, R. W., Strauss, U. P. (1969): Polyelectrolytes, pp. 781-861 in Encyclopedia of Polymer Science and Technology, Vol. 10 (H. F. Mark, N. G. Gaylord, and N. M. Bikales, eds.), Wiley Interscience, New York.

Badgley, W. J., Mark, H. (1949): Osmometry and viscometry of polymer solutions, pp. 75-112 in High Molecular Weight Compounds (Frontiers in Chemistry, Vol. VI), (R. E. Burk and Oliver Grummit, eds.), Interscience, New York.

Baldwin, R. L., van Holde, K. E. (1960): Sedimentation of high polymers, Adv. Polymer Sci., 1:451-511.

Battista, O. A. (1958): Fundamentals of High Polymers, Chap. 4, Reinhold, New York.

Benoit, H. (1968): Use of light scattering and hydrodynamic methods for determining the overall conformation of helical molecules, J. Chem. Phys., 65:23-30.

Billmeyer, Jr., F. W. (1964): Principles of light scattering, Chap. 56 in Treatise on Analytical Chemistry (I. M. Kolthoff and P. J. Elving, eds.), Part I, Vol. 5, Wiley Interscience, New York.

——. (1965): Characterization of molecular weight distributions in high polymers, J. Polymer Sci., C8:161-178.

——. (1966): Measuring the weight of giant molecules, Chemistry, 39: 8-14.

——. (1969): Recent advances in determining polymer molecular weights and sizes, Appl. Polymer Symposia, 10:1-6.

——. (1972): Synthetic Polymers, Doubleday, Garden City, New York.

Billmeyer, Jr., F. W., Kokle, V. (1964): The molecular structure of polyethylene. XV. Comparison of number-average molecular weights by various methods, J. Am. Chem. Soc., 86:3544-3546.

Bonnar, R. O., Dimbat, M., Stross, F. H. (1958): Molecular-Average Molecular Weights, Interscience, New York.

Bowen, T. J. (1970 : An Introduction to Ultracentrifugation, Wiley Interscience, New York.

Brandrup, J., Immergut, E. H. (1975): Polymer Handbook, John Wiley, New York.

Braun, D., Cherdron, H., Keru, W. (1972): Techniques of Polymer Synthesis and Characterization, Wiley Interscience, New York.

Brice, B. A., Halwer, M. (1951): A differential refractometer, J. Opt. Soc. Am., 41:1033-1037.

Burge, David E. (1963): Osmotic coefficients in aqueous solutions. Studies with the vapor pressure osmometer, J. Phys. Chem., 67:2590-2593.

Bushuk, W., Benoit, H. (1958): Light-scattering studies of copolymers. I. Effect of heterogeneity of chain composition on the molecular weight, Can. J. Chem., 36:1616-1626.

Cantow, M. J. R. (1967): Polymer Fractionation, Academic, New York.

Carpenter, D. K. (1966): Light-scattering study of the molecular weight distribution of polypropylene, J. Polymer Sci., A-2, 4:923-942.

Carr, Jr., C. I., Zimm, B. H. (1950): Absolute intensity of light scattering from pure liquids and solutions, J. Chem. Phys., 18:1616-1626.

Chiang, R. (1964): Characterization of high polymers in solutions—with emphasis on techniques at elevated temperatures, Chap. XII in Newer Methods of Polymer Characterization (B. Ke, ed.), Wiley Interscience, New York.

Coll, H., Stross, F. H. (1968): Determination of molecular weights by equilibrium osmotic-pressure measurements, pp. 10-27 in Characterization of Macromolecular Structure (D. McIntyre, ed.), National Academy of Sciences Publication No. 1573, Washington, D.C.

Collins, E. A., Baris, Billmeyer, F. W. (1973): Experiments in Polymer Science, Wiley Interscience, New York.

Cowie, J. M. G. (1966): Estimation of unperturbed polymer dimensions from viscosity measurements in non-ideal solvents, Polymer, 7:487-495.

———. (1974): Polymers: Chemistry and Physics of Modern Materials, Chap. 8, Intext Educational Publishers, New York.

Cragg, L. H. (1946): The terminology of intrinsic viscosity and related functions, J. Colloid Sci., 1:261-269.

Debye, P. J. (1944): Light scattering analysis, J. Appl. Phys., 15:338.

———. (1946): The terminology of intrinsic viscosity and related functions, J. Colloid Sci., 1:261-269.

———. (1946): Light scattering in solutions, J. Appl. Phys., 15:338-342.

———. (1947): Molecular-weight determination by light scattering, J. Phys. Coll. Chem., 51:18-32.

———. (1957): How giant molecules are measured, Sci. Am., 197:90.

Debye, P., Bueche, A. M. (1948): Intrinsic viscosity, diffusion, and sedimentation rates of polymers in solutions, J. Chem. Phys., 16: 573-579.

Einstein, A. (1910): Theory of the opalescence of homogeneous liquids and liquid mixtures in the neighborhood of the critical state, Ann. Physik, 33:1275-1298.

Elias, H. G. (1968): Dynamic osmometry, pp. 28-50 in Characterization of Macromolecular Structure (D. McIntyre, ed.), Natural Academy of Sciences Publication No. 1573, Washington, D.C.

———. (1975). Macromolecules Structure and Properties, Synthesis and Materials, Plenum, New York.

Ezrin, M. (1968): Determination of molecular weight by ebulliometry, pp. 3-9 in Characterization of Macromolecular Structure (D. McIntyre, ed.), National Academy of Sciences Publication No. 1573, Washington, D.C.

———. (1973): Polymer Molecular Weight Methods, American Chemical Society, Washington, D.C.

Flory, P. J. (1943): Molecular weights and intrinsic viscosities of polyisobutylenes, J. Am. Chem. Soc., 65:372-382.

———. (1953): Principles of Polymer Chemistry, Cornell University Press, Ithaca, New York.

Fujita, H. (1962): Mathematical Theory of Sedimentation Analysis, Academic, New York.

Fuoss, R. M., Mead, D. J. (1943): Osmotic pressures of polyvinyl chloride solutions by a dynamic method, J. Phys. Chem., 47:59-70.

Glover, C. A. (1966): Determination of molecular weights by ebulliometry, pp. 1-67 in Advances in Analytical Chemistry and Instrumentation (C. N. Reilley and F. W. McLafferty, eds.), Vol. 5, Wiley Interscience, New York.

Hellman, M., Wall, L. A. (1962): End-group analysis, Chap. V in Analytical Chemistry of Polymers (G. M. Kline, ed.), Part III, Wiley Interscience, New York.

Holleran, P. M., Billmeyer, Jr., F. W. (1968): Rapid osmometry with diffusible polymers, J. Polymer Sci., B6:137-140.

Huggins, M. L. (1942): The viscosity of dilute solutions of long-chain molecules. IV. Dependence on concentration, J. Am. Chem. Soc., 64: 2716-2718.

Immergut, E. H., Rollin, S., Salkind, A., Mark, H. (1954): New types of membranes for osmotic pressure measurements, J. Polymer Sci., 12:439-443.

Johnson, J. F., Porter, R. S. (1968): Analytical Gel Permeation Chromatography, John Wiley, New York.

Ke, B. (1964): Newer Methods of Polymer Characterization, Wiley Interscience, New York.

Kerker, M. (1969): The Scattering of Light and Other Electromagnetic Radiation, Academic, New York.

Kerker, M., Kratohvil, J. P., Matijevic, E. (1964): Calibration of light-scattering instruments. II. The volume correction, J. Polymer Sci., A2:303-311.

Kirkwood, J. G., Riseman, J. (1948): The intrinsic viscosities and diffusion constants of flexible molecules in solution, J. Chem. Phys., 16: 565-573.

Kraemer, E. O. (1938): Molecular weights of cellulose and cellulose derivatives, Ind. Eng. Chem., 30:1200-1203.

Kratohvil, J. P. (1964): Light scattering, Anal. Chem. Ann. Rev., 36: 458R-472R.

——. (1966): Calibration of light scattering instruments. IV. Corrections for reflection effects, J. Colloid Interface Sci., 21:498-512.

——. (1966): Light scattering, Anal. Chem. Ann. Rev., 38:517R-526R.

Kratohvil, J. P., Dezelic, G., Kerker, M., Matijevic, E. (1962): Calibration of light-scattering instruments: A critical survey, J. Polymer Sci., 57:59-78.

Kratohvil, J. P., Smart, C. (1965): Calibration of light-scattering instruments. III. Absolute angular intensity measurements on Mie scatterers, J. Colloid Sci., 20:875-892.

Krigbaum, W. R., Flory, P. J. (1952): Treatment of osmotic pressure data, J. Polymer Sci., 9:503-588.

——. (1953): Statistical mechanics of dilute polymer solutions. IV. Variation of the osmotic second coefficient with molecular weight, J. Am. Chem. Soc., 75:1775-1784.

Krigbaum, W. R., Roe, R. J. (1967): Measurement of osmotic pressure, Chap. 79 in Treatise on Analytical Chemistry (I. M. Kolthoff and P. J. Elving, eds.), Part I, Vol. 7, Wiley Interscience, New York.

Kurata, M., Iwawa, M., Kamada, K. (1966): Viscosity-molecular weight relationships and unperturbed dimensions of long-chain molecules, pp. IV-1-IV-72 in Polymer Handbook (J. Brandrup and E. H. Immer, eds.), Wiley Interscience, New York.

Livesey, P. J., Billmeyer, Jr., F. W. (1969): Particle-size determination by low-angle light scattering: New instrumentation and a rapid method of interpreting data, J. Colloid Interface Sci., 30:447-472.

Lyons, J. W. (1967): Measurement of viscosity, Chap. 83 in Treatise on Analytical Chemistry (I. M. Kolthoff and P. J. Elving, eds.), Part I, Vol. 7, Wiley Interscience, New York.

Margerison, D., East, G. C. (1967): Introduction to Polymer Chemistry, Chap. 2, Pergamon, New York.

Mark, H. F. (1948): Frontiers in Chemistry, Vol. 5, Interscience, New York.

Mark, H. F., Whitby, G. S. (eds.) (1940): Collected Papers of Wallace Hume Carothers on High Polymeric Substances, Interscience, New York.

Maron, S. H., Lou, R. L. H. (1954): Calibration of light-scattering photometers with Ludox, J. Polymer Sci., 14:29-36.

McCaffery, E. M. (1970): Laboratory Preparation for Macromolecular Chemistry, McGraw-Hill, New York.

McIntyre, D. (1948): Light scattering, ASTM Spec. Techn. Publ., 247:27.

McIntyre, D. (ed.) (1968): Characterization of Macromolecular Structure, National Academy of Sciences Publication No. 1573, Washington, D.C.

McIntyre, D., Gornick, F. (eds.) (1964): Light Scattering from Dilute Polymer Solutions, Gordon and Breach, New York.

Meares, P. (1965): Polymers—Structure and Bulk Properties, Chap. 3, Van Nostrand, Princeton.

Miller, M. L. (1966): The Structure of Polymers, Reinhold, New York.

Moore, J. C. (1964): Gel permeation chromatography, J. Polymer Sci., A2:835.

Moore, W. R. (1967): Viscosities of dilute polymer solutions, Chap. 1 in Progress in Polymer Science (A. D. Jenkins, ed.), Vol. 1, Pergamon, New York.

Morawetz, H. (1965): Macromolecules in Solution, Wiley Interscience, New York.

Morgan, P. W. (1965): Condensation Polymers by Interfacial and Solution Methods, Chap. 10, Wiley Interscience, New York.

Muus, L. T., Billmeyer, Jr., F. W. (1957): The molecular structure of polyethylene. VI. Molecular weight from dissymmetry of scattered light, J. Am. Chem. Soc., 79:5079-5082.

Newitt, E. J., Kokle, V. (1966): Molecular structure of polyethylene. XIII. An improved cryoscopic method for determining number-average molecular weight of polyethylene, J. Polymer Sci., A-2, 4:705-714.

O'Driscoll, K. F. (1964): The Nature and Chemistry of High Polymers, Chap. 5, Reinhold, New York.

Ogg, C. L., Porter, W. L., Willits, C. O. (1945): Determining the hydroxyl content of certain organic compounds; macro and semimicro methods, Ind. Eng. Chem. Anal. Ed., 17:394-397.

Onyon, P. F. (1951): Viscometry, Chap. 6 in Techniques of Polymer Characterization (P. W. Allen, ed.), Butterworths, London.

Parker, D. B. V. (1975): Polymer Chemistry, Applied Science Publishers, Essex, England.

Peaker, F. W. (1959): Light-scattering techniques, Chap. 5 in Techniques of Polymer Characterization (P. W. Allen, ed.), Butterworths, London.

Pohl, H. A. (1954): Determination of carboxyl end groups in a polyester polyethylene terephthalate, Anal. Chem., 26:1614-1616.

Price, G. F. (1959): Techniques of end-group analysis, Chap. 7 in Techniques of Polymer Characterization (P. W. Allen, ed.), Butterworths, London.

Ravve, A. (1967): Organic Chemistry of Macromolecules, Dekker, New York.

Rayleigh, Lord. (1871): On the light from the sky, its polarization and color, Phil. Mag., 41:107-120, 274-279.

———. (1871): On the scattering of light by small particles, Phil. Mag., 41:447-454.

———. (1914): On the diffraction of light by spheres of small relative index, Proc. Roy. Soc., A90:219-225.

Reiff, T. R., Yiengst, M. J. (1959): Rapid automatic semimicro colloid osmometer, J. Lab. Clin. Med., 53:291-298.

Rempp, P., Benoit, H. (1968): Determination of molecular weight, Rubber Chem. Technol., 41:245.

Rodriquez, F. (1970): Principles of Polymer Systems, Chap. 6, McGraw-Hill, New York.

Rolfson, F. B., Coll, H. (1964): Automatic osmometer for determination of number average molecular weights of polymers, Anal. Chem., 36: 888-894.

Rosen, S. L. (1971): Fundamental Principles of Polymeric Materials for Practicing Engineers, Cahners Books, Boston.

Schachman, H. K. (1959): Ultracentrifugation in Biochemistry, Academic, New York.

Schlenker, B. R. (1975): Introduction to Material Science, John Wiley, New York.

Schmidt, A. X., Marlies, C. A. (1948): Principles of High-Polymer Theory and Practice, McGraw-Hill, New York.

Scholte, T. G. (1968): Molecular weights and molecular weight distribution of polymers by equilibrium ultracentrifugation. Part I. Average molecular weights, J. Polymer Sci. A-2, 6:91-109.

———. (1968): Molecular weights and molecular weight distribution of polymers by equilibrium ultracentrifugation. Part II. Molecular weight distribution, J. Polymer Sci. A-2, 6:111-127.

———. (1970): Determination of the molecular weight distribution of polymers from equilibrium in the ultracentrifuge, Eur. Polym. J., 6:51-56.

Schultz, J. M. (1973): Polymer Materials Science, Prentice Hall, Englewood Cliffs, New Jersey.

Seymour, R. B. (1971): Introduction of Polymer Chemistry, Chap. 3, McGraw-Hill, New York.

Seymour, R. B., Owen, D. R. (1973): Characterization of polymers, Paintindia, 9:27.

———. (1973): Polymer characterizations, Australian Paint J., 18:4.

Slade, P. E. (1975): Polymer Molecular Weights, Dekker, New York.

Smoluchowski, M. (1912): Opalescence of gases in the critical condition, Phil. Mag., 23:165-173.

Stabin, J. V., Immergut, E. H. (1954): A high-speed glass osmometer, J. Polymer Sci., 14:209-212.

Staudinger, H. (1928): Ber. Bunsenges. Phys. Chem., 61:2427.

———. (1932): Die Hochmolekularen Organischen Verbindungen, Springer-Verlag, Berlin.

Staudinger, H., Heuer, W. (1930): Highly polymerized compounds. XXXIII. A relation between the viscosity and the molecular weight of polystyrenes, Ber. Bunsenges. Phys. Chem., 63B:222-234.

Stevens, M. P. (1975): Polymer Chemistry, an Introduction, Chap. 2, Addison-Wesley, Reading, Massachusetts.

Stockmayer, W. H., Casassa, E. F. (1952): The third virial coefficient in polymer solutions, J. Chem. Phys., 20:1560-1566.

Svedberg, T., Pederson, K. O. (1940): The Ultracentrifuge, Clarendon, Oxford.

Svensson, H., Thompson, T. E. (1961): Translational diffusion methods in protein chemistry, Chap. 3 in Analytical Methods of Protein Chemistry, (P. Alexander and R. J. Block, eds.), Vol. 3, Pergamon, New York.

Tanford, C. (1961): Physical Chemistry of Macromolecules, Sec. 17-23, John Wiley, New York.

Tomlinson, C., Chylewski, C., Simon, W. (1963): The thermoelectric microdetermination of molecular weight-III, Tetrahedron, 19:949-960.

Van de Hulst, H. C. (1957): Light scattering by small particles, John Wiley, New York.

Van Holde, K. E. (1967): Measurement of sedimentation, Chap. 80 in Treatise on Analytical Chemistry (I. M. Kolthoff and P. J. Elving, eds.), Part I, Vol. 7, Wiley Interscience, New York.

Van Oene, H. (1968): Measurement of the viscosity of dilute polymer solutions, pp. 353-367 in Characterization of Macromolecular Structure (D. McIntyre, ed.), National Academy of Sciences Publication No. 1573, Washington, D.C.

Vaughan, M. F. (1960): Gel permeation chromatography, Nature, 188:55.

Wachter, A. H., Simon, W. (1969): Molecular weight determination of polystyrene standards by vapor pressure osmometry, Anal. Chem., 41: 90-94.

Waltz, J. E., Taylor, G. B. (1947): Determination of the molecular weight of nylon, Anal. Chem., 19:448-450.

Weissberg, S. G., Rothman, S., Wales, M. (1962): in Analytical Chemistry of Polymers (G. M. Kline, ed.), Pt. II, Wiley Interscience, New York.

Williams, J. W. (ed.) (1963): Ultracentrifugal Analysis in Theory and Experiment, Academic, New York.

Williams, J. W., van Holde, Kensal, E., Baldwin, R. L., Fujita, H. (1958): The theory of sedimentation analysis, Chem. Rev., 58:715-806.

Zimm, B. H. (1948): The scattering of light and the radial distribution function of high polymer solutions, J. Chem. Phys., 16:1093-1099.

———. (1948): Apparatus and methods for measurement and interpretation of the angular variation of light scattering: Preliminary results on polystyrene solutions, J. Chem. Phys., 16:1099-1116.

Zimm, B. H., Kelb, R. W. (1959): J. Polymer Sci., 37:19.

Zimm, B. H., Myerson, I. (1946): A convenient small osmometer, J. Am. Chem. Soc., 68:911-912.

5

Testing and Characterization of Polymers

Public acceptance of polymers is usually associated with an assurance of quality based on a knowledge of successful long-term and reliable tests. In contrast, much of the dissatisfaction with synthetic polymers is related to failures which possibly could have been prevented by proper testing, design, and quality control. The American Society for Testing and Materials (ASTM), through its committees D-1 on paint and D-20 on plastics, has developed many standard tests which should be referred to by all producers and consumers of finished polymeric materials. There are also cooperating groups in many other technical societies: the American National Standards Institute (ANSI), an International Standards Organization (ISO), and standards societies such as the British Standards Institution (BSI) in England, the Deutsche Normenausschuss (DNA) in Germany, and comparable groups in every developed nation throughout the entire world.

A number of testing techniques have already been considered in Chaps. 3 and 4. Here we will concentrate on the areas of physical testing and spectronic, including thermal, characterization. Most of these techniques can be directly applied to nonpolymeric materials such as small molecular organics, inorganic salts, and metals.

5.1 TYPICAL STRESS-STRAIN CURVES

As shown in Fig. 5.1, Carswell and Nason assigned polymers into five classifications. The soft and weak class (a), such as polyisobutylene, is characterized by a low modulus of elasticity, low yield point, and moderate time-dependent elongation. The Poisson ratio, i.e., the ratio of contraction to elongation for class (a) polymers is 0.5 which is similar to that of liquids.

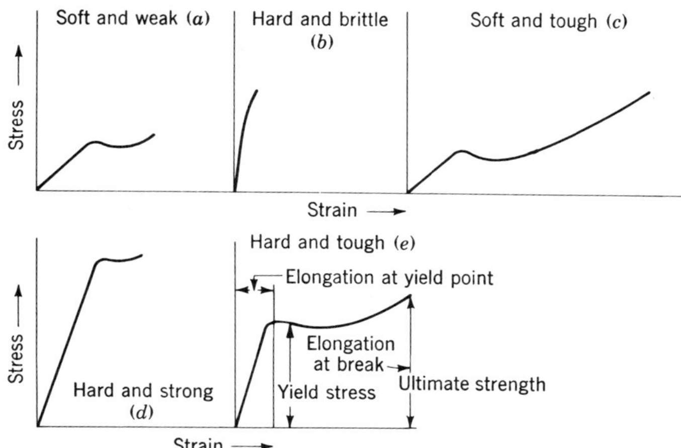

FIGURE 5.1 Typical stress-strain curves for plastics. (From Introduction to Polymer Chemistry by R. Seymour, McGraw-Hill, New York, 1971. Used with permission of McGraw-Hill Book Company.)

In contrast, the Poisson ratio of hard and brittle class (b) polymers, like polystyrene, approaches 0.3. Class (b) polymers are characterized by a high modulus of elasticity, a poorly defined yield point, and little elongation before failure. However, class (c) polymers, such as plasticized PVC, have a low modulus of elasticity, high elongation, and a well-defined yield point. Since class (c) polymers stretch after the yield point, the area under the curve, which represents toughness, is greater than that in class (b).

Rigid PVC is representative of hard and strong class (d) polymers. These polymers have a high modulus of elasticity and high yield strength. The curve for hard and tough class (e) polymers, such as ABS copolymers, shows moderate elongation prior to the yield point followed by nonrecoverable elongation. In general, the behavior of all classes is Hookean, prior to the yield point. The reversible recoverable elongation prior to the yield point, called the elastic range, is the result of the bending and stretching of covalent bonds in the polymer backbone. This useful portion of the stress-strain curve may also include some recoverable uncoiling of polymer chains. Irreversible slippage of polymer chains is the predominant mechanism after the yield point.

Since these properties are time dependent, class (a) polymers may resemble class (d) polymers if the stress is applied rapidly, and vice versa. These properties are also temperature dependent. Hence, the properties of class (c) polymers may resembly class (b) polymers when the temperature

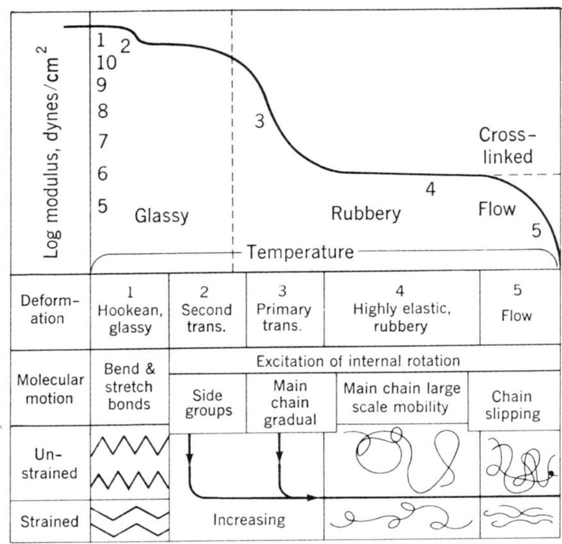

FIGURE 5.2 Characteristic effects of temperature on the properties of a typical polymer. (From Introduction to Polymer Chemistry by R. Seymour, McGraw-Hill, New York, 1971. Used with permission of McGraw-Hill Book Company.)

is decreased. The effects of temperature and the mechanisms of elongation are summarized in Fig. 5.2.

5.2 PHYSICAL TESTS

Tensile strength, which is a measure of the ability of a polymer to withstand pulling stresses, is usually measured by pulling a dumbbell specimen such as the one shown in Fig. 5.3 in accordance with ASTM-D638-72. These test specimens, like all others, must be conditioned under standard conditions of humidity (50%) and temperature (23°C) before testing. The ultimate tensile strength is equal to the load which caused failure (L) divided by the minimum cross-sectional area (A).

Flexural strength, or cross-breaking strength, is a measure of the bending strength or stiffness of a bar test specimen used as a simple beam in accordance with ASTM-D790-71. As shown in Fig. 5.4, the flexural strength is based on the load required to rupture a simple beam before its deflection is 5%. The ultimate tensile strength in kilograms per square centimeter is equal to $3Pl/2bd^2$, where P = load causing failure, l = length of span, b = width of specimen, and d = thickness of specimen.

Compressive strength, or the ability of a specimen to resist crushing forces, is measured by crushing a cylindrical specimen in accordance with ASTM-D695-69. The ultimate compression strength in kilograms per square centimeter is equal to the load which caused failure (L) divided by the minimum cross-sectional area (A).

Impact strength is a measure of toughness or the ability of a specimen to withstand a sharp blow, such as being dropped from a specific height. As shown in Fig. 5.5, impact resistance may be determined by measuring the energy of a pendulum required to break a notched plastic specimen.

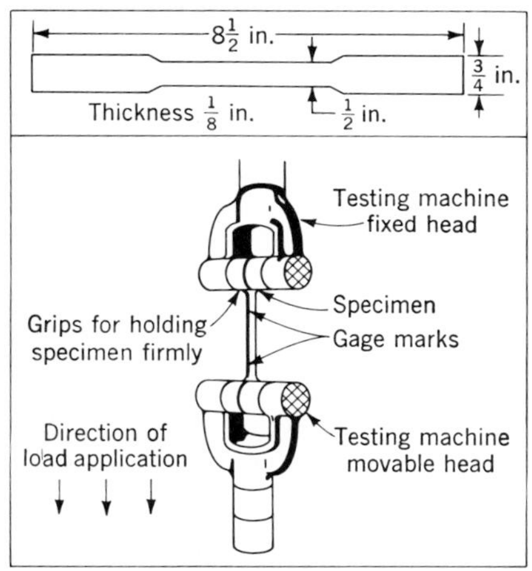

FIGURE 5.3 Typical tensile test. (From Introduction to Polymer Chemistry by R. Seymour, McGraw-Hill, New York, 1971. Used with permission of McGraw-Hill Book Company.)

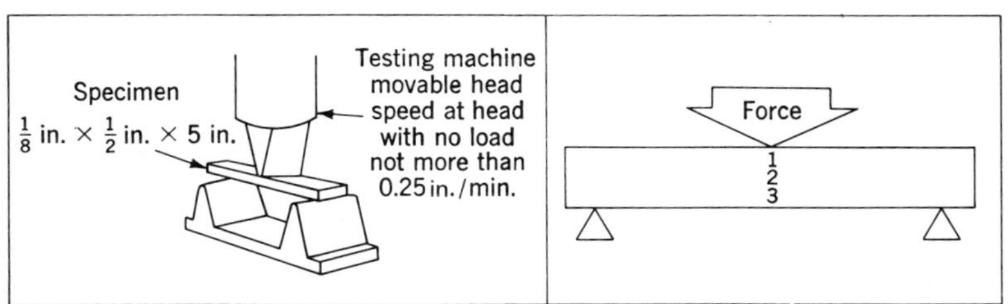

FIGURE 5.4 Typical flexural strength test. (From Introduction to Polymer Chemistry by R. Seymour, McGraw-Hill, New York, 1971. Used with permission of McGraw-Hill Book Company.)

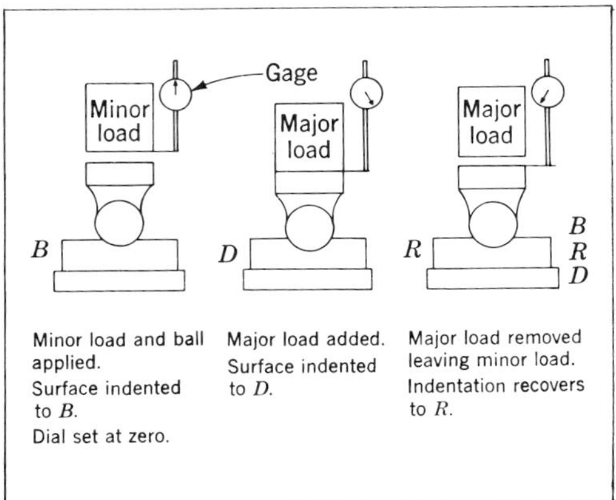

FIGURE 5.5 Rockwell hardness test. (From Introduction to Polymer Chemistry by R. Seymour, McGraw-Hill, New York, 1971. Used with permission of McGraw-Hill Book Company.)

An unnotched specimen is used in the Charpy test (ASTM-D256-73), while a notched specimen is used in the Izod impact test. Since the results of these impact tests are controversial, other tests simulating actual use have been developed, such as dropping specimens from specific heights.

Elongation is measured by the tensile test shown in Fig. 5.3. The percentage of elongation is equal to the change in dimensions divided by the original length of the specimen multiplied by 100, i.e.,

$$\%El = \frac{\Delta l}{l} \times 100$$

Shear strength is a measure of the load required to cause failure in the area of the sheared specimen in accordance with ASTM-D732-46 (1969). This test, which was revised in 1969, utilizes a punch-type shear fixture for testing flat specimens. The shear strength (S) is equal to the load (L) divided by the area (A).

The stiffness or modulus of elasticity (E) may be determined for tensile, flexural, or compressive strength by dividing the stress by the strain or elongation.

Hardness is a general term which describes a combination of properties such as the resistance to penetration, abrasion, and scratching. Indentation hardness of thermosets may be measured by a Barcol Impressor as described in ASTM-D-2583-67 (1972). A shore durometer is used to measure the penetration hardness of elastomers and soft thermoplastics.

Rockwell hardness tests [ASTM-D785-65 (1970)], depicted in Fig. 5.5, measure hardness in progressive numbers on different scales corresponding to the size of the ball indentor used. The scale symbols of R, L, M, E, and K correspond to the loads of 60, 60, 100, 100, and 150 kg, respectively. The diameter of the ball indentor decreases as one goes from R to K.

Scratch hardness may be measured on Mohs scale, which ranges from 1 for talc to 10 for diamonds or by scratching with pencils of specified hardness (ASTM-D-3363). Hardness may also be measured by the number of bounces of a ball or the amount of rocking by a Sward Hardness Rocker. Abrasion resistance may be measured by the loss in weight caused by the rubbing of the wheels of a Taber-abrader (ASTM-D-1044).

The tests for change in dimensions of a polymer under long-term stress, called creep or cold flow (ASTM-D674-56), are no longer recommended by ASTM. ASTM-D-671 describes suggested tests for fatigue or endurance of plastics under repeated flexure.

Several electrical tests are essential for the evaluation of plastics in electrical applications. These include the dielectric constant (permittivity; ASTM-D150-74) which is the ratio of the capacitance of the polymer and air and dielectric strength, or dielectric breakdown voltage (ASTM-D149-75). The latter is the maximum applied voltage that a polymer can withstand for 1 min divided by the thickness of the sample in mils (1×10^{-3} in.).

Measurement of the volume resistivity or bulk specific resistance, p, is one of the easiest, most straightforward, and most useful electrical property determinations of a material. Specific resistance is one of the few physical quantities which exhibits values differing by more than 10^{23} for materials which are readily available under conditions common to our experience. This large range of conductivity is basic to the wide use of electricity and electrical devices. Conductive materials such as copper exhibit a p value of about 10^{-6} ohm-cm, whereas good insulators such as polytetrafluorethylene and polyethylene exhibit p values of about 10^{17} ohm-cm.

Material response is typically studied utilizing either direct (constant) applied voltage, dc, or alternating applied voltage, ac. The ac response as a function of frequency, is characteristic of the material. In the future these "electrical spectra" may be utilized routinely as a product identification tool, much like infrared spectroscopy.

The volume resistivity, or the reciprocal of conductance, is defined as the electrical resistance between opposite faces of a cube of unit dimensions (ASTM-D257-78). The arc resistance, or resistance to tracking, is considered as the minimum time required for a high-voltage discharge to find a conducting carbonized path across the surface of a polymer as evidenced by the disappearance of the arc into the test specimen (ASTM-D495-73).

The power factor is the energy required for the rotation of the dipoles of a polymer in an applied electrostatic field of increasing frequency. These values, which typically range from 1.5×10^{4} for polystyrene to 5×10^{-2} for plasticized cellulose acetate, increase at T_g because of increased chain mobility. The loss factor is the product of the power factor and the dielectric constant.

Several thermal tests are also essential for predicting the performance of polymers at elevated temperatures. Thermal conductivity, or K factor (ASTM-C-177-71), is the time rate of heat flow (Q) required to attain a steady state in temperature of a sample having a thickness (L) and an area (A). ΔT is the difference in temperature between a hot plate and a cooling plate above and below the test sample. The thermal conductivity (K) in BTU per inch per hour per square feet per degrees Fahrenheit is calculated from the following equation:

$$K = \frac{QL}{A\,\Delta T} \tag{5.1}$$

The coefficient of linear thermal expansion (α) (ASTM-D696-79) is equal to the change in length of a sample (ΔL) divided by its length (L) and the change in temperature (ΔT) during the test, i.e., $\alpha = \Delta L/L\Delta T$. The specific heat is the energy required to raise the temperature of 1 g of polymer 1°C. These values, which may also be calculated from the summation of the atomic specific heats for the repeating unit, range from 0.2 to 0.4 cal/°C, and are higher than the specific heats of metals.

The glass transition temperature (T_g; ASTM D-3418-75) is the temperature at which there is an absorption or release of energy as the temperature is raised or lowered. T_g may be determined from differential thermal analysis (DTA), differential scanning calorimetry (DSC), or torsional braid analysis (TBA), techniques which are discussed later in this chapter.

The softening point of relatively soft polymers (ASTM-D1525-75) is the temperature at which a flat-ended Vicat needle with a cross section of 1 mm^2 penetrates a test specimen to a depth of 1 mm under a specified load which is usually 1 kg.

As shown in Fig. 5.6, the heat deflection temperature (ASTM-D-648-72) is determined by noting the temperature at which a simple beam under a load of 264 or 66 psi deflects 0.01 in.

The brittleness temperature of plastics (ASTM-D-746-72) and plastic film [ASTM-D-1790-62 (1970)] is the temperature at which 50% of test samples fail an impact test.

Flammability tests for polymers include tests for ignition (ASTM-D-1929-77), rate of burning of cellular plastics (ASTM-D-1692-74), many flammability tests, such as ASTM-D-635-74, measurements of smoke density (ASTM-D-2843-70), and the oxygen index (OI) test (ASTM-D-2863-74). The last is the minimum concentration of oxygen in an oxygen-nitrogen mixture that will support candlelike combustion. Flammability tests are useful for comparative purposes, but because of the presence of many variables in actual fires, they are not reliable for assuring lack of flammability in large-scale fires.

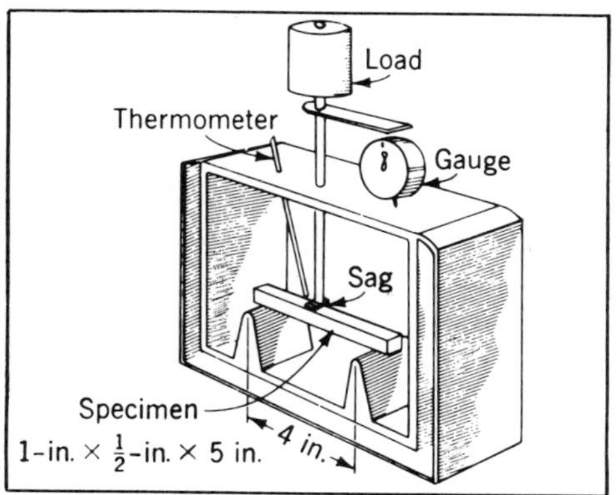

FIGURE 5.6 Deflection temperature test. (From Introduction to Polymer Chemistry by R. Seymour, McGraw-Hill, New York, 1971. Used with permission of McGraw-Hill Book Company.)

Since many polymers are resistant to attack by corrosives, tests for the corrosion resistance of polymers are particularly important. ASTM-D-543-67 (1977) measures weight and dimensional changes of test samples immersed for 7 days in many different test solutions. These tests may be coupled with tensile tests. Other ASTM tests include those under accelerated service conditions [ASTM-D756-78 (1971)], water absorption [ASTM-D570-63 (1972)], and environmental stress cracking of ethylene plastics (ESCR; ASTM-D1693-70).

As shown in Fig. 5.7, the ESCR test measures the time of failure of scored test samples which are bent 180° and inserted in a solution of standard detergent. Many failures of polymers are the result of molecular changes which can be detected by the use of appropriate instrumentation.

5.3 SPECTRONIC CHARACTERIZATION OF POLYMERS

The index of refraction (n), which is the ratio of the velocity of light in a vacuum to the velocity of light in a transparent polymer, is characteristic for each polymer. This value, which is also a function of molecular weight, may be determined by use of an Abbe refractometer [ASTM-D542-50 (1970)].

Differences in indices of refraction may be measured by phase-contrast microscopy, and the structure of spherulites may be studied using crossed polarizers in a polarized light microscope. Melting points may be determined when the latter is equipped with a hot stage. Thickness may be measured in nanometers using interference microscopy.

The morphology of polymers may be investigated by electron microscopy and by scanning electron microscopy (SEM). While SEM is limited to

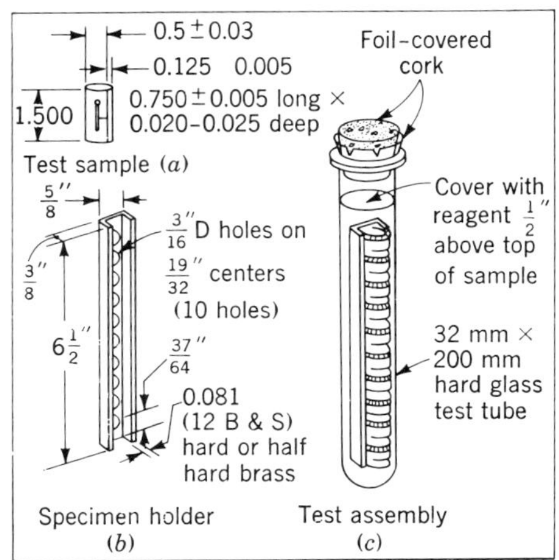

FIGURE 5.7 Environmental stress cracking test. (From Introduction to Polymer Chemistry by R. Seymour, McGraw-Hill, New York, 1971. Used with permission of McGraw-Hill Book Company.)

images in the 5 to 10 nm range, magnifications of over 200,000 are possible with electron microscopy.

Most monomers and polymers may be identified by infrared spectroscopy (IR) in which the energy, in the wavelength range of 1 to 50 nm, is associated with molecular vibration and vibration-rotation spectra of polymer molecules. These motions are comparable to small molecules of similar structure (model compounds).

For example, as shown in Fig. 5.8, the IR spectrum of polystyrene is sufficiently characteristic that it is used as a standard for checking instrumenta

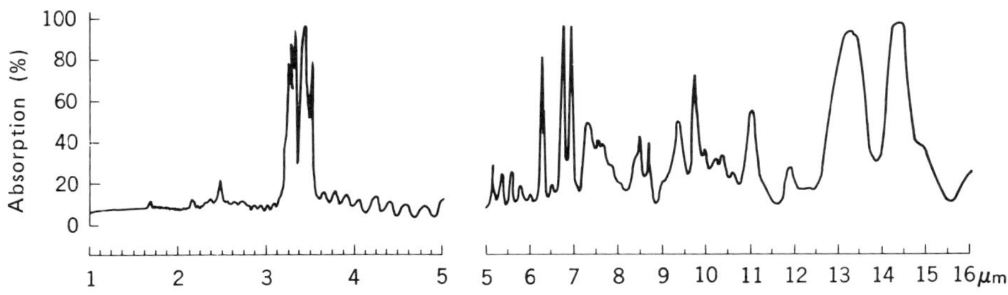

FIGURE 5.8 Infrared spectrum of a polystyrene film. (From Introduction to Polymer Chemistry by R. Seymour, McGraw-Hill, New York, 1971. Used with permission of McGraw-Hill Book Company.)

operation. The repeating unit of polystyrene (C_8H_8) has 16 atoms, and since it has no symmetry, all vibrations are active, i.e., 3° each of rotational and translational freedom and 42° of vibrational freedom (3n - 6).

The bands in the range of 8.7 to 9.7 μm are characteristic, but not identified as to origin, and are said to be in the "fingerprint" region. Typical C—H stretching vibrations are at 3.3, 3.4, and 3.5 μm, and out-of-plane bending of aromatic C—H bonds are at 11.0 and 14.3 μm. Characteristic C—C stretching vibrations are at 6.2 and 6.7 μm. Characteristic bands for other typical groups in polymers are shown in Table 5.1.

TABLE 5.1 Absorption Bands for Typical Groups in Polymers

Group	Type of vibration	Wavelength (λ, μm)	Wave number (V, cm^{-1})
CH_2	Stretch	3.38-3.51	2,850-2,960
	Bend	6.82	1,465
	Rock	13.00-13.80	725-890
CH_3	Stretch	3.38-3.48	2,860-2,870
	Bend	6.9	1,450
H R C=C H H	C—H stretch	3.25-3.30	3,030-3,085
	C—H bend in plane	7.10-7.68	1,300-1,410
	C—H bend out of plane	10.10-11.00	910-990
	C—C stretch	6.08	1,643
H R C=C H R	C—H stretch	3.24	3,080
	C—H bend in plane	7.10	1,410
	C—H bend out of plane	11.27	888
	C—C stretch	6.06	1,650
Benzene	C—H bend out of plane	14.50	690
OH	Stretch	2.7-3.2	3,150-3,700
SH	Stretch	3.9	2,550
Aliphatic acid	C=O stretch	5.85	1,710
Aromatic acid	C=O stretch	5.92	1,690
CCl	Stretch	12-16	620-830
CN	Stretch	4.8	2,200

The relative amounts of styrene and acrylonitrile in the copolymer in the ultraviolet (UV) spectrogram in Fig. 5.9 may be determined from the relative areas of absorption bands for styrene and acrylonitrile at wave numbers 1600 and 2240 cm^{-1}, respectively.

Ultraviolet spectroscopy has less applicability to the characterization of polymers than IR, but it is useful in detecting aromatics, such as polystyrene, and appropriate additives, such as antioxidants, which exhibit characteristic absorption in the UV region. The absorption of the charge transfer constant of styrene-acrylonitrile-$ZnCl_2$ at different temperatures is shown in Fig. 5.9.

While IR spectroscopy is most useful for the identification of polymers, proton magnetic resonance spectroscopy (pmr) is more useful for elucidating polymer structure. Nuclear protons in the hydrogen atoms in polymers have random orientation, but these protons tend to be oriented, i.e., aligned with or against the field, in a strong magnetic field.

Absorption of energy by these protons under proper conditions of field strength and frequency, called resonance, causes a spin flip which is displayed on a recorder. The absorption of energy at different frequencies is influenced by neighboring electrons. Thus, as shown in Fig. 5.10, maleic anhydride, vinyl acetate, and the charge transfer complex of these two monomers have different characteristic spectra relative to the internal

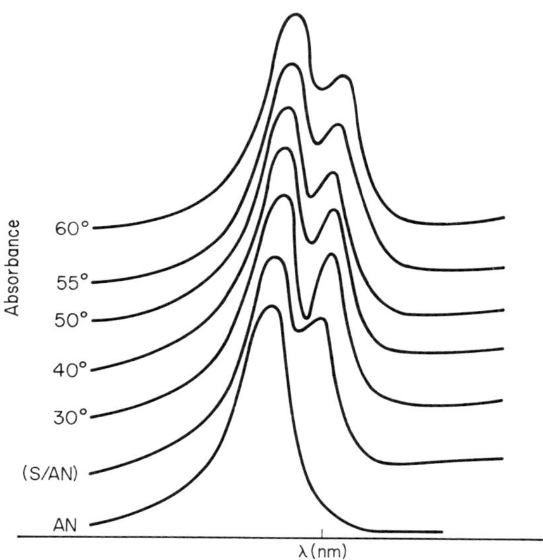

FIGURE 5.9 Ultraviolet spectra of styrene-acrylonitrile (SAN $ZnCl_2$ in t-butanol at 25, 30, 40, 50, 55, and 60°C, and styrene at 25°C. [R. Seymour, G. Stahl, D. Garner, and R. Knapp, Polymer Preprints, 17(1):219 (1976). With permission from the Division of Polymer Chemistry, ACS.]

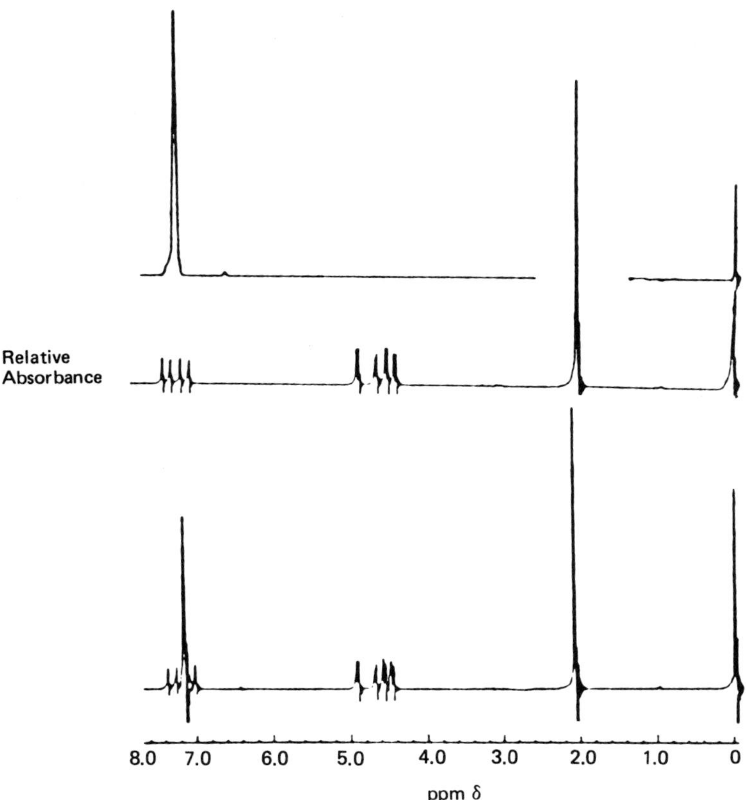

FIGURE 5.10 PMR spectra of maleic anhydride and vinyl acetate and the charge transfer complex of these two monomers at 25°C. [R. Seymour, D. Garner, G. Stahl, and L. Sanders, Polymer Preprints, 17(2):663 (1976). With permission from the Division of Polymer Chemistry, ACS.]

reference standard, tetramethylsilane, which is given a value of 0 and 10 ppm on the δ and τ scales, respectively.

The characteristic spectra and structures of polyolefins are shown in Fig. 5.11 and Table 5.2. As shown in Fig. 5.11, the ratio of the area of the pmr peaks, may be used to determine molecular structure based on the ratios of methyl to methylene groups present.

Because of the small but consistent concentrations of carbon-13 present in all organic compounds, it is necessary to use more sophisticated nmr spectroscopy (^{13}C-nmr) for determining the effect of neighboring electrons on these nuclei. However, ^{13}C-nmr spectroscopy is an extremely valuable tool for the investigation of polymer structure. A representative ^{13}C-nmr spectrum of the alternating copolymer of styrene and acrylonitrile is shown in Fig. 5.12.

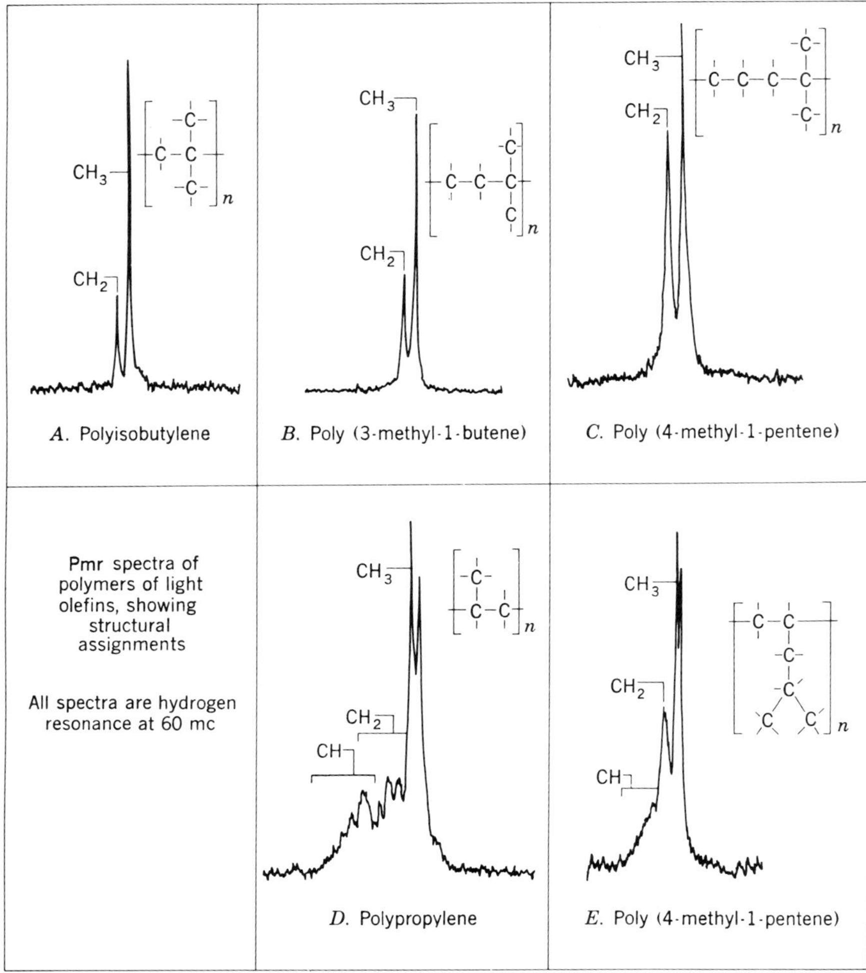

FIGURE 5.11 PMR peaks for hydrocarbon polymers. (With permission of N. Chamberlain, F. Stehling, K. Bartz, and J. Reed, Esso Research and Engineering Co.)

Electron paramagnetic resonance (epr), or electron spin resonance (esr), spectroscopy is a valuable tool for measuring the relative abundance of unpaired electrons present in macroradicals. For example, as shown in Fig. 5.13, macroradicals are formed by the homogeneous cleavage of nylon chains when these filaments are broken, and the concentration of macroradicals increases as the stress is increased.

TABLE 5.2 Relationships of Methyl and Methylene Groups in Polymers in Fig. 5.11

Polymer	Structure	CH_3:CH_2
Polyisobutylene	CH_3 H | —C—C— H | CH_3	2:1
Poly(3-methyl-1-butene)[a]	CH_3 H H | —C—C—C— H H | CH_3	1:1
Poly(4-methyl-1-pentene)	CH_3 H H H | —C—C—C—C— H H H | CH_3	2:3
Polypropylene	CH_3H | | —C—C— | | H H	1:1
Poly(4-methyl-1-pentene)[a]	H H | —C—C— H | CH_2 | H_3C—C—CH_3 | H	2:2

[a]According to Chamberlain, the pmr measurements were used to show an unexpected structure for poly(3-methyl-1-butene) and two different structures for poly(4-methyl-1-pentene).

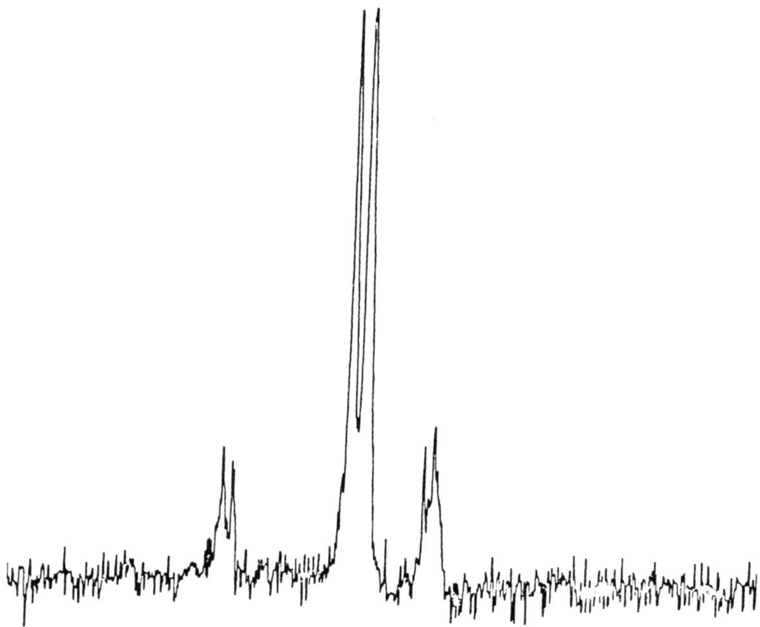

FIGURE 5.12 Representative ^{13}C-nmr spectra of styrene-acrylonitrile (SAN) alternating copolymer. [R. Seymour, G. Stahl, D. Garner, and R. Knapp, Polymer Preprints, 17(1):220 (1976). With permission from the Division of Polymer Chemistry, ACS.]

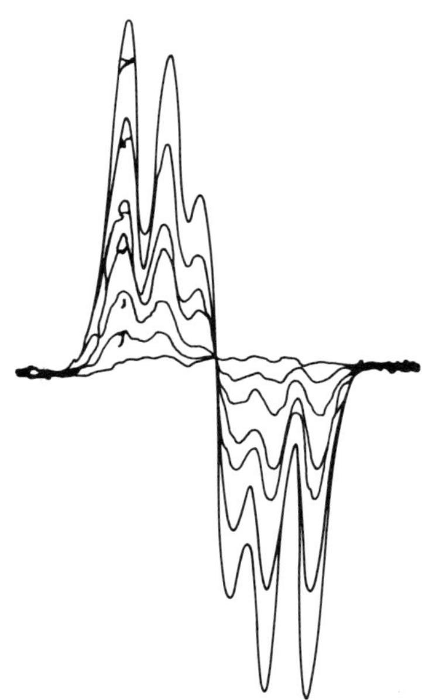

FIGURE 5.13 EPR spectra for nylon-66 fibers broken under increasing stress.

X-ray diffraction has been used to determine crystalline structure and conformations in polymers. Raman spectroscopy, including laser-Raman spectroscopy, has been used to study the microstructure of polymers such as carbon-carbon double bond stretching vibrations.

5.4 THERMAL ANALYSIS

Major instrumentation involved with the generation of thermal property behavior of materials includes thermal gravimetric analysis (TGA), differential scanning calorimetry (DSC), differential thermal analysis (DTA), torsional braid analysis (TBA), thermal mechanical analysis (TMA), and pyrolysis gas chromatography (PGC).

One of the simplest techniques is pyrolysis gas chromatography (PGC) in which the gases, resulting from the pyrolysis of a polymer, are analyzed by gas chromatography. This technique may be used for qualitative and quantitative analysis. The latter requires calibration with known amounts of a standard polymer pyrolyzed under the same conditions as the unknown. Representative PGC pyrograms of polyvinyl acetate and alternating and random copolymers of vinyl acetate and maleic anhydride and the copolymer of styrene and acrylonitrile are shown in Figs. 5.14 and 5.15.

There are several different modes of thermal analysis described as DSC. DSC is a technique of nonequilibrium calorimetry in which the heat flow into or away from the polymer is measured as a function of temperature or time. This is different from DTA where the temperature difference between a reference and a sample is measured as a function of temperature or time. Presently available DSC equipment measures the heat flow by maintaining a thermal balance between the reference and sample by changing a current passing through the heaters under the two chambers. For instance, the heating of a sample and reference proceeds at a predetermined rate until heat is emitted or consumed by the sample. If an endothermic occurrence takes place, the temperature of the sample will be less than that of the reference. The circuitry is programmed to give a constant temperature for both the reference and the sample compartments. Excess current is fed into the sample compartment to raise the temperature to that of the reference. The current necessary to maintain a constant temperature between the sample and reference is recorded. The area under the resulting curve is a direct measure of the heat of transition.

The advantages of DSC and DTA over a good adiabatic calorimeter include speed, low cost, and the ability to use small samples. Sample size can range from 0.5 mg to 10g. A resultant plot of ΔT as a function of time or temperature is known as a thermogram. Since the temperature difference is directly proportional to the heat capacity, the curves resemble inverted specific heat curves. A typical DSC thermogram of a block copolymer of vinyl acetate and acrylic acid is shown in Fig. 5.16. The distinctions between DSC and DTA are becoming less clear with the advent of new instrumentation which uses components of both DSC and DTA.

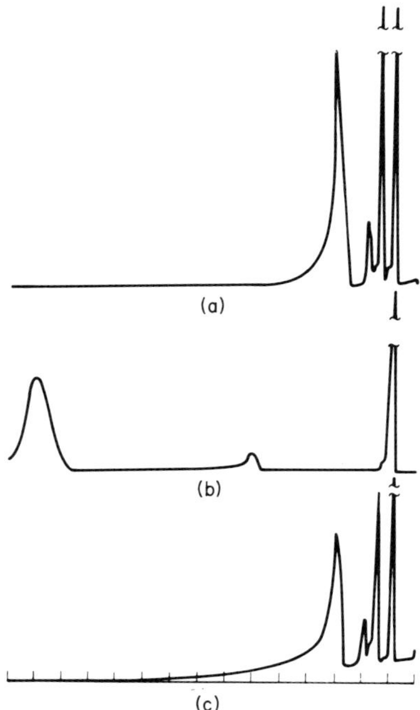

FIGURE 5.14 Gas chromatography pyrograms of the homopolymer of vinyl acetate and the alternating and random copolymers of vinyl acetate and maleic anhydride. [R. Seymour, D. Garner, G. Stahl, and L. Sanders, Polymer Preprints 17(2):665 (1976). With permission from the Division of Polymer Chemistry, ACS.]

Possible determinations from DSC and DTA measurements include the following: (1) heat of transition, (2) heat of reaction, (3) sample purity, (4) phase diagram, (5) specific heat, (6) sample identification, (7) percentage incorporation of a substance, (8) reaction rate, (9) rate of crystallization or melting, (10) solvent retention, and (11) activation energy. Thus, thermocalorimetric analysis can be a quite useful tool in describing the chemical and physical relationship of a polymer with respect to temperature.

In thermogravimetric analysis (TGA), a sensitive balance is used to follow the weight change of a polymer as a function of time or temperature. Usual sample sizes for commercial instruments are in the range of 0.1 mg to 10 g with heating rates of 0.1 to 50°C/min. The most usual literature heating rates are 10, 15, 20, 25, and 30°C/min. In making both TGA and thermocalorimetric measurements, the same heating rate and flow of gas should be employed to give the most comparable thermograms.

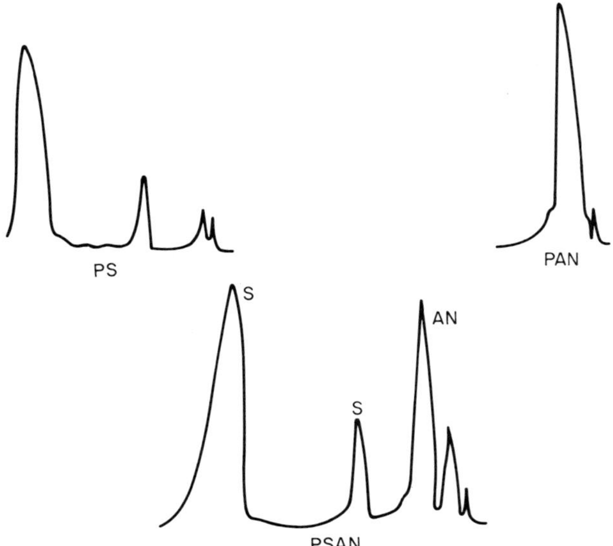

FIGURE 5.15 Representative PGC pyrograms of polystyrene (PS), polyacrylonitrile (PAN), and poly(styrene-co-acrylonitrile) (PSAN). [R. Seymour, G. Stahl, D. Garner, and R. Knapp, Polymer Preprints, 17(1):221 (1976). With permission from the Division of Polymer Chemistry, ACS.]

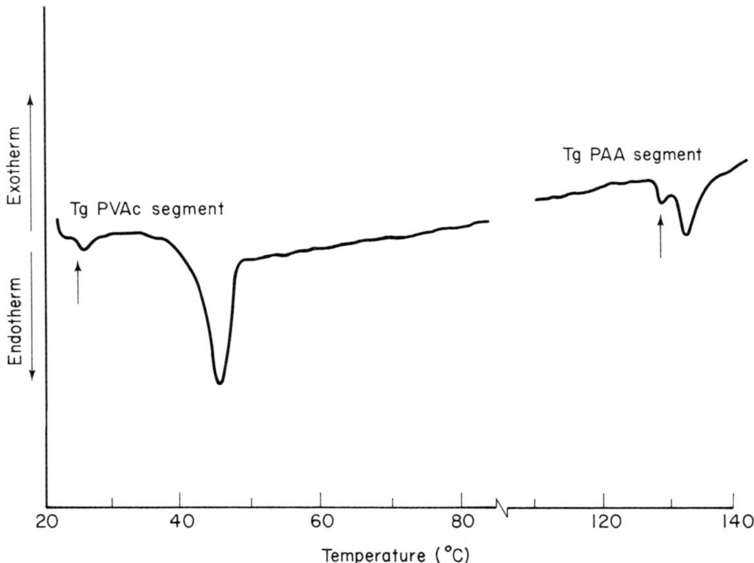

FIGURE 5.16 Typical DSC thermogram of a block copolymer of vinyl acetate and acrylic acid [P(VAc-b-AA)].

TGA can allow determination of the following: (1) sample purity, (2) identification, (3) solvent retention, (4) reaction rate, (5) activation energy, and (6) heat of reaction.

Thermomechanical analysis (TMA) measures the mechanical response of a polymer as a function of temperature. Typical measurements as a function of temperature include the following: (1) expansion properties, i.e., expansion of a material leading to the calculation of the linear expansion coefficient; (2) tension properties, i.e., the measurement of shrinkage and expansion of a material under tensile stress, e.g., elastic modulus; (3) dilatometry, i.e., volumetric expansion within a confining medium, e.g., specific volume; (4) single fiber properties, i.e., tensile response of single fibers under a specific load, e.g., single-fiber modulus; and (5) compression properties, such as measuring softening or penetration under load.

Compressive, tensile, and single-fiber properties are usually measured under some load, yielding information about softening points, modulus changes, phase transitions, and creep properties. For compressive measurements, a probe is positioned on the sample and loaded with a given stress. A record of the penetration of the probe into the polymer is obtained as a function of temperature. Tensile properties can be measured by attaching the fiber to two fused quartz hooks. One hook is loaded with a given stress. Elastic modulus changes are recorded by monitoring a probe displacement.

In torsional braid analysis (TBA) the changes in tensile strength as the polymer undergoes thermal transition is measured as a function of temperature and sometimes also as a function of the applied frequency of vibration of the sample. As thermal transitions are measured, irreversible changes such as thermal decomposition or cross linking are observed, if present. In general, a change in T_g or change in the shape of the curve (shear modulus versus temperature) during repeated sweeps through the region, such as a region containing the T_g, is evidence of irreversible change. The name TBA is derived from the fact that measurements are made on fibers which are "braided" together to give test samples connected between or onto vicelike attachments or hooks.

DSC, DTA, TMA, and TBA analyses are all interrelated, all signaling changes in thermal behavior as a function of heating rate or time. TGA is also related to the others in the assignment of phase changes to observed weight changes.

Recent trends include increased emphasis on coupling thermal techniques and on coupling thermal techniques with other analysis techniques, such as mass spectrometry (MS) of the off-gases produced by thermolysis or pyrolysis of polymers. Useful combinations include TG-MS, GC-MS, TG-GC-MS, and PGC-MS, with intercorrelation of data from IR, nmr, GPC, and EM of analyzed samples at different heating times and temperatures.

The polymer softening range, while not a specific thermodynamic property, is a valuable "use" property. It is normally a simple and readily obtainable property. Softening ranges generally lie between the polymers' T_g and T_m. Some polymers do not exhibit a softening range but rather undergo a solid state decomposition before softening.

Softening ranges are dependent on the technique and procedure used to determine them. Thus, listings of softening ranges should be accompanied by the specific technique and procedure employed for the determination. The following are techniques often used for the determination of polymer softening range.

The capillary technique is analogous to the technique employed to determine melting points of typical organic compounds. The sample is placed in a capillary tube and heated with the temperature recorded from beginning to end of melting. Control of the heating rate lends more importance to the measurements. Instruments such as the Fisher-Johns Melting Point Apparatus are useful in this respect.

Another technique calls for a plug or film (or other suitable form) of the polymer to be stroked along a heated surface whose temperature is being increased until the polymer sticks to the surface. A modification of this utilizes a heated surface containing a temperature gradient between the ends of the surface.

The Vicat needle method consists of determining the temperature at which a 1-mm penetration of a needle (having a point with an area of 1 mm) occurs on a standard sample (1/8-in. thick, minimum width, 3/4-in.) at a specified heating rate (often 50°C/hr) under specific stress (generally less than 1 kg). This is also referred to as the heat deflection point.

In the ring and ball method the softening range of a sample is determined by noting the temperature at which the sample, held within a horizontal ring, is forced downward by the weight of a standard steel ball supported by the sample. The ball and ring are generally heated by inserting them in a bath.

It is important that softening range data can serve as guides to proper temperatures for melt fabrication, such as melt pressing, melt extruding, and molding. It is also an indication of the product's thermal stability.

SUMMARY

1. The American Society for Testing and Materials (ASTM) and comparable organizations throughout the world have established meaningful standards for the testing of polymers.

2. The mechanical properties of plastics may be classified by five stress-strain curves which show the yield point, elongation, and toughness of various classes of plastics.

3. The test for tensile strength, i.e., the measure of the ability of a polymer to withstand pulling stresses, is described in ASTM standard D638-72.

4. The test for flexural strength, or the measure of bending strength of a polymer, is described by ASTM-D790-71.

5. The test for compressive strength, or the measure of the crushing resistance of a polymer, is described by ASTM-D695-60.

6. The test for impact strength, or the measure of toughness of a polymer, is described by ASTM-D256-73.

7. Hardness, which implies resistance to penetration or abrasion and scratching, is described by several ASTM tests.

8. Many electrical tests which are essential for polymers used in electrical applications are described by ASTM tests.

9. ASTM tests have been developed for T_g, softening point, heat deflection temperature, and brittleness at low temperatures.

10. Listed among the ASTM flammability tests is the oxygen index test which defines the minimum oxygen content in an oxygen-nitrogen mixture that will support combustion of a plastic, burning like a candle.

11. ASTM test D-543-67 (1971) measures the changes in weight and dimensions of plastic test specimens immersed in selected standard liquids for 7 days.

12. Most monomers and polymers may be identified qualitatively and quantitatively by IR spectroscopy.

13. Proton and carbon-13 nmr are useful for elucidating polymer structure.

14. The mechanism in fiber rupture and the concentration of primary radicals or macroradicals may be investigated using epr spectroscopy.

15. PGC, in which products of pyrolysis are analyzed by gas chromatography, is an excellent tool for polymer analysis.

16. DTA and DSC, which provide information on thermal transitions, may also be used for the identification of polymers.

17. The stability of polymers at elevated temperatures may be determined by TGA.

GLOSSARY

A: Area.

Abbe refractometer: An instrument used for measuring the index of refraction.

alpha (α): Coefficient of expansion.

arc resistance: Resistance to tracking by a high-voltage discharge.

ASTM: American Society for Testing and Materials.

ASTM-D20: Committee responsible for standards for plastics.

Barcol impressor: An instrument used to measure the resistance of a polymer to penetration or indentation.

BSI: British Standards Institution.

BTU: British thermal unit.

Charpy test: An impact test.

chemical shifts: Peaks in pmr spectroscopy.

^{13}C-nmr: Nuclear magnetic resonance spectroscopy based on the effect of neighboring electrons on carbon-13 nuclei.

coefficient of expansion: Change in dimensions per degree Celsius.

compressive strength: Resistance to crushing forces.

ΔT: Difference in temperature.

dielectric constant: Ratio of the capacitance of a polymer to that of air or a vacuum.

dielectric strength: Maximum applied voltage that a polymer can withstand.

differential scanning calorimetry: Measurement of the differences in changes in enthalpy of a heated polymer and a reference standard based on power input.

differential thermal analysis: Measurement of the difference in the temperature of a polymer and a reference standard when heated.

DNA: Deutsche Normenausschuss (German standard tests).

DSC: Differential scanning calorimetry.

DTA: Differential thermal analysis.

elastic range: The range on a stress-strain curve below the yield point.

environmental stress cracking: Cracking of polyolefins in liquid media such as liquid detergents.

epr: Electron paramagnetic resonance.

ESCR: Environmental stress cracking.

esr: Electron spin resonance.

flexural strength: Resistance to bending.

glass transition temperature: Lowest temperature at which segmental motion of polymer chains exists.

heat deflection temperature: The temperature at which a simple loaded beam undergoes a definite deflection.

impact strength: Measure of toughness.

index of refraction: The ratio of the velocity of light in a vacuum to that in a transparent polymer.

infrared spectroscopy: A technique used for the characterization of polymers based on their molecular vibration and vibration-rotation spectra.

IR: Infrared.

ISO: International Standards Organization.

Izod: An impact test.

K factor: A measure of thermal conductivity.

l: Length of a sample.

L: Thickness of test specimen in thermal conductivity test.

loss factor: Power factor multiplied by dielectric constant.

modulus: Stiffness of a polymer.

Mohs scale: A hardness scale ranging from 1 for talc to 10 for a diamond.

nmr: Nuclear magnetic resonance spectroscopy.

OI: Oxygen index.

oxygen index: A test for the minimum oxygen concentration in a mixture of oxygen and nitrogen that will support a candlelike flame of a burning polymer.

PGC: Pyrolysis gas chromatography.

phase-contrast microscopy: Measurement of differences in indices of index of refraction.

pmr: Spectroscopy based on proton or hydrogen magnetic resonance.

Poisson's ratio: The ratio of contraction to elongation of a polymer.

power factor: Electrical energy required to rotate the dipoles in a polymer while in an electrostatic field.

Q: Rate of heat flow.

Rockwell hardness: A measure of indentation resistance.

SEM: Scanning electron microscopy.

shear strength: Resistance to shearing forces.

shore durometer: A simple instrument used to measure resistance of a polymer to penetration of a blunt needle.

standard testing conditions: 23°C, 50% humidity.

Sward hardness rocker: A rocking device used as a measure of hardness.

Tabor abraser: A mechanical rotator used to test abrasion resistance.

tensile strength: Resistance to pulling stresses.

T_g: Glass transition temperature.

TGA: Thermogravimetric analysis.

thermogravimetric analysis: Measurement of the loss in weight when a polymer is heated.

UV: Ultraviolet.

Vicat needle: One used under load to penetrate polymer surfaces.

volume resistivity: Electrical resistance between opposite forces of a 1-in. cube.

yield point: The point on a stress-strain curve below which there is reversible recovery.

EXERCISES

1. What is the most important standards organization in the United States?
2. What is the tensile strength (TS) of a test sample of PMMA which is 1.25 cm square with a thickness of 0.32 cm, if failure occurs at 282 kg?
3. What is the tensile strength (TS) of a test sample of PMMA which is 1.27 cm square with a thickness of 0.32 cm, if failure occurs at 282 kg?
4. What is the compressive strength (CS) of a 10 cm long plastic rod which has a cross section of 1.27 cm × 1.27 cm which fails under a load of 3500 kg?
5. If a sample of polypropylene measuring 5 cm elongates to 12 cm, what is the percentage of elongation:
6. If the tensile strength is 705 kg cm^{-2} and the elongation is 0.026 cm/cm, what is the tensile modulus?
7. Define creep.
8. What is the value of Poisson's ratio for hevea rubber at (a) 25°C, and (b) -65°C?
9. What changes occur in a polymer under stress before the yield point?
10. What changes occur in a stressed polymer after the yield point?
11. How could you estimate relative toughness of polymer samples from stress-strain curves?
12. What effect will a decrease in testing temperature have on tensile strength?
13. What effect will an increase in the time of testing have on tensile strength?

14. Is the statement correct that a polymer with a notched impact strength of 2 ft lb per in. of notch is twice as tough as one with a value of 1 ft lb per in. of notch?
15. Why are electrical tests for polymers important?
16. Which is the better insulator: (a) a polymer with a low or (b) a high K factor?
17. Why are the specific heats of polymers higher than those of metals?
18. What are the standard heat deflection loads in metric units?
19. Why is the use of the term flame-proof plastics incorrect?
20. Which plastic will be more resistant when immersed in 25% sulfuric acid at 50°C: (a) HDPE, (b) PMMA, or (c) PVAc?
21. What happens to indices of refraction values at T_g?
22. How does the index of refraction change when the molecular weight of a polymer is increased?
23. How many degrees of vibrational freedom are present in polypropylene?
24. What is the ultraviolet region of the spectrum?
25. Which would absorb in the UV region: (a) polystyrene, (b) hevea rubber, (c) PVC?
26. What technique would you use to determine crystallinity in a polymer?
27. What thermal instrumental technique would you use to determine T_g?

BIBLIOGRAPHY

Alexander, L. E. (1969): X-Ray Diffraction Methods in Polymer Science, John Wiley, New York

Alfrey, T. (1948): Mechanical Behavior of Polymers, Interscience, New York.

Allen, L. B., Chellis, L. N. (1966): Flammability tests in Testing of Plastics (J. V. Schmitz, ed.), Vol. 2, Chap. 11, Wiley Interscience, New York.

Altgelt, K. H., Moore, J. C. (1967): GPC, in Polymer Fractionation (M. J. R. Cantow, ed.), Chap. 4, Academic, New York.

American Society for Testing and Materials, 1976 Book of ASTM Standards, Parts 26, 34, 36, Plastics, American Society for Testing and Materials, Philadelphia.

Anderson, H. C. (1966): TGA, in Techniques and Methods of Polymer Evaluation (P. E. Slade and L. T. Jenkins, eds.), Vol. I, Dekker, New York.

Baer, E. (ed.) (1964): Engineering Design for Plastics, Reinhold, New York.

Bekkedahl, N. (1969): Volume dilatometry, J. Res. Nat. Bur. Stand., 43:145.

Bellamy, L. J. (1958): The Infrared Spectra of Complex Molecules, 2d ed., John Wiley, New York.

Bergen, R. L. (1966): Stress relaxation tests, in Testing of Polymers (J. V. Schmitz, ed.), Vol. 2, Chap. 1, Wiley Interscience, New York.

Bikales, N. M. (1971): Mechanical Properties of Polymers, Wiley Interscience, New York.

Billmeyer, Jr., F. W., Saltzman, M., Principles of Color Technology, Wiley Interscience, New York.

Bobbitt, J. M. (1963): Thin Layer Chromatography, Reinhold, New York.

Boguslavskii, L., Vannikov, A. (1970): Organic Semiconductors and Biopolymers, Plenum, New York.

Bovey, F. A. (1973): C-13-NMR of polypeptides, Polymer Preprints, 14:163.

Bovey, F. A., Schilling, F. C., Kwei, T. K., Frisch, A. L. (1977): Carbon-13-NMR of Polymers, Polymer Preprints, 18:704.

Braude, E. A., Nachod, F. C. (1955): Determination of Organic Structures by Physical Methods, Academic, New York.

Braun, D., Cherdron, H., Kern, W. (1972): Techniques of Polymer Synthesis and Characterization, Wiley Interscience, New York.

Brown, W. E. (ed.) (1969): Testing of Polymers, Vol. IV, Interscience Div., John Wiley, New York.

Bueche, F. (1962): Physical Properties of Polymers, Wiley-Interscience, New York.

Bulkin, B. J. (1976): Raman spectra of polymers, Polymer Preprints, 17:754.

Carey, R. H. (ed.) (1964): Simulated service testing in the plastics industry, ASTM Spec. Tech. Publ., 375.

Carraher, C. E. (1977): Resistivity measurements, J. Chem. Ed., 54:576.

Carraher, C. E., Sheats, J., Pittman, C. U. (1978): Organometallic Polymers, Academic, New York.

Carswell, T. S., Nason, H. K. (1944): Classification of polymers, Mod. Plastics, 21:121.

Chamberlain, N. F., Stehling, F. C., Bartz, K. W., Reed, J. J. R. (1965): NMR Data for H^1, Esso Research and Engineering Company, Baytown, Texas.

Chen, H. Y. (1976): C-13 NMR spectra of polyolefins, Polymer Preprints, 17:688.

Chiu, J. (1966): Application of thermogravimetry to the study of high polymers, Appl. Poly. Symp., 2:25-43.

———. (1974): Polymer Characterization by Thermal Methods of Analysis, Dekker, New York.

Clark, D. T. (1974): ESCA applications, Polymer Sci. Technol., 5A:241.

Collins, E. A., Bares, J., Billmeyer, Jr., F. W., Experiments in Polymer Science, John Wiley, New York.

Conley, R. T. (1966): Infrared Spectroscopy, Allyn and Bacon, Boston.

Corten, H. T. (1971): Composite Materials: Testing and Design, ASTM, Philadelphia.

Cowie, J. M. G. (1973): Polymers: Chemistry and Physics of Modern Materials, Chaps. 8, 9, 12, Intext Educational, New York.

Craver, C. D. (1971): Polymer Characterization, Plenum, New York.

Cross, A. D. (1964): Introduction to Practical Infrared Spectroscopy, 2nd ed., Butterworths, London.

Dawkins, J. V., Yeadon, G. (1977): High performance GPC with silica microspheres: Annual Meeting, ACS, Chicago, Illinois, August 28, 1977, preprinted in Polymer Preprints, 18(2):227.

Dohany, J. E., Stefanow, H. (1975): DSC of films, Org. Coat. Plast. Chem., 35:83.

Elliott, A. (1969): Infrared Spectra and Structure of Organic Long-Chain Polymers, St. Martin's, New York.

Ferguson, R. C. (1967): High frequency NMR spectra of polymers, ACS Div. Polymer Chem. Polymer Preprints, 8:1026.

Ferry, J. D. (1967): Viscoelastic Properties of Polymers, John Wiley, New York.

Fischer, E. W. (1964): Electron diffraction, Chap. 7 in Newer Methods of Polymer Characterization (B. Ke, ed.), Wiley Interscience, New York.

Frisch, K. (1972): Electrical Properties of Polymers, Technomic, Westport, Connecticut.

Gardner, H., Sward, G. (1962): Physical and Chemical Examination of Paints, Varnishes, Lacquers and Colors, 12th ed., Henry A. Gardner Laboratory, Bethesda, Maryland.

Garn, P. D. (1965): Thermoanalytical Methods of Investigation, Academic, New York.

Garrett, T. B., Goldfarb, L. (1977): Dilatometric and DSC observations, J. Appl. Polymer Sci., 21:1395.

Gordon, P. K., Gordon, R. (1965): Paint and Varnish Manual, Formulation and Testing, Wiley Interscience, New York

Gutman, F., Lyons, L. (1967): Organic Semiconductors, John Wiley, New York.

Haken, J. K. (1974): Gas Chromatography of Coating Materials, Dekker, New York.

Hall, R. W. (1959): in Chap. 2, Techniques of Polymer Characterization (P. W. Allen, ed.), Butterworths, London.

Hallimond, A. D. (1970): The Polarizing Microscope, Vickers, York, England.

Hartman, B., Lee, G. F. (1977): Torsional braid analysis, J. Appl. Polymer Sci., 21:1341.

Haslam, J., Willis, H. A. (1965): Identification and Analysis of Plastics, Van Nostrand, Princeton.

Helfinstine, J. D. (1977): Charpy impact test of composites, ASTM Spec. Tech. Publ. STO 617.

Henniker, C. K. (1967): IR Spectrometry of Industrial Polymers, Academic, New York.

Hilado, C. L. J. (1968): Flammability tests for cellular plastics, ACS Div. Org. Coatings and Plastics Chem., 28:265.

Hummel, D. O. (1971): IR Spectra of Polymers, Wiley Interscience, New York.

Ingram, D. J. E. (1958): Free Radicals as Studied by EPR, Academic, New York.

Ives, G. C., Mead, J. A., Riley, M. M. (1971): Handbook of Plastic Test Methods, CRC Press, Cleveland, Ohio.

Jeffery, J. W. (1971): Methods in X-Ray Crystallography, Academic, New York.

Johnson, J. F., Porter, R. S., Cantow, M. J. R. (1966): GPC, Rev. Macromol. Chem., 1:393.

Kambe, K., Garn, P. D. (1975): Thermal Analysis, Halsted, New York.

Karas, F. (ed.) (1964): Dielectric Properties of Polymers, Plenum, New York.

Katon, J. (ed.) (1968): Organic Semiconducting Polymers, Dekker, New York.

Ke, B. (1964): DTA, Chap 9 in Newer Methods of Polymer Characterization, Wiley Interscience, New York.

Keinath, S. E., Kumler, P. L., Boyer, R. R. (1975): ESR Studies, Polymer Preprints, 16:120.

Kissinger, H. E., Newman, S. B. (1962): DTA, Chap. 4 in Analytical Chemistry of Polymers (G. M. Kline, ed.), Pt. II, Wiley Interscience, New York.

Kline, G. M. (1956): Analytical Chemistry of Polymers, Wiley Interscience, New York.

Klug, H. P., Alexander, L. E. (1954): X-Ray Diffraction Procedures, John Wiley, New York.

Le Chatelier, H. (1877): DTA, Bull. Soc. Fr. Mineral., 10:204.

Lever, A. E., Rhys, J. (1968): The Properties and Testing of Plastics Materials, 3rd ed., Temple Press, London.

Mackenzie, R. C. (1970): Differential Thermal Analysis, Vol. 1, Fundamental Aspects, Academic, New York.

———. (1962): DTA Data, Cleaver-Hume Press, London.

Manley, T. R. (1963): DTA, Techniques of Polymer Science, SCI Monograph 17, Gordon and Breach, New York.

Mark, H. F., Gaylord, N. G., Bikales, N. M. (eds.) (1964-1970): Encyclopedia of Polymer Science and Technology, Wiley Interscience, New York (14 volumes + supp.).

Martin, C., Gourdenne, A. (1976): NMR of polyurethanes, Polymer Preprints, 17:773.

Matiellio, J. J. (1944, 1946): Protective and Decorative Coatings, Vols. 4 and 5, John Wiley, New York.

McCaffery, E. M. (1970): Laboratory Preparation for Macromolecular Chemistry, McGraw-Hill, New York.

McCall, D. W., Slichter, W. P. (1964): High resolution NMR, Chap 8 in Newer Methods of Polymer Characterization (B. Ke, ed.), Wiley Interscience, New York.

McDonald, S. A., Daniels, C. A., Davidson, J. A. (1977): Electron microscopy of PVC latex, J. Colloig Interface Sci., 59:342.

Merriam, C. N., Ginsberg, T., and Robeson, L. M. (1976): Mechnical testing during cure, Coatings Plastic Preprints, 36:358.

Milby, R. V. (1973): Plastic Technology, Sect. III, McGraw-Hill, New York.

Miller, G. W. (1969): The thermal characterization of polymers, Appl. Poly. Symp., 10:35-72.

Moore, J. C. (1964): GPC, J. Polymer Sci., 2A:835.

Nielsen, L. E. (1966): Mechanical Properties of Polymers, Reinhold, New York.

Over, J. E. (1976): Characterization of coatings by C-13 and proton NMR Coatings Plastic Preprints, 36:121.

Pake, G. E. (1962): Paramagnetic Resonance, Benjamin, New York.

Payne, H. F. (1954): Organic Coating Technology, Chap. 15, John Wiley, New York.

Pople, J. A., Schneider, W. G., Bernstein, H. J. (1959): High-Resolution Nuclear Magnetic Resonance, McGraw-Hill, New York.

Porter, R. S., Johnson, J. F. (1968): Analytical Calorimetry, Plenum, New York.

Posner, A. S. (1954): X-Ray diffraction, Chap 2 in Analytical Chemistry of Polymers (G. M. Kline, ed.), Vol. 2, Wiley Interscience, New York.

Potts, W. J. (1965): ATR spectroscopy, ACS Div. Org. Coatings and Plastics Chem., Preprints, 25:364.

Ramani, S. V., Williams, D. P. (1977): Notched and unnotched fatigue behavior of composites, Sci. Tech. Aerosp. Rep., 15:1.

Randolph, A. F. (ed.) (1960): SPI Plastics Engineering Handbook, Chap. 24, Reinhold, New York.

Richardson, J. H. (1971): Optical Microscopy for the Material Sciences, Dekker, New York.

Ritchie, P. D. (ed.) (1965): Physics of Plastics, Van Nostrand, Princeton.

Roberts, J. D. (1959): Nuclear Magnetic Resonance, McGraw-Hill, New York.

Rodriquez, F. (1970): Principles of Polymer Systems, Chaps. 9, 15, McGraw-Hill, New York.

Rogers, C. E. (1964): Permeability vs. chemical resistance, Chap. 9 in Engineering Design for Plastics (E. Baer, ed.), Reinhold, New York.

Roylance, D. K., DeVries, K. L. (1976): ESR studies of polymer fracture, Polymer Preprints, 17:720.

Saunders, K. J. (1966): The Identification of Plastics and Rubbers, Chapman and Hall, London.

Schmitz, J. V. (ed.) (1965-1967): Testing of Polymers, Vols. 1-3, Wiley Interscience, New York.

Schroeder, L. R., Cooper, S. K. (1975): IR thermal analysis of polyamides, Polymer Preprints, 17:743.

Seymour, R. B. (1965): Characterization of polymers by index of refraction and density measurements, Plastics World, 20:16.

———. (1974): Resin characterization, Paintindia, 8:13.

———. (1976): Chemical resistance of non-metallic materials, Treatise on Analytical Chemistry III, 3 sect. DI:341.

Seymour, R. B., Owen, D. R. (1973): Characterization of block copolymers, Australian Paint J., 18:4.

Seymour, R. B., Stahl, G. A. (1975): Recording dilatometer, Rev. Sci. Instrum., 46:16.

Seymour, R. B., Wood, H., Owen, D. R. (1977): Turbidimetric titration, Pop. Plast., 22:21.

Silverstein, R. M., Bassler, G. C. (1963): Spectrometric Identification of Organic Compounds, Chap. 4, John Wiley, New York.

Slade, P. E., Jenkins, L. T. (1966): Thermal analysis, in Techniques and Methods of Polymer Evaluation, Vol. I, Dekker, New York.

Slade, P. E., Jenkins, P. E. (1974): Thermal Characterization Techniques, Dekker, New York.

Slichter, W. P., Davis, D. D. (1968): NMR studies of polymer solutions, Macromolecules, 1:47.

Smith, L. A. (1965): Infrared spectroscopy, Chap. 66 in Treatise on Analytical Chemistry (I. M. Kolthoff and P. J. Elving, eds.), Part I, Vol. 6, Wiley Interscience, New York.

Smothers, W. J., Chiang, J. (1959): DTA, Chemical Publishing Company, New York.

Sohma, J., Sahaguchi, M. (1976): ESR Studies of Polymer Radicals Produced by Mechanical Destruction, Springer-Verlag, New York.

Stannett, V., Yasuda, H. (1965): Gas and vapor permeation, Chap. 13 in Testing of Polymers (J. V. Schmitz, ed.), Vol. I, Wiley Interscience, New York.

Statton, W. O. (1965): The theory of X-ray studies of polymers, Chap. 6 in Newer Methods of Polymer Characterization (B. Ke, ed.), Wiley Interscience, New York.

Stevens, M. P. (1969): Characterization and Analysis of Polymers by Gas Chromatography, Dekker, New York.

———. (1975): Polymer Chemistry, an Introduction, Chap. 4, Addison-Wesley, Reading, Massachusetts.

Swift, H. F. (1970): Electron Microscopes, Barnes and Noble, New York.

Tanford, C. (1965): Physical Chemistry of Macromolecules, Chap. 2, John Wiley, New York.

Tarin, P. M., Thomas, E. L. (1977): Electron microscopic study of spherulies, Annual Meeting ACS, Chicago, August 28, 1977, preprinted in Polymer Preprints, 18(2):249.

Thornton, P. R. (1968): Scanning Electron Microscopy, Chapman and Hall, London.

Tobolsky, A. V. (1960): Properties and Structures of Polymers, John Wiley, New York.

Truett, W. L. (1977): The characterization of polymers by pyrolysis, annual meeting ACS, Chicago, August 28, 1977, preprinted in Polymer Preprints, 18(2):107.

Tryon, M., Horowitz, E. (1961): Ultraviolet spectrophotometry, Chap. 7 in Analytical Chemistry of Polymers (G. M. Kline, ed.), Part 2, Interscience, New York.

Vaughn, M. F. (1960, 1962): GPC, Nature, 188:55; 195:801.

Von Hippel, H. (1954): Dielectric Measurements and Applications, John Wiley, New York.

Wake, W. C. (1969): The Analysis of Rubber and Rubber-Like Polymers, 2nd ed., John Wiley, New York.

Ward, I. M. (1971): Mechanical Properties of Solid Polymers, Wiley Interscience, New York.

Weiss, E. (1966): Ozone resistance, Chap. 9 in Testing of Polymers (J. V. Schmitz, ed.), Vol. 2, Wiley Interscience, New York.

Weissberger, A. (1960): Techniques of Organic Chemistry, Wiley Interscience, New York.

Wiberg, K. B., Nist, B. J. (1962): Interpretation of NMR Spectra, Benjamin, New York.

Williams, T. I. (1950): An Introduction to Chromatography, Chemical Publishing Company, New York.

Winding, C. C., Hiatt, G. D. (1961): Polymeric Materials, McGraw-Hill, New York.

Wunderlich, B. (1970): Differential thermal analysis, Chap. XVII in Physical Methods of Chemistry, (A. Weissberger, ed.), Part IV, Wiley Interscience, New York.

Zbinden, R. (1964): Infrared Spectroscopy of High Polymers, Academic, New York.

6

Naturally Occurring Polymers

One of the strongest and rapidly growing areas of polymers is that of natural polymers. Our bodies are largely composed of polymers: DNA, RNA, proteins, and polycarbohydrates. These are related to aging, awareness, mobility, strength, and so on, all the characteristics that contribute to our being alive. Many medical, health, and biological projects and advances are concerned with materials which are at least in part polymeric. There is an ever-increasing emphasis on molecular biology, i.e., chemistry applied to natural systems. Thus, an understanding of polymeric principles is advantageous to those desiring to pursue a career related to our natural environment.

Physically there is no difference in the behavior, study, or testing of natural and synthetic polymers, and information techniques suitable for application to synthetic polymers are equally applicable to natural polymers.

While the specific chemistry and physics dealing with synthetic polymers are complicated, the chemistry and physics of natural polymers are even more complex, complicated by a number of related factors, including (1) many natural polymers are composed of different, often similar, repeat units; (2) a greater dependency on the exact natural polymer environment; (3) the question of the real structure of the natural polymer in its natural environment; and (4) the fact that polymer shape and size are even more important to natural polymers relative to synthetic polymers.

Industrially we are undergoing a reemergence of the use of natural polymers in many new and old areas since natural polymers are typically regenerable resources nature can continue to synthesize as we harvest them. Many natural polymers are also present in large quantities. For instance, cellulose makes up about one-third of the bulk of the entire vegetable kingdom, being present in corn stocks, tree leaves, carrot tops, grass, and so on. With the realization that we must conserve and regulate our chemical resources comes the awareness that we must find substitutes for resources that are not self-generating, such as oil, gas, and metals—thus the underlying reason for the increasing emphasis in polymer chemistry toward the use and modification of natural, regenerable polymers by industry.

6.1 POLYSACCHARIDES

The most important polysaccharides are cellulose and starch. These may be hydrolyzed by acids or enzymes to lower molecular weight carbohydrates (oligosaccharides) and finally to D-glucose. The latter is the building block, or mer, for carbohydrate polymers, and since it cannot be hydrolyzed further, it is called a monosaccharide. Cellobiose and maltose, which are the repeating units in cellulose and starch, are disaccharides, consisting of two molecules of D-glucose joined together through carbon atoms 1 and 4.

The D-glucose units in cellobiose are joined by a β-acetal linkage while those in maltose are joined by an α-acetal linkage as shown in Fig. 6.1. The hydroxyl groups in the β form of D-glucose are present in the equatorial positions, and the hydroxyl on carbon 1 (the anomeric carbon atom) in the α form is in the axial position. While the chair forms shown for D-glucose, cellobiose, and maltose, exist in all disaccharides and polysaccharides, simple Boeseken-Haworth perspective planar hexagonal rings will be used for simplicity in showing polymeric structures of most carbohydrates.

Accordingly, the molecular structures of cellobiose and maltose are shown in Figs. 6.2 and 6.3. The hydrogen atoms on the terminal carbon 1 and 4 atoms have been deleted to show the bonding present in cellulose and amylose starch. Amylodextrin is a highly branched polysaccharide with branches present on carbon 6.

Cellulose is a polydisperse polymer with a $\overline{DP}$ of 3500 to 36,000. Native cellulose is widely distributed in nature and is the principal constituent of cotton, kapok, flax, hemp, jute, ramie, and wood. Flax has a $\overline{DP}$ of 36,000 or an average molecular weight of 5,900,000. Regenerated cellulose, such as rayon and cellophane, is produced by precipitating solutions of native cellulose in a nonsolvent.

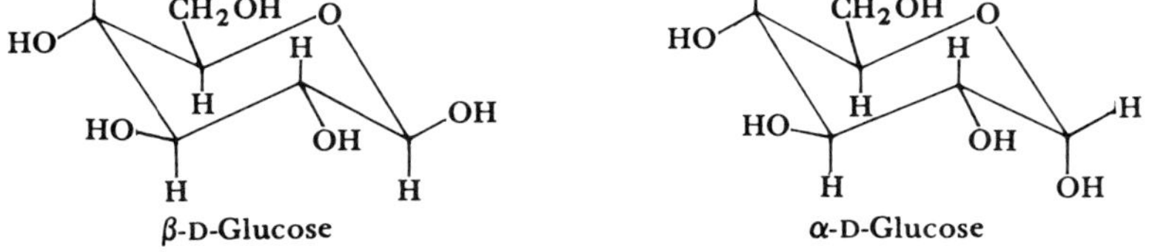

FIGURE 6.1 Chair forms of α and β D-glucose present in an equilibrium of 36% α and 64% β in aqueous solutions.

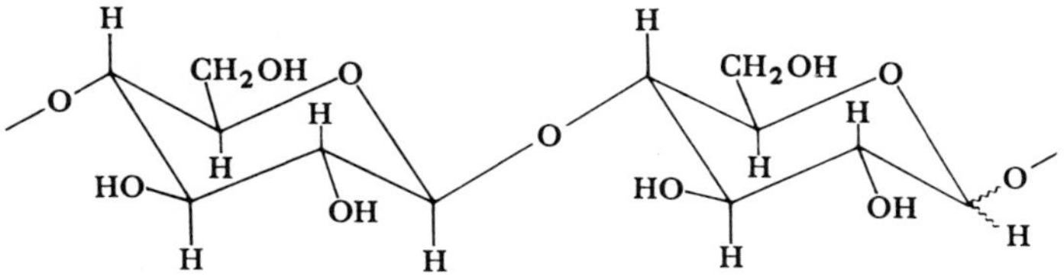

FIGURE 6.2 Chair form of cellobiose repeating unit in cellulose.

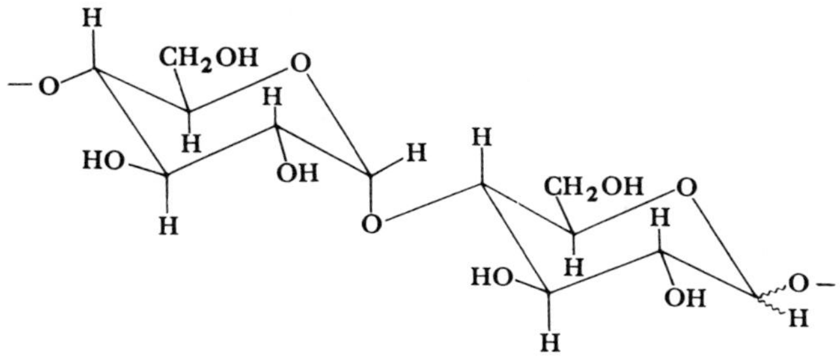

FIGURE 6.3 Chair form of maltose repeating unit in amylose.

Cellulose, which comprises more than one-third of all vegetable matter, is the world's most abundant organic compound. Approximately 50 billion tons of this renewable resource are produced annually by land plants which absorb 4×10^{20} cal of solar energy. Natural cotton fibers, which are the seed hairs from Gossypium, are about 1 to 2 cm in length and about 5 to 20 μm in diameter. The molecules in native cellulose are present in threadlike strands or bundles called fibrils.

While the celluloses are often largely linear polymers, they are not soluble in water because of the presence of strong intermolecular hydrogen bonds, and sometimes the presence of a small amount of cross linking. Highly ordered crystalline cellulose has a density as high as 1.63 g cm^{-3}, while amorphous cellulose has a density as low as 1.47 g cm^{-3}. High molecular weight native cellulose, which is insoluble in 17.5% aqueous sodium hydroxide solution, is called α cellulose. The fraction that is soluble in 17.5% sodium hydroxide solution, but insoluble in 8% solution is called β cellulose, and that which is soluble in 8% sodium hydroxide solution is called γ cellulose.

Strong caustic solutions penetrate the crystal lattice of α cellulose and produce an alkoxide called alkali, or soda cellulose. Mercerized cotton is produced by aqueous extraction of the sodium hydroxide. Cellulose ethers and cellulose xanthate are produced by reactions of alkylhalides or carbon disulfide, respectively, with the alkali cellulose.

Most linear celluloses may be dissolved in solvents capable of breaking the strong hydrogen bonds. These solvents include aqueous solutions of inorganic acids, calcium thiocyanate, zinc chloride, lithium chloride, dimethyl dibenzyl ammonium hydroxide, iron sodium tartrate, and cadmium or copper ammonia hydroxide (Schweitzer's reagent). Cellulose is also soluble in hydrazine, dimethyl sulfoxide in the presence of formaldehyde and in dimethyl formamide in the presence of lithium chloride. The average molecular weight of cellulose may be determined by measuring the viscosity of these solutions. The product precipitated by the addition of a nonsolvent to these solutions is highly amorphous regenerated cellulose.

6.2 THE XANTHATE VISCOSE PROCESS

The xanthate viscose process which is used for the production of rayon and cellophane is the most widely used regeneration process. The cellulose obtained by the removal of lignin from wood pump is converted to alkali cellulose. The addition of carbon disulfide to the latter produces cellulose xanthate.

While terminal hydroxyl and aldehyde groups, such as are present in cellobiose, are also present in cellulose, they are not significant because they are present on very long-chain polymeric molecules. For convenience, one may represent cellulose by the semiempirical formula $C_6H_7O_2(OH)_3$. This formula shows the three potentially reactive hydroxyl groups on each repeating unit in the chain.

Presumably, the hydrogen atom of the hydroxyl group on carbon 6 is replaced by the sodium ion in soda cellulose, and, thus, the carbon disulfide reacts with one hydroxyl group only in each anhydroglucose repeating unit as shown by the following equations:

$$[C_6H_7O_2(OH)_3]_n + nNaOH \longrightarrow [(C_6H_7O_2(OH)_2O^-,\ Na^+)]_n \qquad (6.1)$$

Cellulose + Sodium hydroxide ⟶ Soda cellulose

$$[C_6H_7O_2(OH)_2O^-,\ Na^+]_n + nCS_2 \longrightarrow [C_6H_7O_2(OH)_2O\text{—}\underset{\underset{\displaystyle S}{\|}}{C}\text{—}S^-,\ Na^+]_n + nH_2O \qquad (6.2)$$

Soda cellulose + Carbon disulfide ⟶ Cellulose xanthate + Water

The orange-colored xanthate solution, or viscose, is allowed to age and is then extruded as a filament through holes in a spinneret. The filament is converted to cellulose when it is immersed in a solution of sodium bisulfate, zinc sulfate, and dilute sulfuric acid. The tenacity, or tensile strength, of this regenerated cellulose is increased by a stretching process which reorients the molecules so that the amorphous polymer becomes more crystalline. Cellophane is produced by passing the viscose solution through a slit die.

Since an average of only one hydroxyl group in each repeating anhydroglucose unit in cellulose reacts with carbon disulfide, the xanthate product is said to have a degree of substitution (DS) of 1 out of a potential DS of 3. Alkyl halides, including chloroacetic acid, may react with soda cellulose to yield ethers with DS values ranging from 0.1 to 2.9.

The DS of inorganic esters such as cellulose nitrate (CN) may be controlled by the concentration of the esterifying acids. However, in classic esterification with organic acids, an ester with a DS of approximately 3 is obtained. The more polar secondary and primary esters, with DS values of 2 and 1, respectively, are produced by partial saponification of the tertiary ester. The degree of esterification of cellulose solutions in dimethyl sulfoxide may be controlled by the time of reaction.

Partially degraded cellulose is called hydrocellulose or oxycellulose, depending on the agent used for degradation. The term holocellulose is used to describe the residue after lignin has been removed from wood pulp. Cellulose soluble in 17.5% aqueous sodium hydroxide is called hemicellulose. Tables 6.1 and 6.2 describe a number of important textile fibers, including cellulosic fibers.

6.3 CHITIN

The exoskeletons of shellfish, arachnids, and many insects consist of chitin which resembles cellulose, but its repeating unit is acetylated D-glucosamine. The hydroxyl group on carbon 2 of glucose is replaced by an amine group in D-glucosamine. Chitin is soluble in Schweitzer's reagent and dilute aqueous acids. It produces a soluble xanthate when reacted with carbon disulfide. Regenerated deacetylated chitin in the form of filaments and fiber is commercially available.

6.4 STARCH

Starch, which is the second most abundant polysaccharide, is widely distributed in plants where it is stored as reserve carbohydrate in seeds, fruits, tubers, roots, and stems. Starch is a polydisperse polymer which exists as a linear polymer amylose and a highly branched polymer amylodextrin. Starches are usually present in the form of intramolecularly hydrogen-bonded polymer aggregates or granules.

Commercial starch is prepared from corn, white potatoes, wheat, rice, barley, millet, cassava, tapioca, arrowroot, and sorghum. The

TABLE 6.1 Textile Fibers

Fiber name	Definition	Properties	Typical uses	Patent names (assignees)
Acrylic	Acrylonitrile units, 85% or more by weight	Warm; light weight; shape retentive; resilient; quick drying; resistant to sunlight,	Carpeting, sweaters, skirts, baby clothes, socks, slacks, blankets, draperies	Orlon (Du Pont), Acrilan (Monsanto), CHEMSTRAND (Monsanto)
Modacrylic	Acrylonitrile units, 35–85% by weight	Resilient; softenable at low temperatures; easy to dye; abrasion resistant; quick drying; shape retentive; resistant to acids, bases	Simulated fur, scatter rugs, stuffed toys, paint rollers, carpets, hairpieces and wigs, fleece fabrics	Verel (Eastman), Dynel (Union Carbide)
Polyester	Dihydric acid-terephthalic acid ester, 85% or more by weight	Strong, resistant to stretching and shrinking; easy to dye; quick drying; resistant to most chemicals; easily washed, wrinkle resistant; abrasion resistant; retains heat-set pleats and creases (permanent press)	Permanent press wear: skirts, shirts, slacks, underwear, blouses; rope, fish nets, tire cord, sails, thread	Vycron (Beaunit), Dacron (Du Pont), Kodel (Eastman), Fortrel (Fiber Ind., Celanese), CHEMSTRAND (polyester, Monsanto)
Spandex	Segmented polyurethane, 85% or more by weight	Light, soft, smooth, resistant to body oils; stronger and more durable than rubber; can be stretched repeatedly and 500% without breaking; can retain original form, abrasion resistant; no deterioration from perspirants; lotions; detergents	Girdles, bras, slacks, bathing suits, pillows	Lycra (Du Pont)
Nylon	Recurring amide groups	Exceptionally strong; elastic; lustrous; easy to wash; abrasion resistant; smooth, resilient, low moisture absorbency; recovers quickly from extensions	Carpeting, upholstery, blouses, tent, sails, hosiery, suits, stretch fabrics, tire cord, curtains, rope, nets, parachutes	Caprolan (Allied Chemical), CHEMSTRAND (nylon, Monsanto, Astroturf (Monsanto), Celanese Polyester (Fiber Ind., Celanese), Cantrece (Du Pont)

TABLE 6.2 Cellulosic Fibers

Fiber name	Definition	Properties	Typical uses	Patent names (asignees)
Rayon	Regenerated cellulose with substitutes no more than 15% of the hydroxyl groups' hydrogens	Highly absorbent; soft; comfortable; easy to dye; good drapability	Dresses, suits, slacks, blouses, coats, tire cord, ties, curtains, blankets	Avril (FMC Corp.), Cuprel (Beaunit), Zantrel (American Enka)
Acetate	Not less than 92% of the hydroxyl groups are acetylated, includes some triacetates	Fast drying; supple; wide range of dyability; shrink resistant	Dresses, shirts, slacks, draperies, upholstery, cigarette filters	Estron (Eastman), Celanese acetate (Celanese)
Triacetate	Derived from cellulose by combining cellulose with acetic acid and/or acetic anhydride	Resistant to shrinking, wrinkling, and fading; easily washed	Skirts, dresses, sportswear (pleat retention important	Arnel (Celanese)

human digestive tract contains enzymes which are capable of cleaving the α-acetal linkages in starch and producing hydrolysis products, such as dextrins, maltose, and D-glucose.

Amylopectin, which is sometimes called the B fraction, is usually the major type of starch present in grains. However, amylose, which is sometimes called the A fraction, is present exclusively in a recessive strain of wrinkled pea. Since amylopectin serves as a protective colloid, native starch consisting of mixtures of amylose and amylopectin can be suspended in cold water. An opalescent starch paste is produced when this suspension is poured into hot water. In the absence of the amylopectin portion, an amylose solution produces a rigid irreversible gel on standing in a process called retrogradation.

Amylose turns blue when iodine is added and may absorb as much as 20% by weight of this halogen. When iodine is added to dextrins, which are degradation products, they produce a reddish color, depending on $\overline{DP}$. Amylopectin absorbs less than 1% by weight of iodine and yields a violet or pale red color. In addition to its use as food, starch is used as an adhesive and paper and textile sizing agent. Starch forms ethers and esters like cellulose, but these are not used commercially to any great extent.

6.5 OTHER POLYSACCHARIDES

Glycogen, which is the reserve carbohydrate in animals, is a very highly branched polysaccharide similar to amylodextrin. Polyglycuronic acids are polysaccharides in which a carboxylic acid group replaces the hydroxyl group on carbon 6 in the anhydrohexose repeating unit. These water-soluble gums include the galactans and mannans found in pectin, algae, seaweed, gum arabic, agar, gum tragacanth, alginic acid, and other plant gums. Pentosans comparable to these hexosans are also naturally occurring polysaccharides.

Dextran is a high molecular weight branched polysaccharide synthesized from sucrose by bacteria. This polymer consists of anhydroglucose repeating units joined by α-acetal linkages through carbons 1 and 6. Partially hydrolyzed dextran is used as a substitute for blood plasma.

6.6 PROTEINS

The many different monodisperse polymers of amino acids, which are essential components of plants and animals, are called proteins. This word is derived from the Greek proteios, "of chief importance." The twenty different α-amino acids are joined together by peptide linkages

$$
\left(\overset{\overset{\displaystyle O}{\|}}{C} - \overset{\overset{\displaystyle H}{|}}{N} - \underset{\underset{\displaystyle H}{|}}{\overset{\overset{\displaystyle R}{|}}{C}} \right)
$$

and are polyamides or polypeptides. The latter term is often used by biologists to denote oligomers or relatively low molecular weight proteins. (Note the structural similarities and differences between proteins and polyamides-nylons.)

All α-amino acids

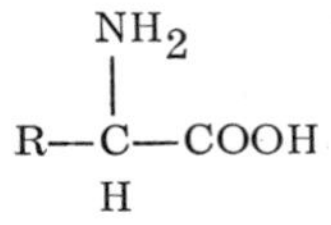

$$\begin{array}{c} NH_2 \\ | \\ R{-}C{-}COOH \\ H \end{array}$$

except glycine

$$\begin{array}{l} NH_2 \\ | \\ H_2C{-}COOH \end{array}$$

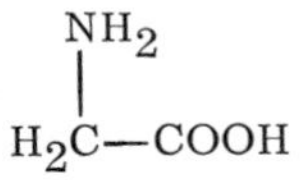

contain a chiral carbon atom and are L-amino acids. Free amino acids are present in aqueous solution at pH values above and below the isoelectric point, but the customary form is a dipolar, or zwitterion

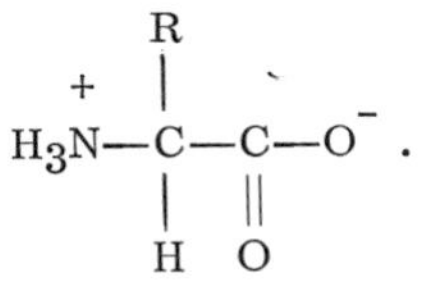

$$\overset{+}{H_3N}{-}\underset{H}{\overset{R}{C}}{-}\underset{O}{\overset{\|}{C}}{-}O^- .$$

Hence, α-amino acids, like other salts, are water-soluble, high melting polar compounds which migrate toward an electrode at pH values other than that of the isoelectric point in a process called electrophoresis.

Proteins may be classified as intermolecularly hydrogen-bonded fibrillar, or hairlike, proteins and as intramolecularly hydrogen-bonded globular proteins. Fibrillar proteins, such as keratin of the hair and nails, collagen of connective tissue, and myosin of the muscle are water-insoluble strong polymers. In contrast, globular proteins such as enzymes, hormones, hemoglobin, and albumin are water-soluble weaker polymers.

Proteins may also be classified as simple polyamides and as conjugated proteins. The latter consist of a protein combined with a prosthetic group. The latter may be a carbohydrate, as in glycoproteins, a nucleic acid, as in nucleoproteins, or a heme, as in hemoglobin.

The amino acids may be neutral, acidic, or basic, in accordance with the relative number of amino and carboxylic acid groups present. For convenience in writing formulas for proteins, the amino acids are represented by abbreviations of three or four letters such as Ala for alanine, Leu for leucine, Try for tryptophan, and Glu for glutamic acid. Thus, a dipeptide could be shown as Ala-Try and a tripeptide as Glu-Leu-Ala.

Proteins may be hydrolyzed by dilute acids, and the mixture of amino acids or residues produced may be separated and identified by paper chromatography. The reagent ninhydrin yields characteristic colored products with amino acids, and these may be determined colorimetrically. This chromatographic technique was developed by Nobel laureates Martin and Synge.

The term primary structure is used to describe the sequence of amino acids units (configuration) in a polypeptide chain. The sequence for N-terminal amino acids in a chain may be determined by use of a technique developed by Nobel laureate Sanger, who reacted the amino end group with 2,4-dinitrofluorobenzene and characterized the yellow aromatic amino acid produced by hydrolysis. This process is repeated after the end amino acid has been hydrolyzed off.

The C-terminal amino acid may be determined by using hydrazine to form hydrazides from the cleaved amino groups. Since the free carboxyl end group is not affected by hydrazine, the terminal amino acid is readily identified. The sequences of amino acids in several polypeptides, such as insulin and trypsin, have been identified by these techniques.

The term secondary structure is used to describe the molecular shape, or conformation, of a protein molecule. Nobel laureate Pauling has shown that a right-handed intramolecularly hydrogen-bonded helical arrangement (α helix) is an important secondary structure when many bulky pendant groups are present on the chain, as shown in Fig. 6.4. The distance between the amino acid repeating units along the chain in an α arrangement is 0.15 nm (1.5 Å).

A β arrangement, or pleated sheet conformation, is predominant when small pendant groups are present in the chain, as in silk fibroin. As shown in Fig. 6.5, the distance between amino acid repeating units along the chain in a β arrangement is 0.35 nm (3.5 Å), i.e., the repeat distance (identity period) is 0.70 nm.

The term tertiary structure is used to designate the shape or folding resulting from the presence of sulfur-sulfur cross-links between polymer chains. This structure requires the presence of cysteine units containing mercapto groups which are oxidized to cystine units containing disulfide groups.

The specificity of enzymatic catalytic activity is dependent on tertiary structure. When ethanol is added to eggs or they are boiled, they lose their physiological activity because of a disruption of folded structure. This reorganization of structure is called denaturation.

While polypeptides can be synthesized by simply heating α-amino acids, the products obtained are random mixtures unless a single amino acid is used. Likewise, nylon-2, which is a homopolypeptide, may be prepared by the Leuch's synthesis from N-carboxy-α-amino acid anhydrides. Polypeptides with specific sequences of amino acids can be prepared by protecting the N-terminal amino group by a reactant such as phthalic anhydride and removing the phthalimide group later by reacting with hydrazine.

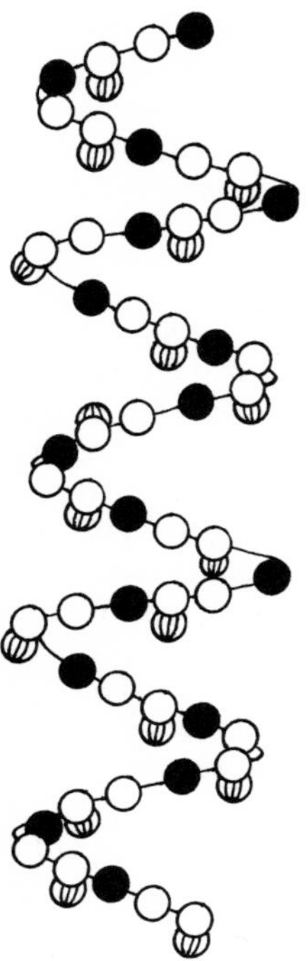

FIGURE 6.4 α-Helix conformation of proteins.

.7 nm

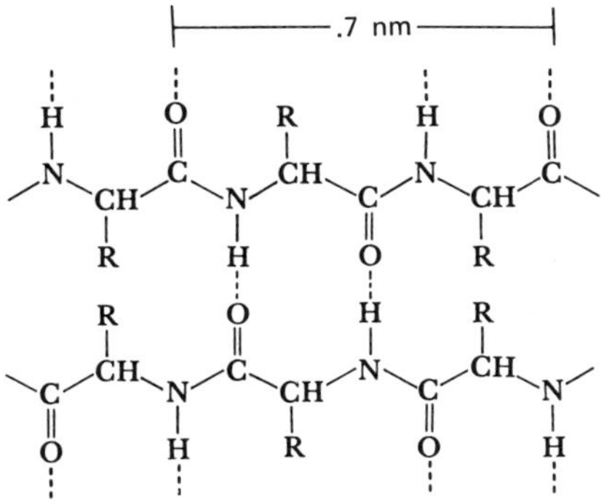

FIGURE 6.5 β Arrangement or pleated sheet conformation of proteins. (M. Stevens, Polymer Chemistry—An Introduction, Addison-Wesley, Reading, Massachusetts, 1975. With permission of Addison-Wesley Publishing Co.)

The most widely used technique is the Merrifield solid phase technique in which all reactions take place on the surface of cross-linked polystyrene beads. Thus, the entire reaction for synthesizing polypeptides with many programmed sequences of amino acids can be carried out automatically in a simple vessel without isolation of any intermediate products.

6.7 NUCLEIC ACIDS

Nucleoproteins, which are conjugated proteins, may be separated into nucleic acids and proteins in aqueous sodium chloride. The name "nuclein," which was coined by Miescher in 1869 to describe products isolated from nuclei in pus, was later changed to nucleic acid. Pure nucleic acid was isolated by Levene in the early 1900s. He showed that either D-ribose or D-deoxyribose was present in what are now known as ribonucleic acid (RNA) and deoxyribonucleic acid (DNA). These specific compounds were originally obtained from yeast and the thymus gland, respectively.

In 1944, Avery showed that DNA was capable of changing one strain of bacteria into another. It is now known that nucleic acids direct the synthesis of proteins. Thus, our modern knowledge of heredity and molecular biology is based on our knowledge of nucleic acids.

The prosthetic group in a nucleoprotein is a phosphoric acid ester of a nucleoside and is called a nucleotide. The nucleoside is a compound consisting of a pentose and heterocyclic bases. The two types of pentose are ribose (in RNA) and deoxyribose (in DNA). There are two classes of heterocyclic bases, namely, pyrimidines, which are simple 1,3-diazines, and purines, which are more complex fused nitrogenous rings consisting of pyrimidine and imidazole rings.

As shown in Fig. 6.6, the deoxyribose present in DNA differs from the ribose present in RNA by the presence of a hydrogen atom instead of a hydroxyl group on carbon atom 2.

The structural formulas for the pyrimidine and purine bases are shown in Fig. 6.7.

Both DNA and RNA contain both purine bases, namely, adenine and guanine, and the pyrimidine base cytosine. Uracil is found in RNA and methyluracil or thymine is found in DNA. (It may help to remember that DNA was originally found in the thymus gland.)

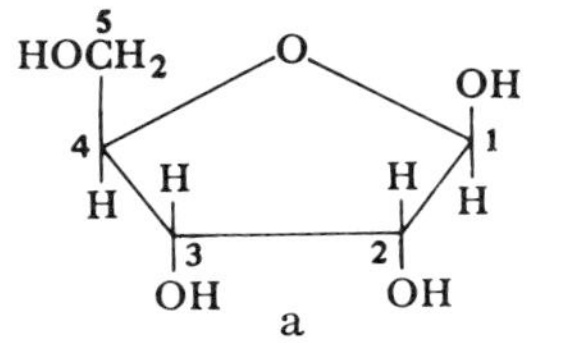

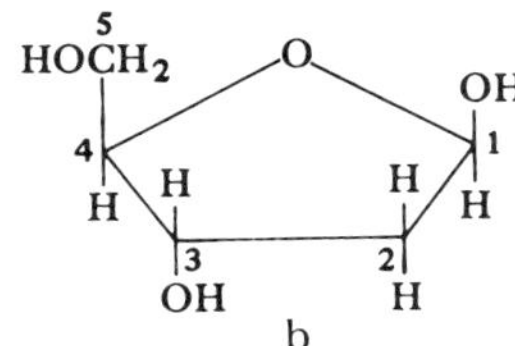

FIGURE 6.6 Boesekin-Haworth structures of (a) ribose and (b) deoxyribose.

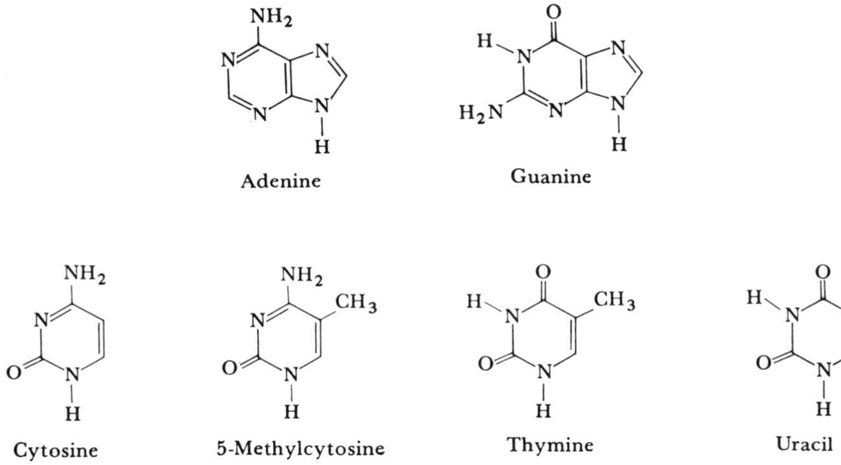

FIGURE 6.7 Structural formulas of purine and pyrimidine bases in nucleic acids.

The basic nitrogen atoms in the purines and pyrimidines are joined to carbon 1, and the phosphate is on carbon 3 in the nucleotides. The names of the nucleotides and nucleosides correspond to the purine or pyrimidine bases present. Thus, the nucleotide shown in Fig. 6.8 is called adenylic acid, since it is the 3'-phosphate ester of the nucleoside adenosine. The corresponding nucleoside for deoxyribose is deoxyadenosine. The other nucleosides of ribose are called guanosine, cytidine, and uridine. The nucleosides of deoxyribose are called deoxycytidine and, simply, thymidine.

Since there are two hydroxyl groups in each deoxyribose, there are two possible phosphoric acid esters. Adenosine forms esters with more than one phosphate group on carbon 5. These are adenosine monophosphate (AMP), the diphosphate (ADP), and the triphosphate (ATP). The hydrolysis of ATP to produce ADP is important in biological energy transfer.

As shown in Fig. 6.9, RNA and DNA are polymers in which the backbone consists of phosphate esters on both carbon 3 and carbon 5 of the pentoses.

The bases on the RNA and DNA chains may be either purines or pyrimidines. Nobel laureates Watson and Crick correctly deduced that DNA existed as a double-stranded helix in which a pyrimidine base on one chain or strand was hydrogen bonded to a purine base on the other chain. As illustrated in Fig. 6.10, the total distance for these pairs is 1.07 nm (10.7 Å). As shown, the base pairs are guanine-cytosine and adenine-thymine (which may be remembered from the mnemonic expression Gee-Cat). A sketch of the DNA double helix is shown in Fig. 6.11.

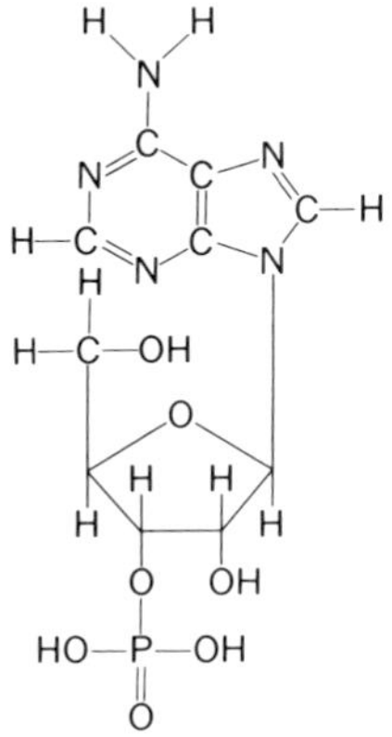

FIGURE 6.8 Adenylic acid, adenosine-3'-phosphate, nucleotide.

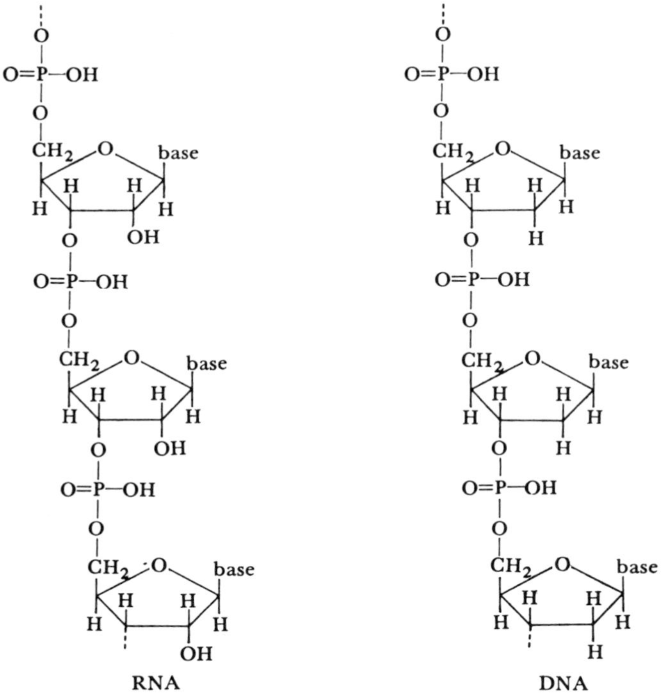

RNA

DNA

FIGURE 6.9 Representative segments of nucleic acid polymeric chains.

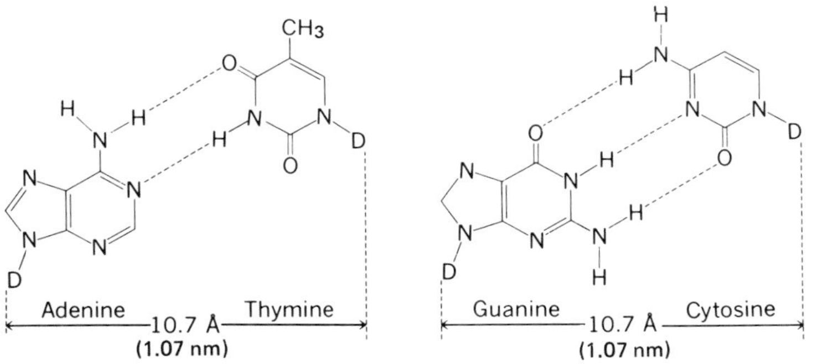

FIGURE 6.10 Allowable base pairs in nucleic acids (DNA).

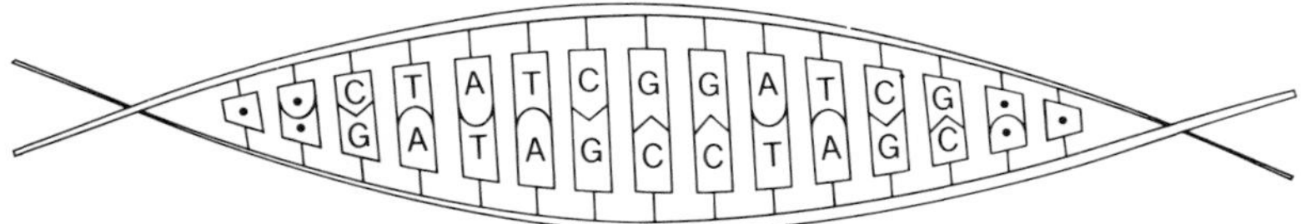

FIGURE 6.11 A schematic representation of the double helix of DNA.

It is now known that the molecular weight of RNA is typically less than that of DNA and that there are at least three different types of RNA, namely, high molecular weight ribosomal RNA (r-RNA), moderate molecular weight transfer RNA (t-RNA), and low molecular weight messenger RNA (m-RNA). These are believed to direct the synthesis of proteins which consist of 20 amino acids arranged in specific sequences. Thus, the total number of possible combinations of amino acids is 2.4×10^{18}.

DNA, which is an essential part of the chromosome of the cell, contains the information for the synthesis of a protein molecule. When the double parent strand splits into two single daughter strands, each strand serves as a template for the formation of another strand with the proper base pairs. The single-stranded DNA also serves as a template for m-RNA. The specific amino acids are brought to the cell by t-RNA, to which the amino acids are joined to the phosphoric acid groups.

There are four different nucleotides (or four different bases) in DNA which provide for 4^2, or 16, dinucleotide combinations and 4^3, or 64, trinucleotides, etc. It is believed that these trinucleotides or codons are present in all known life forms, and that these codons specify the specific amino acids used in protein synthesis. Thus, using U as a symbol for uracil, the codon UUU is specific for phenylalanine (Phe). Most of the code for the 64 combinations of the four bases has been elucidated.

Other examples of codons are AUG and UAG, which are the initiators and terminators of chains. Of course, with 64 codons and only 20 amino acids, plus start and stop signals, many amino acids are represented by as many as three codons. Thus, in addition to UUU, UUC is also a codon for Phe. Mutations can be caused by mistakes in the code and by specific chemical compounds which affect the base pairs.

6.8 NATURALLY OCCURRING POLYISOPRENES

Polyisoprenes

```
    H              H
    |              |
[---C---C===C---C---]
    |   |    |    |     n
    H  CH3   H    H
```

occur in nature as hard plastics called gutta percha and balata and as an elastomer or rubber known as Hevea braziliensis, or natural rubber (NR). Approximately 50% of the 500 tons of gutta percha produced annually is obtained from gutta percha trees grown on plantations in Java and Malaya. Balata and about 50% of the gutta percha used are obtained from trees in the jungles of South America and the East Indies. The first gutta-insulated submarine cable was installed between England and France in 1850. Gutta percha (Palaquium oblongifolium) continues to be used for wire insulation, and both this polyisoprene and balata (Mimusops globosa) are used as the covers for golf balls.

The hardness of these polydisperse naturally occurring crystalline polymers is the result of a trans configuration in 1,4-polyisoprene (see Fig. 6.12). The chain extensions on opposite sides of the double bonds in the polymer chain facilitate good fit and cause inflexibility in these chains.

Gutta percha exists in the planar α form which has an X-ray identity period of 0.87 nm (8.7 Å) and a melting point of 74°C. The α form is transformed to the β form when these trans isomers of polyisoprene are heated above the transition temperature of 68°C. The nonplanar β form has a melting point of 64°C and an identity period of 0.48 nm (4.8 Å). The latter corresponds to the length of the isoprene repeating unit in the polymer chain.

Both trans and cis isomers of polyisoprene are present in chicle which is obtained from the Achras sapota tree in Central America. Since chicle is more flexible than gutta percha, it has been used as a base for chewing gum. Both trans and cis isomers of polyisoprene are also synthesized commercially.

Natural rubber, which is one of the most important biologically inactive, naturally occurring polymers, was used by the Mayan civilization in Central and South America before the twelfth century. In addition to using the latex from the ule tree for waterproofing of clothing, the Western

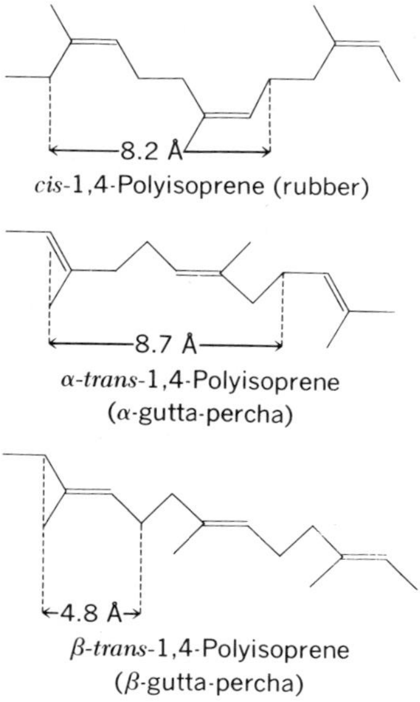

8.2 Å

cis-1,4-Polyisoprene (rubber)

8.7 Å

α-*trans*-1,4-Polyisoprene
(α-gutta-percha)

4.8 Å

β-*trans*-1,4-Polyisoprene
(β-gutta-percha)

FIGURE 6.12 Abbreviated structural formulas for polyisoprenes. (From *Introduction to Polymer Chemistry* by R. Seymour, McGraw-Hill, New York, 1971. Used with permission of McGraw-Hill Book Company.)

hemisphere natives played a game called tlachtli with large rubber balls. The object of this game was to insert the ball into a tight-fitting stone hole in a vertical wall using only the shoulder or thigh. The game ended once a goal was scored, and the members of the losing team were sacrificed to the gods.

While natural rubber, or *caoutchooc*, was brought to Europe by Columbus, little use, beyond erasing pencil marks, was made of this important elastomer until the nineteenth century. Accordingly, Priestly coined the name *India rubber* to describe its major use at that time.

While less than 1% of the world's present supply of natural rubber is obtained from wild rubber trees, most of this elastomer was shipped from Central and South America prior to the twentieth century. The latex, which is an aqueous suspension of 30 to 35% cis-1,4-polyisoprene, occurs in microscopic tubules located between the bark and the cambian layer in the hevea plant. The latex is obtained by collecting the liquid which seeps out after tapping the hevea plants.

Hevea latex is also present in the household decorative rubber plant (*Ficus elastica*), milkweed (*Cryptoslegia grandiflora*), goldenrod (*Solidago*), dandelions (*Taraxacum offinale* and *Koksaghhyz*), creepers (*Landolphia*), and guayule (*Parthenium argentatum*).

In addition to the cultivation of H. braziliensis, experimental plantations have been established for the cultivation of F. elastica, Funtunia, Castilloa, Manihot, Kok-saghyz, and P. argentatum. While F. elastica continues to be used as a decorative plant, the cultivation of all nonhevea rubbers, except guayule, has been abandoned.

Much of the interest in the Russian dandelion and guayule resulted from successful growth in cooler temperature zones. As much as 200 kg of rubber per acre has been obtained from the cultivation of dandelions in Turkestan (Uzbekistan), but this project was abandoned after the development of styrene-butadiene synthetic rubber (SBR). However, natural rubber is being obtained from wild guayule plants in Northern Mexico, and this plant is also being cultivated in the Southwestern United States. Guayule has a rubber content of about 10%. As much as 1500 kg of rubber per hectare may be obtained by crushing this plant.

Approximately 99% of the present supply of natural rubber is obtained from the progenitors of a few thousand seedlings smuggled out of Brazil by Wickham and Cross and cultivated in Ceylon in 1876. The first successful tappings of these trees were made in 1896. The plantations in Malaya and Indonesia now account for over 70% of the world's production of natural rubber.

This widely used elastomer (cis-1,4-polyisoprene), is not produced in nature by the polymerization of isoprene, but by the enzymatic polymerization of isopentenylpyrophosphate

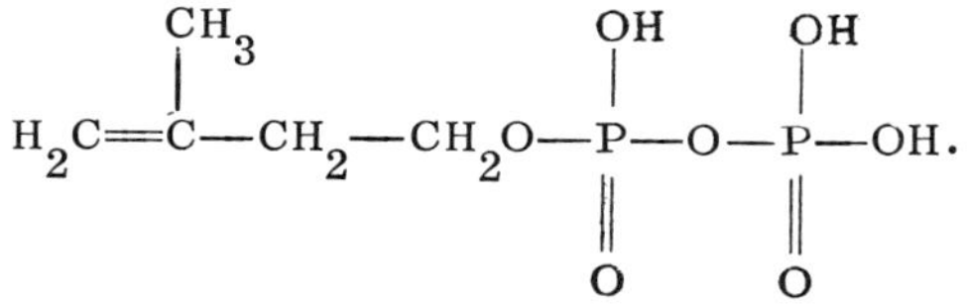

$$H_2C{=}\underset{\displaystyle CH_3}{\overset{|}{C}}{-}CH_2{-}CH_2O{-}\overset{\displaystyle OH}{\underset{\displaystyle \| \atop O}{P}}{-}O{-}\overset{\displaystyle OH}{\underset{\displaystyle \| \atop O}{P}}{-}OH.$$

While the theoretical yield of hevea rubber is 9000 kg per hectare (ha), the best yields to date are 3300 kg/ha (1 ha = 2.47 acres).

Prior to the discovery of the vulcanization or cross linking of hevea rubber with sulfur, by Charles Goodyear in 1858, Faraday had shown that the empirical formula of this elastomer is C_5H_8, and thus rubber is a member of the terpene group. The product obtained by pyrolysis of rubber was named isoprene by Williams in 1860 and converted to a solid (polymerized) by Bouchardat in 1879. Tilden suggested the formula that is now accepted for isoprene:

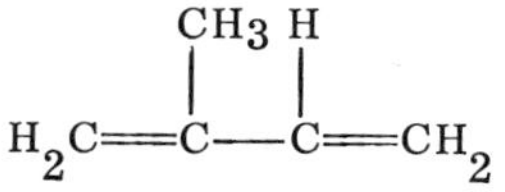

$$H_2C{=}\overset{\displaystyle CH_3}{\overset{|}{C}}{-}\overset{\displaystyle H}{\overset{|}{C}}{=}CH_2$$

Since levulinic aldehyde

$$H_3C-\underset{\underset{O}{\|}}{C}-\overset{\overset{H}{|}}{\underset{\underset{H}{|}}{C}}-\overset{\overset{H}{|}}{\underset{\underset{H}{|}}{C}}-\overset{\overset{H}{|}}{C}=O$$

was produced by ozonolysis, Harries suggested the presently accepted structure for the polymer.

The X-ray identity pattern of stretched natural rubber is 0.82 nm (8.2 Å), which represents two isoprene units in a cis configuration in the polymer chain. Rubber has a glass transition temperature of -85°C, but this is increased as the cross-linked density of vulcanized rubber increases. Unvulcanized rubber undergoes typical reactions of olefins, such as hydrogenation, chlorination, hydrohalogenation, epoxidation, and ozonolysis.

Natural rubber crystallizes when stretched in a reversible process. However, the sample remains in its stretched form (racked rubber) if it is cooled below its T_g. The racked rubber will snap back and approach its original form when it is heated above its T_g. Rubber that has been held in an extended form for long periods of time does not return to its original form immediately when the stress is relieved, since a relaxation process must occur before it decays completely to its original length. The delay in returning to the original form is called hysteresis.

These and other elastic properties of NR and other elastomers above the T_g are based on long-range elasticity. Stretching causes an uncoiling of the polymer chains, but these chains assume the most probable conformations if the stress is removed after a short period of time. Some slippage of chains occurs if the rubber is held in the stretched position for long periods of time.

The absence of strong intermolecular forces, the presence of pendant methyl groups, and the crankshaft action associated with the cis isomer all contribute to the flexibility of the natural rubber molecule. The introduction of a few cross-links by vulcanization with sulfur reduces slippage of the chains, but still permits flexibility in the chain sections between cross-links (principal sections).

When a strip of natural rubber (NR) or synthetic rubber (SR) is stretched at a constant rate, the tensile strength required for stretching (stress, s) increases slowly until an elongation (strain, γ) of about 500% is observed. This initial process is associated with an uncoiling of the polymer chains in the principal sections.

Considerably more stress is required for greater elongation to about 800%. This rapid increase in modulus (G) is associated with better alignment of the polymer chains along the axis of elongation, crystallization, and decrease in entropy (ΔS). The work done in the stretching process (W_{el}) is equal to the product of the retractile force (f) and the change in length (dl). Therefore, the force is equal to the work per change in length (dl).

$$W_{el} = f\,dl \qquad \text{or} \qquad f = \frac{W_{el}}{dl} \tag{6.3}$$

W_{el} is equal to the change in Gibbs free energy (dG), which under conditions of constant pressure, is equal to the change in internal energy (dE) minus the product of the change in entropy and the Kelvin temperature.

$$f = \frac{W_{el}}{dl} = \frac{dG}{dl} = \frac{dE}{dl} - T\frac{dS}{dl} \tag{6.4}$$

The first term in (6.4) is important in the initial low-modulus stretching process, and the second term predominates in the second high-modulus stretching process.

As observed by Gough in 1805 and confirmed by Joule in 1859, the temperature of rubber increases as it is stretched, and the stretched sample cools as it snaps back to its original condition. (This is easily confirmed by rapidly stretching a rubber band and placing it to your lips, noting that heating has occurred, and then rapidly releasing the tension and again placing the rubber band to your lips.) This effect was expressed mathematically by Kelvin and Clausius in the 1850s. The ratio of the rate of change of the retractive force (df) to the change in Kelvin temperature (dT) in an adiabatic process is equal to the specific heat of the elastomer (C_p) per degree temperature (T) times the change in temperature (dT) with the change in length (dl).

$$\frac{df}{dT} = -\frac{C_p}{T}\frac{dT}{dl} \tag{6.5}$$

Equation (6.5) may be transformed as shown in (6.6) to an equation which states that unlike most solids, natural rubber (and other elastomers) contract when heated.

$$\frac{dT}{df} = -\frac{T}{C_p}\frac{dl}{dT} \tag{6.6}$$

In the process of adding various essential ingredients or additives to crude rubber in a process called compounding, the rubber is masticated on a two-roll mill or in an intensive mixer at an elevated temperature in the presence of air. This mechanical action cleaves some of the carbon-carbon covalent bonds and produces macroradicals with lower $\overline{DP}$ values than the original macromolecule. The coupling of these macroradicals may be prevented if chain transfer agents called peptizers are present. As shown in the following equation, loosely bonded atoms or groups are abstracted from the chain transfer agent and a dead polymer is produced.

$$\sim\!\!\sim CH_2{-}CH_2{-}CH_2{-}CH_2\sim\!\!\sim \xrightarrow{E} \sim\!\!\sim CH_2{-}\dot{C}H_2 + {}^{\bullet}CH_2{-}CH_2\sim\!\!\sim$$

Rubber molecule Macroradicals

$$\sim\!\!\sim CH_2{-}\dot{C}H_2 + HSR \longrightarrow \sim\!\!\sim CH_2{-}CH_3 + \cdot SR \qquad (6.7)$$

Macroradical, Chain transfer agent, Dead polymer, Free radical

$$\sim\!\!\sim CH_2{-}\dot{C}H_2 + \cdot SR \longrightarrow \sim\!\!\sim CH_2{-}CH_2{-}SR$$

Macroradical, Free radical, Dead polymer

Vulcanization of both natural and synthetic rubber is the cross-linking reaction carried out on the greatest industrial scale. The exact mechanism varies with the employed vulcanization technique. Physical cross linking occurs through the mechanical cleaving of the carbon-carbon bond as noted above with subsequent rejoining of different chains.

$$\sim\!\!\sim CH_2{-}\dot{C}H_2 + \sim\!\!\sim CH_2{-}\dot{C}H_2 \longrightarrow \begin{matrix} \sim\!\!\sim CH_2{-}CH_2 \\ | \\ \sim\!\!\sim CH_2{-}CH_2 \end{matrix}$$

$$\sim\!\!\sim CH_2{-}\dot{C}H_2 + \sim\!\!\sim CH_2{-}CH_2\sim\!\!\sim \longrightarrow \sim\!\!\sim CH_2{-}CH_3 + \sim\!\!\sim CH_2{-}\underset{\bullet}{C}H\sim\!\!\sim$$

$$\begin{matrix} \sim\underset{\bullet}{C}HCH_2\sim \\ + \\ \sim\dot{C}HCH_2\sim \end{matrix} \longrightarrow \begin{matrix} \sim CHCH_2\sim \\ | \\ \sim CHCH_2\sim \end{matrix} \qquad (6.8)$$

Peroxide-initiated cross linking proceeds by homolytic abstraction of a polymer chain hydrogen followed by radical recombination. With

$$R{-}O{-}O{-}R \longrightarrow 2\,RO^{\bullet}$$

$$RO^{\bullet} + \sim\!\!\sim CH_2{-}CH_2\sim\!\!\sim \longrightarrow ROH + \sim\!\!\sim CH_2{-}\underset{\bullet}{C}H\sim\!\!\sim \qquad (6.9)$$

$$\begin{matrix} \sim\underset{\bullet}{C}HCH_2\sim \\ + \\ \sim\dot{C}HCH_2\sim \end{matrix} \longrightarrow \begin{matrix} \sim CHCH_2\sim \\ | \\ \sim CHCH_2\sim \end{matrix}$$

unsaturated polymer hydrogen abstraction probably occurs largely at the allylic position.

$$\sim CH_2CH{=}CHCH_2\sim + RO\cdot \longrightarrow \sim\dot{C}HCH{=}CHCH_2\sim + ROH \qquad (6.10)$$

The oldest method of vulcanization utilizing sulfur appears in part to occur through an ionic pathway involving addition to a double bond forming an intermediate sulfonium ion which subsequently abstracts a hydride ion or donates a proton, forming new cations for chain propagation. Other propagation steps may also occur.

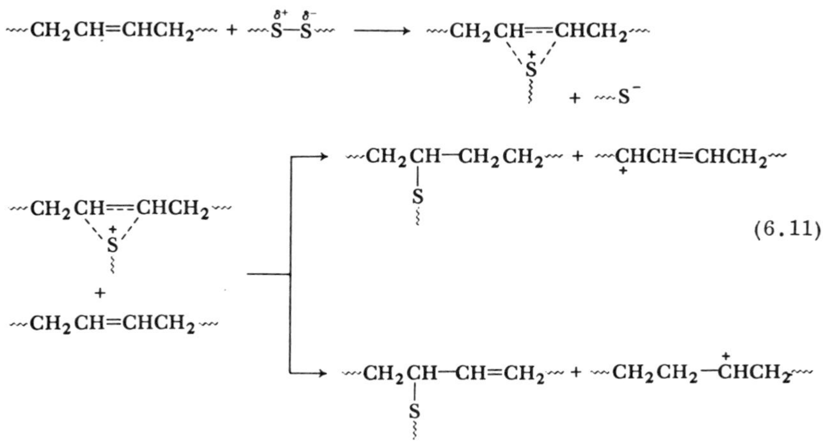

$$\sim CH_2CH{=}CHCH_2\sim + \sim\overset{\delta+}{S}{-}\overset{\delta-}{S}\sim \longrightarrow \sim CH_2\underset{\underset{\sim}{S^+}}{CH{=}{=}CH}CH_2\sim + \sim S^-$$

$$\sim CH_2\underset{\underset{\sim}{S^+}}{CH{=}{=}CH}CH_2\sim + \sim CH_2CH{=}CHCH_2\sim \longrightarrow \begin{cases} \sim CH_2\underset{\underset{\sim}{S}}{CH}{-}CH_2CH_2\sim + \sim\overset{}{\underset{+}{C}}HCH{=}CHCH_2\sim \\ \sim CH_2\underset{\underset{\sim}{S}}{CH}{-}CH{=}CH_2\sim + \sim CH_2CH_2{-}\overset{+}{C}HCH_2\sim \end{cases} \qquad (6.11)$$

Cold vulcanization can occur by dipping thin portions of rubber into carbon disulfide solutions of S_2Cl_2.

$$2\sim CH{=}CH\sim + S_2Cl_2 \longrightarrow \sim\underset{\underset{Cl}{|}}{CH}{-}S{-}\underset{\underset{Cl}{|}}{CH}\sim + S \qquad (6.12)$$

The long time required for vulcanization of rubber by heating with sulfur was shortened drastically by Oenslager, who used organic amines as catalysts, or accelerators, for the vulcanization of rubber in 1912. The most widely used accelerators are derivatives of 2-mercaptobenzothiazole (Captax). Other frequently used accelerators are zinc dimethyldithiocarbamate and tetramethylthiuram disulfide.

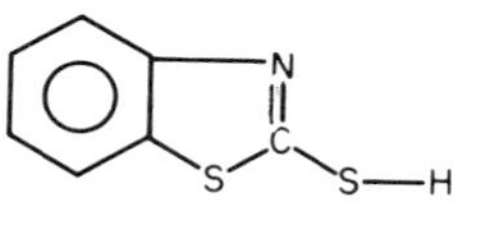

2-Mercaptobenzothiazole

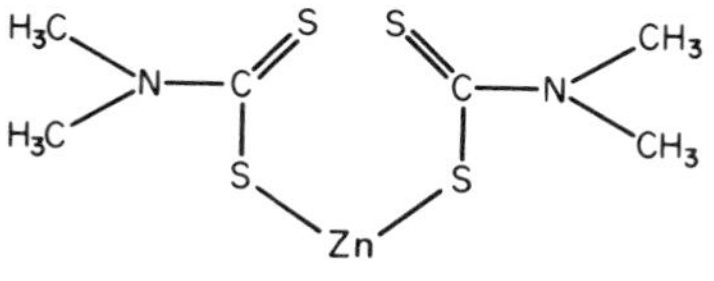

Zinc dimethydithiocarbamate

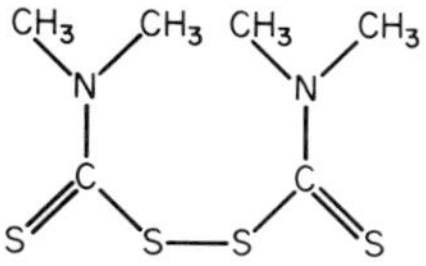

Tetramethylthiuram
disulfide

Rubber-compounding formulations also include antioxidants, such as phenyl-β-naphthylamine, which retard the degradation of rubber at elevated temperatures, and carbon black, which serves as a reinforcing agent. Amorphous silica is used in place of carbon black in compounding recipes for the white side walls of pneumatic tires. Since β-naphthylamine is said to be carcinogenic, relatively pure phenyl-β-naphthylamine should be used. The key to prevention of rubber oxidation by an antioxidant depends on its ability to stop the propagation reaction and the chain reaction, or on its ability to destroy peroxides.

$$R^{\cdot} + O_2 \longrightarrow RO_2^{\cdot} \qquad \text{Propagation}$$

$$RO_2^{\cdot} + R'H \longrightarrow R^{\cdot} + R'O_2H \qquad \text{Chain reaction} \tag{6.13}$$

$$R'O_2H + AH\ (\text{antioxidant}) \longrightarrow \text{Stable products} \qquad \text{peroxide destruction}$$

While natural rubber and cotton account for over 40% of total elastomer and fiber production, only relatively small amounts of natural plastics and resins are used commercially. The principal products of this type are casein, shellac, asphalt or bitumen, rosin, and polymers obtained by the drying (polymerization) of unsaturated oils.

Shellac, which was used by Edison for molding his first phonograph records and as an alcoholic solution (spirit varnish) for coating wood, is a cross-linked polymer consisting to a large extent of derivatives of aleuritic acid (9,10,16-trihydroxyhexadecanoic acid). Shellac is excreted by small coccid insects (Coccus lacca) which feed on the twigs of trees in Southeastern Asia. Over 20 lakshas (Sanskrit for 100,000), or 2 million insects, must be dissolved in ethanol to produce 1 kg of shellac.

While naturally occurring bitumens were used by the ancients for caulking and water proofing, they now account for less than 5% of this type of material. Large deposits of natural bitumens are located at Trinidad and Bermudez Lake in the West Indies and Venezuela, respectively. Gilsonite, which was named after its discoverer, is found in Utah and Colorado. Most of today's asphaltic materials are obtained from petroleum-still residues.

Cold molded-filled asphaltic compositions have been used for battery cases and electrical components. Hot-melt asphaltic compositions may be converted to non-Newtonian fluids by passing air into the melt. Both blown and regular asphalt are used in highway construction, roofing, and flooring construction, and for waterproofing.

Rosin, the residue left in the manufacture of turpentine by distillation, is a mixture of the diterpene, abietic acid, and its anhydride. It is nonpolymeric but is used in the manufacture of synthetic resins and varnishes. Ester gum, a cross-linked ester, is obtained by the esterification of rosin with glycerol or pentaerythritol.

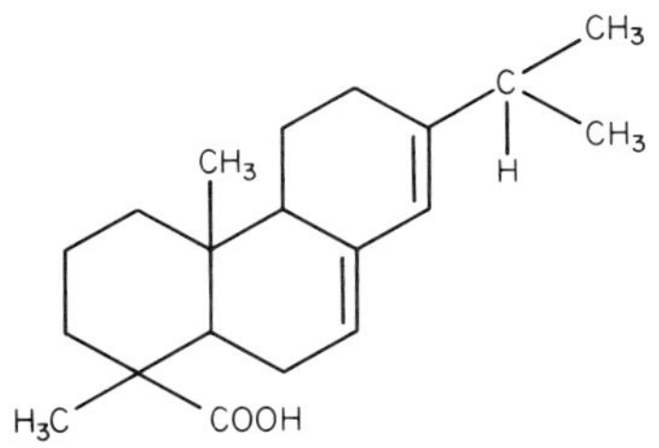

Abietic acid

Lignin is the noncellulosic constituent of wood. Next to cellulose, lignin is the major constituent of wood. Since its removal is the major step in the production of paper pulp, tremendous quantities of lignin are available as a byproduct of paper manufacture. Lignin is a complex polyphenolic, relatively low molecular weight, polymer probably containing units as described in Fig. 6.13. Its sulfonic acid derivative is used as an extender for phenolic resins, as a wetting agent for applications such as oil drilling muds, and for the production of vanillin. This last use accounts for less than 0.01%, and all other uses account for less than 1% of this byproduct.

Many natural resins are fossil resins exuded from trees thousands of years ago. Recent exudates are called recent resins, and those obtained from dead trees are called semifossil resins. Humic acid is a fossil resin found with peat, brown coal, or lignite deposits throughout the world. It is a carboxylated phenoliclike polymer used as a soil conditioner, as a component of oil drilling muds, and as a scavenger for heavy metals.

Amber is a fossil resin found in the Baltic Sea regions, and sandarac and copals are found in Morocco and Oceania, respectively. Other copal resins, such as pontiac, kauri, manila, congo, batu, and so on, are named after the geographical location of the deposit.

Casein, a protein from milk, under the name of Galalith has been used as a molding resin and as an adhesive. Unsaturated oils found in linseed, soybean, safflower, tung, octicica, and menhaden are used as drying oils in surface coatings at an annual rate of over 300 thousand tons. Other

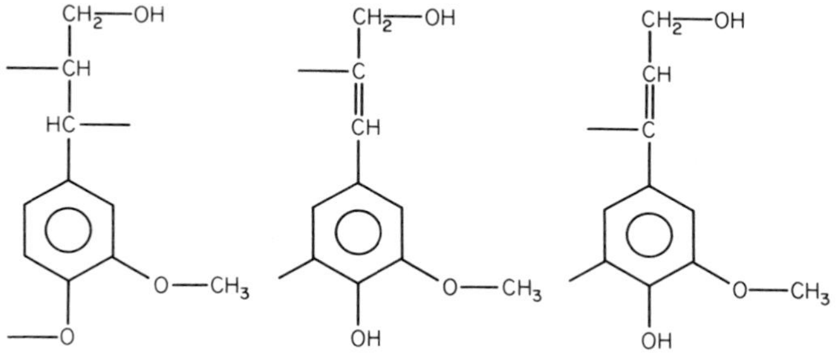

FIGURE 6.13 Possible units contained within lignin.

regenerated protein sources include soya beans (glycinin), maize (zein), and ground nuts (arachin).

Synthetic polymeric fibers, plastics, elastomers, and coatings have displaced the natural polymeric products to a large extent. However, the latter are renewable resources independent of the supply of petroleum. Thus, their use will continue to increase as long as there is sufficient land available for the cultivation of both food and polymeric crops.

SUMMARY

1. Cellulose and starch, which are the most important polysaccharides, are hydrolyzed by acids to D-glucose, which is a monosaccharide. The disaccharides cellobiose and maltose are precursors of glucose in this hydrolysis. D-glucose exists in two different chair conformations called α and β D-glucose. All the hydroxyl groups in the β form are equatorial, and all are equatorial in the α form except the hydroxyl group on carbon 1, which is axial. Cellobiose and cellulose are dimers of β-D-glucose, and maltose and starch are polymers of α-D-glucose.

2. Cellulose is a linear polydisperse polymer whose molecules are often present as fibrils, because of strong intermolecular hydrogen bonding. Soda cellulose, prepared by the actions of strong caustic or cellulose, reacts with carbon disulfide to produce a soluble xanthate and with alkylhalides to produce ethers. Regenerated cellulose in the form of filaments (rayon) or sheets (cellophane) is produced when soluble cellulose xanthate (viscose) is precipitated in aqueous acid solutions.

3. A celluloselike product consisting of repeating units of acetylated D-glucosamine is found in the exoskeleton of shellfish. Amylose is a linear polymer, while amylopectin is a branched polymer. The former forms a blue occlusion compound with iodine. Glycogen is a readily hydrolyzable highly branched polymer of D-glucose.

4. Proteins are polyamides consisting of some 20 different α-amino acids joined through peptide linkages

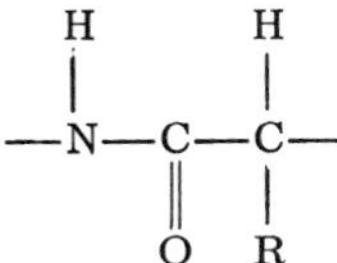

Since α-amino acids exist as dipolar ions, they are insoluble and high melting and do not migrate to charged poles at their isoelectric points. Since they do migrate at other pH values, the process of electrophoresis may be used to separate amino acids and proteins. Proteins with high intermolecular hydrogen bonding are fibrillar, and those with intramolecular hydrogen bonding are globular. Proteins may be hydrolyzed by weak mineral acids to α-amino acids, and the latter may be separated by paper chromatography and identified by the addition of ninhydrin.

5. The sequence of amino acids in the primary structure (configuration) may be determined by reactions with the amine or carboxyl end groups followed by controlled hydrolysis. The secondary structure or conformation may be a right-handed intramolecularly hydrogen-bonded helix or an intermolecularly bonded pleated sheet. The shape or folding in the tertiary structure is dependent on the presence of sulfur-sulfur cross-links. Polypeptides may be synthesized by protecting one of the functional groups before condensation. The preferred solid-phase polymerization technique takes place on the surface of cross-linked polystyrene beads.

6. The nucleic acid separated from nucleoproteins is a nucleotide, which may be hydrolyzed to phosphoric acid and a nucleoside. The latter consists of ribose (in RNA) or deoxyribose (in DNA) and purine and pyrimidine bases. All nucleic acids contain adenine, guanine, and cytosine. RNA contains uracil, and DNA contains thymine (3-methyluracil). The polymer backbone consists of phosphate esters of the hydroxyl groups in the 3 and 5 positions. The RNA polymer forms a single helix, but DNA forms a double helix capable of replication. The double helix is held together by the hydrogen bonds of purine-pyrimidine pairs from separate chains. The allowable pairs are guanine-cytosine and adenine-thymine. RNA exists in three different molecular weights, namely, messenger, transfer, and ribosomal RNA. The 64 possible DNA trinucleotides provide 64 codons which specify the amino acids used in protein synthesis.

7. The hard naturally occurring plastics, balata and gutta percha, are trans isomers of the naturally occurring elastic cis-1,4-polyisoprene, which is natural rubber (Hevea braziliensis). The polymer chain of amorphous natural rubber and other elastomers uncoils during stretching and returns to its original low-entropy form above its T_g. However, if it is held in the stretched position for long periods of time, a relaxation process takes place before it returns completely to its original length.

8. Slippage of chains is prevented but elasticity is retained when a few cross-links are present between the principal sections of elastomers. The original low-modulus stretching process is related to a change in internal energy per unit length. The more important high-modulus stretching process which follows is related to a change in entropy, resulting from the alignment of chains and crystallization.

9. Unlike other solids, stretched rubber contracts when heated. The long-range elasticity of rubber is dependent on the absence of strong intermolecular forces, the presence of a pendant methyl group, and a cis configuration, which aid the crankshaft-type motion. In addition to sulfur, the compounding ingredients of rubber include accelerators, antioxidants, and fillers, such as carbon black.

GLOSSARY

A: An abbreviation for adenine.

accelerator: A catalyst for the vulcanization of rubber.

acetal linkage: The linkage between anhydroglucose units in polysaccharides.

adenine: A purine base present in nucleic acids.

adenosine: A nucleoside based on adenine.

adenosine phosphates: Phosphoric acid esters of adenosine.

adenylic acid: A nucleotide based on adenine.

ADP: Adenosine diphosphate.

alkali cellulose: Cellulose that has been treated with a strong caustic solution.

α-amino acid: A carboxylic acid with an amino group on the carbon next to the carboxyl group.

α arrangement: That present in an α helix.

α cellulose: Cellulose that is insoluble in a 17.5% caustic solution.

α helix: A right-handed helical conformation.

amorphous silica: A filler used with polymers.

AMP: Adenosine monophosphate.

amylodextrin: A highly branched starch polymer with branches or chain extensions on carbon 6 of the anhydroglucose repeating units.

amylose: A linear starch polymer.

antioxidant: A compound that retards the degradation of a polymer.

ATP: Adenosine triphosphate.

axial bonds: Bonds that are perpendicular and above or below the plane of the hexose ring, such as the hydroxy group on carbon 1 in α-D-glucose.

balata: A naturally occurring plastic (trans-1,4-polyisoprene).

β arrangement: A pleated sheetlike conformation.

β cellulose: Cellulose soluble in 17.5% but insoluble in 8% caustic solution.

Boeseken-Haworth projections: Planar hexagonal rings used for simplicity, instead of the staggered chain forms, to show the structure of saccharides such as D-glucose.

C: An abbreviation for cytosine.

carbohydrate: An organic compound with an empirical formula of CH_2O.

carbon black: Finely divided carbon used for the reinforcement of rubber.

casein: Milk protein.

cellobiose: A disaccharide consisting of two D-glucose units joined by a β-acetal linkage. It is the repeating unit in the cellulose molecule.

cellophane: A sheet of cellulose regenerated by the acidification of an alkaline solution of cellulose xanthate.

cellulose: A linear polysaccharide consisting of many anhydroglucose units joined by β-acetal linkages.

cellulose xanthate: The reaction product of soda cellulose and carbon disulfide.

chair form: The most stable conformation of a six-membered ring like D-glucose, is named because of its slight resemblance to a chair in contrast to the less-stable boat conformation.

chitin: A polymer of acetylated glucosamine present in the exoskeletons of shellfish.

chromatography: A separation technique based on the selective absorption of the components present.

codon: A trinucleotide with three different bases which provides the necessary information for protein synthesis.

collagen: A protein present in connective tissue.

compounding: The process of adding essential ingredients to a polymer such as rubber.

conjugated protein: The combination of a protein and a prosthetic group, such as a nucleic acid.

C-terminal amino acid: One with a carboxylic acid end group.

cytosine: A pyrimidine base present in nucleic acids.

degree of substitution (DS): A number that designates the average number of reacted hydroxyl groups in each anhydroglucose unit in cellulose or starch.

denaturation: The change of conformation of a protein resulting from heat or chemical reactants.

deoxyribonucleic acid (DNA): A nucleic acid in which deoxyribose units are present.

dextran: A high molecular weight branched polysaccharide synthesized from sucrose by bacteria.

dextrin: Degraded starch.

D-glucose: A hexose obtained by the hydrolysis of starch or cellulose.

dipeptide: A dimer formed by the condensation of two amino acids.

disaccharide: A dimer of D-glucose or other monosaccharide, such as cellobiose.

DNA: Deoxyribonucleic acid.

drying: Jargon used to describe the cross-linking of unsaturated polymers in the presence of air and a heavy metal catalyst (drier).

DS: Degree of substitution.

enzyme: A protein with specific catalytic activity.

equatorial bonds: Bonds that are essentially parallel to the plane of the hexose ring, such as those in β-D-glucose.

ester gum: The ester of rosin and glycerol.

fibrillar: Hairlike, an insoluble intermolecularly hydrogen-bonded protein.

fibrils: Naturally occurring threadlike strands or bundles of fibers.

fossil resins: Resins obtained from the exudate of prehistoric trees.

G: An abbreviation for guanine.

Galalith: Casein plastics.

γ cellulose: Cellulose and derivatives soluble in 8% caustic solution.

globular: Nonfibrous soluble proteins containing intramolecular hydrogen bonds.

glycine: The simplest and only nonchiral α-amino acid.

glycogen: A highly branched polysaccharide which serves as the reserve carbohydrate in animals.

guanine: A purine base present in nucleic acids.

guayule: A shrub containing rubber.

gutta percha: A naturally occurring plastic (trans-1,4-polyisoprene).

Hevea braziliensis: Natural rubber.

hexosans: Polysaccharides in which the repeating units are six-membered (pyranose) rings.

hormones: Organic compounds having specific biological effects.

humic acid: A polymeric aromatic carboxylic acid found in lignite.

hydrocellulose: Cellulose degraded (depolymerized) by hydrolysis.

isoelectric point: The pH at which an amino acid does not migrate to either the positive or the negative pole in a cell.

keratin: A fibrillar protein.

latex: A stable dispersion of polymer particles in water.

lignin: The noncellulosic resinous component of wood.

long-range elasticity: The theory of rubber elasticity.

macroradical: A high molecular weight free radical.

maltose: A disaccharide consisting of two D-glucose units joined by an α-acetal linkage. It is the repeating unit in the starch molecule.

mer: The repeating unit in a polymeric chain.

mercerized cotton: Cotton fiber that has been immersed in caustic solution, usually under tension, and washed with water to remove the excess caustic.

monosaccharide: A simple sugar, such as D-glucose, which cannot be hydrolyzed further.

myosin: A protein present in muscle.

native cellulose: Naturally occurring cellulose.

ninhydrin: A triketohydrindene hydrate which reacts with α-amino acids to produce characteristic blue to purple compounds.

NR: Symbol for natural rubber.

N-terminal amino acid: One with an amino end group.

nucleoside: The product obtained when phosphoric acid is hydrolyzed off a nucleotide.

nucleotide: A nucleic acid.

oligosaccharide: A relatively low molecular weight polysaccharide.

oxycellulose: Cellulose degraded (depolymerized) by oxidation.

paper chromatography: A technique used for separating amino acids in which paper serves as the stationary phase.

pentosans: Polysaccharides in which the repeating units are five-membered (furanose) rings.

peptide linkage: $-\overset{\overset{\displaystyle O}{\|}}{C}-\overset{\overset{\displaystyle H}{|}}{N}-$

polyglycuronic acids: Also known as uronic or glycuronic acids, naturally occurring polysaccharides in which the hydroxyl on carbon 6 has been oxidized to form a carboxylic acid group.

polypeptide: A protein; term often used for low molecular weight proteins.

polysaccharide: A polymer consisting of many hexose units, such as anhydroglucose.

primary structure: A term used to describe the primary configuration present in a protein chain.

prosthetic group: A nonproteinous group conjugated with a protein. Derived from the Greek prosthesic, an addition.

protein: A polyamide in which the building blocks are α-amino acids joined by peptide linkages.

purine base: Compounds consisting of two fused heterocyclic rings, namely, a pyrimidine and an imidazole ring.

pyrimidine: A 1,3-diazine.

racked rubber: Stretched rubber cooled below its T_g.

rayon: Cellulose regenerated by acidification of a cellulose xanthate (viscose) solution.

recent resins: Resins obtained from the exudate of living trees.

regenerated cellulose: Cellulose obtained by precipitation from solution.

retrogradation: An irreversible gel produced by the aging of aqueous solutions of amylose starch.

ribonucleic acid (RNA): A nucleic acid in which ribose units are present.

RNA: Ribonucleic acid: m-RNA, messenger RNA; r-RNA, ribosonal RNA; t-RNA, transfer RNA.

rosin: A naval stores product consisting primarily of abietic acid anhydride.

Schweitzer's solution: An ammoniacal solution of copper hydroxide.

secondary structure: A term used to describe the conformation of a protein molecule.

semifossil resins: Resins obtained from the exudate of dead trees.

shellac: A natural polymer obtained from the excreta of insects in Southeastern Asia.

soda cellulose: Cellulose that has been treated with a strong caustic solution.

starch: A linear or branched polysaccharide consisting of many anhydroglucose units joined by α-acetal linkages. Amylose starch is a linear polymer, while amylodextrin is a branched polymer.

T: Thymine.

tenacity: A term for the tensile strength of fibers.

terpene: A class of hydrocarbons having the empirical formula C_5H_8.

tertiary structure: The shape or folding of a protein resulting from sulfur-sulfur cross-links.

thymine: A pyrimidine base present in DNA.

U: Uracil.

uracil: A pyrimidine base present in RNA.

viscose: An alkaline solution of cellulose xanthate.

zwitterion: A dipolar ion of an amino acid

$$H_3N^+\!-\!\underset{\displaystyle H}{\overset{\displaystyle R}{\underset{|}{\overset{|}{C}}}}\!-\!COO^-$$

EXERCISES

1. Why is starch digestible by humans; why is cellulose not digestible by humans?
2. How does cellobiose differ from maltose?
3. Why is cellulose stronger than amylose?

4. How does the monosaccharide hydrolytic product of cellulose differ from that of starch?
5. Which has the higher molecular weight: (a) α, or (b) β cellulose?
6. How many hydroxyl groups are present on each anhydroglucose unit in cellulose?
7. Which would be more polar—tertiary or secondary cellulose acetate?
8. Why would you expect chitin to be soluble in hydrochloric acid?
9. Which is more apt to form a helix: (a) amylose or (b) amylopectin?
10. Why is pectin soluble in water?
11. Define a protein in polymer science language.
12. Which α-amino acid does not belong to the L series?
13. To which pole will an amino acid migrate at a pH above its isoelectric point?
14. Why is collagen stronger than albumin?
15. What are three requirements of a strong fiber?
16. Which protein would be more apt to be present in a helical conformation: (a) a linear polyamide with small pendant groups, or (b) a linear polyamide with bulky pendant groups?
17. What is the difference between the molecular weight of (a) ribose and (b) deoxyribose?
18. What is the repeating unit in the polymer chain of DNA?
19. Which is more acidic: (a) a nucleoside or (b) a nucleotide?
20. What base found in DNA is not present in RNA?
21. Why would you predict helical conformations for RNA and DNA?
22. If the sequence on one chain of a double helix is ATTACGTCAT, what is the sequence of the adjacent chain?
23. Why is it essential to have trinucleotides rather than dinucleotides as codons for directing protein synthesis?
24. How do the configurations differ for (a) gutta percha and (b) natural rubber?
25. What is the approximate Poisson's ratio of rubber?
26. Will the tensile force required to stretch rubber increase or decrease as the temperature is increased?
27. Does a stretched rubber band expand or contract when heated?

28. List three requirements for an elastomer.
29. Why is there an interest in the cultivation of guayule?
30. Are the polymerization processes for synthetic and natural cis-polyisoprene (a) similar or (b) different?
31. What does the production of levulinic aldehyde as the product of the ozonolysis of natural rubber tell you about the structure of NR?
32. Why doesn't cold racked rubber contract readily?
33. Why does a rubber band become opaque when stretched?
34. What is the most important contribution to retractile forces in highly elongated rubber?
35. What is present in a so-called unvulcanized rubber compound?
36. What happens to a free radical, such as (·SR), during the mastication of rubber?
37. Why aren't natural plastics used more?
38. What type of solvent would you choose for shellac?
39. What type of solvent would you choose for asphalt?
40. Which is a polymer: (a) rosin, or (b) ester gum?
41. If the annual production of paper is 100 million tons, how much lignin is discarded annually?
42. Is an article molded from Galalith valuable?

BIBLIOGRAPHY

Abraham, H. (1960-1963): Asphalts and Allied Substances, 6th ed., Van Nostrand, Princeton.

Alexander, S. H. (1975): The chemistry and technology of bituminous coatings, Chap. 45 in Applied Polymer Science (J. K. Craver and R. W. Tess, eds.), Organic Coatings and Plastics Chemistry Division of the American Chemical Society, Washington, D.C.

Allen, P. W. (1972): Natural Rubber and Synthetics, Halsted, New York.

American Society for Testing Materials (1974): Rubber and Related Products, Philadelphia.

Asimov, I. (1962): The Genetic Code, New American Library, New York.

Barron, H. (1947): Modern Rubber Chemistry, Chapman & Hall, London.

Brauns, F. E. (1952): The Chemistry of Lignin, Academic, New York.

Briston, J. H. (1974): Plastic Fibers, Halsted, New York.

Boker, H. (1974): Natural and Synthetic Polymers, Dekker, New York.

Carraher, C. E., Tsuda, M. (1980): Modification of Polymers, ACS Symposium Series, Washington, D.C.

Chargaff, E., Davidson, J. N. (1955, 1960): The Nucleic Acids, Vols. I-III, Academic, New York.

Cook, P. G. (1956): Latex: Natural and Synthetic, Chapman & Hall, London.

Cowan, J. C. (1975): Chemistry and technology of drying oils, Chap. 36 in Applied Polymer Science (J. K. Craver and R. W. Tess, eds.), Organic Coatings and Plastics Chemistry Division of the American Chemical Society, Washington, D.C.

Davidson, J. N. (1972): The Biochemistry of Nucleic Acids, Academic, New York.

Dickerson, R. E., Geir, O. O. (1969): The Structure and Action of Proteins, Academic, New York.

DuBois, J. H. (1972): Plastics History, U.S.A., Chap. 1, Cahners Books, Boston.

Dunn, A. S. (1975): Rubber and Rubber Elasticity, John Wiley, New York.

Dyke, S. F. (1960): The Carbohydrates, Interscience, New York.

Fisher, H. L. (1957): Chemistry of Natural and Synthetic Rubbers, Reinhold, New York.

Floyd, D. E., Wittcoff, H. (1975): Chemistry and technology of polyamide resins in coatings, Chap. 47 in Applied Polymer Science (J. K. Craver and R. W. Tess, eds.), Organic Coatings and Plastics Division of the American Chemical Society, Washington, D.C.

Fox, S., Foster, J. (1957): Protein Chemistry, John Wiley, New York.

Frazer, R. D. B., MacRae, T. P. (1974): Conformations in Fibrous Proteins, Academic, New York.

Goldstein, I. S. (1976): The place of cellulose under energy scarcity, Polymer Preprints, 17:234.

Goodman, M. (1976): Biopolymers—new frontier, Polymer Preprints, 17:235.

Guthrie, R. D., Honeyman, J. (1964): An Introduction to the Chemistry of Carbohydrates, Clarendon, Oxford.

Harborne, J. B., Van Sumers, C. F. (1975): The Chemistry and Biochemistry of Plant Proteins, Academic, New York.

Harper, C. A. (1975): Handbook of Plastics and Elastomers, McGraw-Hill, New York.

Heinish, K. F. (1974): Dictionary of Rubber, Halsted, New York.

Hicks, E. (1961): Shellac, Chemical Publishing Company, New York.

Hoiberg, A. J. (1964): Bituminous Material: Asphalts, Tar and Pitches, Wiley Interscience, New York.

Inch, E. W. (1974): Plastics and Rubber, Philosophical Library, New York.

Ingram, V. M. (1972): Biosynthesis of Macromolecules, Benjamin Publications, New York.

Jeu, Y., McSweeney, E. E. (1975): Chemistry and technology of tall oil and naval stores, Chap. 51 in Applied Polymer Science (J. K. Craver and R. W. Tess, eds.), Organic Coatings and Plastics Division of the American Chemical Society, Washington, D.C.

Katsoyannis, P. S. (1974): The Chemistry of Polypeptides, Plenum, New York.

LeBras, J. (1965): Introduction to Rubber, Hart, New York.

Mandelkern, L. (1972): An Introduction to Macromolecules, Chap. 4, Springer-Verlag, New York.

Mantell, C. L., Kopf, C. W., Curtis, J. L., Rogers, E. M. (1942): The Technology of Natural Resins, John Wiley, New York.

Mazzarelli, R. A. A. (1974): Natural Chelating Polymers, Pergamon, New York.

McCormick, C. (1979): Cellulose solution, J. Polymer Sci., Polymer Letters, 17:479.

Merrifield, R. B. (1975): Solid phase peptide synthesis, Polymer Preprints, 16:135.

Meyer, K. H. (1959): Natural and Synthetic High Polymers, 2d ed., Interscience, New York.

Morton, M. (1973): Rubber Technology, Van Nostrand-Reinhold, New York.

Ott, E., Spurlin, H. M., Grafflin, M. W. (1955): Cellulose and Cellulose Derivatives, Vol. 5, Interscience, New York.

Pearl, I. A. (1967): The Chemistry of Lignin, Dekker, New York.

Perutz, M. F. (1962): Proteins and Nucleic Acids, Elsevier, Amsterdam.

Pettit, G. R. (1975): Synthetic Peptides, Academic, New York.

Pigman, W. (1957): The Carbohydrates, Academic, New York.

Plastics and Rubber Institute (1976): Progress of Rubber Technology, London.

Raave, A. (1967): Organic Chemistry of Macromolecules, Chaps. 20, 21, Dekker, New York.

Rebenfield, L. (1975): Chemistry and technology of fibers, Chap. 40 in Applied Polymer Science (J. K. Craver and R. W. Tess, eds.), Organic Coatings and Plastics Division of the American Chemical Society, Washington, D.C.

Scheraga, A. A. (1961): Protein Structure, Academic, New York.

Sekhar, B. C. (1976): More latex from trees, Polymer Preprints, 17:233.

Seymour, R. B. (1972): Introduction to Polymer Chemistry, Chap. 4, McGraw-Hill, New York.

——. (1975): Modern Plastics Technology, Chap. 14, Reston, Reston, Virginia.

Seymour, R. B., Johnson, E. J. (1977): Solutions of cellulose in organic solvents, Chap. 19 in Structure-Solubility Relationships in Polymers (F. W. Harris and R. B. Seymour, eds.), Academic, New York.

——. (1978). Acetylation of cellulose solutions, J. Polymer Sci. Chem. Ed., 16:1.

Smith, F., Montgomery, R. (1959): The Chemistry of Plant Gums and Mucilages, Reinhold, New York.

Stevens, H. P., Stevens, W. H. (1940): Rubber Latex, Chemical Publishing, New York.

Stevens, M. P. (1975): Polymer Chemistry, an Introduction, Chap. 15, Addison-Wesley, Reading, Massachusetts.

Thames, S. F. (1977): Tung oil—Past, present and future, Coatings Plastics Preprints, 37:90.

Treloar, L. R. G. (1975): The Physics of Rubber Elasticity, Oxford University Press, New York.

Van Derveer, D., Lowe, K. E. (1975): Fiber Conservation and Utilization, Miller Freeman, San Francisco.

Vollmert, B. (1973): Polymer Chemistry, Chap. 3, Springer-Verlag, New York.

Walter, P., Meienhofer, J. (1976): Peptides, Ann Arbor Publishers, Ann Arbor, Michigan.

Wheelons, M. A. (1974): Injection Molding of Rubber, Halsted, New York.

Whistler, R. L., BeMiller, J. N. (1966): Industrial Gums, W. A. Benjamin, New York.

Whistler, R. L., Smart, C. L. (1953): Polysaccharide Chemistry, Academic, New York.

——. (1963): Methods in Carbohydrate Chemistry, Vol. 3, Academic, New York.

Winspear, G. C. (ed.) (1968): Rubber Handbook, R. T. Vanderbilt, New York.

Wrinch, D. (1965): Chemical Aspects of Polypeptide Chain Structures and the Cyclol Theory, Plenum, New York.

Yescumbe, E. R. (1976): Plastic and Rubber, Applied Science Publishers, Essex, England.

Zelinski, R. P. (1975): Chemistry and technology of rubber, Chap. 28 in Applied Polymer Science (J. K. Craver and R. W. Tess, eds.), Organic Coatings and Plastics Chemistry Division, American Chemical Society, Washington, D.C.

7

Step-Reaction Polymerization or Polycondensation Reactions

7.1 COMPARISON BETWEEN POLYMER TYPE AND KINETICS OF POLYMERIZATION

There is a large but not total overlap between the terms condensation polymers and stepwise kinetics and the terms addition (or sometimes the term vinyl) and chain kinetics. In this section we will describe briefly each of these four terms and illustrate their similarities and differences.

The terms addition and condensation polymers were first proposed by Carothers and are based on whether the repeating unit of the polymer contains the same atoms as the monomer. An addition polymer has the same atoms as the monomer in its repeating unit,

$$\mathrm{H_2C{=}CHX} \longrightarrow \left(\begin{array}{cc} \mathrm{H} & \mathrm{H} \\ | & | \\ \mathrm{C} - & \mathrm{C} \\ | & | \\ \mathrm{H} & \mathrm{X} \end{array} \right) \tag{7.1}$$

the atoms in the polymer backbone typically being only carbon. Condensation polymers contain fewer atoms within the polymer repeating unit than the reactants because of the formation of byproducts during the polymerization process, with the polymer backbone typically containing atoms of more than one element.

$$\mathrm{X{-}A{-}R{-}A{-}X + Y{-}B{-}R'{-}B{-}Y \longrightarrow \left(A{-}R{-}A{-}B{-}R'{-}B \right)} \tag{7.2}$$

where A—X can be

$$-\mathrm{NH_2},\quad -\mathrm{SH},\quad -\overset{\displaystyle \mathrm{O}}{\overset{\|}{\mathrm{C}}}-\mathrm{NH_2},\quad -\mathrm{OH},\quad -\mathrm{NOH}$$

where Y—B can be

$$-\underset{\underset{O}{\|}}{C}-OH, \quad -\underset{\underset{O}{\|}}{C}-Cl, \quad -\overset{\overset{O}{\|}}{\underset{\underset{R}{|}}{P}}-Cl, \quad -\overset{\overset{O}{\|}}{\underset{\underset{O}{\|}}{S}}-Cl$$

The corresponding polymerizations can then be called addition polymerizations and condensation polymerizations.

The term stepwise kinetics, or step-growth kinetics, refers to polymerizations in which polymer molecular weight increases in a slow, steplike manner as reaction time increases.

Polyesterification in a bulk polymerization process will be utilized to illustrate stepwise growth. Polymer formation begins with one dialcohol (diol) molecule reacting with one diacid molecule, forming what we will call one repeating unit of the eventual polyester.

$$HO-\overset{\overset{O}{\|}}{C}-R-\overset{\overset{O}{\|}}{C}-OH + HO-R'-OH \xrightarrow{-H_2O} HO-\overset{\overset{O}{\|}}{C}-R-\overset{\overset{O}{\|}}{C}-O-R'-OH \quad (7.3)$$

This alcohol-acid unit can now react with either an alcohol or acid giving a chain capped with either two active alcohol functional groups or two active acid groups.

$$HO\text{-}\overset{\overset{O}{\|}}{C}\text{-}R\text{-}\overset{\overset{O}{\|}}{C}\text{-}O\text{-}R'\text{-}OH + \begin{cases} HO\text{-}\overset{\overset{O}{\|}}{C}\text{-}R\text{-}\overset{\overset{O}{\|}}{C}\text{-}OH \xrightarrow{-H_2O} HO\text{-}\overset{\overset{O}{\|}}{C}\text{-}R\text{-}\overset{\overset{O}{\|}}{C}\text{-}O\text{-}R'\text{-}O\text{-}\overset{\overset{O}{\|}}{C}\text{-}R\text{-}\overset{\overset{O}{\|}}{C}\text{-}OH \\ HO\text{-}R'\text{-}OH \xrightarrow{-H_2O} HO\text{-}R'\text{-}O\text{-}\overset{\overset{O}{\|}}{C}\text{-}R\text{-}\overset{\overset{O}{\|}}{C}\text{-}O\text{-}R'\text{-}OH \end{cases} \quad (7.4)$$

The chain capped with the two alcohol groups can now condense with a molecule containing an acid group, while the molecule capped with two acid functional groups can react with a molecule containing an alcohol functional group. This continues through the monomer matrix wherever molecules of the correct unlike functionality having the necessary energy of activation and correct geometry collide. The net effect is that dimer, trimer, tetramer, and so on, molecules are formed

$$HO-R'-O-\overset{\overset{O}{\|}}{C}-R-\overset{\overset{O}{\|}}{C}-O-R'-OH + HO-\overset{\overset{O}{\|}}{C}-R-\overset{\overset{O}{\|}}{C}-OH \xrightarrow{-H_2O}$$
$$HO-R'-O-\overset{\overset{O}{\|}}{C}-R-\overset{\overset{O}{\|}}{C}-O-R'-O-\overset{\overset{O}{\|}}{C}-R-\overset{\overset{O}{\|}}{C}-OH \xrightarrow{etc.} \quad (7.5)$$

$$\mathrm{HO{-}\overset{O}{\overset{\|}{C}}{-}R{-}\overset{O}{\overset{\|}{C}}{-}O{-}R'{-}O{-}\overset{O}{\overset{\|}{C}}{-}R{-}\overset{O}{\overset{\|}{C}}{-}OH + HO{-}R'{-}OH \xrightarrow{-H_2O}}$$
$$\mathrm{HO{-}\overset{O}{\overset{\|}{C}}{-}R{-}\overset{O}{\overset{\|}{C}}{-}O{-}R'{-}O{-}\overset{O}{\overset{\|}{C}}{-}R{-}\overset{O}{\overset{\|}{C}}{-}O{-}R'{-}OH \xrightarrow{etc.}} \qquad (7.6)$$

and, along with the monomers, are consumed rapidly without any large chains being formed throughout the system until the reaction progresses toward total reaction of the chains with themselves. The molecular weight of the total system increases slowly in a stepwise manner. Considering A molecules to be diacid molecules and B to represent alcohol molecules (diols), we can construct a system containing ten each of A and B, and assuming a random number condensations of unlike functional groups, we can calculate changes in DP, maximum DP, and the percentage of unreacted monomer (Fig. 7.1). The maximum DP for this system is ten AB units. For this system, while the percentage of reacted monomer increases rapidly, both system $\overline{DP}$ and highest DP increases slowly. Figures 7.2 and 7.3 graphically show this stepwise growth as a function of both reaction time and reaction temperature T. It should be noted that the actual plot of molecular weight as a function of reaction time depends on the particular kinetic dependency for the particular system in question and need not be linear (Fig. 7.2).

Chain growth reactions require initiation to begin chain growth. Here let us consider that the initiation of styrene molecules in a bulk reaction system occurs by means of a free radical initiator R$^{\bullet}$. This free radical quickly adds to a styrene monomer, shifting the unpaired, free electron away from the adding free radical. This new active chain, containing an unpaired electron, again adds to another styrene monomer, again with the unpaired electron shifting toward the chain end. This continues again and again, eventually forming a long polystyrene chain,

$$\mathrm{R^{\cdot} + H_2C{=}CH(C_6H_5) \longrightarrow R{-}CH_2{-}CH^{\cdot}(C_6H_5)} \qquad \text{Initiation} \qquad (7.7)$$

$$\mathrm{R{-}CH_2{-}CH^{\cdot}(C_6H_5) + H_2C{=}CH(C_6H_5) \longrightarrow R{-}CH_2{-}CH(C_6H_5){-}CH_2{-}CH^{\cdot}(C_6H_5)} \qquad (7.8)$$

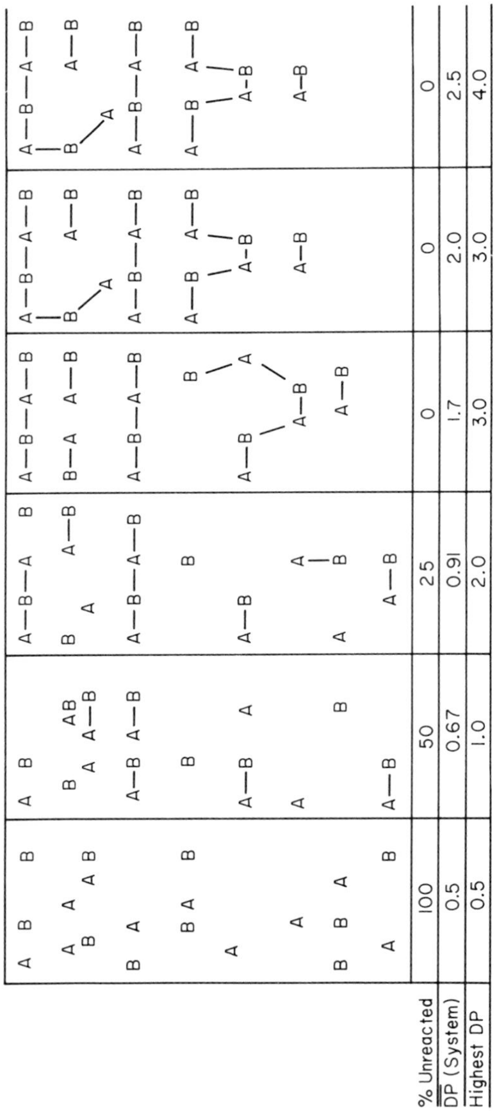

% Unreacted	100	50	25	0	0	0
$\overline{\overline{DP}}$ (System)	0.5	0.67	0.91	1.7	2.0	2.5
Highest DP	0.5	1.0	2.0	3.0	3.0	4.0

FIGURE 7.1 Chain length dependency on reaction time and extent of monomer reaction for a stepwise kinetic model.

$$\mathrm{R-CH_2-\underset{C_6H_5}{CH}-CH_2-\underset{C_6H_5}{CH^{\cdot}} + H_2C{=}\underset{C_6H_5}{CH} \rightarrow R-CH_2-\underset{C_6H_5}{CH}-CH_2-\underset{C_6H_5}{CH}-CH_2-\underset{C_6H_5}{CH^{\cdot}}} \tag{7.9}$$

$$\mathrm{R-CH_2-\underset{C_6H_5}{CH}-CH_2-\underset{C_6H_5}{CH}-CH_2-\underset{C_6H_5}{CH^{\cdot}} + H_2C{=}\underset{C_6H_5}{CH} \longrightarrow \longrightarrow \longrightarrow \longrightarrow \cdots} \tag{7.10}$$

$$\mathrm{R{-}\!\left[CH_2-\underset{C_6H_5}{CH}\right]\!{-}H}$$

Polystyrene

growth continuing until some termination reaction renders the chain inactive. Since polymerization occurs only with active chains (i.e., chains containing an unpaired electron), and since the concentration of growing chains is maintained at a quite low concentration at any given time, long chains are formed rapidly, although most of the bulk of the styrene system remains unreacted. Again we can construct a system illustrating the dependency of chain length on reaction extent and reaction time. Let us consider a system containing 20 styrene molecules (since styrene can react with itself the

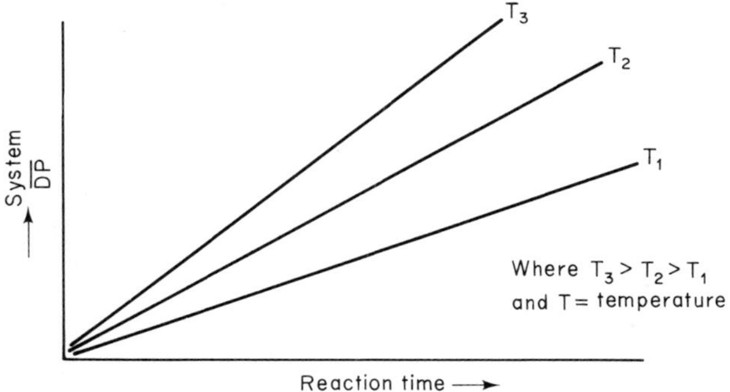

FIGURE 7.2 System molecular weight for stepwise kinetics as a function of reaction time and reaction temperature.

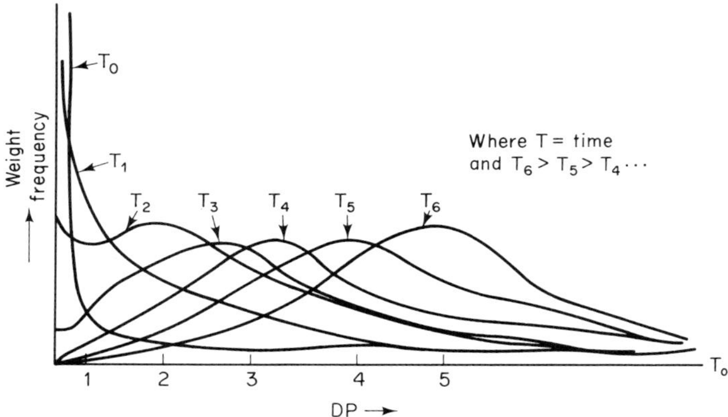

FIGURE 7.3 Molecular weight distribution for stepwise kinetics as a function of extent of reaction.

system can be constructed with like molecules). For easier comparison with Fig. 7.4 we will define for this case only that each repeating unit requires two styrene (AA) units. While the $\overline{DP}$ for the entire system does not increase at a markedly different rate than for the stepwise kinetic model, the DP for the longest chain increases rapidly. Further, the percentage of unreacted monomers remains high throughout the system, and in actual bulk and solution polymerizations of styrene the percentage of unreacted styrene monomers typically far outnumber the number of polymer chains. For chain-growth polymerizations it is usual to plot molecular weight of only material that had become a free radical as a function of reaction time, giving plots such as those in Figs. 7.5 and 7.6. Both average chain length and molecular weight distribution remain approximately constant throughout much of the polymerization.

Most addition polymers are formed from polymerizations exhibiting chain-growth kinetics. This includes the typical polymerizations of the vast majority of vinyl monomers such as ethylene, styrene, vinyl chloride, propylene, methyl acrylate, and vinyl acetate. Further, most condensation polymers are formed from systems exhibiting stepwise kinetics. Industrially this includes the formation of polyesters and polyamides. Thus, there is a large overlap between the terms addition polymers and chain-growth kinetics and the terms condensation polymers and stepwise kinetics. The following are examples illustrating the lack of adherence to the above.

1. The formation of polyurethanes and polyureas typically occurs in the bulk solution through kinetics that are clearly stepwise, and the polymer backbone is heteroatomed, yet there is no byproduct released through the condensation of the isocyanate with the diol or diamine because condensation

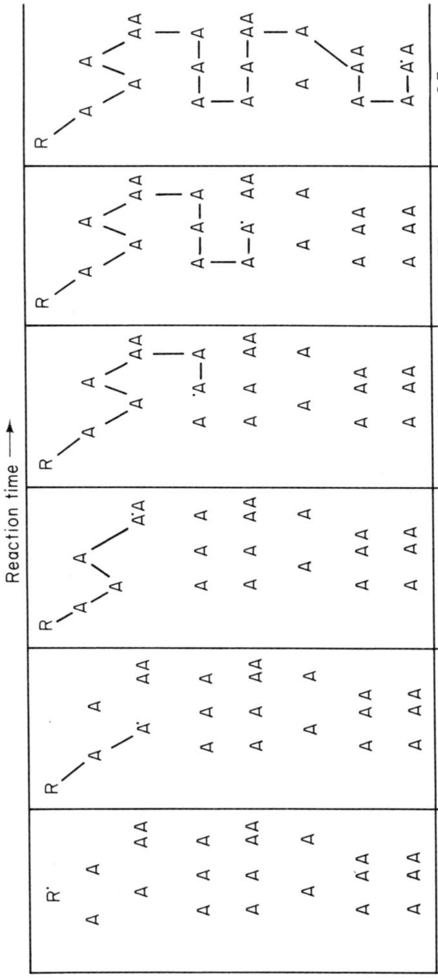

Reaction time ⟶

% Unreacted	100	90	80	70	55	25
$\overline{DP}$ (System)	0.5	0.53	0.59	0.67	0.83	1.7
Highest DP	0.5	1.0	2.0	3.0	4.5	7.5

FIGURE 7.4 Molecular weight for chain-growth kinetics as a function of reaction time and extent of reaction.

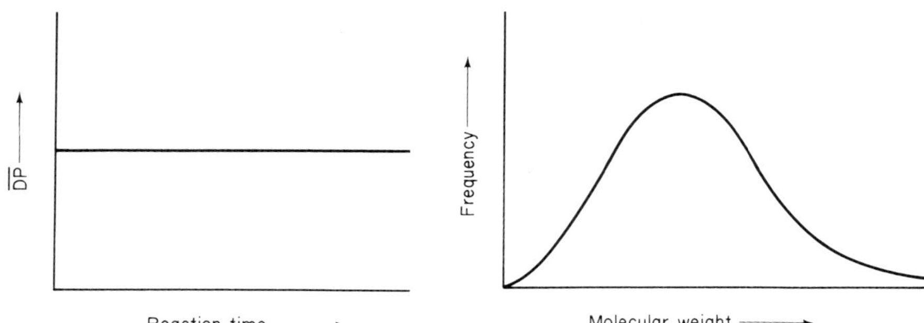

FIGURE 7.5 Idealized molecular weight of reacted polymers as a function of reaction time for chain-growth kinetics.

FIGURE 7.6 Molecular weight distribution for chain-growth kinetics.

occurs through internal rearrangement and shift of the hydrogen—neither necessitating expulsion of a byproduct.

$$OCN\text{-}(CH_2)_6\text{-}NCO + HO\text{-}(CH_2)_5\text{-}OH \longrightarrow$$

$$\left(\overset{O}{\overset{\|}{C}}-\overset{H}{\overset{|}{N}}-(CH_2)_6-\overset{H}{\overset{|}{N}}-\overset{O}{\overset{\|}{C}}-O-(CH_2)_5-O \right) \tag{7.11}$$

$$OCN\text{-}(CH_2)_6\text{-}NCO + H_2N\text{-}(CH_2)_5\text{-}NH_2 \longrightarrow$$

$$\left(\overset{O}{\overset{\|}{C}}-\overset{H}{\overset{|}{N}}-(CH_2)_6-\overset{H}{\overset{|}{N}}-\overset{O}{\overset{\|}{C}}-\overset{H}{\overset{|}{N}}-(CH_2)_5-\overset{H}{\overset{|}{N}} \right) \tag{7.12}$$

2. The Diels-Alder condensation of a bisdiene and benzoquinone clearly forms an addition polymer, one possessing only carbon atoms in its backbone and where no byproduct is given up, yet the polymer is formed through a stepwise kinetic process.

$$\text{(bisdiene)}-(CH_2)_6-\text{(bisdiene)} + \text{(benzoquinone)} \longrightarrow \left[-(CH_2)_6- \cdots \overset{O}{\|} \cdots \underset{O}{\|} \cdots \right] \tag{7.13}$$

3. Internal esters (lactones) are readily polymerized by chainwise, acid-catalyzed ring openings without explusion of a byproduct, yet the resulting polyester is clearly a condensation polymer exhibiting a heteroatomed polymeric backbone. Further, the 6-carbon polyester is also formed using typical stepwise polycondensation of ω-hydroxycarboxylic acid.

$$\text{(caprolactone)} \xrightarrow{H^+} -\!\!\left[\overset{O}{\overset{\|}{C}} \!-\!(CH_2)_5\!-\!O \right]\!\!- \quad \text{and} \quad HO\!-\!(CH_2)_5\!-\!CO_2H \xrightarrow{\Delta} \tag{7.14}$$

$$-\!\!\left[\overset{O}{\overset{\|}{C}} \!-\!(CH_2)_5\!-\!O \right]\!\!- +$$

4. Nylon-6, clearly a condensation polymer, is readily formed from either the internal amide (lactam) through a chainwise kinetic polymerization, or from the stepwise reaction of the ω-amino acid.

$$\text{(caprolactam)} \xrightarrow{H^+} -\!\!\left[\overset{O}{\overset{\|}{C}} \!-\!(CH_2)_5\!-\!\overset{H}{\overset{|}{N}} \right]\!\!- \tag{7.15}$$

and

$$H_2N(CH_2)_5CO_2H \xrightarrow{\Delta} -\!\!\left[\overset{O}{\overset{\|}{C}} \!-\!(CH_2)_5\!-\!\overset{H}{\overset{|}{N}} \right]\!\!- + H_2O \tag{7.16}$$

5. A wholly hydrocarbon polymer can be made using the typical chainwise polymerization of polyethylene, through a chainlike polymerization of 1,8-dibromooctane utilizing the Wurtz reaction, or through the chain-growth boron trifluoride-catalyzed polymerization of diazomethane.

$$CH_2{=}CH_2 \longrightarrow -(CH_2-CH_2)- \tag{7.17}$$

$$BrH_2C(CH_2)_6CH_2Br \xrightarrow{2Na} -(CH_2)- + 2NaBr \tag{7.18}$$

$$CH_2N_2 \xrightarrow{BF_3} -(CH_2)- + N_2 \tag{7.19}$$

6. Polyethylene oxide can be formed from either the usual catalyzed chainwise polymerization of ethylene oxide or the less usual condensation by means of a stepwise process of ethylene glycol.

$$\text{H}_2\text{C}\overset{\text{O}}{—}\text{CH}_2 \xrightarrow{H^+} \left(\!-CH_2-CH_2-O-\right)\!- \quad (7.20)$$

$$\underset{\text{OH}}{\text{CH}_2}-\underset{\text{OH}}{\text{CH}_2} \longrightarrow \left(\!-CH_2-CH_2-O-\right)\!- + H_2O \quad (7.21)$$

7. Further interfacially formed typical condensation polymers, such as polyurethanes, polyesters, polyamides, and polyureas, typically are formed on a microscopic level in a chain-growth manner due to comonomer migration limits and the highly reactive nature of the reactants employed for such interfacial polycondensations.

Thus, a number of examples clearly illustrate the lack of total overlap associated with describing the nature of the polymer backbone and the kinetics of formation for that polymer.

7.2 INTRODUCTION

While condensation polymers account for only a small percentage of all synthetic polymers, most natural polymers are of the condensation form. The first all-synthetic polymer, Bakelite, was produced by the stepwise condensation of phenol and formaldehyde, and many of the other synthetic polymers available before World War II were produced using stepwise polycondensations of appropriate reactants.

As shown by Carothers in the 1930s, the chemistry of condensation polymerizations is essentially the same as classic condensation reactions resulting in the formation of monomeric esters, amides, and so on, the principle difference being that the reactants used for polymer formation are bifunctional instead of monofunctional.

The similarity between the kinetics explaining stepwise polycondensation reactions and the kinetics explaining monofunctional aminations and esterifications, for example, is evident. Experimentally, both kinetic approaches are found to be essentially identical. Usual activation energies (30 to 60 kcal/mol) call for only about one collision in 10^{12} to 10^{15} to be effective in producing product at 100°C, whereas for the vinyl reactions between R° and a vinyl-monomer, activation energies are small (2 to 5 kcal/mol), with most collisions of proper orientation being effective in lengthening the chain. This is in agreement with the slowness of stepwise processes compared with radical chain processes. The rate constant of individual polycondensation steps is essentially independent of chain length, being similar to that of the "small-molecule" condensation. This is responsible for the stepwise growth pattern of such polycondensations, since addition of a unit does not greatly increase the reactivity of the now-growing end, whereas for radical and ionic vinyl polymerizations the active radical or ionic site is transmitted to the growing chain end, giving an end which is quite reactive. Table 7.1 contains a listing of a number of industrially important condensation polymers.

7.3 STEPWISE KINETICS

While more complicated situations can occur, we will consider only the kinetics of simple polyesterification. The kinetics of most other common condensations follow an analogous pathway.

For uncatalyzed reactions where the diacid and diol are present in equimolar amounts, one diacid is experimentally found to act as a catalyst. The experimental rate expression dependencies are described in the usual manner as follows:

$$\text{Rate of polycondensation} = -\frac{d[A]}{dt} = k[A]^2[D] \tag{7.22}$$

where [A] represents the diacid concentration and [D] the diol concentration.

Where [A] = [D] we can write

$$-\frac{d[A]}{dt} = k[A]^3 \tag{7.23}$$

Rearrangement gives

$$-\frac{d[A]}{[A]^3} = kdt \tag{7.24}$$

Integration of the above over the limits of $A = A_0$ to $A = A_t$ and $t = t_0$ to $t = t$ gives

$$2kt = \frac{1}{[A_t]^2} - \frac{1}{[A_0]^2} = \frac{1}{[A_t]^2} + \text{constant} \tag{7.25}$$

It is convenient to express (7.25) in terms of extent of reaction p, where p is defined as the fraction of functional groups that have reacted at time t. Thus 1 - p is the fraction of groups unreacted. A_t is in turn $A_0 \cdot (1 - p)$, i.e.,

$$A_t = A_0(1 - p) \tag{7.26}$$

TABLE 7.1 Structures, Properties, and Uses of Some Synthetic Condensation-Type Polymers

Type (common name)	Characteristic repeating unit	Typical reactants	Typical properties	Typical uses
Polyamide (nylon)	$\left[\overset{H}{\overset{\vert}{N}}-\overset{O}{\overset{\Vert}{C}}-R-\overset{O}{\overset{\Vert}{C}}-\overset{H}{\overset{\vert}{N}}-R \right]$	$H_2-N-R-\overset{O}{\overset{\Vert}{C}}-OH$ $H_2NRNH_2 + HO-\overset{O}{\overset{\Vert}{C}}-R-\overset{O}{\overset{\Vert}{C}}-OH$ $H_2NRNH_2 + Cl-\overset{O}{\overset{\Vert}{C}}-R-\overset{O}{\overset{\Vert}{C}}-Cl$ $(CH_2)_x$ ring closed by $C{=}O$ and $N-H$ *	Good balance of properties, high strength, good elasticity and abrasion resistance, good toughness, favorable solvent resistance, only fair outdoor weathering properties, fair moisture resistance	Fibers—about 1/2 of all nylon fiber produced goes into tire cord (tire replacement); rope, cord, belting and fiber cloths, thread, hose, undergarments, dresses; plastics—use as an engineering material, substitute for metal in bearings, cams, gears rollers; jackets on electrical wire
Polyurethane	$\left[\overset{H}{\overset{\vert}{N}}-\overset{O}{\overset{\Vert}{C}}-O-R-O-\overset{O}{\overset{\Vert}{C}}-\overset{H}{\overset{\vert}{N}}-R \right]$	$OCN-R-NCO + HO-R-OH$	Elastomers—good abrasion resistance, hardness, good resistance to grease and good elasticity; fibers—high elasticity, excellent rebound; coatings—good resistance to solvent attack and abrasion, good flexibility and impact resistance; foams—good strength per weight, good rebound, high impact strength	Four major forms utilized—fibers, elastomers, coatings cross-linked foams; elastomers—small industrial wheels, heel lifts; fibers—swimsuits and foundation garments; coatings—floors where high impact and abrasion resistance are required, such as dance floors; bowling pins; foams—pillows, cushions

Polyurea	$+NH-C(=O)-NH-R-NH-C(=O)-NH-R+$	$OCN-R-NCO + H_2N-R-NH_2$	High T_g, fair resistance to greases, oils, solvents	Not widely utilized
Polyester	$+O-C(=O)-R-C(=O)-O-R+$	$HO-R-OH + Cl-C(=O)-R-C(=O)-Cl$ $HO-R-OH + HO-C(=O)-R-C(=O)-OH$ $HO-R-C(=O)-OH$ **	High T_g, high T_m, good mechanical properties to about 175°C, good resistance to solvent and chemicals; fibers—good crease resistance and rebound, low moisture absorption, high modulus, good resistance to abrasion; film—high tensile strength (almost equal to that of some steel), stiff, high resistance to failure on repeated flexing, fair tear strength, high impact strength	Fibers—garments, permanent press and "wash and wear" garments, felts, tire cord; film—magnetic recording tape, high grade films
Polyether	$+O-R+$	$+CH_2+_x$ O (cyclic ether)	Good thermoplastic behavior, water solubility, generally good mechanical properties, moderate strength and stiffness (similar to polyethylene)	Sizing for cotton and synthetic fibers; stabilizers for adhesives, binders, and film-formers in pharmaceuticals; thickeners; production of films

* repeat unit $+C(=O)+CH_2+_{x}NH+$

** repeat unit $+O-R-C(=O)+$

(continued)

TABLE 7.1 (continued)

Type (common name)	Characteristic repeating unit	Typical reactants	Typical properties	Typical uses
Polycarbonate	$+O-R-O-\overset{O}{\overset{\|}{C}}+$	$COCl_2 + HO-R-OH$ 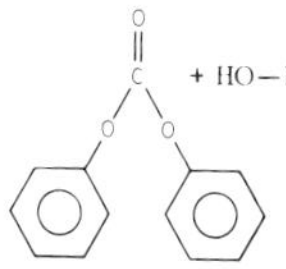 $+ HO-R-OH$	Crystalline thermoplastic with good mechanical properties, high impact strength, good thermal and oxidative stability, transparent, self-extinguishing, low moisture absorption	Machinery and business
Phenol-formaldehyde resins	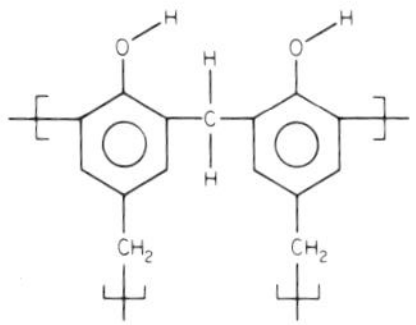	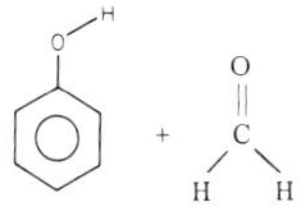	Good heat resistance, dimensional stability and resistance to cold flow; good resistance to most solvents; good dielectric properties	Used in molding applications; phonograph records; electrical, radio, televisions, appliance, and automotive parts where their good dielectric properties are of use; filler; missile nose cones; impregnating paper; varnishes; decorative laminates for wall coverings; electrical parts, such as printed circuits; countertops, toilet seats; coatings for electrical wire; adhesive for plywood, sandpaper, brake linings and abrasive wheels

Polyacetal	$+\!O-R-O-CH_2\!+$	$HO-R-OH + (RO)_2CH_2$	Intermediate physical properties	No large industrial application
Polyanhydride	$+\!\overset{O}{\overset{\Vert}{C}}-O-\overset{O}{\overset{\Vert}{C}}-R\!+$	$HO-\overset{O}{\overset{\Vert}{C}}-R-\overset{O}{\overset{\Vert}{C}}-OH$	Medium to poor T_g and T_m, medium physical properties	No large industrial application
Polysulfides	$+\!S_x-R\!+$ $+\!\overset{S}{\overset{\Vert}{S}}-\overset{S}{\overset{\Vert}{S}}-R\!+$ $+\!S-S-R\!+$	$Cl-R-Cl + Na_2S_x$ $Cl-R-Cl + Na_2S_4$ $Cl-R-Cl$ (oxidation)	Outstanding oil and solvent resistance, good gas impermeability, good resistance to aging and ozone, bad odors, low tensile strength, poor heat resistance	Solvent resistant and gas resistant elastomer—such as gasoline hoses and tanks, gaskets, diaphragms
Polysiloxane	$+\!\underset{R}{\overset{R}{Si}}-O\!+$	$Cl-\underset{R}{\overset{R}{Si}}-Cl + H_2O \rightarrow HO-\underset{R}{\overset{R}{Si}}-OH \rightarrow$ polymer	Available in a wide range of physical states—from liquids to greases, to waxes to to resins to rubbers; excellent high and moderate low temperature physical properties; resistant to weathering and lubricating oils	Fluids—cooling and dielectric fluids, in waxes and polishes, as antifoam and release agents, for paper and textile treatment; elastomers—gaskets, seals, cable and wire insulation, hot liquids and gas conduits, surgical and prosthetic devices, sealing compounds; resins—varnishes, industrial paints, encapsulating and impregnating agents
Polyphosphate and polyphosphonate esters	$+\!\underset{R}{\overset{O}{\overset{\Vert}{P}}}-O-R-O\!+$	$Cl-\underset{R}{\overset{O}{\overset{\Vert}{P}}}-Cl + HO-R-OH$	Good fire resistance, fair adhesion, moderate moisture stability, fair temperature stability	Additive to promote flame retardance, adhesive for glass (since refractive index of some esters is about the same as that of glass), certain pharmaceutical applications, surfactant

Substitution of the expression for A_t from (7.26) into (7.25) and rearrangement gives

$$2A_0^2 kt = \frac{1}{(1 - p)^2} + \text{constant} \tag{7.27}$$

A plot of $1/(1 - p)^2$ as a function of time should then be linear with the slope $2A_0$ k from which k is determinable. Determination of k at different temperatures enables the calculation of activation energy.

The number-average degree of polymerization $\overline{DP}_N$ can be expressed as

$$\overline{DP}_N = \frac{\text{number of original molecules}}{\text{number of molecules at a specific time t}} = \frac{N_0}{N} = \frac{A_0}{A_t} \tag{7.28}$$

Thus,

$$\overline{DP}_N = \frac{A_0}{A_t} = \frac{A_0}{A_0(1 - p)} = \frac{1}{1 - p} \tag{7.29}$$

The relationship given in (7.29) is called the Carothers equation because it was first found by Carothers while working with the synthesis of nylons—polyamides. For an essentially quantitative synthesis of polyamides where p is 0.9999, the $\overline{DP}$ was found to be approximately equal to 10,000, the value calculated using (7.29).

$$DP = \frac{1}{1 - p} = \frac{1}{1 - 0.9999} = \frac{1}{0.0001} = 10,000 \tag{7.30}$$

$$nH_2N\!\left(CH_2\right)_6NH_2 + nClC(=O)\!\left(CH_2\right)_8C(=O)Cl \xrightarrow{OH^-}$$

Hexamethylene-diamine   Sebacyl chloride

$$\left[\!-N(H)\!\left(CH_2\right)_6N(H)C(=O)\!\left(CH_2\right)_8C(=O)-\right]_n + nHCl \tag{7.31}$$

Nylon-610   Hydrogen chloride

The $\overline{DP}$ of 10,000 calculated above for nylon-610 is more than adequate for a strong fiber. Actually, it would be difficult to force such a high molecular weight polymer through the small holes in the spinneret in the melt extrusion process used for fiber production.

The many possible nylons are coded to show the number of carbon atoms in the amine and acid repeating units, respectively. The most widely used nylon fiber is nylon-66.

The high value of p would be decreased and the value of $\overline{DP}$ also decreased accordingly if a competing cyclization reaction occurred.

Since the values of k at any temperature may be determined from the slope (kA_0) of the line when $1/(1 - p)^2$ is plotted against t, one may determine $\overline{DP}_N$ at any time t from the expression

$$(\overline{DP}_N)^2 = 2kt[A_0]^2 + \text{constant} \tag{7.32}$$

Returning again to consider the synthesis of polyesters, generally much longer reaction times are required to effect formation of high polymer in uncatalyzed esterifications than for acid- or base-catalyzed systems. Since the added acid or base is a catalyst, its apparent concentration does not change with time, thus it need not be included in the kinetic rate expression. In such cases the reaction follows the rate expression

$$\text{Rate of polycondensation} = -\frac{d[A]}{dt} = k[A][B] \tag{7.33}$$

For [A] = [B] we have

$$-\frac{d[A]}{dt} = k[A]^2 \tag{7.34}$$

which gives on integration and subsequent substitution

$$kt = \frac{1}{A_t} + \text{constant} = \frac{1}{A_0(1 - p)} + \text{constant} \tag{7.35}$$

Rearrangement gives

$$A_0 kt = \frac{1}{1 - p} + \text{constant} \tag{7.36}$$

which predicts a linear relationship of $1/(1 - p)$ with reaction time. This is shown in Fig. 7.7.

For such second-order reactions, $\overline{DP}_N = [A_0]kt + 1$. The effect of time on $\overline{DP}$ can be demonstrated using $A_0 = 2$ mol/liter and $k = 10^{-2}$ liter/mol-sec at the reaction times of 1800, 3600, and 5400 sec. Thus, $\overline{DP}$ increases from 37 to 73 to 109.

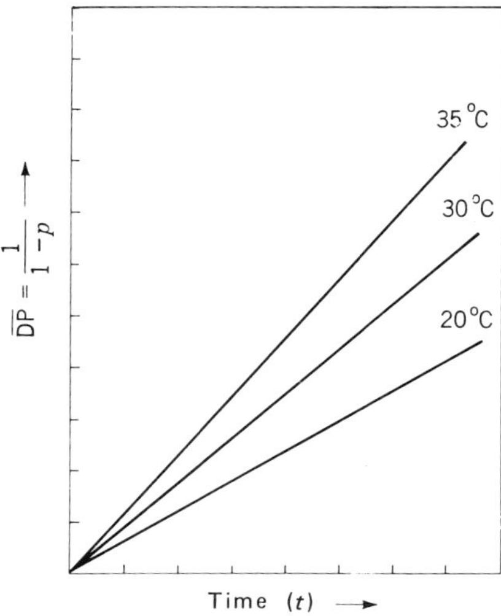

FIGURE 7.7 Plot of chain length as a function of reaction time for the acid catalyzed condensation of ethylene glycol with terephthalic acid. (From Introduction to Polymer Chemistry by R. Seymour, McGraw-Hill, New York, 1971. Used with permission of McGraw-Hill Book Company.)

$$\overline{DP} = 1 + (10^{-2})\ (2)\ (1800) = 37$$
$$\overline{DP} = 1 + (10^{-2})\ (2)\ (3600) = 73 \qquad (7.37)$$
$$\overline{DP} = 1 + (10^{-2})\ (2)\ (5400) = 109$$

Useful high molecular weight linear polymers are not obtained unless the value for the fractional conversion p is at least 0.990, i.e., a $\overline{DP}$ greater than 100.

It is important to note that the rate constant k for reactions of monofunctional compounds is essentially the same as that for difunctional compounds and hence these k values, which are essentially unchanged during the reaction, can be used for polycondensation reactions. Likewise, as is the case with reactions of small molecules, the rate constant k increases with temperature in accordance with the Arrhenius equation shown below. The energies of activation (E_a) are also comparable to those for monofunctional reactants.

$$K = Ae^{-E_a/RT} \qquad (7.38)$$

7.4 GENERAL STEP-REACTION POLYMERIZATION

From equations such as (7.36) it is possible to derive expressions describing the molecular weight distribution of such a stepwise polymerization at any extent of polymerization. The same relationship is more easily derived from statistical considerations. The following statistical treatment assumes the reaction rate to be independent of chain length.

One may write a general equation for the formation of a linear polymer by the step reaction of bifunctional reactants A and B as follows:

$$nA + nB \longrightarrow A(BA)_{n-1}B \tag{7.39}$$

The probability of finding a repeating unit AB in the polymer is p, and the probability of finding n - 1 of these repeating units in the polymer chain is p^{n-1}. Likewise, the probability of finding an unreacted molecule of A or B is 1 - p. Thus, the probability (p_n) of finding a chain with n repeating units $(BA)_n$ is

$$p_n = (1 - p)p^{n-1} \tag{7.40}$$

Hence, the probability of the total number of repeating units $(BA)_n$, where N is equal to the total number of molecules, is

$$N_n = N(1 - p)p^{n-1} \tag{7.41}$$

Since

$$\frac{N_0}{N} = \frac{1}{1 - p} \qquad N = N_0(1 - p) \tag{7.42}$$

Therefore,

$$N_n = N_0(1 - p)^2 p^{n-1} \tag{7.43}$$

The corresponding weight-average molecular weight distribution W_n may be calculated from the relationship $W_n = nN_n/N_0$ as follows:

$$W_n = \frac{nN_0(1 - p)^2 p^{n-1}}{N_0} = n(1 - p)^2 p^{n-1} \tag{7.44}$$

The relationships shown in (7.41) and (7.42) demonstrate that high values of $p(>0.99)$ are essential in order to produce either high N_n or high W_n values. The number-average molecular weight M_n and weight-average molecular weight M_w calculated from (7.41) and (7.42) are as follows:

$$M_n = \frac{N_n(mN_n)}{N} = \frac{m}{1 - p} \tag{7.45}$$

where m = the molecular weight of the mer and

$$M_w = \frac{m(1 + p)}{1 - p} \tag{7.46}$$

Thus, the index of polydispersity M_w/M_n for the most probable molecular weight distribution becomes $1 + p$, as shown below:

$$\frac{M_w}{M_n} = \frac{m(1 + p)/(1 - p)}{m/(1 - p)} = 1 + p \tag{7.47}$$

Thus, when p is equal to 1 the index of polydispersibility for the most probable distribution for step-reaction polymers is 2.

Because the value of p is essentially 1 in some step-reaction polymerizations, the products obtained under normal conditions have very high molecular weights and are difficult to process. It is obvious that the value of p may be reduced by using a slight excess of one of the reactants or by quenching the reaction before completion. Thus, if a reaction is quenched when the fractional conversion p is 0.995, $\overline{DP}$ will be equal to 200.

If more than 1 mol of B is used with 1 mol of A, the ratio of A/B, or r, may be substituted in the modified Carothers equation as shown below:

$$\overline{DP} = \frac{\text{total nA at p}}{\text{total nA at rp}} = \frac{n[1 + (1 + 1/r)]/2}{n[1 - p + (1 - rp/r)]/2} = \frac{1 + (1/r)}{1 - p + [(1 - rp)/r]} \tag{7.48}$$

Therefore,

$$\overline{DP} = \frac{r}{r} \; \frac{r + 1}{r(1 - p) + (1 - rp)} = \frac{1 + r}{(1 + r) - 2rp} \tag{7.49}$$

Thus, if $r = 0.97$ and $p \simeq 1$, $\overline{DP}$ is equal to

$$DP = \frac{1 + r}{(1 + r) - 2rp} = \frac{1 + 0.97}{1 + 0.97 - 2(0.97)} = \frac{1.97}{0.03} = 66 \tag{7.50}$$

The $\overline{DP}$ value of 66 is above the threshold limit of 50 required for polyamide fibers.

Since quenching the reaction or adding a stoichiometrical excess of one reactant is not economical, the commercial practice is to add a calculated amount of a monofunctional reactant. Acetic acid is used as the monofunctional reactant in the synthesis of polyamides and polyesters. In this case, one may employ a functionality factor (f) which is equal to the average number of functional groups present per reactive molecule. While the value of f in the preceding examples has been 2.0, it may be reduced to lower values and used in the following modified Carothers equation:

$$DP = \frac{A_0}{A_0[1 - (pf/2)]} = \frac{2}{2 - pf} \tag{7.51}$$

Thus, if 1 mol% of A is used with equimolar quantities of A, f = 2(0.99) + 0.01 = 1.99. If we substitute this value of f in (7.51), we obtain a $\overline{DP}$ of 200 when $p \simeq 1$.

7.5 POLYESTERS

In his first experiments, after he joined the duPont Company, Carothers attempted to produce fibers from aliphatic polyesters. He condensed adipic acid with ethylene glycol, but since the fractional conversion (p) was less than 0.95, the $\overline{DP}$ of these polyesters was less than 20. He could have solved the problem by use of the Schotten-Baumann reaction or by ester interchange, but he shelved this work in favor of the thermal decomposition of purified ammonium salts in which the fractional conversation (p) was essentially 1.0 (this subject is continued in Sec. 7.6).

Useful commercial polyesters, called glyptals and alkyds, had been prepared before Carothers conducted his investigations. These processes, like other esterifications, had low fractional conversions, but they were useful as coatings (not fibers) because of high $\overline{DP}$ values resulting from cross linking.

When the functionality in (7.51) is greater than 2, cross linking occurs. Thus, in spite of some unavoidable "wasted loop reactions," it is possible to have gelation occur when the fractional conversation values are low.

For example, if p = 0.95, $\overline{DP}$ is equal to 400 when 1 mol of phthalic anhydride is condensed with 0.9 mol of ethylene glycol and 0.1 mol of glycerol. In this case f = 0.9(2) + 0.3 = 2.1. If the hydric compounds consisted of 0.8 mol of ethylene glycol and 0.2 mol of glycerol, f = 2.2 and the calculated $\overline{DP}$ is infinity. Hence, if the formation of wasted loops is not great, a cross-linked gel would be obtained.

In the statistical approach to the requirements for incipient gelation, one introduces a branching coefficient α which is defined as the probability that a reactant with a value for f of greater than 2.0 is connected to a linear chain segment or to another multifunctional reactant or branch point. The critical value for incipient gelation (α_c) is the probability that more than one of the f - 1 chain segments on the branch unit will be connected to another branch unit, i.e., $\alpha_c = (f - 1)^{-1}$ or $1/(f - 1)$. Thus, when f = 2.2, $\alpha_c = 0.83$.

Glyptal polyesters were produced by heating glycerol and phthalic anhydride in 1901. Since the secondary hydroxyl is less active than the terminal primary hydroxyls in glycerol, the first product formed at conversions of less than 70% is a linear polymer. As shown in the following equation, a crosslinked coating is produced by further heating.

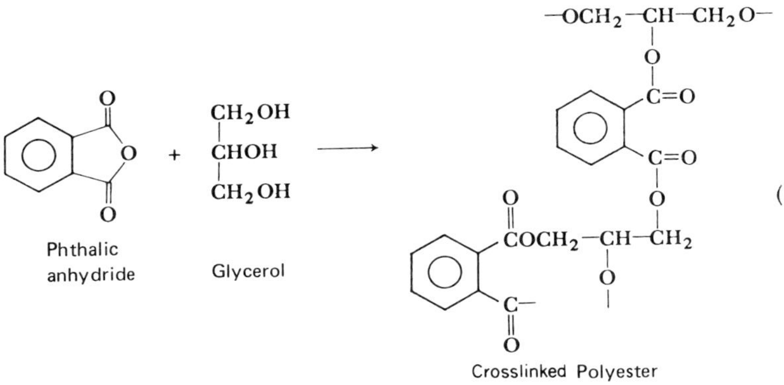

Phthalic anhydride + CH_2OH–CHOH–CH_2OH (Glycerol) $\longrightarrow$ Crosslinked Polyester (7.52)

Alkyds were synthesized by Kienle in the 1920s from trifunctional alcohols and dicarboxylic acids. Unsaturated oils called drying oils were transesterified with the phthalic anhydride in the reaction so that an unsaturated polyester was obtained.

The extent of cross linking or "drying" of these alkyds in the presence of a soluble lead or cobalt catalyst or drier was dependent on the amount of unsaturated oil present. The terms short oil, medium oil, and long oil alkyd are used to signify the "oil length" obtained by use of 30 to 50%, 50 to 65%, and 65 to 80% of unsaturated oil, respectively.

The term alkyd is sometimes used to describe all polyesters produced from the condensation of a polybasic acid and a polyhydric alcohol. Thus, the terms nonoil and oil-free alkyds have been used to distinguish between the principal types of polyesters. The terms saturated and unsaturated polyesters are also widely used. The chain reaction mechanism of the curing of these unsaturated polymers will be discussed in Chap. 8.

Another type of unsaturated polyester is produced by the condensation of ethylene glycol with phthalic anhydride and maleic anhydride. These polyesters may be dissolved in styrene and used as cross-linking resins for the production of fibrous glass-reinforced plastics.

$$\underset{\text{Maleic anhydride}}{\text{(maleic anhydride ring)}} + \underset{\text{Ethylene glycol}}{\begin{matrix} H_2COH \\ | \\ H_2COH \end{matrix}} \longrightarrow \underset{\text{Unsaturated polyester}}{-\overset{H}{\underset{H}{C}}-\overset{H}{\underset{H}{C}}-O-\overset{O}{\overset{\|}{C}}-\overset{H}{C}=\overset{H}{C}-\overset{O}{\overset{\|}{C}}-O-} \tag{7.53}$$

The difficulties encountered by Carothers in his attempted preparation of crystalline high molecular weight linear fibers were overcome by an ester interchange reaction with ethylene glycol and dimethyl terephthalate. More recently, terephthalic acid has been used directly. Polyesters may also be produced from the reaction of terephthalic acid and ethylene oxide. The classic reaction for producing Dacron, Kodel, and Terylene fibers and Dacron film is shown below.

$$\underset{\text{Dimethyl terephthalate}}{nH_3C-O-\overset{O}{\overset{\|}{C}}-C_6H_4-\overset{O}{\overset{\|}{C}}-O-CH_3} + \underset{\text{Ethylene glycol}}{nHO(CH_2)_2OH} \xrightarrow[\Delta \; -2nCH_3OH]{CH_3ONa} \underset{\text{Polyethylene terephthalate}}{\left[-O-\overset{O}{\overset{\|}{C}}-C_6H_4-\overset{O}{\overset{\|}{C}}-O(CH_2)_2O-\right]_n} + 2nCH_3OH \tag{7.54}$$

Polyester fibers (PET), which are now the world's leading synthetic fibers, are produced at an annual rate of over 1.5 million tons in the USA. Biaxially oriented PET film is one of the strongest polymeric films available.

Since polyethylene terephthalate has a melting point of 240°C, it is difficult to mold. However, polybutylene terephthalate produced from butylene glycol has a melting point of 170°C and is more readily molded. It is a strong, highly crystalline engineering plastic.

Polycarbonates, which are polyesters of the unstable carbonic acid, are relatively stable polymers which were originally produced by the reaction of phosgene with bisphenol A [2,2 -bis(4-hydroxyphenyl) propane]. This unusually tough transparent plastic is available under the trade names of Lexan (General Electric) and Merlon (Mobay). Polycarbonates may also be produced by ester interchange between diphenyl carbonate and bisphenol A. The equation for the classic preparation of polycarbonates is shown in (7.55).

The melting point of polycarbonates is decreased from 225 to 195°C when the methyl pendant groups are replaced by propyl groups. The polycarbonate prepared from bis(4-hydroxyphenyl) ether also has a lower melting point and lower glass transition temperature.

$$HO-C_6H_4-C(CH_3)_2-C_6H_4-OH + Cl-\overset{O}{\overset{\|}{C}}-Cl \longrightarrow \left[-O-C_6H_4-C(CH_3)_2-C_6H_4-O\overset{O}{\overset{\|}{C}}- \right]_n + 2HCl \tag{7.55}$$

Bisphenol A + Phosgene → Polycarbonate + Hydrogen chloride

As shown in (7.56), a highly crystalline, high temperature-resistant polymer is produced by the self-condensation of an ester of p-hydroxybenzoic acid. This poly-p-benzoate, which is marketed under the tradename of Ekonol, has a melting point greater than 900°C (probably decomposes before 900°C).

$$mR\overset{O}{\overset{\|}{C}}-O-C_6H_4-\overset{O}{\overset{\|}{C}}-OR' \longrightarrow \left[-O-C_6H_4-\overset{O}{\overset{\|}{C}}- \right]_m + mR\overset{O}{\overset{\|}{C}}-OR' \tag{7.56}$$

p-Hydroxybenzoic acid ester → Poly-p-benzoate

7.6 SYNTHETIC POLYAMIDES

The first polyesters produced by Carothers had relatively low molecular weights because of low fractional conversions. He was successful in producing higher molecular weight polymers by shifting the equilibrium by the removal of the water produced. However, these aliphatic polyesters, which he called "super polymers," lacked stiffening groups in the chain and thus had melting points that were too low for laundering and ironing.

His next step was to increase the fractional conversion (p) by making salts by the reaction of hexamethylenediamine and adipic acid. These were recrystallizable from ethanol. Thus, a high molecular weight polyamide known generally as nylon, which had a melting point of 265°C, could be produced by the thermal decomposition of this pure, equal molar nylon-66 salt, as shown by (7.57).

$$HO_2C(CH_2)_4CO_2H + H_2N(CH_2)_6NH_2 \longrightarrow$$

$$[^-O_2C(CH_2)_4CO_2^-][H_3\overset{+}{N}(CH_2)_6\overset{+}{N}H_3] \xrightarrow{heat} \left[-\overset{O}{\overset{\|}{C}}(CH_2)_4\overset{O}{\overset{\|}{C}}NH(CH_2)_6NH- \right]_n + 2H_2O$$

Adipic acid + 1,6 - Hexanediamine $\xrightarrow{heat}$ Nylon 66 + Water (7.57)

Since the molecular weight of the original nylon-66 produced by Carothers in 1938 was higher than he desired, he added 1% of acetic acid to the reactants in order to reduce the $\overline{DP}$ value. Because of the stiffening effect of the amide groups, the melting point of nylon-66 is 200°C greater than that of the corresponding polyester. The melting point of nylons (PA) increases as the number of methylene groups between amide groups in the chain are reduced.

Since the chains of nylons having an even number of carbon atoms between the amide groups pack better, their melting points are higher than comparable nylons with odd numbers of carbon atoms. The melting points decrease and the water resistance increases as the number of methylene groups between amide groups is increased.

Aromatic nylons prepared from terephthalic acid (Kevlar) have very high melting points and are called aramides. The solubility and ease of fabrication of aramides is improved by the preparation of ordered copolyamides. For example, a copolymer consisting of meta-benzamide and isophthalamide units is more readily processed than polyortho-phenylene phthalamide.

Because of the presence of the bulky methoxymethyl pendant group, the hydrogen-bonding forces are reduced, the melting point is reduced, and the flexibility is increased in methoxymethylated nylon-66. Comparable results are observed when nylon-66 is condensed with ethylene oxide. The equations for these reactions are shown below.

$$\left[\text{NH(CH}_2)_6\text{NH}\overset{\text{O}}{\overset{\|}{\text{C}}}(\text{CH}_2)_4\overset{\text{O}}{\overset{\|}{\text{C}}}\right]_n \xrightarrow[\text{CH}_3\text{OH},\ \text{OH}^-]{\text{CH}_2\text{O}} \left[\text{NH(CH}_2)_6\underset{\text{CH}_2\text{OCH}_3}{\underset{|}{\text{N}}}\overset{\text{O}}{\overset{\|}{\text{C}}}(\text{CH}_2)_4\overset{\text{O}}{\overset{\|}{\text{C}}}\right]_n \qquad (7.58)$$

nylon-66 methoxymethylated nylon-66

$$\sim\underset{\text{H}}{\underset{|}{\text{N}}}-\overset{\text{O}}{\overset{\|}{\text{C}}}\sim + \text{CH}_2\overset{\text{O}}{-}\text{CH}_2 \longrightarrow \sim\underset{\text{CH}_2\text{CH}_2\text{OH}}{\underset{|}{\text{N}}}-\overset{\text{O}}{\overset{\|}{\text{C}}}\sim \qquad (7.59)$$

nylon-66 ethoxylated nylon-66

Comparable changes in physical properties are observed when branched dicarboxylic acids and branched diamines are used as the reactants for producing nylons. Thus, nylons produced from α-methyladipic acid and hexamethylenediamine and from adipic acid and 3-methylhexamethylene diamine have melting points that are at least 80°C less than that of nylon-66. These nylons are not suitable for fiber use because of the presence of branches on the chain.

7.7 POLYIMIDES

As shown in the following equation, polyimides (PI) with melting points greater than 600°C are produced by the condensation of an aliphatic diamine and a dianhydride, such as pyromellitic anhydride. It is customary to carry out this reaction stepwise to produce a soluble prepolymer (polyamic acid) which is insolubilized when heated. However, the product of the first step is insoluble when aromatic diamines are used. (Again decomposition may occur prior to 600°C.)

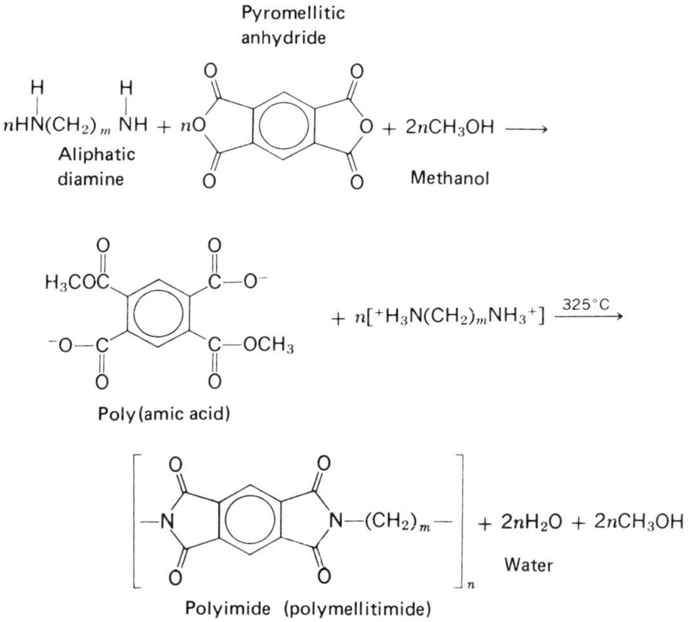

Pyromellitic anhydride

$n\mathrm{HN(H)(CH_2)_m N(H)H} + n\mathrm{O(C=O)_2C_6H_2(C=O)_2O} + 2n\mathrm{CH_3OH} \longrightarrow$

Aliphatic diamine — Methanol

$\mathrm{H_3COC(=O)}$, $\mathrm{C(=O)-O^-}$, $\mathrm{^-O-C(=O)}$, $\mathrm{C(=O)-OCH_3}$ on benzene ring $+ n[\mathrm{^+H_3N(CH_2)_mNH_3^+}] \xrightarrow{325°C}$ (7.60)

Poly(amic acid)

$\left[-\mathrm{N(C=O)_2C_6H_2(C=O)_2N}-(\mathrm{CH_2})_m- \right]_n + 2n\mathrm{H_2O} + 2n\mathrm{CH_3OH}$

Water

Polyimide (polymellitimide)

7.8 POLYBENZIMIDAZOLES AND RELATED POLYMERS

Many heterocyclic polymers have been produced in an attempt to develop high temperature resistant polymers for aerospace applications. Among these are the polybenzimidazoles (PBI) which, as shown by the following equation, are prepared from aromatic tetramines and esters of dicarboxylic aromatic acids. In the standardized procedure, the reactants are heated at temperatures below 300°C in order to form a soluble prepolymer which is converted to the final insoluble polymer by heating at higher temperatures.

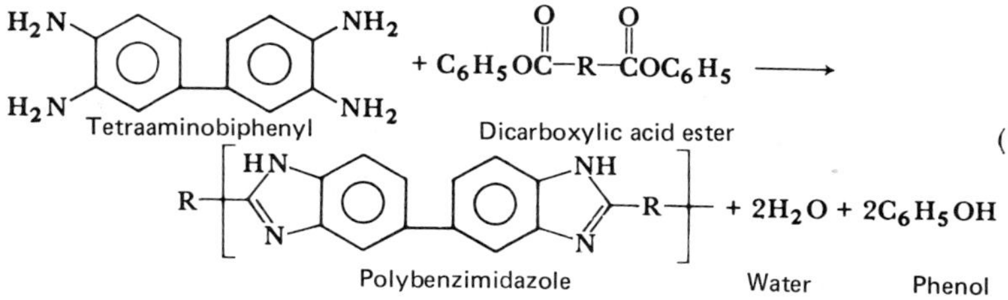

$$\underset{\text{Tetraaminobiphenyl}}{(H_2N)_2C_6H_3{-}C_6H_3(NH_2)_2} + \underset{\text{Dicarboxylic acid ester}}{C_6H_5O\overset{O}{\overset{\|}{C}}{-}R{-}\overset{O}{\overset{\|}{C}}OC_6H_5} \longrightarrow \underset{\text{Polybenzimidazole}}{\left[R \text{—(benzimidazole—benzimidazole)—} R \right]} + \underset{\text{Water}}{2H_2O} + \underset{\text{Phenol}}{2C_6H_5OH} \qquad (7.61)$$

Polymers such as PBI have a weak link in the single covalent bond connecting the phenyl rings in biphenyl. This weakness is overcome by the synthesis of a ladder polymer which, as shown by the formula for polyquinoxaline, has two covalent bonds throughout the chain. Thus, the integrity of the polymer is maintained even if one bond is broken. This requirement is also met by spiropolymers, such as the intractable spiroketalpolymers produced by the condensation of 1,4-cyclohexanedione and pentaerythritol, as shown below.

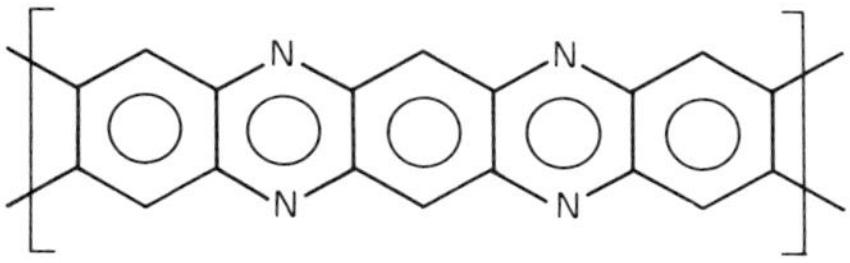

Polyquinoxaline
(a ladder polymer)

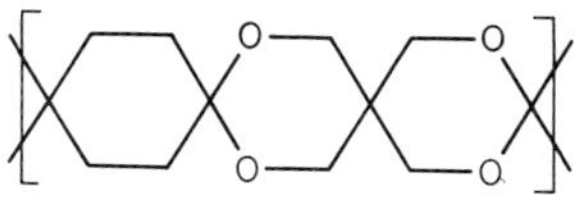

Spiroketal polymer
(a spiropolymer)

7.9 POLYURETHANES AND POLYUREAS

Urethanes, or carbamates, are well-known organic compounds which were formerly used for the characterization of alcohols. Since the fractional conversion (p) of the reaction is relatively high, Bayer was able to prepare numerous useful polyurethanes (PU) by the reaction of dihydric alcohols and diisocyanates. For example, a crystalline polymeric fiber (Perlon U) may be prepared by the reaction of 1,4-butanediol and hexamethylene diisocyanate as shown in the following equation.

$$\underset{\text{1,4 - Butanediol}}{n\mathrm{HO(CH_2)_4OH}} + \underset{\text{Hexamethylene diisocyanate}}{n\mathrm{OCN(CH_2)_6NCO}} \longrightarrow \underset{\text{Polyurethane}}{\left[\mathrm{-O-(CH_2)_4O-\overset{}{\underset{\|}{\underset{O}{C}}}-\overset{H}{N}(CH_2)_6\overset{H}{N}-\underset{\|}{\underset{O}{C}}-} \right]_n} \qquad (7.62)$$

Reactants with an even number of carbon atoms as used in (7.62) produce higher-melting polymers than those with an odd number of carbon atoms. The melting point is decreased as the number of methylene groups is increased, and increased by the incorporation of stiffening groups such as phenylene groups.

Isocyanates react with water to produce unstable carbamic acids which decompose to form diamines and carbon dioxide, which acts as a blowing agent. Hence, polymeric foams are produced when traces of moisture are present in the reactants. Since many of these foams are formed in situ and isocyanates are toxic, it is preferable to use isocyanate terminated prepolymers. The latter are prepared from flexible or rigid hydroxyl-terminated polyesters or polyethers.

Cross-linked polyurethane coatings, elastomers, or foams may be produced by using an excess of the diisocyanate which reacts with the urethane hydrogen to produce an allophanate, or by incorporating polyols such as glycerol or pentaerythitol in the reactant mixture. The diamines produced by the decomposition of carbamic acids react with diisocyanates to produce polyureas. Equations for the formation of an allophanate and a polyurea are shown below.

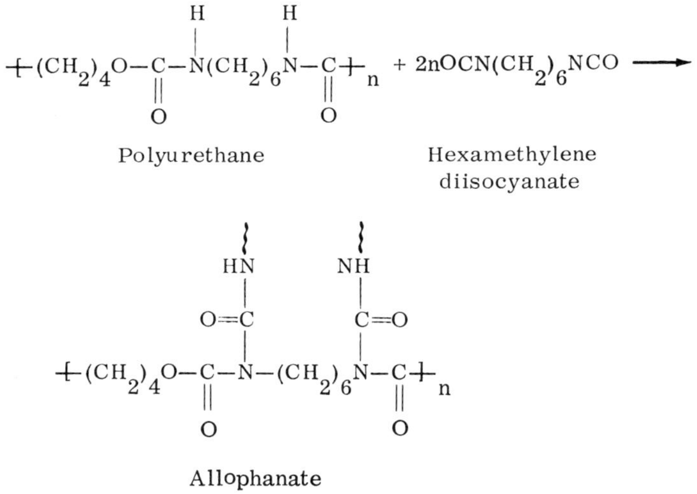

$$\left[(CH_2)_4O-\underset{\underset{O}{\|}}{C}-\overset{H}{\overset{|}{N}}(CH_2)_6\overset{H}{\overset{|}{N}}-\underset{\underset{O}{\|}}{C} \right]_n + 2nOCN(CH_2)_6NCO \longrightarrow$$

Polyurethane Hexamethylene diisocyanate

$$\left[(CH_2)_4O-\underset{\underset{O}{\|}}{C}-\overset{\overset{\wr}{HN}-\overset{|}{}}{}\overset{O=C}{\overset{|}{N}}-(CH_2)_6-\overset{C=O\;(NH\wr)}{\overset{|}{N}}-\underset{\underset{O}{\|}}{C} \right]_n \qquad (7.63)$$

Allophanate

$$n\;OCN-C_6H_3(CH_3)-NCO + nH_2NRNH_2 \longrightarrow \left[\overset{H}{\overset{|}{N}}-\underset{}{\overset{O}{\overset{\|}{C}}}-\overset{H}{\overset{|}{N}}-C_6H_3(CH_3)-\overset{H}{\overset{|}{N}}-\underset{\underset{O}{\|}}{C}-\overset{H}{\overset{|}{N}}-R \right]_n \qquad (7.64)$$

Diamine Polyurea

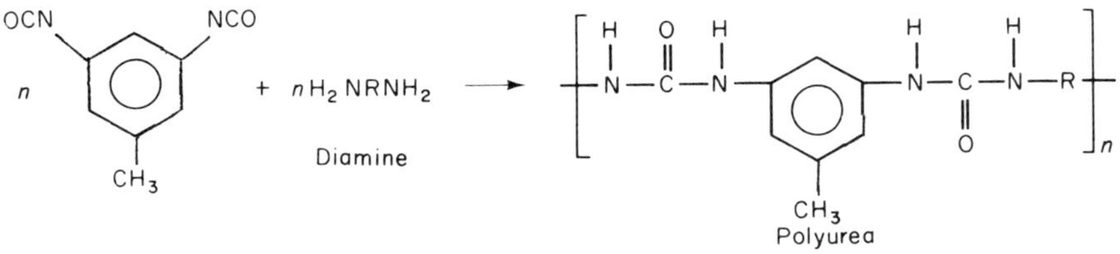

7.10 POLYSULFIDES

Thiokol, which was the first synthetic elastomer, was synthesized by Patrick by the condensation of alkylene dichlorides and sodium polysulfides in the 1920s. These solvent-resistant elastomers have limited use because of their foul odor. They may be reduced to liquid polymers (LP-2) which may be reoxidized to solid elastomers in caulking material and in solid rocket propellant formulations. The equations for the production of these alkylene polysulfides are shown below.

$$n\mathrm{Cl}\!+\!\mathrm{CH_2}\!+_2\mathrm{O}\!+\!\mathrm{CH_2}\!+_2\mathrm{Cl} + n\mathrm{Na_2S_x} \longrightarrow$$

bis(2-Chloroethyl) ether — Sodium polysulfide

$$\text{+}\!\!\text{+}\mathrm{CH_2}\!+_2\mathrm{O}\!+\!\mathrm{CH_2}\!+_2\mathrm{S_x}]_n + n\mathrm{NaCl}$$

Polyethylene sulfide — Sodium chloride

$$[-(\mathrm{CH_2}\!+_2\mathrm{O}\!+\!\mathrm{CH_2}\!+_2\mathrm{S_x}-]_n \xrightarrow{\mathrm{Na_2SO_3}} \text{+}\!\!\text{+}\mathrm{CH_2}\!+_2\mathrm{O}\!+\!\mathrm{CH_2}\!+_2\mathrm{S}\!+\!\mathrm{H}$$

$$+ \mathrm{Na_2S_2O_3} \qquad (7.65)$$

$$2\text{+}\!\!\text{+}\mathrm{CH_2}\!+_2\mathrm{O}\!+\!\mathrm{CH_2}\!+_2\mathrm{S}\!+_n\mathrm{H} + \mathrm{PbO_2} \longrightarrow$$

Liquid

$$\text{+}\!\!\text{+}\mathrm{CH_2}\!+_2\mathrm{O}\!+\!\mathrm{CH_2}\!+_2\mathrm{S}\!+_2 + \mathrm{PbO} + \mathrm{H_2O}$$

Solid

Polyphenylene sulfide (Ryton) is a solvent-resistant plastic that is useful in high temperature service. This crystalline polymer is synthesized from p-dichlorobenzene as shown by the following equation:

$$\mathrm{Cl}-\mathrm{C_6H_4}-\mathrm{Cl} \xrightarrow[\mathrm{S + Na_2CO_3}]{\mathrm{Na_2S\ or}} \left[\!-\mathrm{C_6H_4}-\mathrm{S}-\!\right] \qquad (7.66)$$

7.11 POLYETHERS

Polyphenylene oxide (PPO; Noryl) is a high temperature resistant polymer produced by the oxidative coupling of 2, 6-disubstituted phenols. As shown by the following equation, this step-growth polymerization is based on a room temperature oxidation by the bubbling of oxygen through a solution of the phenol in the presence of copper(I) chloride and pyridine.

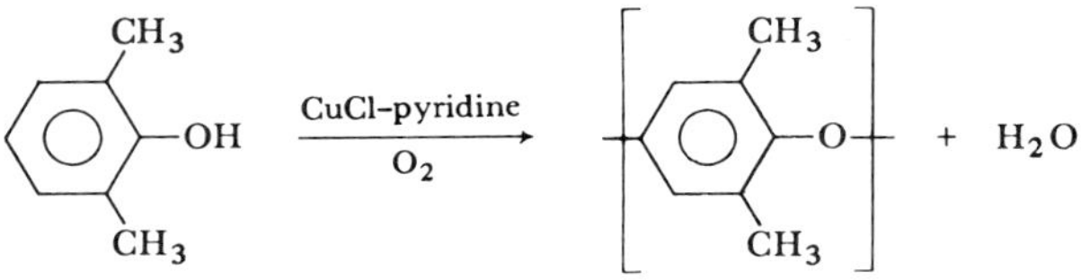

$$\text{2,6-(CH}_3)_2\text{C}_6\text{H}_3\text{-OH} \xrightarrow[O_2]{\text{CuCl-pyridine}} \left[\text{-C}_6\text{H}_2(\text{CH}_3)_2\text{-O-} \right] + H_2O \tag{7.67}$$

Epoxy resins (ethoxyline resins), under the tradenames of Araldite and Epon, were synthesized in the 1940s by a step-reaction polymerization between epichlorohydrin and bisphenol A. The $\overline{DP}$ of the prepolymer produced in this reaction is dependent on the ratio of the reactants. The low molecular weight liquid prepolymer is cured, or cross-linked, at room temperature by the addition of alkylene polyamines and at high temperatures by the addition of cyclic carboxylic anhydrides. The equations for the production and curing of these widely used molding, laminating, and surface-coating resins are shown below.

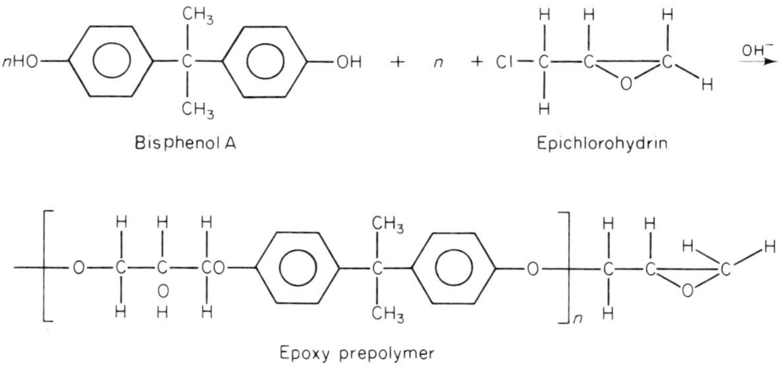

$$n\text{HO-C}_6\text{H}_4\text{-C(CH}_3)_2\text{-C}_6\text{H}_4\text{-OH} + n + \text{Cl-CH}_2\text{-}\underset{\diagdown O \diagup}{\text{CH-CH}_2} \xrightarrow{OH^-}$$

Bisphenol A   Epichlorohydrin

$$\left[\text{-O-CH}_2\text{-CH(OH)-CH}_2\text{O-C}_6\text{H}_4\text{-C(CH}_3)_2\text{-C}_6\text{H}_4\text{-O-} \right]_n \text{CH}_2\text{-}\underset{\diagdown O \diagup}{\text{CH-CH}_2} \tag{7.68}$$

Epoxy prepolymer

$$\text{Epoxy prepolymer} + \begin{matrix}\text{alkylene polyamine}\\ \text{or}\\ \text{cyclic anhydride}\end{matrix} \longrightarrow \text{cured epoxy resin} \tag{7.69}$$

The high molecular weight thermoplastics called phenoxy resins are produced by the hydrolysis of high molecular weight linear epoxy resins. These transparent resins, whose structures resemble epoxy resins, do not contain epoxide groups. They may be molded, as such, or cross-linked, through the hydroxy pendant groups by diisocyanates or cyclic anhydrides.

Furan resins are produced by the acid-catalyzed polymerization of furfuryl alcohol or the products obtained by the condensation of this chemurgic product or furfural with acetone or maleic anhydride. The dark-colored resins produced from these unsaturated compounds are characterized by excellent resistance to alkalis, solvents, and nonoxidizing acids.

7.12 POLYSULFONES

While aliphatic polysulfones have been produced from the copolymerization of ethylene and sulfur dioxide, the more important polysulfones are the amorphous aromatic polymers. These high-impact polymers are produced by a Friedel-Crafts condensation of sulfonyl chlorides, as shown in the following equation. The engineering polymers (Astrel or Udel) polysulfone, polyethersulfone, and polyphenylsulfone have a heat deflection temperature of 174, 201, and 204°C, respectively.

$$C_6H_5{-}O{-}C_6H_4{-}SO_2Cl \xrightarrow{AlCl_3} \left[C_6H_4{-}O{-}C_6H_4{-}SO_2 \right] + HCl$$

Diphenylene oxide sulfonyl chloride — Poly(aryl sulfone) — Hydrogen chloride

(7.70)

7.13 PHENOLIC AND AMINO PLASTICS

Baekeland showed that a relatively stable resole prepolymer could be obtained by the controlled condensation of phenol and formaldehyde under alkaline conditions. These linear polymers (PF) may be readily converted to infusible cross-linked polymers called resites by heating or by the addition of mineral acids. As shown by the following equation, the early products produced when formaldehyde is condensed with phenol are hydroxybenzyl alcohols. The linear resole polymer is called an A-stage resin, and the cross-linked resite is called a C-stage resin.

$$C_6H_5OH + H_2C{=}O \xrightarrow{OH^-} C_6H_4(OH)CH_2OH \xrightarrow{H_2C{=}O} C_6H_2(OH)(CH_2OH)_3$$

Phenol — Formaldehyde — o-Methylolphenol (saligenin) — Trimethylolphenol

(7.71)

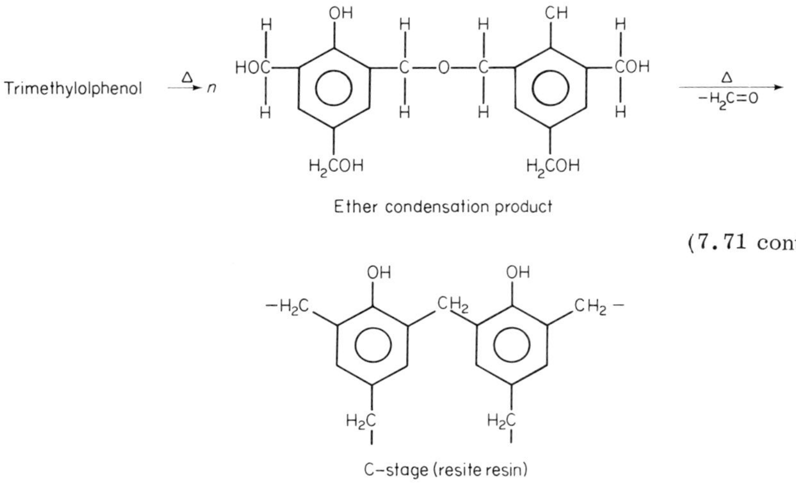

Trimethylolphenol $\xrightarrow{\Delta}$ n [ether condensation product structure] $\xrightarrow[-H_2C=O]{\Delta}$

Ether condensation product

(7.71 cont.)

C-stage (resite resin)

Baekeland recognized that the trifunctional phenol would produce network polymers and hence used difunctional ortho- or para-substituted phenols to produce soluble linear paint resins. As shown by the following equation, linear thermoplastic polymers may be produced by alkaline or acid condensation of formaldehyde with phenolic derivatives such as para-cresol.

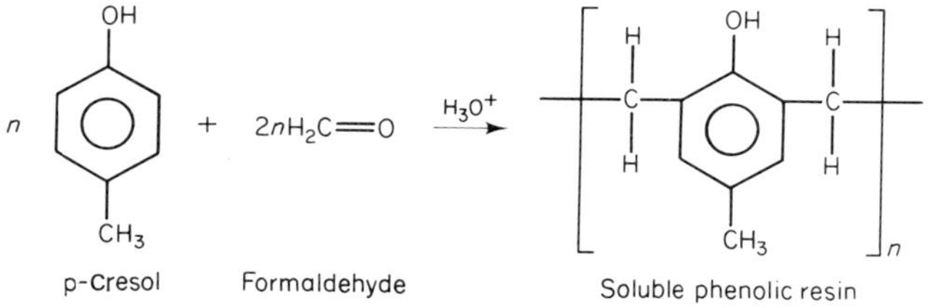

$$n\ \text{p-Cresol} + 2nH_2C{=}O \xrightarrow{H_3O^+} \text{Soluble phenolic resin} \tag{7.72}$$

p-Cresol Formaldehyde Soluble phenolic resin

Since the acid condensation of 1 mol of phenol with 1.5 mol of formaldehyde produced infusible C-stage products, Baekeland reduced the relative amount of formaldehyde used and made useful novolac resins in a two-step process. Thus, a stable A-stage novolac resin is produced by heating 1 mol of phenol with 0.8 mol of formaldehyde in the presence of sulfuric acid.

The A-stage resin thus produced, after the removal of water by vacuum distillation, is cooled to yield a solid which is then pulverized. The additional formaldehyde required to convert this linear polymer to an infusible thermoset resin is supplied by hexamethylenetetramine. The latter, which is admixed with the pulverized A-stage resin, is produced by the condensation of formaldehyde and ammonia.

Other essential ingredients, such as attrition ground wood (wood flour) filler, pigments, and lubricants, are also admixed with the resin and hexamethylenetetramine. The A-stage resin in this mixture is advanced, or further polymerized, by passing it through heavy heated rolls, through an extruder or a heated heavy-duty mixer. The term phenolic molding compound is applied to the granulated product containing the B-stage novolac resin.

The phenolic molding compound is converted to the infusible C-stage by heating it under pressure in cavities in a compression molding press. Plywood and other laminates are produced by heating and pressing a series of sheets coated with liquid resole resin. Articles such as automobile distributor heads are molded from novolac molding compounds. The equation for making and curing novolac resins is shown below.

$$n\,C_6H_5OH \;+\; 2nH_2C{=}O \xrightarrow{H_3O^+} \left[-CH_2-C_6H_3(OH)-CH_2- \right]_n \xrightarrow[\text{Hexamethylene tetramine}]{(CH_2)_6N_4} \left[-CH_2-C_6H_2(OH)(CH_2-)-CH_2- \right]_n \qquad (7.73)$$

Phenol Formaldehyde A-stage novolac

C-stage novolac

While the condensation of urea and formaldehyde had been described in 1884, urea-formaldehyde resins (UF) were not patented until 1918. Comparable products based on the condensation of formaldehyde and melamine (2,4,6-triamino-1,3,5-triazine) were not patented until 1939. The term amino resins is now used to describe both urea and melamine-formaldehyde (MF) resins.

Urea and melamine are tetra- and hexa-functional molecules, respectively. However, the formation of network polymers is prevented by adding alcohols such as n-butanol and by condensing with formaldehyde at low temperature under alkaline conditions. While phenolic resins have better moisture and weather resistance than urea resins, the latter are preferred for light-colored objects.

For example, the interior layers of laminated countertops are held together by phenolic resins, but either urea or melamine resins are used for the decorative surface. Melamine plastics are more resistant to heat and moisture than UF and are used for the decorative surface. Melamine plastics are more resistant to heat and moisture than UF and are used for the manufacture of plastic dinnerware. As shown by the following equations, the intermediate reaction products are methylol derivatives. Also, cyclization occurs when urea-formaldehyde resins are cured in the presence of acids.

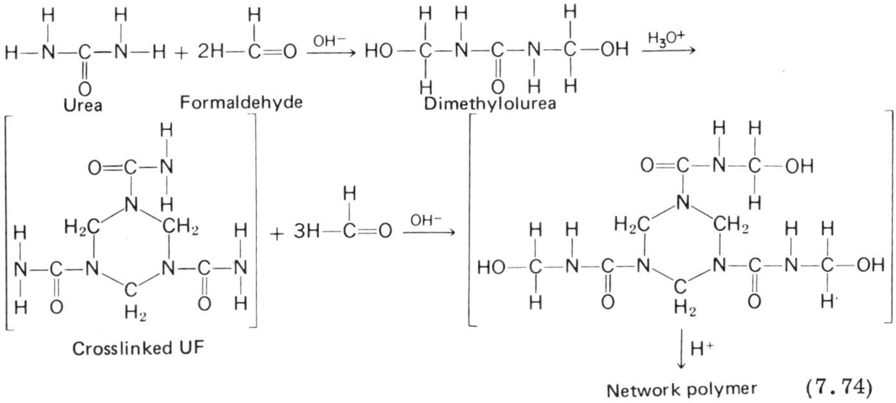

$$H_2N{-}\overset{O}{\overset{\|}{C}}{-}NH_2 + 2H{-}\overset{H}{\overset{|}{C}}{=}O \xrightarrow{OH^-} HO{-}CH_2{-}NH{-}\overset{O}{\overset{\|}{C}}{-}NH{-}CH_2{-}OH \xrightarrow{H_3O^+}$$

Urea Formaldehyde Dimethylolurea

$$\left[\text{Crosslinked UF: } H_2N{-}CO{-}N\!<\!(CH_2{-}N(CONH_2){-}CH_2)\!>\!N{-}CO{-}NH_2\right] + 3H{-}\overset{H}{\overset{|}{C}}{=}O \xrightarrow{OH^-} \left[HO{-}CH_2{-}NH{-}CO{-}N\!<\!(CH_2{-}N(CO{-}NH{-}CH_2OH){-}CH_2)\!>\!N{-}CO{-}NH{-}CH_2{-}OH\right] \xrightarrow{H^+} \text{Network polymer} \qquad (7.74)$$

Crosslinked UF

Network polymer (7.74)

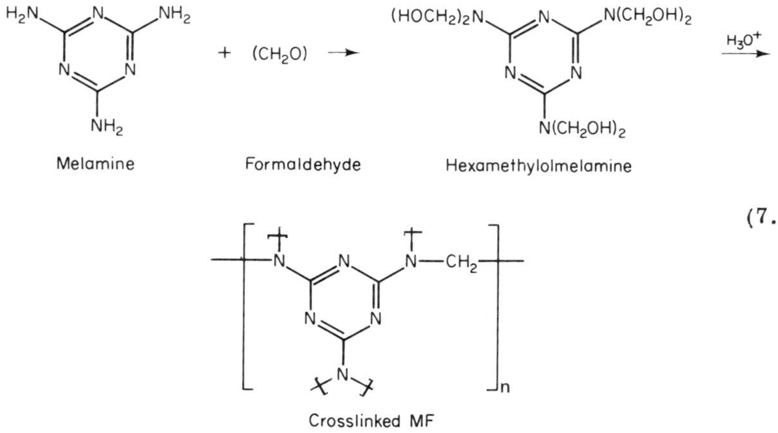

$$\underset{\text{Melamine}}{C_3N_3(NH_2)_3} + \underset{\text{Formaldehyde}}{(CH_2O)} \longrightarrow \underset{\text{Hexamethylolmelamine}}{C_3N_3[N(CH_2OH)_2]_3} \xrightarrow{H_3O^+} \left[\,{-}N{-}C_3N_3(N<){-}N{-}CH_2{-}\,\right]_n \qquad (7.75)$$

Crosslinked MF

As shown in Table 7.2, amino resins, phenolic resins, epoxy resins, saturated and unsaturated polyester resins, nylons, and polyurethanes are produced on a relatively large scale by step-reaction polymerization. Synthetic fibers, thermoplastics, thermosetting plastics, adhesives, coatings, and plastic foams are produced by this technique. However, few synthetic

TABLE 7.2 Production of Polymers in the USA by Step-Reaction Polymerization in 1978 (thousands of metric tons)

Synthetic fibers	
Nylon	1193
Polyester	1818
Total	3011
Thermosetting plastics	
Phenolics	700
Polyesters	524
Ureas	475
Epoxies	141
Melamines	100
Total	1940
Coatings	
Alkyds	215
Total for principal synthetic step-reaction polymers	5166

elastomers are produced by step-reaction polymerization, and actually most synthetic polymers are produced by chain-reaction polymerization, which is discussed in the next chapter.

7.14 GENERAL INFORMATION ON STEP-REACTION POLYMERIZATION

Since the average molecular weight increases with conversion, useful high molecular weight linear polymers may be obtained by step-reaction polymerization when the fractional conversion (p) is high (above 0.99). The concentration of reactants decreases rapidly in the early stages of polymerization, and a polymer with many different molecular weights will be present in the final product. The requirement for a linear polymer is a functionality of 2. Network polymers are usually produced when the functionality is greater than 2. The original reactants and all products resulting from their condensation may react to produce higher molecular weight species. The rate constant k is similar to that of corresponding condensation reactions with monofunctional groups and remains essentially unchanged with higher molecular weight species.

7.15 POLYCONDENSATION MECHANISMS

Proposed mechanisms for polycondensations are essentially the same as those proposed in the organic chemistry of smaller molecules. Here we will only briefly consider several examples to illustrate this similarity between proposed mechanisms for reactions involving smaller molecules and those which eventually produce polymers. For instance, the synthesis of polyamides (nylons) can often be envisioned as a simple S_N2 type of Lewis acid-base reaction with the Lewis base nucleophilic amine attacking the electron-poor, electrophilic carbonyl site followed by loss of a proton. A similar mechanism can be proposed for most polyesterifications.

$$\sim R-\overset{\delta-}{N}H_2: + \overset{\delta-}{O}=\overset{\delta+}{C}(\sim)-\overset{\delta-}{X} \rightleftharpoons \sim R-\overset{\oplus}{N}H(H\cdots X^{\ominus})-C(=O)\sim \rightleftharpoons \sim R-NH-C(=O)\sim \qquad (7.76)$$

$$R-\ddot{O}^{\delta-}H: + \overset{\delta-}{O}=\overset{\delta+}{C}(\sim)-\overset{\delta-}{X} \rightleftharpoons R-\overset{+}{O}(H\cdots X^{\ominus})-C(=O)\sim \rightleftharpoons \sim R-O-C(=O)\sim \qquad (7.77)$$

and a related pathway

$$\sim R-\overset{\delta+}{C}(=\overset{\delta-}{O})-X + H-\ddot{O}-R\sim \rightleftharpoons$$

$$\sim R-C(X)(-\ominus:\ddot{O}:\leftarrow H)-\overset{\oplus}{O}(H)-R\sim \rightleftharpoons \sim R-C(X)(-:\ddot{O}-H)-O-R\sim$$

$$\rightleftharpoons \sim R-C(=O)-O-R\sim + HX \qquad (7.78)$$

Below are a number of resonance forms for the isocyanate moiety illustrating the overall electrophilic nature of the carbon atom, giving overall an electron arrangement which can be described by

$$\overset{}{R}-\overset{\delta-}{N}=\overset{\delta+}{C}=\overset{\delta-}{O}$$

Polyurethane formation occurs with attack of the nucleophilic alcohol at the electron-poor isocyanate-carbon with a proton shift followed by a rearrangement to the urethane linkage.

$$R-\ddot{N}=C=\ddot{O}: \longleftrightarrow R-\overset{\ominus}{\ddot{N}}-\overset{\oplus}{C}=\ddot{O}: \longleftrightarrow R-N=\overset{\oplus}{C}-\overset{\ominus}{\ddot{\underset{..}{O}}}: \longleftrightarrow$$

$$R-\overset{\ominus}{\underset{..}{\ddot{N}}}-C\equiv\overset{\oplus}{O}: \longleftrightarrow R-\overset{\oplus}{N}\equiv C-\overset{\ominus}{\ddot{\underset{..}{O}}}: \tag{7.79}$$

$$\sim R-\overset{\delta-}{N}=\overset{\delta+}{C}=\overset{\delta-}{O} + H\overset{\delta-}{\ddot{O}}-R\sim \longrightarrow \sim R-\overset{\ominus}{N}-C(=O)-\overset{\oplus}{O}(H)-R\sim$$

$$\longrightarrow \sim R-N=C(-O^{\ominus})-\overset{+}{O}(H)-R\sim \longrightarrow \sim R-\underset{}{N(H)}-C(=O)-O-R\sim \tag{7.80}$$

Polyether formations, such as the formation of polyethylene oxide from ethylene oxide, can occur either through acid or base catalysis as depicted below.

$$\overset{\delta-}{O}(CH_2CH_2)^{\delta+} + H^{\oplus} \longrightarrow H-\overset{\oplus}{O}(CH_2CH_2) \longrightarrow {}^{\oplus}CH_2-CH_2-OH \xrightarrow{\overset{\delta-}{O}(CH_2CH_2)^{\delta+}}$$

$$\oplus CH_2-CH_2-O-CH_2-CH_2-CH_2-OH \rightarrow \rightarrow \rightarrow +CH_2-CH_2-O+ \tag{7.81}$$

$$\underset{\delta+}{\overset{\delta-}{\text{O}}}\text{(epoxide)} + X^{\ominus} \longrightarrow {}^{\ominus}O{-}CH_2{-}CH_2{-}X \xrightarrow[\delta+]{\overset{\delta-}{\text{O}}\text{(epoxide)}}$$

$$^{\ominus}O{-}CH_2{-}CH_2{-}O{-}CH_2{-}CH_2{-}X \rightarrow \rightarrow \rightarrow \left(CH_2{-}CH_2{-}O\right) \tag{7.82}$$

where X = $^{\ominus}$OH, $^{\ominus}$OR. The topic of polyether formation is further dealt with in Sec. 7.1.

Again, the mechanistic pathways suggested for condensations involving smaller molecules can generally be directly applied to polycondensation processes.

7.16 SYNTHETIC ROUTES

The previous sections contain the general synthesis for a number of important condensation polymers. Here we will consider briefly the three main synthetic techniques typically utilized in the synthesis of condensation polymers. This will be followed by a discussion of some considerations that must be taken into account when choosing a given synthetic procedure utilizing specific examples to illustrate the points.

The melt technique is also referred to by other names to describe the same or similar processes. These names include high melt, bulk melt, and simply bulk or neat. The melt process is an equilibrium-controlled process in which polymer is formed by driving the reaction toward completion, usually by removal of the byproduct. For polyesterifications involving the formation of water or HCl, the driving force is the elimination, generally by a combination of reduced pressure and applied heat, of the water or HCl. Reactants are introduced along with any added catalyst to the reaction vessel. Heat is applied to melt the reactants, permitting their necessary intimate contact. Heating can be maintained at the reaction melt temperature or

$$Cl{-}\overset{\overset{O}{\|}}{C}{-}R{-}\overset{\overset{O}{\|}}{C}{-}Cl + HO{-}R{-}OH \rightleftarrows \rightleftarrows \rightleftarrows \ldots\ldots \left(\overset{\overset{O}{\|}}{C}{-}R{-}\overset{\overset{O}{\|}}{C}{-}O{-}R{-}O\right) + HCl \tag{7.83}$$

$$HO{-}\overset{\overset{O}{\|}}{C}{-}R{-}\overset{\overset{O}{\|}}{C}{-}OH + HO{-}R{-}OH \rightleftarrows \rightleftarrows \rightleftarrows \ldots\ldots \left(\overset{\overset{O}{\|}}{C}{-}R{-}\overset{\overset{O}{\|}}{C}{-}O{-}R{-}O\right) + H_2O \tag{7.84}$$

increased above it. Pressure is reduced. Typical melt polycondensations take several hours to several days before the desired polymeric product is achieved. Yields are of necessity high.

Solution condensations are also equilibrium processes, with the reaction often driven by removal of the byproduct by distillation or by salt formation with added base. Reactants generally must be more reactive in comparison with the melt technique, since lower temperatures are employed, with a number of solution processes occurring near room temperature. Solvent entrapment is a problem, but since a reaction may occur under considerably reduced temperatures compared to the melt technique, thermally induced side reactions are minimized. Side reactions with the solvent have been a problem in some cases. Because the reactants must be quite energetic, many condensations are not suitable for the solution technique.

The interfacial technique, while an old technique, has only recently gained popularity with the work of Morgan and Carraher in the 1960s and 1970s. Many of the reactions can be carried out under essentially nonequilibrium conditions. The technique is heterophasic, with two fast-reacting reactants dissolved in a pair of immiscible liquids, one of which is usually water. The aqueous phase typically contains the Lewis base—a diol, diamine, or dithiol—along with any added base, or other additive. The organic phase consists of a Lewis acid such as an acid chloride contained in a suitable organic solvent such as benzene, chloroform, diethyl ether, toluene, octane, or carbon tetrachloride. Reaction occurs near the interface (hence the name). The technique offers the ability to synthesize a wide variety of polymers ranging from modification of cotton, polyester synthesis, synthesis of nucleic acids, and synthesis of polycarbonates, the latter being the only polymer produced on a large industrial scale using the interfacial technique. Figure 7.8 describes a simple assembly that can be rapidly put together to form nylon with the interfacial technique. (A note of caution: diamine, carbon tetrachloride, and acid chloride are harmful, and the reaction should be carried out with adequate ventilation and other necessary safety procedures, including rubber gloves.) A few drops of phenolphthalein added to the aqueous phase will give a more colorful nylon material. While aqueous-organic solvent systems are the rule, there are a number of other interfacial systems which have been developed, including solid-liquid, liquid-gas, and nonaqueous liquid systems. With all the potential that the interfacial offers it has not attracted wide industrial use because of the high cost of the necessarily quite reactive monomers and the added expense of trying to cope with solvent removal and recovery.

In principle, any dibasic acid will condense with any diol or diamine. In practice, few such condensations have been utilized on an industrial scale for a variety of reasons, including availability of inexpensive comonomers in large quantity and undesirable chemical and physical properties of the synthesized polymer. For instance, several companies were interested in the synthesis of aromatic amines for commercial use. Aromatic amines

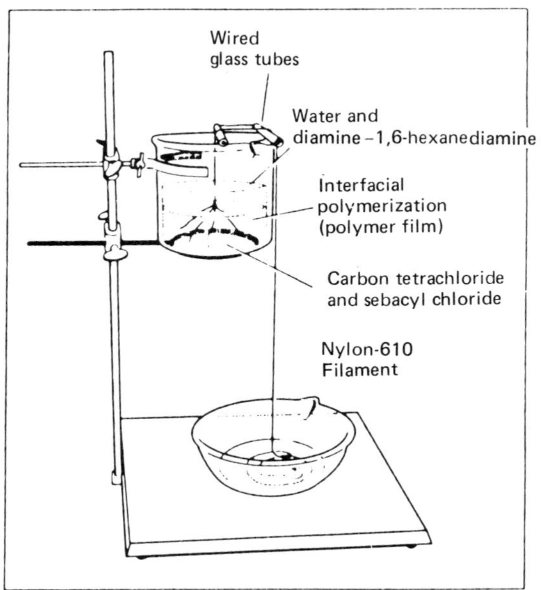

FIGURE 7.8 Self-propelled interfacial spinning of nylon-610 in the "nylon rope trick." (R. Seymour and J. Higgins, Experimental Organic Chemistry, Barnes and Noble, New York, 1971. With permission of Barnes and Noble Publishing Company.)

offered much greater tear resistance and strength compared with an aliphatic nylon such as nylon-66. While aromatic amines could be synthesized using several routes, each produced a solid nylon which was only with difficulty soluble in a limited number of undesirable solvents. Solution of the nylon was necessary for fabrication of the polymer. Morgan and others noted that some polymers formed with rapid stirring would remain in solution for different times. Today, aromatic amides, under the name aramides, are synthesized using rapidly stirred systems which permit the aromatic nylon to remain in solution long enough to permit fabrication.

Polyethylene terephthalate is the best known polyester being used as a film (tradenames such as Mylar) and as a fiber (tradenames such as Dacron and Terylene). It can be produced using any of the three major polycondensation procedures. It can be rapidly prepared from the acid chloride using the aqueous interfacial system, giving poor to good yield and short to long chain lengths. Due to the excessive cost of acid chlorides, the interfacial technique of synthesis is presently ruled out industrially. In solution and bulk, polymerization rate is slow, so excess ethylene glycol is employed to increase the esterification rate. The use of excess diol, while producing the polyester at an acceptable rate, effectively decreases molecular weight. This is overcome by subsequent removal of the excess ethylene glycol. The necessity of using two steps in the production of high molecular weight polyester is undesirable both time- and material-wise.

$$\mathrm{Cl{-}\overset{O}{\overset{\|}{C}}{-}C_6H_4{-}\overset{O}{\overset{\|}{C}}{-}Cl} + \mathrm{HO{-}CH_2{-}CH_2{-}OH} \longrightarrow \longrightarrow \left[\mathrm{\overset{O}{\overset{\|}{C}}{-}C_6H_4{-}\overset{O}{\overset{\|}{C}}{-}O{-}CH_2{-}CH_2{-}O}\right]_n + \mathrm{HCl} \tag{7.85}$$

$$\mathrm{HO_2C{-}C_6H_4{-}CO_2H} + \mathrm{HO{-}CH_2{-}CH_2{-}OH} \longrightarrow \longrightarrow \left[\mathrm{\overset{O}{\overset{\|}{C}}{-}C_6H_4{-}\overset{O}{\overset{\|}{C}}{-}O{-}CH_2{-}CH_2{-}O}\right]_n + \mathrm{H_2O} \tag{7.86}$$

Terephthalic acid is insoluble in most common organic solvents and is also high melting ($>300°C$), compounding the problem of utilizing it directly for bulk and solution syntheses. Thus, the transesterification reaction utilizing the dimethyl ester of terephthalic acid with removal of methanol and subsequent removal of the "excess" glycol offers an attractive alternative. Yet because the necessary technology, including facilities, are already present to handle terephthalic acid itself, this alternative will probably not become a major part in the industrial synthesis of polyethylene terephthalate. Thus, consideration of previous investment of time and facilities are important in deciding the particular polycondensation technique utilized.

$$\mathrm{HO_2C{-}C_6H_4{-}CO_2H} + \mathrm{CH_3OH} \rightleftharpoons \mathrm{H_3C{-}O{-}\overset{O}{\overset{\|}{C}}{-}C_6H_4{-}\overset{O}{\overset{\|}{C}}{-}O{-}CH_3} \tag{7.87}$$

$$H_3C-O-\overset{O}{\overset{\|}{C}}-C_6H_4-\overset{O}{\overset{\|}{C}}-O-CH_3 + HO-CH_2-CH_2-OH \rightleftarrows$$

$$HO-CH_2-CH_2-O-\overset{O}{\overset{\|}{C}}-C_6H_4-\overset{O}{\overset{\|}{C}}-O-CH_2-CH_2-OH$$

$$HO-CH_2-CH_2-O-\overset{O}{\overset{\|}{C}}-C_6H_4-\overset{O}{\overset{\|}{C}}-O-CH_2-CH_2-OH \rightleftarrows \rightleftarrows \qquad (7.87\ \text{cont.})$$

$$\cdots\!\left[\overset{O}{\overset{\|}{C}}-C_6H_4-\overset{O}{\overset{\|}{C}}-O-CH_2-CH_2-O\right]_n\!\!- \;+\; HO-CH_2-CH_2-OH$$

Table 7.3 contains a comparison of the three systems. Other often-noted liabilities, strengths, and comparisons of the systems include the following. A characteristic of melt polycondensations is that they are slow and require that conversion be high before high polymer is formed. Most melt systems utilize less reactive reactants than called for in solution and interfacial systems. Thus, higher temperatures are necessary to achieve a reasonable reaction rate. Undesirable side reactions, depolymerization, and degradation of thermally unstable reactants and products can occur at such elevated temperatures. On the other hand, the less reactive reactants are generally less expensive than those called for in solution and interfacial syntheses. The need for near-equivalence of reactants to achieve high polymers is much greater for the melt process than for the other two processes. Solution and interfacial systems have the added expense of solvent utilized in the reaction system and subsequent solvent removal from the polymer. The solution and interfacial systems are often collectively known as the low-temperature methods. Assets of the low-temperature methods often cited include use of cis, trans, or optically active structures without rearrangement; direct polymerization to polymer coatings, fibrous particles, small articles, wires, fibers, and films; and the possible synthesis of thermally unstable products and use of thermally unstable reactants. Most industrial processes utilize the melt and solution techniques although the interfacial technique is gaining limited use.

TABLE 7.3 Comparison of Requirements Between Different Polycondensation Techniques

Requirement	Melt	Solution	Interfacial
Temperature	High	Limited only by MP and BP of solvents utilized—generally about room temperature	
Stability to heat	Necessary	Unnecessary	Unnecessary
Kinetics	Equilibrium, stepwise	Equilibrium, stepwise	Often nonequilibrium; chainlike on a macroscopic level
Reaction time	1 hr to several days	Several minutes to 1 hr	Several minutes to 1 hr
Yield	Necessarily high	Low to high	Low to high
Stoichiometric equivalence	Necessary	Less necessary	Often unnecessary
Purity of reactants	Necessary	Less necessary	Less necessary
Equipment	Specialized, often sealed	Simple, open	Simple, open
Pressure	High, low	Atmospheric	Atmospheric

SUMMARY

1. Many naturally occurring and some synthetic polymers are produced by condensation reactions which are described kinetically by the term step-reaction polymerization. Since a high fractional conversion (p) is required, only a relatively few useful linear polymers, such as polyesters, including polycarbonates plus polyamides, polyurethanes, polyureas, polysulfides, polyoxides, and polysulfones, may be synthesized by step reactions. However, this technique may be used to produce network polymers even when the fractional conversion is relatively low. Phenolic, epoxy, urea, and melamine resins are produced by step-reaction polymerization.

2. Since the fractional conversions are very high, useful polymers may be produced by the step-wise condensation of a bifunctional acyl or

sulfonyl chloride with a diamine or glycol. The rate constant k for these second- and third-order reactions is similar to corresponding reactions of monofunctional reactants and is essentially unchanged as the reactions proceed through dimers, tetramers, octamers, oligomers, and higher molecular weight polymers. This rate constant increases with temperature in accordance with the Arrhenius equation.

3. The degree of polymerization $\overline{DP}$ of a reaction of bifunctional reactants may be calculated from the Carothers' equation, $\overline{DP} = 1/(1 - p)$. However, this value will be changed if cyclization occurs to form "wasted loops." Since this is a step reaction, $\overline{DP}$ increases with time.

4. The index of polydispersity $\overline{M}_w/\overline{M}_n$ for the most probable molecular weight distribution is 1 + p for certain stepwise kinetics. When the value of p is very high, the $\overline{DP}$ may be lowered by the inclusion of a small amount of a monofunctional reactant so that the functionality (f) is reduced below 2.

5. High molecular weight linear polyesters may be produced by ester interchange or by interfacial condensation (Schotten-Baumann reaction). When the functionality of one of the reactants is greater than 2, branching may occur and incipient gelation (α_c) or cross linking may take place. The critical value for α_c is $1/(f - 1)$.

6. The cross linking of polyesters produced from phthalic anhydride and glycerol may be controlled using relatively low-temperature conditions under which the secondary hydroxyl group is not esterified until the temperature is increased. The cross linking of unsaturated polyesters such as alkyds occurs by so-called drying reactions in which cross linking occurs in the presence of oxygen.

7. High molecular weight polyamides, such as nylon-66, may be produced by the thermal decomposition of pure salts of the diamine and dicarboxylic acid reactants. The melting point of these polyamides is decreased as the number of methylene groups in the reactants is increased or if pendant groups are present. The introduction of stiffening groups such as phenylene groups increases the melting point. Polyimides, polybenzimidazoles, polyquinoxaline, and spiroketal polymers have many stiffening groups in the chains and are useful at high temperatures.

8. Polyurethanes and polyureas are produced by the room temperature reaction of a diisocyanate with a dihydric alcohol or a diamine, respectively. When water is present in the reactants, unstable carbamic acids are produced which decompose to form carbon dioxide which serves as a blowing agent for foam production.

9. Flexible and rigid polysulfides are produced by a Williamson condensation of aliphatic reactants and a Wurtz condensation of aromatic reactants, respectively. Rigid polyoxides are produced by the low-temperature oxidative coupling of hindered phenols. Stable rigid aromatic polysulfones are produced by the Friedel-Crafts condensation of phenyl sulfonyl chlorides.

10. Low molecular weight epoxy resins are produced by the condensation of epichlorohydrin and dihydroxy compounds such as bisphenol A. These prepolymers, which contain hydroxyl pendant groups and epoxy end groups, may be cured at room temperature by the reaction of polyamines and at elevated temperature by the reaction with cyclic anhydrides.

11. Linear phenolic and amino resins may be produced by the condensation of formaldehyde with phenol, urea, or melamine under alkaline conditions at moderate temperatures. These A-stage resole resins may be advanced almost to incipient gelation (B-stage) by heating and cured to the C-stage by heating at higher temperatures or by the addition of acids. Novolac resins may be produced under acid conditions by condensing formaldehyde with an excess of phenol. These A-stage linear resins are advanced to the B-stage by heating with hexamethylenetetramine under moderate conditions, and cured to the C-stage in a mold at higher temperatures.

12. When the functionality of phenol, urea, or melamine is reduced to 2 by the incorporation of substituents, the condensation with formaldehyde yields soluble thermoplastics.

GLOSSARY

advancing: Polymerizing further.

alkyds: Originally used to describe oil-modified polyesters, but now used for many polyester plastics and coatings.

allophanates: The reaction product of a urethane and an isocyanate.

α: Symbol for branching coefficient.

α_c: Critical value for incipient gelation.

amino resins: A term used to describe urea and melamine-formaldehyde resins.

Araldite: Tradename for an epoxy resin.

aramides: Aromatic polyamides.

A-stage: A linear prepolymer of phenol and formaldehyde.

Baekeland, Leo: The inventor of phenol-formaldehyde resins.

Bakelite: A polymer produced by the condensation of phenol and formaldehyde.

bifunctional: A molecule with two active functional groups.

bisphenol A: 2,2'-bis(4-hydroxyphenyl)propane.

B-stage: An advanced A-stage resin.

C: Concentration at a temperature (T).

C, A: Concentration at a time T.

C_0, A_0: Original concentration.

carbamate: A urethane.

carbamic acids: Unstable compounds which decompose spontaneously to produce amines and carbon dioxide.

Carothers' equation: 1/(1 - p).

Carothers, W. H.: The inventor of nylon who also developed the kinetic equations for the step-reaction polymerization.

compression molding press: A press that uses external pressure to force a heat-softened molding compound into a die to produce a molded article.

condensation reaction: A reaction in which two molecules react to produce a third molecule and a byproduct such as water.

cyclization: Ring formation.

Dacron: Tradename for a polyester fiber.

drier: A catalyst for cross linking by oxygen. Driers are soluble heavy metal salts such as cobalt naphthenate.

drying: Cross linking of an unsaturated polymer in the presence of oxygen.

drying oil: An unsaturated oil like tung oil.

E_a: Energy of activation.

Ekanol: Tradename for poly-p-benzoate.

engineering plastics: Those with physical properties good enough for use as structural materials.

Epon: Tradename for an epoxy resin.

epoxy resin: A polymer produced by the condensation of epichlorohydrin and a dihydric alcohol or by the epoxidation of an unsaturated compound.

ester interchange: The reaction between an ester of a volatile alcohol and a less volatile alcohol in which the lower boiling alcohol is removed by distillation.

filament: The extrudate when a polymer melt is forced through a hole in a spinneret.

functionality: The number of active functional groups in a molecule.

functionality factor: The average number of functional groups present per reactive molecule in a mixture of reactants.

furan resin: One produced from furfuryl alcohol or furfural.

gel point: The point at which cross linking begins.

glyptals: Polyesters, usually cross-linked by heating at elevated temperatures.

hexamethylenetetramine: A crystalline solid obtained by the condensation of formaldehyde and ammonia.

incipient gelation: The point at which $\overline{DP}$ equals infinity.

interfacial polymerization: One in which the polymerization reaction takes place at the interface of two immiscible liquids.

k: Symbol for rate constant.

Kodel: Tradename for a polyester fiber.

ladder polymer: A double-chained, temperature-resistant polymer.

laminate: Layers of sheets of paper or wood adhered by resins and pressed together like plywood.

long oil alkyd: One obtained in the presence of 65 to 80% of an unsaturated oil.

MF: Melamine-formaldehyde resin.

medium oil alkyd: An alkyd obtained in the presence of 50 to 65% of an unsaturated oil.

melamine-formaldehyde resin: A resin produced by the condensation of melamine and formaldehyde.

methylol: $-CH_2OH$.

molding compound: A name used to describe a mixture of a resin and essential additives.

N: Number of molecules.

network polymer: Infusible cross-linked polymer.

nonoil alkyd: An oil-free alkyd containing no unsaturated oils.

novolac: Polymers prepared by the condensation of phenol and formaldehyde under acidic conditions.

nucleophilic substitution: A reaction in which a nucleophilic reagent (Greek, nucleus loving) displaces a weaker nucleophile or base and the latter becomes the leaving group.

nylon: A synthetic polyamide.

nylon-610 (PA): A polyamide synthesized from a 6-carbon diamine and a 10-carbon dicarboxylic acid.

nylon rope trick: The preparation of a polyamide by the Schotten-Baumann reaction of a diacyl chloride and a diamine.

nylon salt: A salt of a diamine and a dicarboxylic acid used as the precursor of nylon.

oil length: A term used to indicate the relative percentage of unsaturated oils used in the production of alkyds.

ordered copolyamides: Polymers produced from a mixture of diamine and dicarboxylic acid reactants of different types.

p: Fractional conversion or fractional yield.

PA: Symbol for polyamide.

PBI: Symbol for polybenzimidazole.

Perlon U: A tradename for PU.

PF: A phenolic resin.

phenoxy resin: A polymer with hydroxyl pendant groups resembling an epoxy resin without epoxy groups.

PI: Polyimide.

polyamide: A polymer with repeating units of

$$-\overset{\displaystyle H}{\overset{|}{N}}-\overset{\displaystyle O}{\overset{\|}{C}}-R-$$

poly(benzimidazole) (PBI): A temperature-resistant heterocyclic polymer.

polycarbonate (PC): A polymer with the repeating unit of

$$-O-\overset{\displaystyle O}{\overset{\|}{C}}-OR-$$

polyester: A polymer with the repeating unit of

$$-\overset{\displaystyle O}{\overset{\|}{C}}OR-$$

polyethylene terephthalate: A linear polyester used for fibers.

polyimide (PI): A temperature-resistant heterocyclic polymer.

polyphenylene oxide: A polymer with the repeating unit

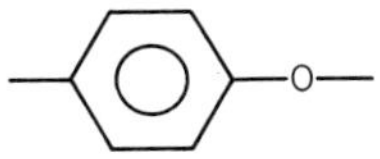

$$-\langle\bigcirc\rangle-O-$$

polyphenylene sulfide: A polymer with the repeating unit

$$-\langle\bigcirc\rangle-S-$$

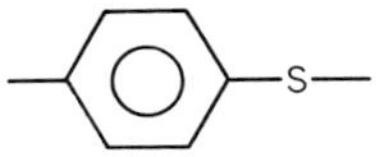

polysulfide: A polymer with the repeating unit $-(RS)_X-$

polysulfone: A polymer with sulfone groups (SO_2) in its backbone.

polyurea: A polymer with the repeating unit of

$$-R-\underset{\text{H}}{\overset{}{N}}-\underset{\|\atop O}{C}-\underset{\text{H}}{N}-$$

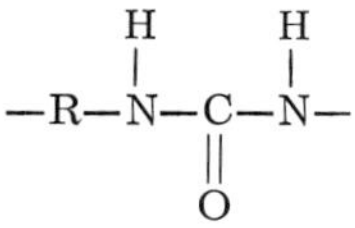

polyurethane (PU): A polymer with the repeating unit of

$$-O-\overset{O}{\overset{\|}{C}}-\overset{H}{\overset{|}{N}}-R-$$

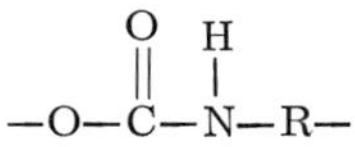

prepolymer: A low molecular weight material (oligomer) capable of further polymerization produced by step-reaction polymerization.

PU: Polyurethane.

r: Molar ratio of reactants.

resite: A cross-linked resole.

resole: A linear polymer prepared by the condensation of phenol and formaldehyde under alkaline conditions.

Ryton: Tradename for polyphenylene sulfide.

Schotten-Baumann reaction: A reaction between an acyl chloride and an alcohol or amine in the presence of sodium hydroxide or pyridine.

second-order reaction: A reaction in which the rate is proportional to the concentration of one reactant to the second power or to the product of two reactants to the first power.

short oil alkyd: An alkyd obtained in the presence of 30 to 50% of an unsaturated oil.

spiropolymer: One having a structure resembling a spiral and thus consisting of a double chain.

step-reaction polymerization: Polymerization in which polyfunctional reactants react to produce larger units in a continuous stepwise manner.

t: Time in seconds.

T: Degrees Kelvin.

TDI: 2,4-tolylene diisocyanate.

Thiokol: Tradename for a polysulfide elastomer.

UF: Symbol for urea-formaldehyde resin.

unsaturated polyester: A term used to describe alkyds with unsaturated chains, particularly those produced by the condensation of maleic anhydride with ethylene glycol.

urea-formaldehyde resin: A resin produced by the condensation of urea and formaldehyde.

wasted loops: The formation of cyclic compounds instead of polymers.

wood flour: A filler produced by the attrition grinding of wood.

EXERCISES

1. Which of the following will yield a polymer when condensed with adipic acid: (a) ethanol, (b) ethylene glycol, (c) glycerol, (d) aniline, or (e) ethylenediamine?
2. Could Carothers have produced strong polyester fibers by ester interchange or Schotten-Baumann reactions using aliphatic reactants?
3. Which would be more useful as a fiber: (a) polyethylene terephthalate or (b) polyhexylene terephthalate?
4. If the fractional conversion in an ester interchange reaction is 0.99999, what would be the $\overline{\mathrm{DP}}$ of the polyester produced?
5. Use the logarithmic form of the Arrhenius equation to show that the value of the rate constant k increases as the temperature increases.
6. What is the first product produced when a molecule of sebacyl chloride reacts with a molecule of ethylene glycol?
7. What is the next product formed in question 6?

8. How would you improve the strength of the filament produced in the nylon rope trick without changing the reactants?

9. Name the product produced by the condensation of adipic acid and tetramethylenediamine.

10. In which reaction would you expect the more "wasted loops": the reaction of oxalyl chloride with (a) ethylenediamine, or (b) hexamethylenediamine?

11. Which system would be more apt to produce "wasted loops": (a) a dilute solution or (b) a concentrated solution?

12. If the values of A_0 and k are 10 mol liter^{-1} and 10^{-3} liter mol sec^{-1}, respectively, how long would it take to obtain a $\overline{DP}$ of 37?

13. Which will yield the lower index of dispersibility: (a) p = 0.999 or (b) p = 0.90?

14. If you used a 2% molar excess of bisphenol A with TDI, what would be the maximum $\overline{DP}$ obtainable:

15. Why would the product obtained in question 14 be a useful fiber assuming $\overline{DP}$ = 100?

16. Assuming a value of 0.999 for p, what would be the $\overline{DP}$ of a polyester prepared from equimolar quantities of difunctional reactants in the presence of 1.5 mol% of acetic acid?

17. What is the functionality of a mixture consisting of 0.7 mol of ethylene glycol, 0.05 mol of ethanol, and 0.25 mol of glycerol?

18. What is the critical value of f for incipient gelation in the mixture described in question 17?

19. What is the functionality of a mixture consisting of 0.4 mol of pentaerythritol and 0.6 mol of diethylene glycol?

20. Which would be the better fiber: one made from an ester of (a) terephthalic acid, or (b) phthalic acid?

21. What would be the deficiency of a nylon film that was stretched in one direction only?

22. Which would be more flexible? (a) polybutylene terephthalate or (b) polyhexylene terephthalate?

23. Which would be more apt to deteriorate in the presence of moisture: (a) Lexan molding powder or (b) Lexan sheet?

24. How could you flexibilize Ekanol?

25. How would you prepare a nylon with greater moisture resistance than nylon-66?
26. How would you prepare a nylon that would be less "clammy" when used as clothing?
27. Which would be higher melting: (a) a polyamide or (b) a polyester with similar numbers of methylene groups in the repeating units?
28. Why is a methoxymethylated nylon more flexible than nylon?
29. Which would perform better at high temperatures: (a) a polyimide or (b) polyquinoxaline?
30. Isn't it wasteful to decompose a diisocyanate by hydrolysis to produce foams?
31. How would you prepare a hydroxyl-terminated polyester?
32. How would you prepare a more flexible polyalkylene sulfide than the one shown in Sec. 7.10?
33. Why is Ryton stiffer than Thiokol?
34. Why do polyurethanes and epoxy resins have good adhesive properties?
35. Why are furan resins relatively inexpensive?
36. Why is it necessary to add hexamethylenetetramine to a novolac molding compound?
37. Could you produce a soluble novolac resin from resorcinol?
38. Can you explain why there are so many terms used, such as novolac, resole, etc., in phenolic resin technology?
39. Why isn't Bakelite used for dinnerware?
40. Which of the following could be a nonpetrochemical plastic: (a) Bakelite, (b) urea plastics, or (c) melamine plastics?
41. Which would produce the better fiber, the reaction product of phthalic acid and (1) 1,4-butanediol or (b) 2-hydroxybutanol?

BIBLIOGRAPHY

Allcock, H. R. (1967): Heteroatom Ring Systems and Polymers, Academic, New York.

Androva, N. A., Bessonov, M. I., Rudakov, L. A. (1970): Polimides—A New Class of Thermally Stable Polymers, Technomic, Stanford, Connecticut.

Baeyer, A. (1878): Phenol-formaldehyde condensates, Ber. Bunsenges. Phys. Chem., 5:280, 1094.

Bailey, F. E., Koleske, J. V. (1976): Poly(ethylene oxide), Academic, New York.

Bamford, C. H., Tipper, C. F. (1976): Non-Radical Polymerization, Elsevier, Amsterdam.

Bayer, O. (1941): Polyurethanes, Ann., 549:286.

Bayer, O., Muller, E. (1960): Polyurethanes, Agnew. Chem., 72:934.

Bertozzi, E. F. (1968): Polysulfide elastomers, Rubber Chem. Technol., 41:114.

Billmeyer, F. W. (1971): Textbook of Polymer Science, Chap. 8, Wiley Interscience, New York.

Bjorksten, J., Tovey, H., Harker, B., Henning, J. (1956): Polyesters and Their Applications, Reinhold, New York.

Boyd, W. H., Merriam, C. N. (1975): Chemistry and Technology of Phenolic Resins, Chap. 48 in Applied Polymer Science (J. K. Craven and R. W. Tess, eds.), Organic Coatings and Plastics Chemistry Division of ACS, Washington, D.C.

Brydson, J. A. (1975): Plastic Materials, Newnes-Butterworths, Kent, England.

Burnett, G. M. (1954): Mechanism of Polymer Reactions, Interscience, New York.

Carothers, W. H. (1929): An introduction to the general theory of condensation polymers, J. Am. Chem. Soc., 51:2548-2559.

——. (1938): Nylon, U.S. Patent 2,130,947.

Carothers, W. H., Arvin, J. A. (1929): Polyesters, J. Am. Chem. Soc., 51:2560.

Carraher, C. E. (1972): Group IVA polymers by the interfacial technique, Inorg. Macromol. Rev., 1:271.

Carswell, T. S. (1947): Phenoplasts, Their Structure, Properties and Chemical Technology, Interscience, New York.

Christopher, W. F., Fox, D. W. (1962): Polycarbonates, Reinhold, New York.

Corkum, R. T., Herbes, W. F., Lanes, L. C., Oldham, W. N. (1964): Melamines, Chap 9 in Manufacture of Plastics (W. M. Smith, ed.), Reinhold, New York.

Cowie, J. M. G. (1973): Polymers: Chemistry and Physics of Modern Materials, Chap. 2, Intext Educational Publishers, New York.

Delmonte, J. (1966): Furane resins, Mod. Plastics, 44:172.

Dombrow, B. A. (1957): Polyurethanes, Reinhold, New York.

Doyle, E. N. (1974): The Development of Polyurethane Products, McGraw-Hill, New York.

Dunlap, A. P., Peters, F. N. (1953): The Furans, Reinhold, New York.

Eaborn, C. (1960): Organosilicon Compounds, Academic, New York.

Fettes, E. M., Jorczak, J. S. (1956): Polysulfides, Chap. 11 in Polymer Processes (C. E. Schildknecht, ed.), Interscience, New York.

Flory, P. J. (1946): Fundamental principles of condensation polymerization, Chem. Rev., 39:137-197.

———. (1953): Principles of Polymer Chemistry, Cornell University Press, Ithaca, New York.

Floyd, D. E. (1958): Polyamide Resins, Reinhold, New York.

Frisch, K. C. (1972): Cyclic Monomers, Wiley Interscience, New York.

———. (1976): Urethane coatings, Chap. 54 in Applied Polymer Chemistry (J. K. Craven and R. W. Tess, eds.), Organic Coatings and Plastics Chemistry Division of ACS, Washington, D.C.

Frisch, K. C., Reegen, S. L. (1973): Advances in Urethane Science and Technology, Technomic, Westport, Connecticut.

Gingold, K. (1973): Soviet Urethane Technology, Technomic, Westport, Connecticut.

Gould, D. F. (1959): Phenolic Resins, Reinhold, New York.

Hill, J. W., Carothers, W. H. (1932, 1933): Polyanhydrides, J. Am. Chem. Soc., 54:1569; 55:5023.

Hill, R. (1953): Fibers from Synthetic Polymers, Elsevier, Amsterdam.

Howard, G. J. (1961): The molecular weight distribution of condensation polymers, pp. 185-231 in Progress in High Polymers (J. C. Robb and F. W. Peaker, eds.), Vol. 1, Academic, New York.

Hutz, C. E. (1964): Epoxy resins, Chap. 13 in Manufacture of Plastics (W. M. Smith, ed.), Reinhold, New York.

Inderfurth, K. H. (1953): Nylon Technology, McGraw-Hill, New York.

Jorczak, J. S. (1959): Polysulfide polymers, Chap. 15 in Introduction to Rubber Technology (M. Morton, ed.), Reinhold, New York.

Kienle, R. H. (1930, 1936): Alkyds, Ind. Eng. Chem., 22:590; 55:229T.

Kirshenbaum, G. S. (1973): Polymer Science Study Guide, Section B, Chap. 1, Gordon and Breach, New York.

Kohan, M. I. (1974): Nylon Plastics, SPE, Greenwich, Connecticut.

Kovacic, P., Kyriakis, A. (1961): Polyphenylenes, J. Am. Chem. Soc., 83:1697.

Kunin, R. (1972): Ion Exchange Resins, Robert E. Krieger, Huntington, New York.

Lawrence, J. R. (1960): Polyester Resins, Reinhold, New York.

Lee, H., Neville, K. (1966): Handbook of Epoxy Resins, McGraw-Hill, New York.

Lenz, R. W. (1967): Organic Chemistry of Synthetic High Polymers, Wiley Interscience, New York.

———. (1969): Applied reaction kinetics: Polymerization reaction kinetics, Ind. Eng. Chem., 61:67-75.

———. (1970): Applied polymerization reaction kinetics, Ind. Eng. Chem., 62:54-61.

Mark, H. F. (1943): The mechanism of polymerization, Chap. 1 in The Chemistry of Large Molecules (R. E. Burke and O. Gummit, eds.), Interscience, New York.

Mark, H., Tobolsky, A. V. (1950): Physical Chemistry of High Polymeric Systems, Interscience, New York.

Mark, H. F., Whitby, G. S. (eds.) (1940): The Collected Papers of Wallace Hume Carothers, Interscience, New York.

Martens, C. R. (1961): Alkyd Resins, Reinhold, New York.

Martin, R. W. (1956): The Chemistry of Phenolic Resins, John Wiley, New York.

Martin, S. M., Patrick, J. C. (1936): Thiokol, Ind. Eng. Chem., 28:1144.

Marvel, C. S. (1959): An Introduction to the Organic Chemistry of High Polymers, John Wiley, New York.

———. (1967): Polyaromatic heterocycles, Proceedings of the Robert A. Welch Foundation Conference in Chemistry Research, 10th Polymers, Houston.

May, C. A., Tanaka, Y. (1973): Epoxy Resins: Chemistry and Technology, Dekker, New York.

McGregor, R. R. (1954): Silicones and Their Uses, McGraw-Hill, New York.

Meals, R. N., Lewis, F. M. (1959): Silicones, Reinhold, New York.

Megson, N. J. L. (1958): Phenolic Resin Chemistry, Academic, New York.

Milby, P. V. (1973): Plastics Technology, McGraw-Hill, New York.

Millich, F., Carraher, C. E. (1977): Interfacial Synthesis, Dekker, New York.

Morgan, P. W. (1965): Condensation Polymers by Interface and Solution Methods, Wiley, New York.

Morgan, P. W., Kwolek, S. L. (1959): The Nylon Rope Trick, J. Chem. Ed., 36:182-184.

Mukamal, H., Harries, F. W., Stille, J. K. (1967): Polyphenylenes, J. Polymer Sci., Pt. A-1, 5:272.

Odian, G. (1970): Principles of Polymerization, McGraw-Hill, New York.

Ogorkiewiz, R. M. (1974): Thermoplastics—Properties and Design, John Wiley, New York.

Parker, D. B. V. (1975): Polymer Chemistry, Applied Science Publishers, Essex, England.

Patton, T. C. (1962): Alkyd Resins Technology, Wiley Interscience, New York.

Shechter, L., Wynstra, J., Kurkjy, R. P. (1956): Epoxy resins, Ind. Eng. Chem., 48:86, 94.

Sittig, M. (1972): Polyamide Fiber Manufacture, Noyes Data Corporation, Park Ridge, New Jersey.

Skeist, I. (1958): Epoxy Resins, Reinhold, New York.

Smith, A. L. (1975): Analysis of Silicones, Wiley Interscience, New York.

Soloman, D. H. (1974): Step Growth Polymerizations, Dekker, New York.

Somerville, G. R., Jones, P. D. (1975): Epoxy resin chemistry and technology, Chap. 52 in Applied Polymer Science (J. K. Craven and R. W. Tess, eds.), Organic Coatings and Plastics Chemistry of ACS, Washington, D.C.

Sorenson, W. R., Campbell, T. W. (1968): Preparative Methods of Polymer Chemistry, 2nd ed., Wiley Interscience, New York.

Spitzer, W. C. (1964): Alkyd resins, Offic. Dig. Fed. Soc. Paint Technol., 36:16.

Stevens, M. P. (1975): Polymer Chemistry, an Introduction, Chap. 9, Addison-Wesley, Reading, Massachusetts.

Stille, J. K., Campbell, T. W. (1972): Condensation Monomers, Wiley Interscience, New York.

Stivala, S. S. (1956): Epoxy resins, Chap. 10 in Polymer Processes (C. E. Schildknecht, ed.), Interscience, New York.

Suen, T. J. (1956): Condensations with formaldehyde, Chap. 8 in Polymer Processes (C. E. Schildknecht, ed.), Interscience, New York.

Vale, C. P. (1950): Aminoplastics, Cleaver-Hume Press, London.

Vollmert, B. (1973): Polymer Chemistry, Chap. 22, Springer-Verlag, New York.

Whinfield, J. R. (1946): Terylene, Nature, 158:930.

Whitehouse, A. A. K., Pritchett, E. G. K. (1955): Phenolic Resins, Plastics Institute, London.

Williams, D. J. (1971): Polymer Science and Engineering, Chap. 3, Prentice Hall, Englewood Cliffs, New Jersey.

8

Ionic Chain-Reaction and Complex Coordinative Polymerization (Addition Polymerization)

In contrast to the slow step-reaction polymerization discussed in Chap. 7, chain-reaction polymerization is usually rapid, and the initiated species continue to propagate until termination. Thus, in the extreme case, one could produce one initiating species which would produce one high molecular weight polymer molecule, leaving all the other monomer molecules unchanged. In any case, the concentration of the monomer, which is usually a derivative of ethylene, decreases continuously throughout the reaction. In contrast to stepwise polymerization, the first species produced is a high molecular weight polymer.

A kinetic chain reaction usually consists of at least three steps, namely, initiation, propagation, and termination. The initiator may be an anion, a cation, a free radical, or a coordination catalyst. While coordination catalysts are the most important commercially, the ionic initiators will be discussed first in an attempt to simplify the discussion of chain-reaction polymerization.

8.1 CATIONIC POLYMERIZATION

The art of cationic polymerization, like many other types of polymerization, is at least a century old. However, the mechanisms for the early reactions were not understood, and, of course, the early scientists did not understand the modern concept of macromolecules. Nevertheless, it is of interest to note that turpentine, styrene, isobutylene, and ethyl vinyl ether were polymerized over a century ago by the use of cationic initiators such as sulfuric acid, tin(IV)chloride, boron trifluoride, and iodine.

The first species produced in these reactions are carbocations, and these were unknown as such prior to World War II. It is now known that pure Lewis acids, such as boron trifluoride or aluminum chloride, are not effective as initiators. A trace of a proton-containing Lewis base, such as water, is also required. As shown in (8.1), the Lewis base coordinates with the electrophilic Lewis acid, and the proton is the actual initiator. Since cations cannot exist alone, they are always accompanied by a counterion, also called a gegenion.

$$\underset{\substack{\text{Lewis}\\ \text{acid}\\ \text{(boron}\\ \text{trifluoride)}}}{BF_3} + \underset{\substack{\text{Lewis}\\ \text{base}\\ \text{(cocatalyst)}}}{H_2O} \rightleftharpoons \underset{\substack{\text{Catalyst-}\\ \text{cocatalyst}\\ \text{complex}}}{H^{\oplus}\ (BF_3OH^-)} \qquad (8.1)$$

Since the required activation energy for ionic polymerization is small, these reactions may occur at very low temperatures. The carbocations, including the macrocarbocations, repel each other, and, hence, chain termination cannot take place by combination, but is usually the result of reaction with impurities.

Both the initiation step and the propagation step are dependent on the stability of the carbocations. Isobutylene (the first monomer to be polymerized commercially by ionic initiators), vinyl ethers, and styrene may be polymerized by this technique. The order of activity for olefins is $(CH_3)_2C{=}CH_2 > CH_3(CH{=}CH_2) > CH_2{=}CH_2$, and for para-substituted styrenes, the order for the substituents is $OCH_3 > CH_3 > H > Cl$. The mechanism is also dependent on the solvent as well as the electrophilicity of the monomer and the nucleophilicity of the gegenion. Rearrangements may occur in ionic polymerizations.

The rate of initiation (R_i) for typical reactions (as shown in the following equation) is proportional to the concentration of the monomer [M] and the concentration of the catalyst-cocatalyst complex [C].

$$\underset{\text{Isobutylene}}{H_2C{=}C(CH_3)_2} + \underset{\substack{\text{Catalyst-}\\ \text{cocatalyst}\\ \text{complex}}}{H^+\ (BF_3OH^-)} \xrightarrow{k_i} \underset{\substack{\text{Carbonium}\\ \text{ion}}}{H_3CC^{\oplus}(CH_3)_2} + \underset{\text{Gegenion}}{BF_3OH^-} \qquad (8.2)$$

$$R_i = k_i[C][M]$$

Propagation, or chain growth, takes place in a head-to-tail configuration as a result of carbocation (M^+) addition to another monomer molecule. The rate constant (k_p) is essentially the same for all propagation steps and is affected by the dielectric constant of the solvent. The rate is fastest in solvents with high dielectric constants, promoting separation of the carbocation-gegenion pairs. The chemical and kinetic equations for propagation are shown in (8.3):

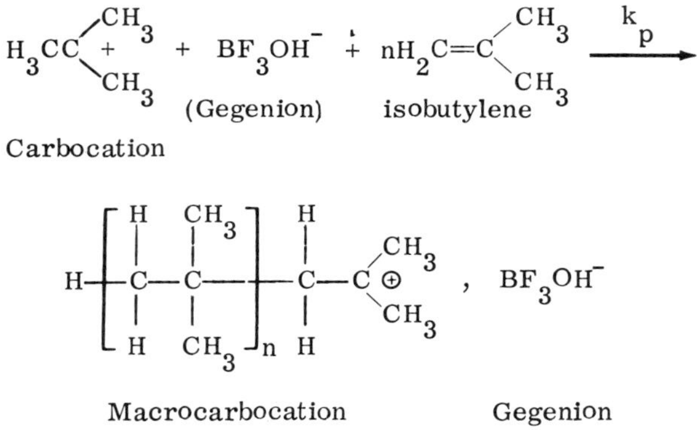

$$\underset{\text{Carbocation}}{H_3CC^{+}(CH_3)_2} + \underset{\text{(Gegenion)}}{BF_3OH^-} + \underset{\text{isobutylene}}{nH_2C{=}C(CH_3)_2} \xrightarrow{k_p}$$

$$\underset{\text{Macrocarbocation}}{H{-}\!\left[\!-CH_2-C(CH_3)_2-\right]_n\!-CH_2-C^{\oplus}(CH_3)_2}\ ,\ \underset{\text{Gegenion}}{BF_3OH^-} \qquad (8.3)$$

$$R_p = k_p[M][M^+]$$

The termination rate R_T, assumed to be a first-order process, is simply the dissociation of the carbonium-gegenion radical forming here BF_3 and H_2O and the now neutral polymer chain, and may be expressed as follows:

$$R_T = k_T[M^+] \qquad (8.4)$$

Termination may take place by chain transfer, in which a proton is transferred to a monomer molecule [M], leaving a cation which may serve as an initiator. The $\overline{DP}$ is equal to the kinetic chain length (ν) when chain transfer occurs. The chemical and kinetic equations for chain transfer are shown below.

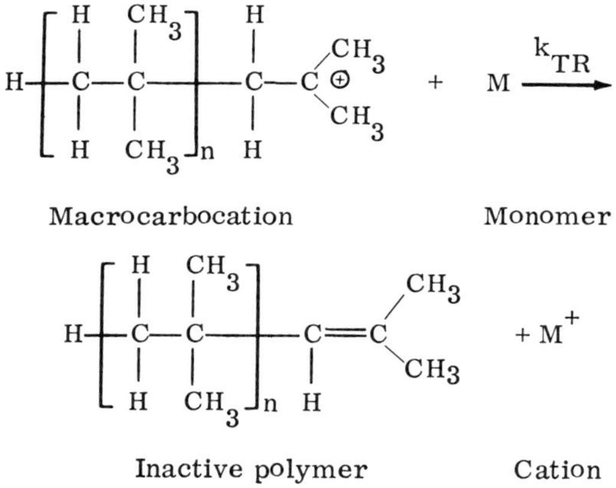

$$\underset{\text{Macrocarbocation}}{H{-}\!\left[\!-CH_2-C(CH_3)_2-\right]_n\!-CH_2-C^{\oplus}(CH_3)_2} + \underset{\text{Monomer}}{M} \xrightarrow{k_{TR}} \qquad (8.5)$$

$$\underset{\text{Inactive polymer}}{H{-}\!\left[\!-CH_2-C(CH_3)_2-\right]_n\!-CH{=}C(CH_3)_2} + \underset{\text{Cation}}{M^+}$$

$$R_{Tr} = k_{Tr}[M][M^+]$$

Since it is difficult to solve these equations which include $[M^+]$, one assumes a steady state in which the rate of initiation equals the rate of termination, giving $R_i = R_T$; and we solve for $[M^+]$ as shown below:

$$k_1C[M] = k_T[M^+] \quad \text{therefore} \quad [M^+] = \frac{k_1[C][M]}{k_T} \tag{8.6}$$

This expression for $[M^+]$ may then be substituted in the propagation rate equation—also the overall rate for cationic polymerization:

$$R_p = k_p[M][M^+] = \frac{k_p k_1 [C][M]^2}{k_T} = k'[C][M]^2 \tag{8.7}$$

We may also determine the value for $\overline{DP}$ when termination, via internal dissociation (8.4), is the dominant step, as follows:

$$\overline{DP} = \frac{R_p}{R_T} = \frac{k_p[M][M^+]}{k_T[M^+]} = \frac{k_p}{k_T}[M] = k''[M] \tag{8.8}$$

However, if chain transfer is the dominant step in the termination of a growing chain,

$$\overline{DP} = \frac{R_p}{R_{Tr}} = \frac{k_p[M][M^+]}{k_{Tr}[M][M^+]} = \frac{k_p}{k_{Tr}} = k''' \tag{8.9}$$

It is important to note that regardless of how termination takes place, the molecular weight of a polymer synthesized by the cationic process is independent of the concentration of the initiator. However, the rate of ionic chain polymerization is dependent on the dielectric constant of the solvent, the resonance stability of the carbonium ion, the stability of the gegenion, and the electropositivity of the initiator.

Polyisobutylene (Vistanex, IM), a variety of butyl rubber, is a tacky polymer with a very low T_g (−70°C) used as an adhesive, a caulking compound, a chewing gum base, and an oil additive. Its use as an oil additive is related to its change in shape with increasing temperature. Since lubricating oil is not a good solvent for polyisobutylene, polyisobutylene is present as a coil at room temperature when mixed with an oil. However, the chain tends to uncoil as the temperature increases and as the oil becomes a better solvent. This effect tends to counteract the decrease in viscosity of the oil as the temperature is increased.

Butyl rubber (IIR), widely used for inner tubes and as a sealant, is produced by the cationic low-temperature copolymerization of isobutylene in the presence of a small amount of isoprene (10%), as shown in Scheme 8.1. Thus, the random copolymer chain contains widely isolated double bonds which assure a low cross-linked density as a result of the formation of large "principal sections" when the butyl rubber is vulcanized or cured. (Copolymers are discussed in Chap. 10.)

$$\text{H}\!-\!\!\left[\begin{array}{cccccc} \text{H} & \text{CH}_3 & & \text{H} & \text{CH}_3\,\text{H} & \text{H} \\ | & | & & | & | \quad | & | \\ \text{C}- & \text{C}- & - & \text{C}- & \text{C}=\text{C}- & \text{C} \\ | & | & & | & & | \\ \text{H} & \text{CH}_3 & & \text{H} & & \text{H} \end{array}\right]_n\!\!-\text{H}$$

Scheme 8.1 A section of a typical repeating unit in the butyl rubber chain.

When the gegenion and the carbocation present in the polymerization of vinyl isobutyl ether form an ion pair in propane at -40°C, stereoregular polymers are produced. The carbocations of vinyl alkyl ethers are stabilized by the delocalization of p electrons in the oxygen atom, and thus these monomers are readily polymerized by cationic initiators. Polyvinyl isobutyl ether

$$\left[\begin{array}{cc} \text{H} & \text{H} \\ | & | \\ \text{C}- & \text{C} \\ | & | \\ \text{H} & \text{OC}_4\text{H}_9 \end{array}\right]_n$$

has a low T_g and is used as an adhesive and as an impregnating resin.

The value of the propagation rate constant (k_p) for vinyl isobutyl ether is 6.5 liters mol^{-1} sec^{-1}. This value decreases as one goes from vinyl ethers to isoprene, isobutylene, butadiene, and styrene. The k_p value for styrene in 1,1-dichloroethane is 0.0037 liter mol^{-1} sec^{-1}.

Commercial polymers of formaldehyde may also be produced by cationic polymerization using boron trifluoride etherate as the initiator. As shown by the following equation, the polymer is produced by ring opening of the trioxane trimer. Since the polyacetal is not thermally stable, the hydroxyl end groups are esterified (capped) by acetic anhydride. The commercial polymer is a strong engineering thermoplastic. Engineering plastics usually have higher modulus and higher heat resistance than general-purpose polymers. The commercial polymer Delrin is produced by anionic polymerization.

$$\frac{n}{3}\ \text{Trioxane} + H^+ \longrightarrow HO\!-\!\!\left[CH_2O\right]_n\!\!-\!H \xrightarrow{Ac_2O} AcO\!-\!\!\left[CH_2O\right]_{n-1}\!\!-\!CH_2OAc \qquad (8.10)$$

Trioxane Polyacetal Stable polyoxymethylene (POM)

Another stable polyacetal [polyoxymethylene—POM; Celcon] is produced commercially by the cationic copolymerization of a mixture of trioxane and dioxolane. As shown in Scheme 8.2, this copolymer contains repeating units from both reactants in the polymer chain. It is believed that the irregularities in the composition of the copolymer hinder the "unzipping" degradation pathway of the polymeric chain.

$$HO\!-\!\!\left[CH_2OCH_2O(CH_2)_2OCH_2O\right]_n$$

Scheme 8.2 A segment of a copolymer chain produced from the cationic copolymerization of trioxane and dioxolane.

Polychloral is a flame-resistant, strong polymer that can be produced by cationic polymerization. The uncapped polymer decomposes at a ceiling temperature of 58°C. Since the polymer does not exist above this temperature, it is called the ceiling temperature T_c. Thus, one may produce solid castings by pouring a hot mixture of trichloroacetaldehyde and initiator into a mold and allowing the polymerization to take place in situ as the mixture cools below the ceiling temperature.

In addition to the production of polyacetals by the ring-opening polymerization of trioxane, this technique was also investigated by Staudinger for the synthesis of polyethers, and is still used for the production of polymers of ethylene oxide (oxirane). Other homologous, cyclic ethers, such as oxetane and tetrahydrofuran, may be polymerized by cationic ring-opening polymerization techniques. Since the tendency for ring cleavage decreases as the size of the ring increases, it is customary to include some oxirane with the reactants as a promotor. The six-membered ring oxacyclohexane is so stable that it does not polymerize even in the presence of a promotor.

As shown in the following equations, an initiator such as sulfuric acid produces an oxonium ion and a gegenion. The oxonium ion then adds to the oxirane, and the macrooxonium ion produced by propagation may then be terminated by chain transfer with water.

$$\underset{\text{Oxirane}}{H_2C\overset{O}{\triangle}CH_2} + \underset{\text{Sulfuric acid}}{H_2SO_4} \rightleftharpoons \underset{\text{Oxonium ion}}{H_2C\overset{\overset{H}{|}}{\overset{O+}{\triangle}}CH_2}, \quad \underset{\text{Gegenion}}{HSO_4^-}$$

$$\underset{\text{Oxonium ion}}{H_2C\overset{\overset{H}{|}}{\overset{O+}{\triangle}}CH_2}, \quad HSO_4^- + n\underset{\text{Oxirane}}{H_2C\overset{O}{\triangle}CH_2} \rightleftharpoons \tag{8.11}$$

$$\underset{\text{Macrooxonium ion}}{H\!\left[O(CH_2)_2\right]_n\overset{+}{O}\!\!<\!\!\begin{array}{l}CH_2\\ |\\ CH_2\end{array}}, \quad \underset{\text{Gegenion}}{HSO_4^-}$$

$$\underset{\text{Macrooxonium ion}}{H\!\left[O(CH_2)_2\right]_n\overset{+}{O}\!\!<\!\!\begin{array}{l}CH_2\\ |\\ CH_2\end{array}}, \quad \underset{\text{Gegenion}}{HSO_4^-} \xrightarrow{H_2O}$$

$$\underset{\text{Dead polymer}}{H\!\left[O(CH_2)_2\right]\!\left[O(CH_2)_2\right]OH} + \underset{\text{Sulfuric acid}}{H_2SO_4}$$

As indicated by the double arrow, the propagation is an equilibrium reaction that tends to hinder the production of high molecular weight polymers. The highest molecular weight products are obtained in polar solvents, such as methylene chloride, at low temperatures (-20° to -100°C).

These water-soluble polymers, which may also be produced by anionic polymerization techniques, are available commercially in several molecular weight ranges under the tradenames of Carbowax and Polyox. In addition to their use as water-soluble bases for cosmetics and pharmaceuticals, these polymers may be added to water to increase its flow rate.

The oxacyclobutane derivative, 3,3-bis-chloromethyloxacyclobutane, may be polymerized by cationic ring-opening polymerization techniques to yield a water-insoluble, crystalline, corrosion-resistant polymer. As shown in Scheme 8.3, this polymer (Penton) has two regularly spaced chloromethylene pendant groups on the polymer chain.

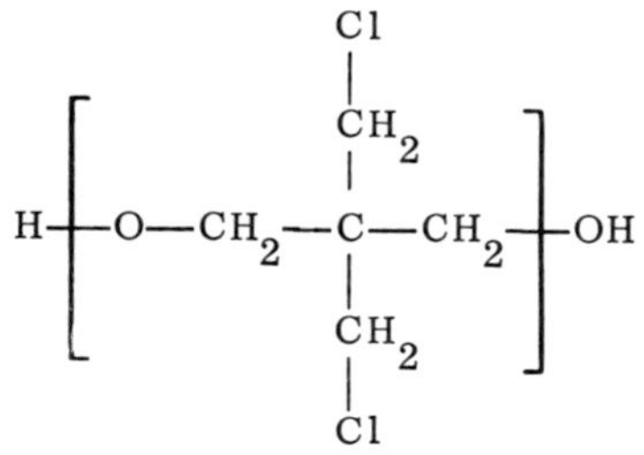

$$H\left[O-CH_2-\underset{\underset{Cl}{|}}{\underset{CH_2}{|}}{\overset{\overset{Cl}{|}}{\overset{CH_2}{|}}{C}}-CH_2\right]OH$$

Scheme 8.3 Poly-3,3-bis-chloromethyloxybutylene.

An acid-soluble polymer, Montrek, has also been produced by the ring-opening polymerization of ethyleneimine (aziridine). This monomer has been classified as a carcinogen and should be used with extreme caution.

While lactams are usually polymerized by anionic ring-opening reactions, N-carboxyl-α-amino acid anhydrides (NCA) may be polymerized by either cationic or anionic techniques. These polypeptide products, which are now called nylon-2, were first produced by Leuchs in 1908 and are called Leuchs' anhydrides. The synthesis may be used to produce homopolypeptides that can be used as model compounds for proteins. As shown in the following equation, carbon dioxide is eliminated in each step of the propagation reaction.

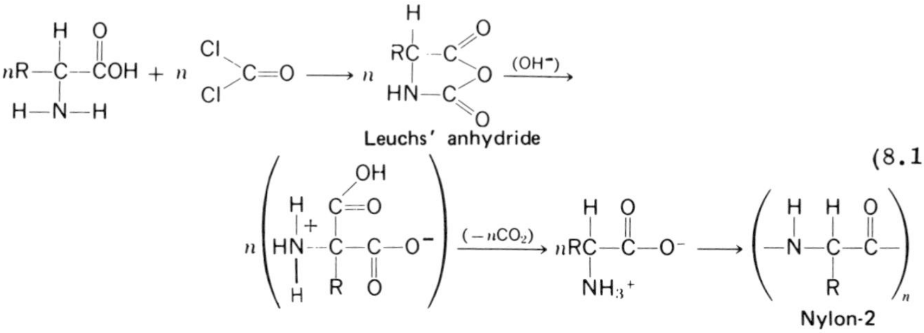

$$nR-\overset{H}{\underset{H-N-H}{C}}-\overset{O}{\overset{\|}{C}}OH + n\,Cl_2C{=}O \longrightarrow n\,\underset{\text{Leuchs' anhydride}}{\left(\begin{array}{c}H\\ RC-C(=O)\\ |\quad\;\; O\\ HN-C(=O)\end{array}\right)} \xrightarrow{(OH^-)}$$

$$n\left(H_2\overset{+}{N}-\overset{\overset{OH}{C=O}}{\underset{R}{C}}-\underset{O}{\overset{}{\underset{\|}{C}}}-O^-\right) \xrightarrow{(-nCO_2)} nR\overset{H}{\underset{NH_3^+}{C}}-\overset{O}{\overset{\|}{C}}-O^- \longrightarrow \underset{\text{Nylon-2}}{\left(-\overset{H}{N}-\overset{H}{\underset{R}{C}}-\overset{O}{\overset{\|}{C}}-\right)_n} \qquad (8.12)$$

Polyterpenes, coumarone-indene resins, and the so-called petroleum resins are produced commercially in relatively large quantities by the cationic polymerization of unsaturated cyclic compounds. These inexpensive resinous products are used as additives for rubber, coatings, floor coverings, and adhesives.

It has been known for some time that cationic polymerizations can produce polymers with stereoregular structures. While a number of vinyl monomers have been evaluated in this regard, much of the work has centered about vinyl ethers. Several general observations have been noted, namely: (1) the amount of stereoregularity is dependent on the nature of the initiator; (2) stereoregularity increases with a decrease in temperature; and (3) the amount and type of polymer (isotactic or syndiotactic) is dependent on the polarity of the solvent. For instance, t-butyl vinyl ether (Scheme 8.4) has the isotactic form emphasized in nonpolar solvents, but the syndiotactic form emphasized in polar solvents.

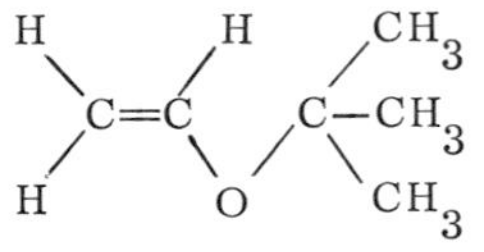

$$\begin{array}{ccccccc} H & & H & & & CH_3 & \\ & \diagdown & \diagup & & \diagup & & \\ & C{=}C & & C{-}CH_3 & & & \\ \diagup & & \diagdown & \diagup & \diagdown & & \\ H & & O & & CH_3 & & \end{array}$$

Scheme 8.4

8.2 ANIONIC POLYMERIZATION

Anionic polymerization was used to produce synthetic elastomers from butadiene at the beginning of the twentieth century. Early investigators used alkali metals in liquid ammonia as initiators, but these were replaced in the 1940s by metal alkyls such as n-butyllithium. In contrast to vinyl monomers with electron-donating groups polymerized by cationic initiators, vinyl monomers with electron-withdrawing groups are more readily polymerized by anionic initiators. Accordingly, acrylonitrile is readily polymerized by anionic techniques, and the order of activity with an amide ion initiator is as follows: acrylonitrile > methyl methacrylate > styrene > butadiene. As might be expected, methyl groups on the α carbon decrease the rate of anionic polymerization, and chlorine atoms on the α carbon increase that activity.

As shown by the following chemical and kinetic equations, potassium amide may be used to initiate the polymerization of acrylonitrile. The propagating species in anionic polymerizations are carbanions instead of carbonium ions, but the initiation, propagation, and chain transfer termination steps in anionic polymerizations are similar to those described for cationic polymerizations.

$$:NH_2^- + H_2C{=}\underset{\displaystyle |}{\overset{\displaystyle CN}{CH}} \xrightarrow{k_i} H_2N\underset{\displaystyle H}{\overset{\displaystyle H}{C}}{-}\underset{\displaystyle H}{\overset{\displaystyle CN}{C}}:^- \tag{8.13}$$

Amide ion   Acrylonitrile   Carbanion

$$R_i = k_i C[M]$$

where C is equal to $[:NH_2^-]$.

$$H_2N\underset{\displaystyle H}{\overset{\displaystyle H}{C}}{-}\underset{\displaystyle H}{\overset{\displaystyle CN}{C}}:^- + nH_2C{=}\overset{\displaystyle CN}{CH} \xrightarrow{k_p} H_2N{\left(\underset{\displaystyle H}{\overset{\displaystyle H}{C}}{-}\underset{\displaystyle H}{\overset{\displaystyle CN}{C}}\right)_n}\underset{\displaystyle H}{\overset{\displaystyle H}{C}}{-}\underset{\displaystyle H}{\overset{\displaystyle CN}{C}}:^- \tag{8.14}$$

Carbanion   Acrylonitrile   Macrocarbanion

$$R_p = k_p[M][M^-]$$

where $[M^-]$ = concentration of carbanion.

$$H_2N{\left(\underset{\displaystyle H}{\overset{\displaystyle H}{C}}{-}\underset{\displaystyle H}{\overset{\displaystyle CN}{C}}\right)_n}\underset{\displaystyle H}{\overset{\displaystyle H}{C}}{-}\underset{\displaystyle H}{\overset{\displaystyle CN}{C}}:^- + NH_3 \xrightarrow{k_{Tr}} H_2N{\left(\underset{\displaystyle H}{\overset{\displaystyle H}{C}}{-}\underset{\displaystyle H}{\overset{\displaystyle CN}{C}}\right)_n}\underset{\displaystyle H}{\overset{\displaystyle H}{C}}{-}\underset{\displaystyle H}{\overset{\displaystyle CN}{CH}} + :NH_2^- \tag{8.15}$$

Macrocarbanion   Ammonia (solvent)   Dead polymer

$$R_{Tr} = k_{Tr}[NH_3][M^-]$$

Since it is difficult to determine the concentration of carbanion $[M^-]$, we assume a steady state in which $R_i = R_{Tr}$ and solve for $[M^-]$, as shown below.

$$k_i C[M] = k_{Tr}[NH_3][M^-] \quad \text{therefore} \quad [M^-] = \frac{k_i}{k_{Tr}} \frac{C[M]}{[NH_3]} \tag{8.16}$$

Thus,

$$R_p = k_p[M][M^-] = [M]\frac{k_p k_i}{k_{Tr}}\frac{C[M]}{[NH_3]} = \frac{[M]^2 C}{[NH_3]}\frac{k_i k_p}{k_{Tr}} = k'\frac{[M]^2 C}{[NH_3]} \tag{8.17}$$

therefore,

$$\overline{DP} = \frac{R_p}{R_{Tr}} = \frac{k_p[M][M^-]}{k_{Tr}[M^-][NH_3]} = \frac{k_p}{k_{Tr}}\frac{[M]}{[NH_3]} = k''\frac{[M]}{[NH_3]} \tag{8.18}$$

Thus, the rate of propagation and the molecular weight are both inversely related to the concentration of ammonia. The activation energy for chain transfer is larger than the activation energy for propagation. The overall activation energy is approximately +38 kcal mol^{-1}. The reaction rate increases and molecular weight decreases as the temperature is increased.

The reaction rate is dependent on the dielectric constant of the solvent, the electronegativity of the initiator, the resonance stability of the carbanion, and the degree of solvation of the gegenion. Weakly polar initiators such as Grignard's reagent may be used when strong electron-withdrawing groups are present on the monomer, but monomers with weak electron-withdrawing groups require more highly polar initiators, such as n-butyl lithium.

Synthetic cis-1,4-polyisoprene is produced at an annual rate of about 76,000 tons by the polymerization of isoprene in a low dielectric solvent, such as hexane, using n-butyl lithium as the initiator. It is assumed that an intermediate cisoid conformation assures the formation of a cis elastomer.

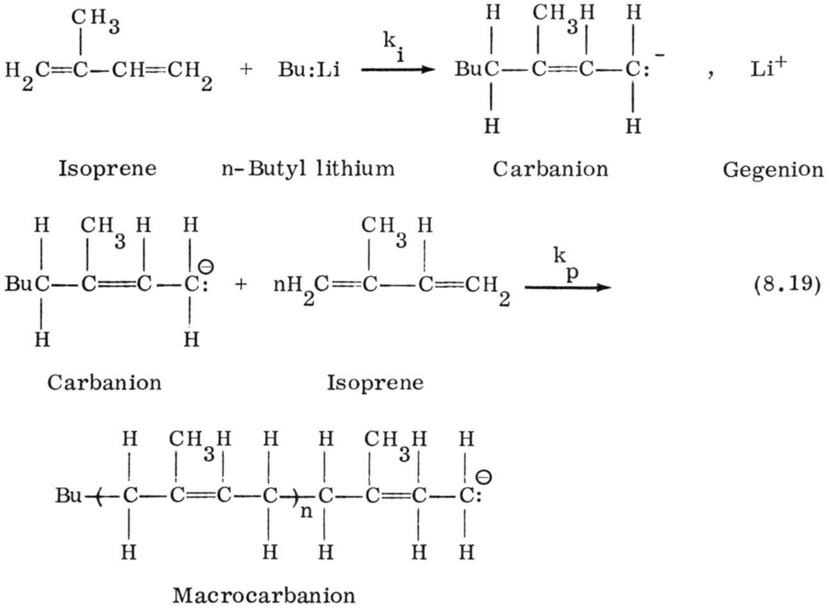

$$H_2C{=}C(CH_3){-}CH{=}CH_2 + Bu{:}Li \xrightarrow{k_i} BuCH_2{-}C(CH_3){=}CH{-}CH_2{:}^- \;,\; Li^+$$

Isoprene n-Butyl lithium Carbanion Gegenion

$$BuCH_2{-}C(CH_3){=}CH{-}CH_2{:}^{\ominus} + nH_2C{=}C(CH_3){-}CH{=}CH_2 \xrightarrow{k_p} \tag{8.19}$$

Carbanion Isoprene

$$Bu{-}(CH_2{-}C(CH_3){=}CH{-}CH_2)_n{-}CH_2{-}C(CH_3){=}CH{-}CH_2{:}^{\ominus}$$

Macrocarbanion

When isoprene is polymerized in a stronger dielectric solvent, such as ethyl ether using butyl lithium or sodium, equal amounts of trans-1,4-polyisoprene and cis-3,4-polyisoprene are produced.

No formal termination step was shown in previous equations, since in the absence of contaminants, the product is a stable macroanion. Szwarc has used the term "living polymers" to describe these active species. Thus, these macroanions may be used to produce a type of copolymer called a block copolymer, in which, as shown in Scheme 8.5, there are long sequences of similar repeating units. Kraton is an ABA block copolymer of styrene (A) and butadiene (B). Termination may be brought about by the addition of water, ethanol, carbon dioxide, or oxygen.

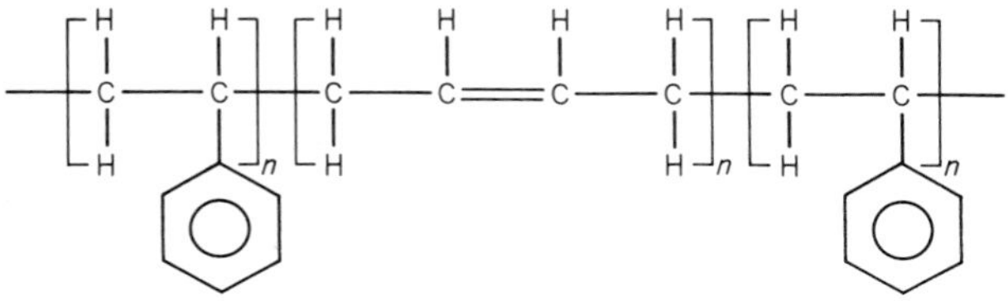

Scheme 8.5 An ABA block copolymer of styrene and butadiene.

In addition to the thermal dehydration of ammonium salts, nylons may also be produced by the anionic ring-opening polymerization of lactams. As shown in (8.20), the polymerization of caprolactam may be initiated by sodium methoxide. This polymer contains six carbon atoms in each repeating unit and is called nylon-6. The term monadic is used to describe nylons such as nylon-6 that have been produced from one reactant. The term dyadic is used to describe nylons such as nylon-66 which have been produced from two reactants.

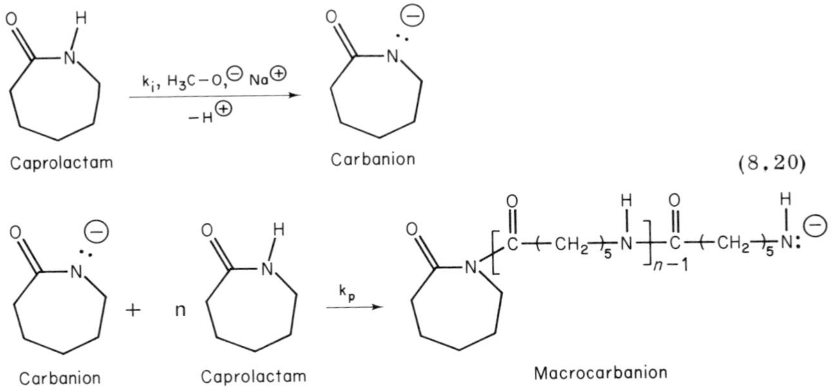

Caprolactam $\xrightarrow[-H^{\oplus}]{k_i,\ H_3C-O^{\ominus}\ Na^{\oplus}}$ Carbanion

Carbanion + n Caprolactam $\xrightarrow{k_p}$ Macrocarbanion (8.20)

The induction period in lactam ring-opening polymerization may be shortened by the addition of an activator, such as acetyl chloride. Nylon-4, nylon-8, and nylon-12 are commercially available and are used as fibers and coatings.

Lactones may also be polymerized by ring-opening anionic polymerization techniques. While the five-membered ring (γ-butyrolactone) is not readily cleaved, the smaller rings readily polymerize to produce linear polyesters. These polymers are used commercially as biodegradable plastics and in polyurethane foams. A proposed general reaction for the ring-opening polymerization of lactones is shown below:

$$\underset{\text{Lactone}}{O{=}C\overset{\frown}{-(CH_2)_x-}O} \xrightarrow[k_i]{B^-} \underset{\text{Cyclic carbanion}}{\overset{B}{\underset{\ominus}{O}}{-}C{-}(CH_2)_x{-}O} \longrightarrow \underset{\text{Carbanion}}{{}^-O{+}CH_2{+}_x\overset{O}{\overset{\|}{C}}{-}B}$$

$$\underset{\text{Carbanion}}{{}^-O(CH_2)_x\overset{O}{\overset{\|}{C}}{-}B} + \underset{\text{Lactone}}{nO{=}C{-}(CH_2)_x{-}O} \xrightarrow{k_p} \tag{8.21}$$

$$\underset{\text{Macrocarbanion}}{{}^-O{+}CH_2{+}_x\overset{O}{\overset{\|}{C}}{-}B{+}\left[(CH_2)_x\overset{O}{\overset{\|}{C}}O\right]_{n-1}{+}CH_2{+}_x\overset{O}{\overset{\|}{C}}{-}B}$$

The stereochemistry associated with anionic polymerization is similar to that observed with cationic polymerization. For soluble anionic initiators at low temperatures, syndiotactic formation is favored in polar solvents, whereas isotactic formation is favored in nonpolar solvents. Thus, the stereochemistry of anionic polymerization appears to be largely dependent on the amount of association the growing chain has with the counterion—as it does for cationic polymerizations.

The stereochemistry of diene polymerization is also affected by solvent polarity. For instance, the proportion of cis-1,4 units is increased by using organolithium or lithium itself as the initiator in the polymerization of isoprene or 1,3-butadiene in nonpolar solvents. We can thus obtain a polymer quite similar to natural hevea rubber using the anionic polymerization of isoprene. With sodium and potassium initiators the amount of cis-1,4 units decreases and trans-1,4 and trans-3,4 units predominate.

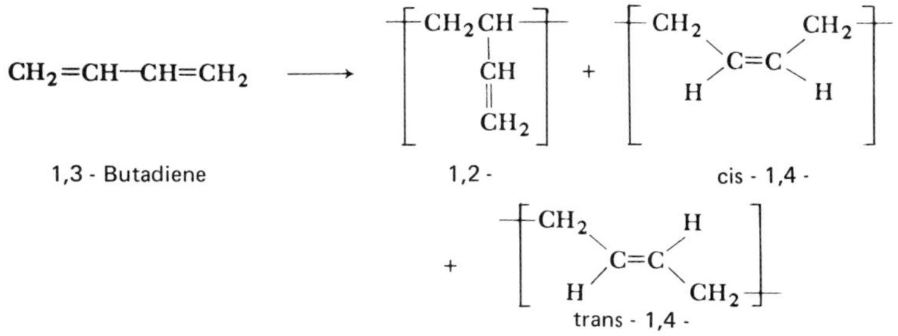

$$CH_2{=}CH{-}CH{=}CH_2 \longrightarrow \left[CH_2CH(CH{=}CH_2)\right] + \left[CH_2(H)C{=}C(H)CH_2\right] \qquad (8.22)$$

1,3 - Butadiene; 1,2 -; cis - 1,4 -

$$+ \left[CH_2(H)C{=}C(H)CH_2\right]$$

trans - 1,4 -

$$CH_2{=}C(CH_3){-}CH{=}CH_2 \longrightarrow \left[CH_2C(CH_3)(CH{=}CH_2)\right] + \left[CH_2CH(C(CH_3){=}CH_2)\right] \qquad (8.23)$$

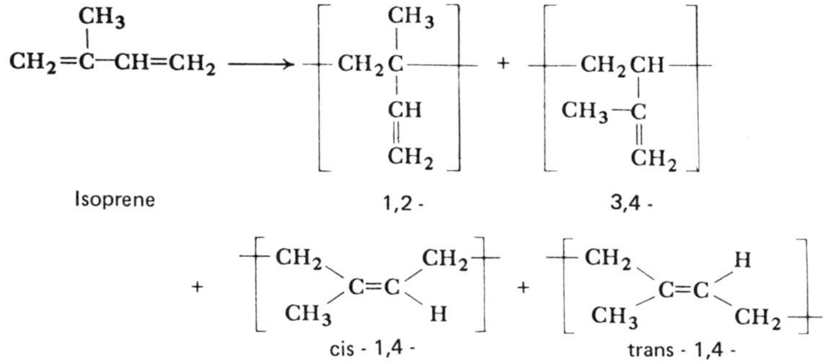

Isoprene; 1,2 -; 3,4 -

$$+ \left[CH_2(CH_3)C{=}C(H)CH_2\right] + \left[CH_2(CH_3)C{=}C(H)CH_2\right]$$

cis - 1,4 -; trans - 1,4 -

8.3 POLYMERIZATION WITH COMPLEX COORDINATION CATALYSTS

Prior to 1950, the only commercial polymer of ethylene was a highly branched polymer called high-pressure polyethylene (extremely high pressures were used in the polymerization process). The technique for making a linear polyethylene was discovered by Nobel laureate Karl Ziegler in the early 1950s. Ziegler prepared high-density polyethylene by polymerizing ethylene at low pressure and ambient temperatures using mixtures of triethylaluminum and titanium tetrachloride. Another Nobel laureate, Giulio Natta, used these complex coordination catalysts to produce crystalline polypropylene. These are now known as Ziegler-Natta catalysts.

In general, a Ziegler-Natta catalyst may be described as a combination of a transition metal compound from groups IV to VIII and an organometallic compound of a metal from groups I to III of the periodic table. It is customary to refer to the transition metal compound, such as $TiCl_4$, as the catalyst, and the organometallic compound, such as diethylaluminum chloride, as the cocatalyst.

Several exchange reactions between catalyst and cocatalyst take place, and some of the Ti(IV) is reduced to Ti(III). It is customary to use either the α, γ, or δ forms, but not the β crystalline form, of $TiCl_3$ as the catalyst for the production of stereoregular polymers. Both the extent of stereoregularity and the rate of polymerization are increased by the addition of triethylamine. Thus, at least 98% of the isotactic polymer is produced when propylene is polymerized in the presence of triethylamine, γ-titanium-(III)chloride, and diethylaluminum chloride.

It is generally agreed that a monomer molecule ($H_2C{=}\overset{R}{\overset{|}{C}}H$) is inserted between the titanium atom and the terminal carbon atom in the growing chain, and that this propagation reaction takes place on the catalyst surface at sites activated by the ethyl groups of the cocatalyst. The monomer molecule is always the terminal group on the chain.

The formation of a π complex is assumed in both the mono- and bimetallic mechanisms. The latter, favored by Natta, involves a cyclic electron-deficient transition complex as shown below:

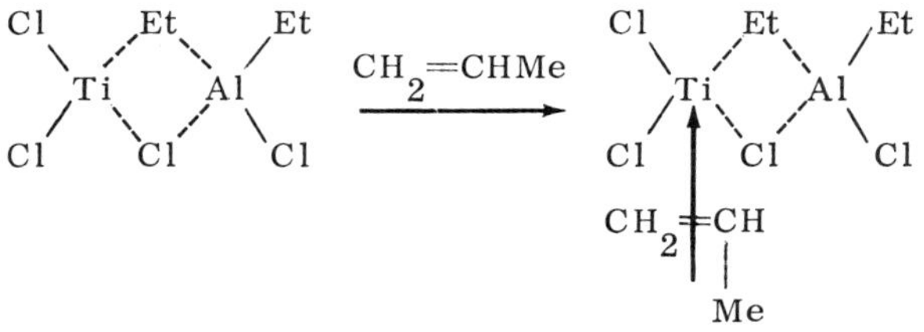

$$Cl_2Ti(\mu\text{-}Et)(\mu\text{-}Cl)AlEtCl \xrightarrow{CH_2=CHMe} Cl_2Ti(\leftarrow CH_2{=}CHMe)(\mu\text{-}Et)(\mu\text{-}Cl)AlEtCl \tag{8.24}$$

In the more generally accepted monometallic mechanism, shown in the following equation, triethylaluminum reacts on the catalyst surface to produce ethyltitanium chloride, at the active site for polymerization of a nonpolar vinyl monomer such as propylene.

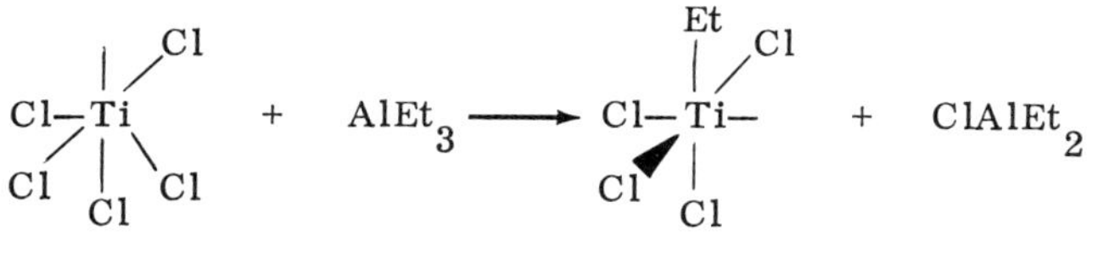

$$TiCl_4\ (\text{Cl}_5\text{Ti}) + AlEt_3 \longrightarrow EtTiCl_3\text{—} + ClAlEt_2 \tag{8.25}$$

Titanium chloride | Triethylaluminum | Ethyltitanium chloride (active center) | Diethylaluminum chloride

Then, as shown by (8.26), propylene forms a π complex with the titanium at the vacant d orbital.

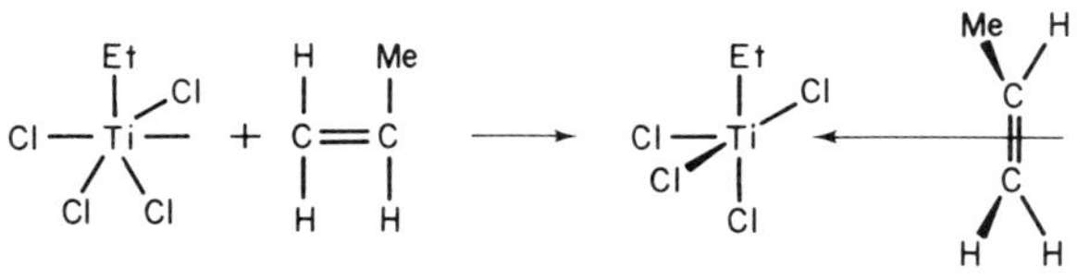

$$EtTiCl_3 + HHC{=}CHMe \longrightarrow EtCl_3Ti \leftarrow (CH_2{=}CHMe) \tag{8.26}$$

Ethyltitanium chloride | Propylene | π Complex

Insertion of the monomer takes place with the formation of a transition state complex, insertion of the monomer, and reformation of an active center in which the ethyl group is now at the end of a propylene group, as shown in the following equation.

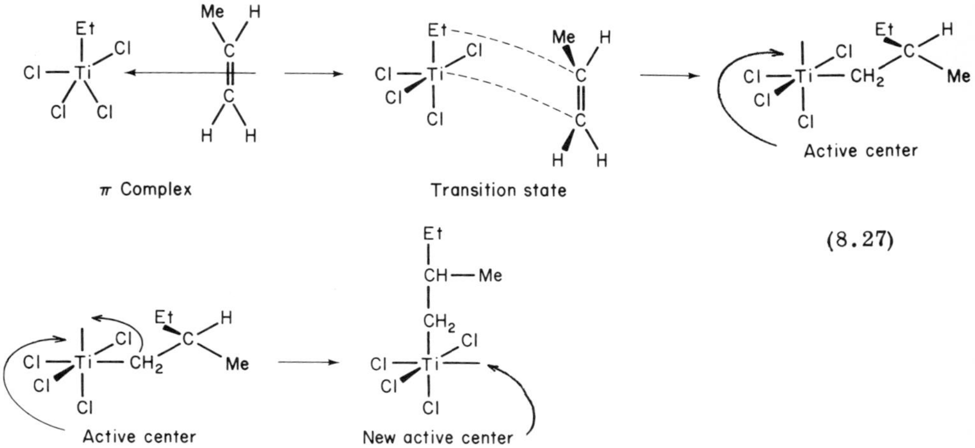

π Complex

Transition state

Active center

(8.27)

Active center

New active center

As shown by (8.28), the process outlined for initiation is repeated for propagation, and stereoregularity is maintained.

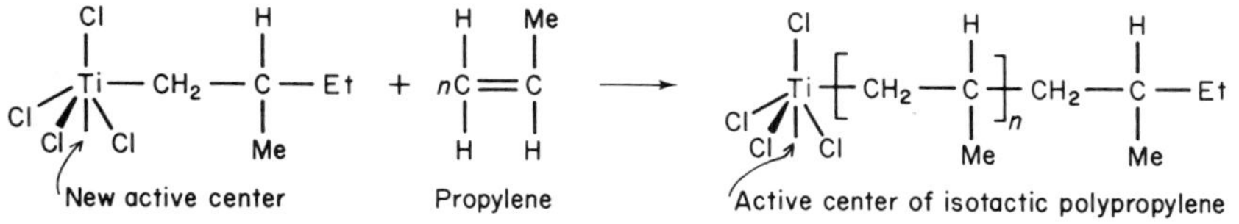

New active center

Propylene

Active center of isotactic polypropylene

(8.28)

For most vinyl monomers, Ziegler-Natta catalysts polymerize to give polymers emphasizing the isotactic form. The degree of stereoregulation appears to be dependent on the amount of exposure of the active site—which is probably a combination of the solid surface and the corners. The more exposed is the catalytic site, typically, the less is the isoatactic fraction in the resulting chains.

The potential versatility is clearly demonstrated in the polymerization of conjugated dienes, such as 1,3-butadiene, where any of the four possible forms—isotactic 1,2; syndiotactic 1,2; trans-1,4; and cis-1,4—can be synthesized in relatively pure form using different Ziegler-Natta catalysis systems.

Molecular weight is regulated to some degree by chain transfer with monomer and with the cocatalyst, plus internal hydride transfer. However, hydrogen is added in the commercial process to terminate the reaction. Low temperatures, at which the alkyl shift and migration are retarded, favor the formation of syndiotactic polypropylene. Commercial isotactic polymer is produced at ambient temperatures. The percentage of polymer insoluble in n-hexane is called the isotactic index.

High-density polyethylene (HDPE) is produced at an annual rate of 1.4 million tons, but most of this is produced using a chromia catalyst supported on silica, i.e., a Phillips catalyst. Some HDPE and PP are produced commercially using a Ziegler-Natta catalyst. This initiator is also used for the production of polybutene and poly-4-methylpentene-1 (TPX). Because of their regular structure, both these polymers are useful at relatively high temperatures. TPX has a melting point of 300°C, and because of its large bulky groups, has a low specific gravity of 0.83.

PP, TPX, and LDPE are less resistant to oxidation than HDPE because of the tertiary carbon atoms present in the chain. Their deterioration by weathering, and other factors is retarded by incorporation of antioxidants (discussed in Chap. 13).

8.4 POLYMERS OF 1,3-BUTADIENE

cis-Polyisoprene, cis-poly-1,4-butadiene (IR), and ethylene propylene copolymer (EP) elastomers can be produced by use of a Ziegler-Natta catalyst. The annual rate of production of IR and EP elastomers is 444,000 and 181,000 tons, respectively. trans-Polyisoprene can be produced using titanium and vanadium catalysts with an alkylaluminum cocatalyst.

1,3-Butadiene may also be polymerized by a heterogeneous catalyst called alfin, since it is derived from an alcohol and an olefin. Alfin, which consists of allylsodium, sodium isoproproxide, and sodium chloride, serves as an initiator for the production of very high molecular weight trans-polybutadienes.

1,3-Dienes, such as 2-methyl-1,3-butadiene, may polymerize to produce cis- or trans-1,4 or 1,2- and 3,4-isotactic and syndiotactic polybutadienes. The Ziegler-Natta catalyst, consisting of a titanium trichloride catalyst, an alkyl aluminum cocatalyst, and a tertiary amine produces essentially 100% cis-poly-1,4-isoprene, while tetra-alkoxy titanates produce essentially 100% poly-3,4-isoprene.

When the ratio of Ziegler-Natta catalyst to cocatalyst is greater than 1 (one), the product is trans-poly-1,4-isoprene. When chromium hexacyanobenzene $[Cr(C_6H_5(CN_6)]$ is used as the catalyst for the polymerization of 1,3-butadiene, stereospecific polymers are obtained. A ratio of cocatalyst to catalyst of 2:1 yields syndiotactic (st) poly-1,2-butadiene, and a ratio of 10:1 yields isotactic (it) poly-1,2-butadiene.

8.5 STEREOREGULARITY

One of the more outstanding areas of research involves the synthesis and characterization of stereoregular polymers. Polymers differing in stereoregularity (tacticity) generally vary with respect to such properties as infrared spectra, X-ray diffraction patterns, solubilities, rate and extent of solubility, and density thermal and mechanical transitions, among others. For instance, the T_g for polymethyl methacrylate is about 105°C for atactic forms, 150°C for isotactic forms, and 115°C for syndiotactic forms. Many of these physical differences are due to the ability, or possibility, of more ordered materials to achieve crystalline orientations.

The stereogeometry of 1- and 1,1-disubstituted vinyl addition polymers has been divided into the three conformations illustrated in (8.29). The isotactic form features a configuration where all the substituents of one kind would all lie on one side, if the molecule were arranged in a linear chain and viewing were done by looking down the "barrow." The syndiotactic form features an alternating arrangement of substituents, whereas a random sequence of substituent placement leads to the atactic configuration. These arrangements assume an adherence to the head-to-tail addition of monomers.

Generally, each substituted vinyl carbon represents a site of asymmetry; it is, in fact, a site of potential optical activity, when included in a polymer chain. Thus, the number of optically active carbons is 2n, where n is the number of asymmetric carbons. Since a polymerizing system can introduce a variety of chain lengths, the total possible number of geometric and chain-length combinations is extremely large. It is quite possible that each polymerization of even common monomers such as styrene might produce many chains as yet not synthesized.

Other geometric possibilities exist for situations involving conjugated double-vinyl compounds. For instance, 1,3-dienes, containing one residual double bond per repeating unit after polymerization, can contain the following different configurations (8.30).

Those derivatives of butadiene which are 1- and 4-disubstituted can be polymerized to produce a polymer having two asymmetric carbon atoms and one double bond per repeating unit. Possible geometric forms are illustrated in Scheme 8.6.

The requirements for obtaining measurable optical activity in polymers are still items of active debate. It is known that whole-chain conformations can contribute to the overall optical activity of polymers. For instance, helical conformations offer a major source of optical rotatory power. In addition to the direct use of stereoregular polymers, such products are currently being used (and further investigated) as "templates" to form other products, some of these possessing stereoregularity.

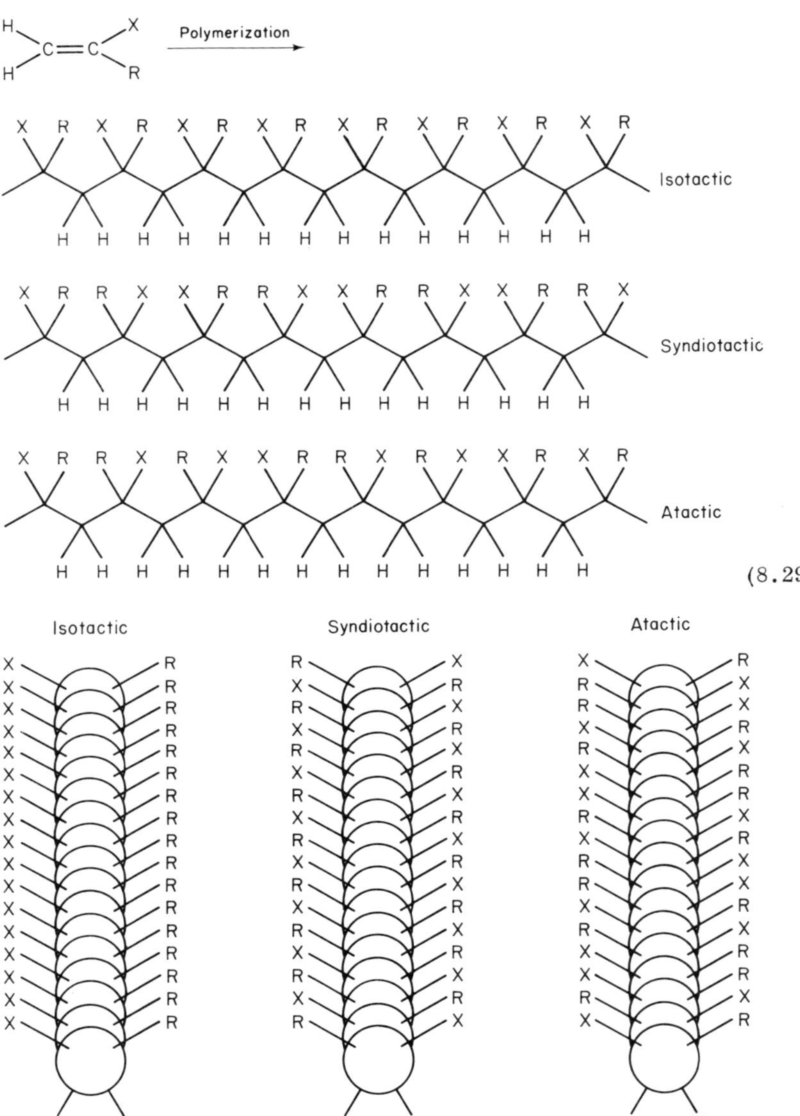
Polymerization
Isotactic
Syndiotactic
Atactic
Isotactic
Syndiotactic
Atactic

(8.29)

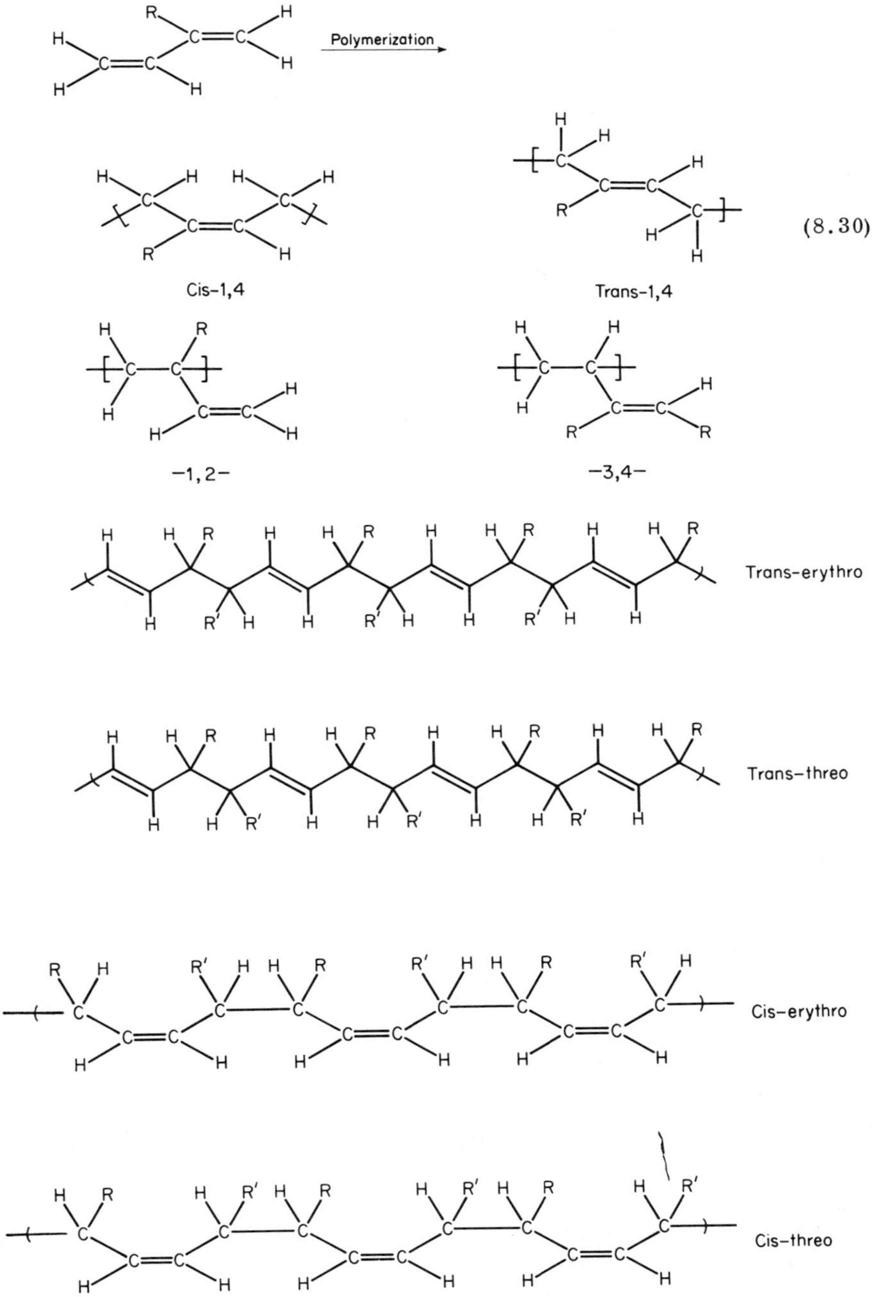

Polymerization

Cis-1,4

Trans-1,4

(8.30)

−1,2−

−3,4−

Trans-erythro

Trans-threo

Cis-erythro

Cis-threo

Scheme 8.6

SUMMARY

1. Chain reactions, including ionic chain polymerization reactions, consist of at least three steps, namely, initiation, propagation, and termination. Because of the repulsion of similarly charged species, termination by coupling seldom occurs. Instead, termination may take place by chain transfer to produce a new ion and a dead polymer. The $\overline{DP}$ of the latter is equal to the kinetic chain length.

2. Sulfuric acid, and Lewis acids with a cocatalyst of water or ether, serve as possible initiators in cationic polymerizations, producing a carbocation and a gegenion. Monomers with electron-donating groups, such as isobutylene and vinyl alkyl ethers, may be polymerized at low temperatures in solvents with high dielectric constants.

3. The degree of polymerization is proportional to the concentration of monomer in cationic polymerization, and the overall rate of polymerization is proportional to the square of the concentration of monomers.

4. In general, the rate of cationic polymerization is dependent on the dielectric constant of the solvent, the resonance stability of the carbocation, the degree of solvation of the gegenion, and the electropositivity of the initiator.

5. Stereoregular polymers are produced at low temperatures in solvents that foster the formation of ion pairs between the carbocation and the gegenion.

6. The stability of formaldehyde polymers is improved by capping the hydroxyl end groups or by copolymerizing with other monomers, such as dioxolane.

7. Water-soluble polymers of ethylene oxide are readily formed, but those of more stable cyclic ethers require a promotor, such as ethylene oxide, for this formation.

8. Nylon-2, a polyamide with a wide variety of pendant groups, may be prepared from N-carboxyl amino acid anhydrides.

9. Monomers with electron-withdrawing groups, such as acrylonitrile, may be polymerized in the presence of anionic initiators, such as butyl lithium.

10. The rate of anionic polymerization is dependent on the dielectric constant of the solvent, the stability of the carbanion, the electronegativity of the initiator, the degree of solvation of the gegenion, and the strength of the electron-withdrawing groups in the monomer.

11. Monadic nylons are produced by the anionic ring opening of lactams, such as caprolactam, yielding nylon-6.

12. Stereospecific polymers of nonpolar monomers may be produced by polymerization with a Ziegler-Natta catalyst. The most widely used system consists of a titanium trichloride catalyst and an alkylaluminum cocatalyst.

13. This mechanism involves a reaction on the surface of $TiCl_3$, activated by the addition of the ethyl group from the cocatalyst. The

monomer adds to this active site to produce a π complex, which forms a new active center by insertion of the monomer between the titanium and carbon atoms. This step is repeated in the propagation reactions, in which the alkyl group from the cocatalyst is always the terminal group.

14. Stereospecific polymers are also produced using alfin and chromia on silica initiators. The former, which consists of allylsodium, sodium isopropoxide, and sodium chloride, yields high molecular weight trans-polydienes.

15. The production of cis- and trans-polydienes, as well as stereospecific poly-1,2-dienes, is influenced by the proper choice of Ziegler-Natta catalysts and the polymerization temperature.

GLOSSARY

alfin: A complex catalyst system consisting of allylsodium, sodium isopropoxide, and sodium chloride.

anionic polymerization: A polymerization initiated by an anion.

aziridine: Ethyleneimine.

block copolymer: A macromolecule consisting of long sequences of different repeating units ($A_nB_nA_n$).

butyl rubber (IIR): A copolymer of isobutylene and isoprene.

C: Catalyst-cocatalyst complex.

capping: Reacting the end groups to produce a stable polymer.

carbanion: A negatively charged organic ion.

carbocation: A positively charged organic ion, i.e., one lacking an electron pair on a carbon atom.

cationic polymerization: Polymerization initiated by a cation and propagated by a carbonium ion.

ceiling temperature: A threshold temperature above which a specific polymer cannot exist.

Celcon: A tradename for a copolymer of formaldehyde and dioxolane,

chain-reaction polymerization: A rapid polymerization based on initiation, propagation, and termination steps.

chain transfer: A process in which a growing chain becomes a dead polymer by abstracting an active group from some other compound.

cocatalyst: The alkylaluminum compound in the Ziegler-Natta catalyst system.

copolymer: A polymer chain containing repeating units from more than one monomer.

copolymerization: A polymerization of a mixture of monomers.

coupling: Joining of two active species.

Delrin: A polyacetal (tradename).

dioxolane: A four-membered cyclic ether containing two carbon and two oxygen atoms in the ring.

dyadic: A polymer produced from more than one reactant.

electrophilic: Electron seeking.

EP: Ethylene-propylene copolymer.

gegenion: A counterion.

IIR: Butyl rubber.

initiation: The start of a chain reaction.

it: Isotactic.

k: Rate constant.

Kraton: A tradename for an ABA block copolymer of styrene-butadiene-styrene.

lactam: A heterocyclic amide with one nitrogen atom in the ring.

lactone: A heterocyclic ester with one oxygen atom in the ring.

Leuchs' anhydride: A cyclic anhydride which decomposes to carbon dioxide and an amino acid.

living polymers: Macroanions.

[M]: Monomer concentration.

$[M^+]$: Carbonium ion concentration.

macroions: Charged polymer molecules.

monadic: A polymer produced from one reactant.

Natta, Giulio: The discoverer of stereospecific polymers.

nylon-4: A polymer with the following repeating unit:

$$-\overset{\displaystyle O}{\overset{\|}{C}}\!-\!(CH_2)_3\!-\!\overset{\displaystyle H}{\overset{|}{N}}-$$

nylon-6: A polymer with the following repeating unit:

$$-\overset{\overset{\displaystyle O}{\|}}{C}-(CH_2)_5-\overset{\overset{\displaystyle H}{|}}{N}-$$

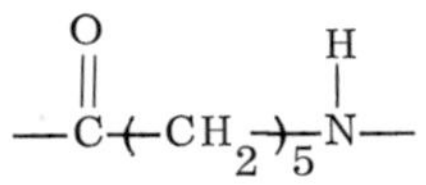

oxacycloalkane: A cyclic compound containing an oxygen atom in the ring.

oxirane: Ethylene oxide.

Penton: A tradename for a polychloroether.

π Complex: A complex formed by a metal with an empty orbital, such as titanium, overlapping with the p orbitals in an alkene.

polyacetal: Polyoxymethylene.

polychloral: A polymer of trichloroacetaldehyde.

polyisobutylene: A polymer with the following repeating units:

$$\left[\begin{array}{cc} H & CH_3 \\ | & | \\ -C- & -C- \\ | & | \\ H & CH_3 \end{array} \right]_n$$

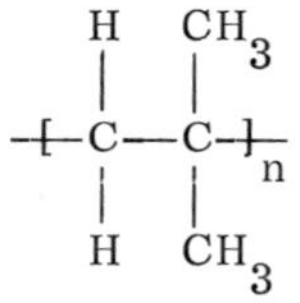

polyoxymethylene: A polymer with the following repeating units:

$$\left[\begin{array}{cc} H & \\ | & \\ -C- & -O- \\ | & \\ H & \end{array} \right]_n$$

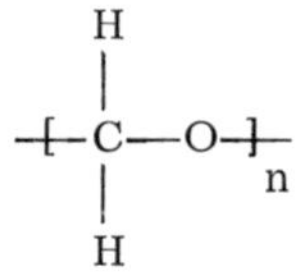

polyvinyl isobutyl ether: A polymer with the following repeating units:

$$\left[\begin{array}{cc} H & H \\ | & | \\ -C- & -C- \\ | & | \\ H & OC_4H_9 \end{array} \right]_n$$

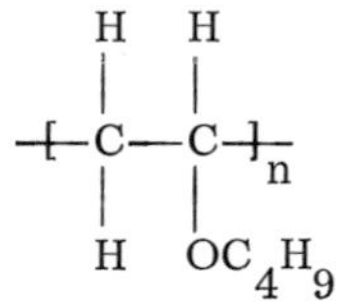

POM: Polyoxymethylene.

PP: Polypropylene.

promotor: A term used for strained cyclic ethers that are readily cleaved.

propagation: The continuous successive chain extension in a chain reaction.

R: Rate.

st: Syndiotactic.

termination: The destruction of active species in a chain reaction.

TPX: Poly-4-methylpentene.

trioxane: A trimer of formaldehyde.

Ziegler, Karl: The discoverer of complex coordination catalysts.

Ziegler-Natta catalyst: $TiCl_3$-AlR_3.

EXERCISES

1. Describe the contents of the reaction flask, 10 min after the polymerization of (a) reactants in step polymerization, such as dimethyl terephthalate and ethylene glycol; and (b) monomer in chain reaction, such as isobutylene.
2. What is the initiator in the polymerization of isobutylene?
3. What is the general name of the product produced by cationic initiation?
4. What reactant besides the monomer is present in cationic chain propagation reactions?
5. What name is used to describe the negatively charged counterion in cationic chain-reaction polymerization?
6. Is a Lewis acid (a) an electrophile, or (b) a nucleophile?
7. Is a Lewis base (a) an electrophile, or (b) a nucleophile?
8. Why isn't coupling a preferred termination step in the cationic chain polymerization of pure monomer?
9. Is the usual configuration of polymers produced by ionic chain polymerization (a) head to tail, or (b) head to head?
10. Which condition would be more apt to produce stereoregular polymers in ionic chain polymerizations: (a) high temperatures or (b) low temperatures?
11. Name (a) a thermoplastic, (b) an elastomer, and (c) a fiber that is produced commercially by ionic chain polymerization.
12. Which technique would you choose for producing a polymer of isobutyl vinyl ether? (a) cationic or (b) anionic?

13. Which technique would you choose for producing a polymer of acrylonitrile: (a) cationic or (b) anionic?

14. Which of the following could be used to initiate the polymerization of isobutylene: (a) sulfuric acid, (b) boron trifluoride etherate, (c) water, or (d) butyl lithium?

15. Which of the following could be polymerized by cationic chain polymerization?

(a) $H_2C{=}C(H){-}CN$

(b) $H_2C{=}C(CH_3)_2$

(c) C_6H_5OH (benzene ring with OH)

(d) $H_2C{-}CH_2$ with bridging O (ethylene oxide)

(e) $H_2C{=}C(H){-}O{-}C_4H_9$

16. Which polymer is more susceptible to oxidation: (a) HDPE, or (b) PP?

17. When termination is by chain transfer, what is the relationship of $\overline{DP}$ and the kinetic chain length?

18. What would be the composition of the product obtained by the cationic low-temperature polymerization of a solution of isobutylene in ethylene?

19. What is the relationship of the rate of initiation (R_i) to the monomer concentration [M] in ionic chain polymerizations?

20. What effect will the use of a solvent with a higher dielectric constant have on the rate of propagation (R_p) in ionic chain polymerization?

21. How does the rate constant k_p change as the yield of polymer increases?

22. Which will have the higher T_g value: (a) polystyrene or (b) polyisobutylene?

23. Which of the following could serve as an initiator for an anionic chain polymerization (a) $AlCl_3 \cdot H_2O$, (b) $BF_3 \cdot H_2O$, (c) butyl lithium, or (d) sodium metal?

24. What species, in addition to a dead polymer, is produced in a chain transfer reaction with a macrocarbonium ion in cationic chain polymerization?

25. What is the relationship of R_i and R_T in a steady-state condition?

26. What is the relationship of $\overline{DP}$ to R_p and R_T?

27. Which would yield the higher molecular weight aldehyde: ozonolysis of (a) natural rubber, or (b) butyl rubber?

28. What percentage of polymer is usually found when a polymer produced by chain-reaction polymerization is heated above its ceiling temperature?

29. What is the relationship of $\overline{DP}$ to initiator concentration in cationic chain polymerization?

30. Can the polymers found in the bottom of a bottle of insolubilized formaldehyde solution be useful?

31. How would you prepare stable polymers from formaldehyde?

32. Why is the thermal decomposition of polymers of formaldehyde called unzipping?

33. Can chloral be polymerized at 60°C?

34. How would you promote the ring-opening polymerization of tetrahydrofuran?

35. How would you increase the rate of flow of water in a fire hose?

36. Why is poly-3,3-bis-chloromethyloxybutylene crystalline?

37. Why must care be used in the polymerization of aziridine?

38. What byproduct is produced when Leuchs' anhydride is polymerized?

39. How could you remove unsaturated hydrocarbons from petroleum or coal tar distillates?

40. What species is produced by the reaction of an anionic chain polymerization initiator and the monomer?

41. What are the propagating species in anionic chain polymerization?

42. Why are polymers produced by the anionic polymerization of pure monomers called "living polymers"?

43. Using the symbols A and B for repeating units in the polymer chain, which of the following is a block copolymer? (a) —ABABAB—, (b) AABABBA—, (c) $—(A)_nB_n—$?

44. What is the most widely used monadic nylon?

45. What is the repeating unit in nylon-4?

46. What is the catalyst and cocatalyst in the most widely used Ziegler-Natta catalyst?

47. Why is β-$TiCl_3$ not used as a polymerization catalyst?

48. What is the principal difference between propagation reactions with butyl lithium and a Ziegler-Natta catalyst?
49. In addition to good strength, clarity, and good resistance to heat and corrosives, what is a unique feature of poly-4-methylpentene-1?
50. Show skeletal structures of cis- and trans-polyisoprene.
51. Write formulas for repeating units in the chains of (a) poly-1,4-isoprene, and (b) poly-1,2-isoprene.
52. What is the most widely used catalyst for the production of HDPE?
53. What elastomer is produced by anionic chain polymerization?
54. What elastomer is produced by use of a Ziegler-Natta catalyst?

APPENDIX

Production of polymers in the United States and Canada in 1978 by ionic chain reaction and complex coordination polymerization (thousands of metric tons) is listed below.

By cationic polymerization	
butyl rubber	146
By anionic polymerization	
polyisoprene	76
By coordination polymerization, including chromia on silica (Phillips catalyst)	
high-density polyethylene (HDPE)	1852
polypropylene plastics	1341
polybutadiene	444
ethylene-propylene copolymer	181
polypropylene fibers	332

BIBLIOGRAPHY

Bailey, F. E., Koleschi, J. V. (1976): Poly(ethylene oxide). Academic, New York.

Chien, J. C. W. (1975): Coordination Polymerization. Academic, New York.

Clark, A. (1969): Olefin polymerization on supported chromium oxide catalysts, Catalysis Rev., 3:145-174.

Coates, G. E. (1960): Organo-metallic Compounds. Methuen, London.

Cooper, W. (1961): Stereospecific Polymerization. Academic, New York.

———. (1963): Chemistry of Cationic Polymerization. MacMillan, New York.

Cossee, P. (1961): In Advances in the Chemistry of Coordination Compounds (S. Kirschner, ed.). Macmillan, New York.

———. (1964): Ziegler-Natta catalysis. I. Mechanism of polymerization of α-olefins with Ziegler-Natta catalysts, J. Catalysis, 3:80-88.

Cowie, J. M. G. (1973): Chaps. 4 and 6 in Polymers: Chemistry and Physics of Modern Materials. Intext Educational Publishers, New York.

Feay, D. C. (1967): Heterogeneous chain growth polymerization, in Organic Chemistry of Synthetic High Polymers, Sec. IV (R. W. Lenz, ed.). Wiley Interscience, New York.

Furukawa, J., and Saegusa, T. (1963): Polymerization of Aldehydes and and Oxides. Wiley Interscience, New York.

Furukawa, J., and Vogl, O. (1976): Ionic Polymerization. Dekker, New York.

Gaylord, N. G., and Mark, H. F. (1959): Linear and Stereoregular Addition Polymers. Interscience, New York.

Goodman, M. (1967): Concepts of Polymer Stereochemistry. Wiley Interscience, New York.

Hancock, E. G. (1973): Propylene. Halsted, New York.

Harwood, J. H. (1963): Industrial Applications of Organometallic Compounds. Reinhold, New York.

Higginson, W. C. E., and Wooding, N. S. (1952): Anionic polymerization. Part I. The polymerization of styrene in liquid ammonia solution catalyzed by potassium amide, J. Chem. Soc., 760-774.

Hogan, J. P., and Banks, R. L. (1955): (Philips Process), U.S. Patent 2,717,888.

Kennedy, J. P. (1975): Cationic Polymerization of Olefins. Wiley Interscience, New York.

Kennedy, J. P., and Johnston, J. E. (1975): Cationic Isomerization Polymerization of Butene and Pentene. Springer-Verlag, New York.

Ketley, A. D. (ed.) (1967): The Stereochemistry of Macromolecules. Vol. 1. Dekker, New York.

———. (1968): The Stereochemistry of Macromolecules. Edward Arnold, New York.

Kresser, T. O. J. (1960): Polypropylene. Reinhold. New York.

Lenz, R. W. (1967): Organic Chemistry of Synthetic High Polymers, Chaps. 14 and 15. Wiley Interscience, New York.

———. (1975): Coordination Polymerization. Academic, New York.

Makowski, H. S., and Lynn, M. (1968): Butyl lithium polymerization of butadiene, ACS Div. Polymer Chem., Polymer Preprints, 9:420, 427.

Margerison, D., and East, G. C. (1967): Introduction to Polymer Chemistry, Chap. 5. Pergamon, New York.

Marvel, C. S. (1959): An Introduction to Organic Chemistry of High Polymers. John Wiley, New York.

Morton, A. A., Bolton, F. H., et al. (1952): Alfin catalysis, Ind. Eng. Chem., 40:2876.

Morton, A. A., and Lanpher, E. J. (1960): Alfin catalyst, J. Polymer Sci., 44:233.

Natta, G. (1958): Ziegler catalysts, J. Inorg. Nucl. Chem., 8:589.

Natta, G., and Danusso, F. (1967): Stereoregular Polymers and Stereospecific Polymerization. Pergamon, New York.

Odian, G. (1970): Principles of Polymerization. McGraw-Hill, New York.

Plesch, P. H. (1963): The Chemistry of Cationic Polymerization. Pergamon, New York.

Raave, A. (1967): Organic Chemistry of Macromolecules. Dekker, New York.

Raff, R. A. V., and Doak, K. W. (eds.) (1964): Crystalline Olefin Polymers. Wiley Interscience, New York.

Reich, L., and Schindler, A. (1966): Polymerization by Organometallic Compounds. Wiley Interscience, New York.

Schildknecht, C. E. (1956): Ionic Polymerization, Polymer Processes, Chap. 6. Interscience, New York.

Schildknecht, C. E., Zoss, A. O., McKinley, C. (1947): Vinyl Alkyl Ethers, Ind. Eng. Chem., 39:180-186.

Seymour, R. B. (1971): Introduction to Polymer Chemistry, Chap. 6. McGraw-Hill, New York.

Sittig, M. (1976): Polyolefin Production Processes, Noyes Data Corp., Park Ridge, New Jersey.

Smith, D. A. (1968): Addition Polymers, Chap. 3. Butterworths, Kent, England.

Stavely, F. W., et al. (1956): Coral rubber, Ind. Eng. Chem., 48:778.

Stevens, M. P. (1975): Polymer Chemistry, An Introduction, Chaps. 6 and 7. Addison-Wesley, Reading, Massachusetts.

Szwarc, M. (1968): Carbanions, Living Polymers and Electron-Transfer Processes. John Wiley, New York.

Thomas, R. M., Sparks, W. J., et al. (1940): Polyisobutylene, J. Am. Chem. Soc., 62:276.

Topchiev, A. V., and Krentsel, B. A. (1962): Polyolefins. Pergamon, New York.

Vollmert, B. (1973): Polymer Chemistry, Chap. 2. Springer-Verlag, New York.

Whitby, B. (1973): Synthetic Rubber. John Wiley, New York.

Wooding, N. W., and Higginson, W. C. E. (1932): Anionic polymerization. Part III. The polymerization of styrene in liquid ammonia catalysed by potassium, J. Am. Chem. Soc., 1178-1180.

Ziegler, K. (1952, 1955): Ziegler catalysts, Angew. Chem., 64:323; 67:541.

9

Free-Radical Chain Polymerization (Addition Polymerization)

Since most synthetic plastics, elastomers, and fibers are prepared by free-radical polymerization, this method is obviously most important from a commercial viewpoint. Table 9.1 contains a listing of a number of commercially important addition polymers. Many of the concepts discussed in Chap. 8 on ionic chain polymerization also apply to free-radical polymerization. However, because of the versatility of this polymerization technique, several new concepts will be introduced in this chapter.

As is the case with other chain reactions, free-radical polymerization is a rapid reaction which consists of the characteristic chain-reaction steps, namely, initiation, propagation, and termination. Unlike the cationic and anionic initiators produced from the heterolytic cleavage of ion pairs such as H^+, HSO_4^- and Bu^-, Li^+, respectively, free-radical initiators are produced by homolytic cleavage of covalent bonds. The formation of free radicals is dependent on high-energy forces or the presence of weak covalent bonds.

9.1 INITIATORS FOR FREE-RADICAL CHAIN POLYMERIZATION

The rate of decomposition of initiators usually follows first-order kinetics and is dependent upon the solvent present and the temperature of polymerization. The latter is usually expressed as a half-life time ($t_{1/2}$) where $t_{1/2} = \ln 2/k_d = 0.693/k_d$. The rate constant ($k_d$) changes with temperature in accordance with the Arrhenius equation as shown below:

$$k_d = Ae^{-Ea/RT} \tag{9.1}$$

TABLE 9.1 Industrially Important Addition Polymers

Name	Repeating unit	Typical properties	Typical uses
Polyacrylonitrile (including acrylic fibers)	$-[CH_2-CH(C\equiv N)]-$	High strength; good stiffness; tough; abrasion resistant; resilient; good flex life; relatively good resistance to moisture and stains, chemicals, insects, and fungi; good weatherability	Carpeting, sweaters, skirts, socks, slacks, baby garments
Polyvinyl acetate	$-[CH_2-CH(O-C(=O)-CH_3)]-$	Water sensitive with respect to physical properties as adhesion and strength; generally good weatherability, fair adhesion	Lower molecular weight used in chewing gums, intermediate in production of polyvinyl alcohol, water-based emulsion paints
Polyvinyl alcohol	$-[CH_2-CH(OH)]-$	Water soluble, unstable in acidic or basic aqueous systems; fair adhesion	Thickening agent for various suspension and emulsion systems, packaging film, wet-strength adhesive
Polyvinyl butyral	$-[CH_2-CH-CH_2-CH]-$ with the two CH groups joined through $-O-CH(C_3H_7)-O-$	Good adhesion to glass; tough; good stability to sunlight; good clarity; insensitive to moisture	Automotive safety glass as the interlayer

Polyvinyl chloride and polyvinylidene chloride (called "the vinyls" or "vinyl resins")	$\left[-CH_2-CHCl-\right]$ $\left[-CH_2-CCl_2-\right]$	Relatively unstable to heat and light, fire resistant; resistant to chemicals, insects, fungi; resistant to moisture	Calendered products such as film sheets and floor coverings; shower curtains, food covers, rainwear, handbags, coated fabrics, insulation for electrical cable and wire, phonograph records
Polytetrafluoroethylene (Teflon)	$\left[-CF_2-CF_2-\right]$	Insoluble in most solvents, chemically inert, low dielectric loss, high dielectric strength, uniquely nonadhesive, low friction properties, constant electrical and mechanical properties from 20 to about 250°C, high impact strength, not hard, outstanding mechanical properties	Coatings to frying pans, etc.; wire and cable insulation; insulation for motors, oils, transformers, generators; gaskets; pump and valve packings; nonlubricated bearings
Polyethylene (low-density, branched)	$\left[-CH_2-CH_2-\right]$	Dependent on molecular weight, branching, molecular weight distribution, etc.; good toughness and pliability over a wide temperature range, outstanding electrical properties, high transparency in thin films, inert chemically, resistant to acids and bases, ages on exposure to light and oxygen, low density, flexible without plasticizer, resilient, high tear strength, moisture resistant	Films; sheeting used in bags, pouches, wrapping produce, textile materials, frozen foods, etc.; drapes, tablecloths; covers for construction, ponds, greenhouses, trash can liners, etc.; electrical wire and cable insulate; coating of foils, papers, other films; squeeze bottles

(continued)

TABLE 9.1 (continued)

Name	Repeating unit	Typical properties	Typical uses
Polyethylene (high-density, linear)		Most of the differences in properties between branched and linear concerns the high crystallinity of the latter; linear polyethylene has a high T_g, T_m, softening range, greater hardness and tensile strength.	Bottles, housewares, toys, films, sheets, extrusion coating, pipes, conduit, wire and cable insulation
Polypropylene	$-\!\!\left[\mathrm{CH_2{-}CH(CH_3)}\right]\!\!-$	Lightest major plastic; its high crystallinity imparts to it high tensile strength, stiffness, and hardness, good gloss, high resistance to marring; high softening range permits polymer to be sterilized; good electrical properties, chemical inertness, moisture resistance	Filament—rope, webbing, cordage; carpeting; injection molding applications in appliance, small houseware, and automotive fields
Polyisoprene (cis-1,4-polyisoprene)	$-\!\!\left[\mathrm{CH_2{-}CH{=}CH{-}CH_2}\right]\!\!-$ (cis)	Structure closely resembling that of natural rubber; properties similar to those of natural rubber	Replacement of natural rubber; natural rubber often preferred because of its greater uniformity and cleanliness
SBR (styrene-butadiene rubber)	Random copolymer	Generally equal or better physical properties than those of natural rubber	Tire treads for cars, inferior to natural rubber with respect to heat buildup and resilience, thus not used for truck tires; belting; molded goods, gum, flooring, rubber shoe soles, electrical insulation, hoses

Butyl rubber (copolymer of isobutylene with small amounts of isoprene added to permit vulcanization)	Amorphous, isoprene—largely in 1,4 structure	Good chemical inertness, low gas permeability, high viscoelastic response to stresses, less sensitive to oxidative aging than most other elastomers, better ozone resistance than natural rubber, good solvent resistance	About 70 to 60% used for inner tubes for tires
Polychloroprene (Neoprene)	Mostly 1,4 product	Outstanding oil and chemical resistance; high tensile strength, outstanding resistance to oxidative degradation and aging; good ozone and weathering resistance; dynamic properties are equal or greater than those of most synthetic rubber and only slightly inferior to those of natural rubber	Can replace natural rubber in most applications; gloves, coated fabrics, cable and wire coatings, hoses, belts, shoe heels, solid tires
Polystyrene	$\left[\!-\mathrm{CH_2}-\mathrm{CH}(\mathrm{C_6H_5})-\!\right]$	Clear; easily colored; easily fabricated; transparent; fair mechanical and thermal properties; good resistance to acids, bases, oxidizing and reducing agents; readily attached by many organic solvents; good electrical insulator	Used for the production of ion-exchange resins, heat- and impact-resistant copolymers, ABS resins, etc., foams, plastic optical components, lighting fixtures, housewares, toys, packaging, appliances, home furnishings
Polymethyl methacrylate	$-\!\left(\mathrm{CH_2}-\mathrm{C}(\mathrm{CH_3})(\mathrm{C{=}O}-\mathrm{O}-\mathrm{CH_3})\right)\!-$	Clear, transparent, colorless, good weatherability, good impact strength, resistant to dilute basic and acidic solutions, easily colored, good mechmechanical and thermal properties, good fabricability, poor abrasion resistance compared to glass	Available in syrups, cast sheets, rods, tubes, and molding and extension compositions; applications where light transmission is needed, such as tail- and signal-light lenses, dials, medallions, brush backs, jewelry, signs, lenses, skylight "glass"

TABLE 9.2 Rate Constants for Common Initiators in Various Solvents[a]

Initiator	Solvent	Temp. (°C)	K_d (sec^{-1})	E_a ($kcal/mol^{-1}$)
2,2'-Azobisisobutyronitrile (AIBN)	Benzene	40	5.4×10^{-7}	30.7
Phenyl-azo-triphenylmethane	Benzene	25	4.3×10^{-6}	26.8
tert-Butyl peroxide (TBP)	Benzene	80	7.8×10^{-8}	34
Cumyl peroxide	Benzene	115	1.6×10^{-5}	40.7
Acetyl peroxide	Benzene	35	9.5×10^{-5}	32.3
Benzoyl peroxide (BPO)	Benzene	30	4.8×10^{-8}	27.8
Lauroyl peroxide	Benzene	30	2.6×10^{-7}	30.4
tert-Butyl hydroperoxide	Benzene	154	4.3×10^{-6}	40.8
tert-Butyl perbenzoate	Benzene	100	1.1×10^{-5}	34.7

[a] All initiators are unstable compounds and should be handled with extreme caution! Data from Polymer Handbook.

The rate constants for several common initiators are listed in Table 9.2. Typical equations for the dissociation of 2,2'-azo-bis-isobutyronitrile (AIBN) and benzoyl peroxide (BPO) are shown below. It should be pointed out that because of recombination, which is solvent dependent, and other side reactions of the free radicals (R·), the initiator efficiency is seldom 100%. Hence, an efficiency factor (f) is employed to show the percentage of effective free radicals produced.

$$\underset{\text{AIBN}}{(CH_3)_2\underset{|}{\overset{}{C}}(CN)-N{=}N-\underset{|}{C}(CN)(CH_3)_2} \xrightarrow[\text{or } 3600\ \text{Å}]{\Delta} \underset{\text{Free radical}}{2(CH_3)_2\underset{|}{C}(CN)\cdot} + N_2 \tag{9.2}$$

$$\underset{\text{BPO}}{C_6H_5-\overset{O}{\overset{\|}{C}}-OO-\overset{O}{\overset{\|}{C}}C_6H_5} \xrightarrow{\Delta} 2C_6H_5-\overset{O}{\overset{\|}{C}}-O\cdot \xrightarrow{\Delta} \underset{\text{Free radical}}{2C_6H_5\cdot} + 2CO_2 \tag{9.3}$$

The rate of decomposition of peroxides such as benzoyl peroxide may be increased by the addition of small amounts of tertiary amines such as N,N-dimethylaniline. The rate of decomposition of initiators may also be increased by exposure to ultraviolet (UV) radiation. For example, AIBN may be decomposed at low temperatures by UV radiation at a wavelength of 360 nm.

9.2 MECHANISM FOR FREE-RADICAL CHAIN POLYMERIZATION

In general, the decomposition of the initiator (I) may be expressed by the following equations in which k_d is the rate or decay constant.

$$I \xrightarrow{k_d} 2R\cdot \tag{9.4}$$

$$R_d = \frac{-d[I]}{dt} = k_d[I] \tag{9.5}$$

where R_d is the rate of decomposition.

Initiation of free-radical chains takes place by addition of a free radical (R·) to a vinyl molecule. Polystyrene plastic (PS) is produced by free radical polymerization at an annual rate of 1.74 million metric tons. The polymerization of styrene (S) will be used as an illustration. Styrene, like many other aromatic compounds, is toxic, and concentrations in the atmosphere should not exceed 10 ppm. It is important to note that the free radical (R·) is present in all polymerizing species and hence, should not be called a catalyst, even though it often is referred to as a catalyst.

$$C_6H_5\cdot + H_2C{=}CH(C_6H_5) \xrightarrow{k_i} C_6H_5{-}CH_2{-}\dot{C}H(C_6H_5) \tag{9.6}$$

Free radical from benzoyl peroxide; Styrene; Styrene–free radical

$$R\cdot + M \xrightarrow{k_i} RM\cdot$$

Free radical; Monomer; New free radical

$$R_i = \frac{d[RM\cdot]}{dt} = k_i[R\cdot][M] \tag{9.7}$$

where R_i is the rate of initiation.

The rate of initiation, which is the rate-controlling step in free-radical polymerization, is also related to the efficiency of the production of two radicals from each molecule of initiator, as shown in the following rate equation:

$$R_i = 2k_d f[I] \tag{9.8}$$

Propagation is a bimolecular reaction (9.9) which takes place by the addition of the new free radical (RM·) to another molecule of monomer (M), and by many repetitions of this step. While there may be slight changes in the propagation rate constant (k_p) in the first few steps, the rate constant is generally considered to be independent of chain length. Hence, the symbols M·, RM·, and RM_nM· may be considered equivalent in rate equations for free-radical chain-reaction polymerization.

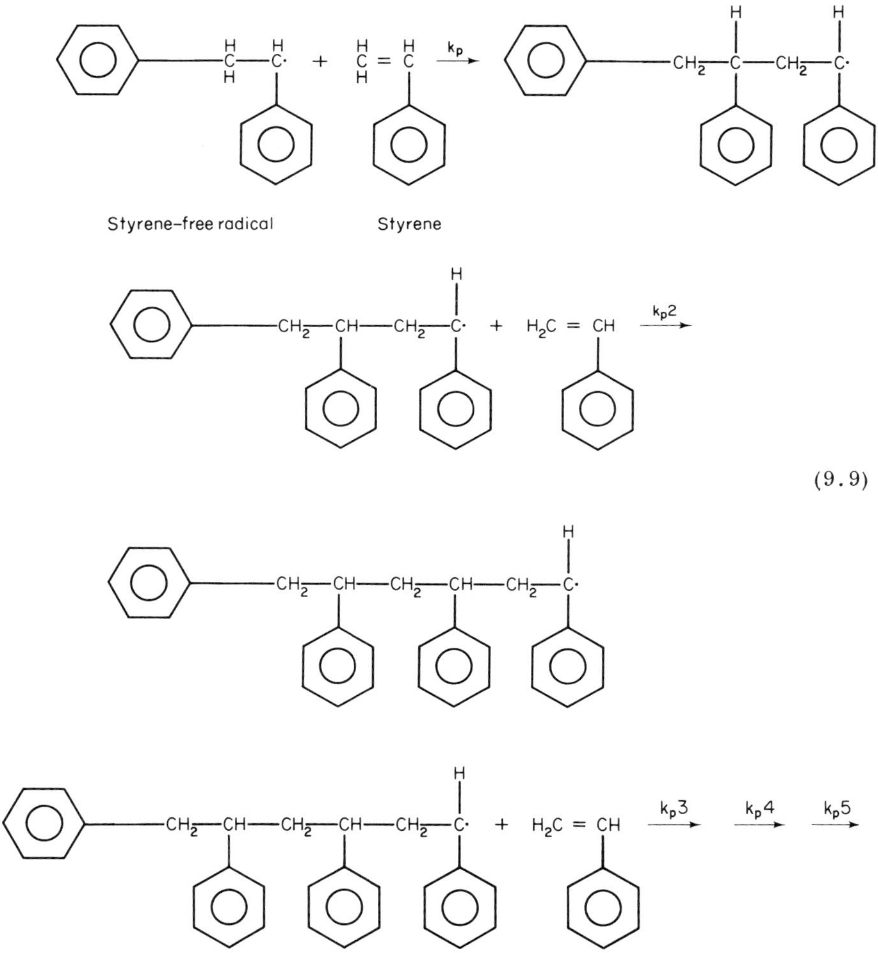

Styrene-free radical + Styrene $\xrightarrow{k_p}$ (9.9)

Styrene-free radical

Styrene

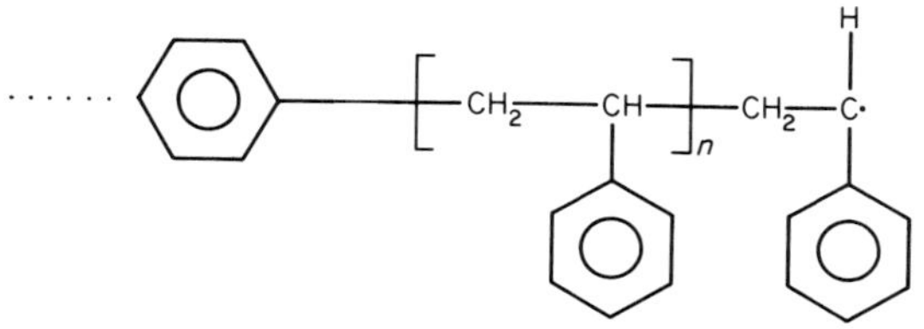

$$\cdots\cdots C_6H_5\text{—}[CH_2\text{—}CH(C_6H_5)]_n\text{—}CH_2\text{—}\dot{C}H(C_6H_5) \qquad (9.9\ \text{cont.})$$

Styrene macroradical

Experimentally it is found that the specific rate constants associated with propagation are approximately independent of chain length; thus, the specific rate constants for each propagation step are considered to be the same, permitting all the propagation steps to be described by a single specific rate constant k_p. Thus, (9.9) can be summed giving the overall propagation expression as

$$\sim\!\!M\cdot + nM \xrightarrow{k_p} \sim\!\!M\text{—}M_{n-1}\text{—}M\cdot$$

or simply

$$M\cdot + nM \xrightarrow{k_p} M\text{—}M_{n-1}\text{—}M\cdot \qquad (9.10)$$

The rate of demise of monomer with time is described as:

$$-\frac{d[M]}{dt} = k_p\,[M\cdot][M] + k_i[R\cdot][M] \qquad (9.11)$$

i.e., monomer consumption occurs only in the steps 2 and 3 described by (9.6) and (9.9).

For long chains the amount of monomer consumed by step 2 (9.6) is small compared with that consumed in step 3 (9.9), permitting (9.11) to be rewritten as:

$$R_p = \frac{-d[M]}{dt} = k_p[M][M\cdot] \qquad (9.12)$$

The polarity of the functional group in the monomers polymerized by free-radical chain polymerization is between the positively inclined monomers, characteristic of undergoing cationic polymerizations, and the negatively inclined monomers, characteristic of undergoing anionic polymerizations. However, as was true for the configuration of growing chains in ionic propagations, head-to-tail arrangement is the customary sequence in free-radical propagation. The functional groups in the vinyl monomers are better stabilizers than the hydrogen atom which would be present as the macroradical end group in a head-to-head arrangement.

Unlike ionic polymerizations, the termination of the growing chain usually takes place by coupling of two macroradicals. Thus, the kinetic chain length (ν) is equal to $\overline{DP}/2$. The chemical and kinetic equations for bimolecular termination are shown below.

$$RM\cdot \quad + \quad \cdot MR \xrightarrow{K_t} RMMR$$

Macroradicals Dead polymer

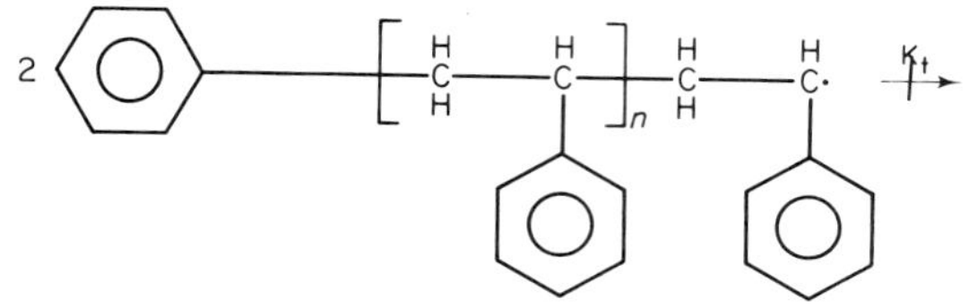

Styrene macroradical (9.13)

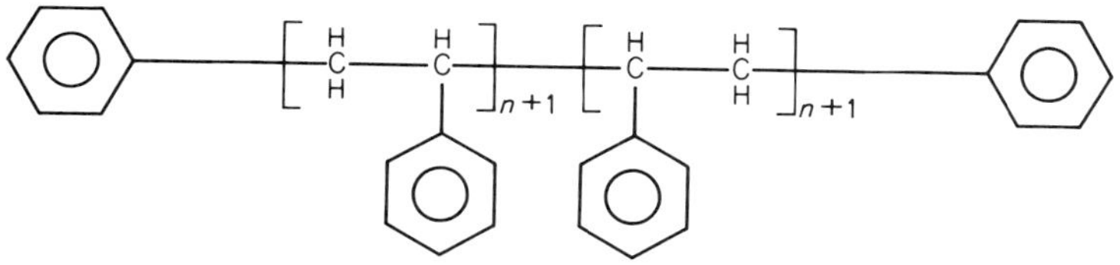

Dead polystyrene

It should be noted that there is a head-to-head configuration at the juncture of the two macroradicals in the dead polymer. The kinetic equation for coupling termination is shown below.

$$R_t = \frac{-d[M\cdot]}{dt} = 2k_t[M\cdot][M\cdot] = 2k_t[M\cdot]^2 \tag{9.14}$$

Termination of free-radical chain polymerization may also take place by disproportionation. This termination process involves chain transfer of a hydrogen atom from one chain end to the free radical chain end of another growing chain. As shown by the following equation, the average kinetic chain length ν of polymers produced by disproportionation is equal to $\overline{DP}$, and one of the dead polymers has a unsaturated chain end.

Styrene macroradicals are usually terminated by coupling. However, while methyl methacrylate macroradicals terminate by coupling at temperatures below 60°C, they tend to terminate by disproportionation at higher temperatures.

Styrene macroradical + Styrene macroradical $\xrightarrow{k_{td}}$ Dead polystyrene + Dead polystyrene

(9.15)

$$R_{Td} = 2k_{Td}[M\cdot]^2 \tag{9.16}$$

$$\nu_t = \frac{R_p}{R_i} = \frac{R_p}{R_T} = \frac{k_p[M][M\cdot]}{2k_{Td}[M\cdot]^2} = \frac{k_p}{2k_{td}}\,\frac{[M]}{[M\cdot]} = \overline{DP} = k'''\,\frac{[M]}{[M\cdot]} \tag{9.17}$$

However, while (9.15) and (9.16) are theoretically important, they contain $[M\cdot]$, which is difficult to experimentally determine and practically of little use. The following is an approach to render such equations more useful by generation of a description of $[M\cdot]$ involving more experimentally accessible terms.

The rate of monomer-radical change is described by:

$$\frac{d[M\cdot]}{dt} = k_i[R\cdot][M] - 2k_t[M\cdot]^2 \tag{9.18}$$

= (monomer-radical formed) - (monomer radical utilized)

It is experimentally found that the number of growing chains is approximately constant over a large extent of reaction. This situation is referred to as a "steady state." For (9.17) this results in $d[M\cdot]/dt = 0$ and

$$k_i[R\cdot][M] = 2k_t[M\cdot]^2 \tag{9.19}$$

Additionally, a steady-state value for the concentration of R· exists, yielding

$$\frac{d[R\cdot]}{dt} = 2k_d f[I] - k_i [R\cdot][M] = 0 \tag{9.20}$$

Solving for [M·] from (9.19) and [R·] from (9.20) gives

$$[M\cdot] = \left(\frac{k_i [R\cdot]M}{2k_t}\right)^{1/2} \tag{9.21}$$

and

$$[R\cdot] = \frac{2k_d f[I]}{k_i [M]} \tag{9.22}$$

Substituting into (9.20) the expression for [R·] from (9.22), we obtain an expression for [M·] (9.22) which contains rapidly determinable variables.

$$[M\cdot] = \left(\frac{k_d f[I]}{k_t}\right)^{1/2} \tag{9.23}$$

We then obtain useful rate and kinetic chain length equations by using the relationship shown above for [M·].

$$R_p = k_p [M][M\cdot] = k_p [M] \left(\frac{k_d f[I]}{k_t}\right)^{1/2} = [M][I]^{1/2} \left(\frac{k_p{}^2 k_d f}{k_t}\right)^{1/2} = k'[M][I]^{1/2} \tag{9.24}$$

where $k' = (k_p{}^2 k_d f/k_t)^{1/2}$

$$R_T = 2k_t [M\cdot]^2 = \frac{2k_t k_d f[I]}{k_t} = 2k_d f[I] \tag{9.25}$$

$$\overline{DP} = \frac{R_p}{R_i} = \frac{k_p [M](k_d f[I]/k_t)^{1/2}}{2k_d f[I]} = \frac{k_p [M]}{2(k_d k_t f[I])^{1/2}}$$

$$= \frac{M}{[I]^{1/2}} \frac{k_p}{(2k_d k_t f)^{1/2}} = \frac{M}{[I]^{1/2}} k'' \tag{9.26}$$

where $k'' = k_p/(2k_d k_t f)^{1/2}$.

Thus, one may make the following conclusions about free-radical chain polymerizations using a chemical initiator:

1. The rate of propagation is proportional to the concentration of the monomer and the square root of the concentration of the initiator.
2. The rate of termination is proportional to the concentration of the initiator.
3. The average molecular weight is proportional to the concentration of the monomer and inversely proportional to the square root of the concentration of initiator.
4. The first chain that is initiated, rapidly produces a high molecular weight polymer.
5. The monomer concentration decreases steadily throughout the reaction and approaches zero at the end.
6. The increases in rates of initiation, propagation, and termination with increases in temperature are in accord with the Arrhenius equation. The energies of activation of initiation, propagation, and termination are approximately 35, 5, and 3 kcal/mol, respectively. Data for typical energies of activation are given in Tables 9.3 and 9.4.
7. Increasing the temperature increases the concentration of free radicals, and thus increases the rate of reactions, but decreases the average molecular weight.
8. If the temperature exceeds the ceiling temperature (T_c), the polymer will decompose and no propagation will take place at temperatures above the ceiling temperature. The ceiling temperature for styrene is 310°C and is only 61°C for α-methylstyrene.

It is interesting to note that because of the great industrial importance of free-radical polymerizations, these are the best studied reactions in all of chemistry. Further, the kinetic approaches described in this chapter are experimentally verified for essentially all the typical free-radical vinyl polymerizations studied.

There is some tendency for the formation of stereoregular segments, particularly at low temperatures, but ionic and coordination catalyst techniques are preferred for the production of stereoregular polymers. For instance, the amount of trans-1,4 is increased from 71% at 100°C to 94% at -46°C for the free-radical polymerization of the diene chloroprene. In fact, the trans-1,4 form appears to be favored for most free-radical polymerizations of dienes. For simple vinyl monomers no clear trend with respect to stereoregular preference has yet emerged.

TABLE 9.3 Energies of Activation for Propagation (E_p) and Termination (E_T) in Free-Radical Chain Polymerization

Monomer	E_p (kcal/mol^{-1})	E_T (kcal/mol^{-1})
Methyl acrylate	7.1	5.3
Acrylonitrile	4.1	5.4
Butadiene	9.3	—
Ethylene	8.2	—
Methyl methacrylate	6.3	2.8
Styrene	7.8	2.4
Vinyl acetate	7.3	5.2
Vinyl chloride	3.7	4.2

[a]Data from Polymer Handbook.

TABLE 9.4 Typical Free-Radical Kinetic Values

k_d	10^{-3} sec^{-1}	E_{ad}	30 to 50 kcal/mol
k_i	10^{3} liter/mol sec	E_{ai}	5 to 7 kcal/mol
k_p	10^{3} liter/mol sec	E_{ap}	4 to 10 kcal/mol
k_t	10^{7} liter/mol sec	E_{at}	0 to 6 kcal/mol

Scheme 9.1 trans-1,4-Polychloroprene.

Chapters 8 and 9 concern themselves mainly with the polymerization of vinyl monomers. Experimentally, only a few vinyl monomers can undergo polymerization by way of anionic, cationic, and free-radical pathways. As would be expected, anionic polymerizations occur mainly with vinyl monomers containing electron-withdrawing substituents, leaving the resulting vinyl portion electron deficient, whereas cationic polymerizations occur mainly with vinyl monomers which contain electron-donating groups. Free-radical polymerizations occur for vinyl monomers that are typically intermediate between electron poor and electron rich. It must be noted that these general tendencies are just that—general tendencies—and that variations do in fact occur. For instance, vinylidene chloride, which contains two chlorine atoms typically considered to be electron withdrawing, does not undergo homopolymerization by an anionic mechanism. Figure 9.1 contains a listing for some of the more common vinyl monomers as a function of type of chain initiation.

9.3 CHAIN TRANSFER

As shown in (9.15), two macroradicals may terminate by chain transfer of a hydrogen atom at one chain end to a free-radical end of another chain in a chain-transfer process called disproportionation. When the abstraction takes place intramolecularly or intermolecularly by a hydrogen atom, some distance from the chain end, branching results. Thus, low-density polyethylene (LDPE), which is produced by a free-radical chain polymerization at extremely high pressure, is highly branched because both types of chain transfer take place during the polymerization of ethylene at high pressure.

Each of these chain-transfer processes causes termination of one macroradical and produces another macroradical. In either case, the unpaired electron is no longer on the terminal carbon atom. The new radical sites serve as branch points for additional chain extension or branching.

As shown by the following equation, short-chain branching is the result of "backbiting" as the chain end assumes a preferred conformation resembling a stable hexagonal ring. The new active center, or branch point, is the result of an abstraction of a hydrogen atom on carbon 6 by the free radical on carbon 1.

H_2		H_2		H_2	
C		C		C	
~H_2C CH_2	$\longrightarrow$	~$\dot{C}$H CH_2	$\xrightarrow{nH_2C{=}CH_2}$	~C(~)H CH_2	
$\dot{C}H_2$ CH_2		H_3C CH_2		H_3C CH_2	(9.27)
C		C		C	
H_2		H_2		H_2	
Ethylene macroradical		New ethylene macroradical		Short-chain branch in LDPE	

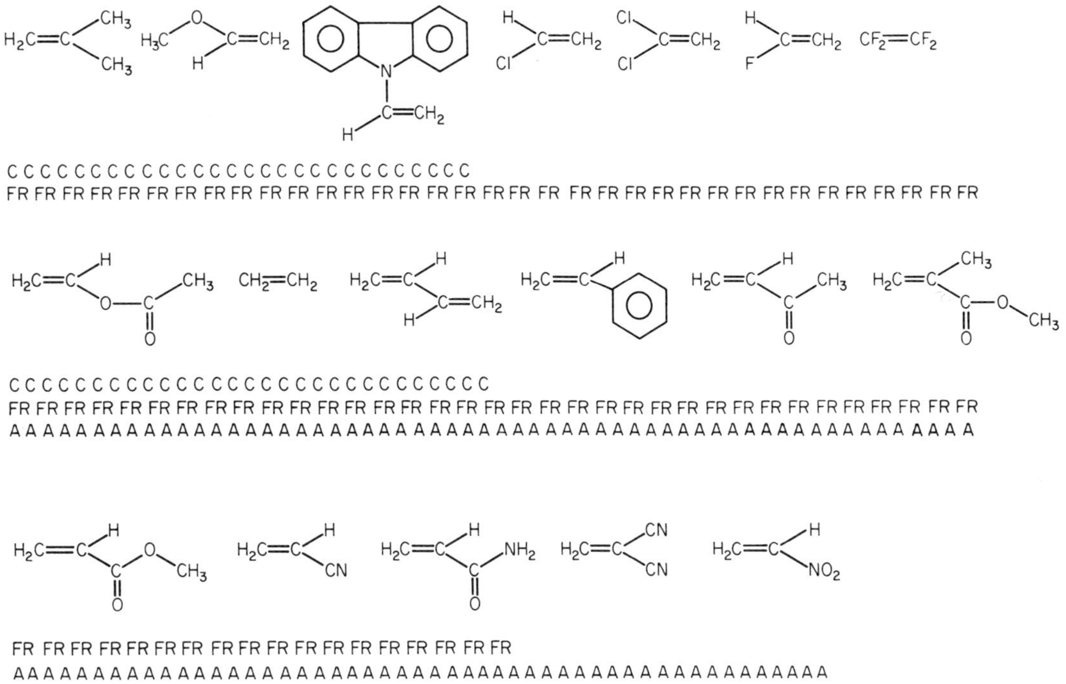

FIGURE 9.1 Type of chain initiation suitable for some common monomers in order of general decrease in electron density associated with the double bond.

As shown in the following equation, long-chain branching takes place as the result of the formation of a branch point by intermolecular chain transfer. Since it is more probable that the new active site will be at a considerable distance from the chain end, the result is a long branch.

$$\sim\!\!\underset{H}{\overset{H}{C}}\!\!\sim \longrightarrow \sim\!\!\underset{H}{\dot{C}}\!\!\sim \xrightarrow{H_2C{=}CH_2} \sim\!\!\underset{H}{\overset{\wr}{C}}\!\!\sim \longrightarrow$$

Dead polymer chain | New macroradical | Long-chain branch in LDPE

$$+ \sim\!\!\underset{H}{\overset{H}{C}}\cdot \longrightarrow \sim CH_3 \tag{9.28}$$

Macroradical | Dead polymer

Chain transfer may also take place with monomer, initiator, solvent, or any other additive present in the polymerization system. Chain transfer to polymer is usually disregarded in the study of chain-transfer reactions, and the emphasis is on chain transfer with solvent or other additive. Thus, while the average chain length is equal to R_p divided by the sum of all termination reactions, it is customary to control all termination reactions except the chain-transfer reaction under investigation. The chain transfer to all other molecules, except solvent or additive, is typically negligible.

This chain-transfer reaction decreases the average chain length in accordance with the concentration of S. The resulting degree of polymerization ($\overline{DP}$) is equal to that which would have been obtained without the solvent or additive plus a factor related to the product of the ratio of the rate of propagation (R_p) to the rate of chain transfer (R_{tr}) and the ratio of the concentration of the monomer [M] to the concentration of solvent of chain-transfer agent [S].

The Mayo equation, which yields positive slopes when the data is plotted, is the reciprocal relationship derived from the previously cited equation. The ratio of the rate of cessation or termination by transfer to the rate of propagation is called the chain-transfer constant (C_5). The latter is related to relative bond strengths in the solvent or additive molecule and the stability of the new free radical produced. The Mayo equation is shown below.

$$\frac{1}{\overline{DP}_0} = \frac{1}{\overline{DP}} + C_s \frac{[S]}{[M]} \tag{9.29}$$

As shown in Fig. 9.2, the molecular weight of polystyrene is reduced when it is polymerized in solvents, and the reduction or increase in slope

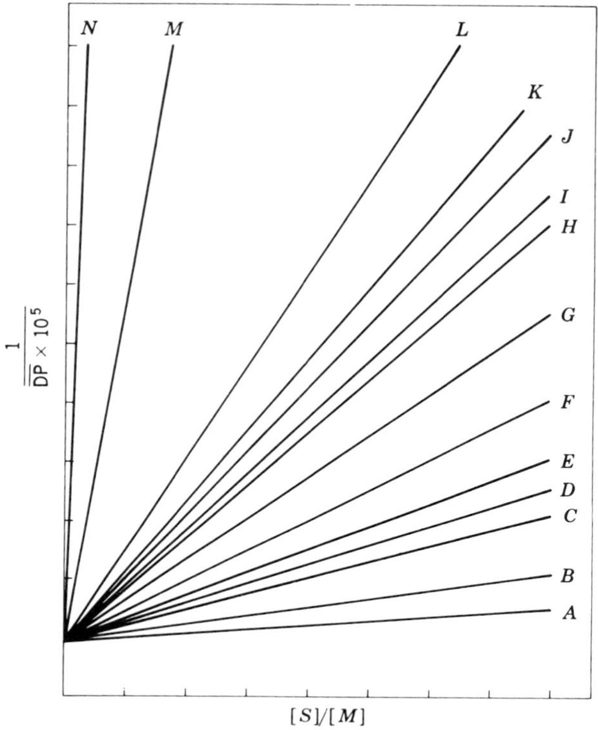

FIGURE 9.2 Molecular weight of polystyrene as a function of solvent and solvent concentration; A = benzene, B = toluene, C = n-heptane, D = chloroform, E = ethylbenzene, F = cumene, G = sec-butylbenzene, H = phenol, I = m-cresol, J = p-cresol, K = o-cresol, L = carbon tetrachloride, M = carbon tetrabromide, N = n-butylmercaptan, [S] = concentration of chain transfer agent, [M] = concentration of styrene monomer. (From Introduction to Polymer Chemistry to R. Seymour, McGraw-Hill, New York, 1971. Used with permission of McGraw-Hill Book Company.)

is related to the chain-transfer efficiency of the solvent. The slopes in this graph are equal to C_S.

Chain-transfer agents have been called regulators (of molecular weight). When used in large proportions, they are called telogens, since they produce low molecular weight polymers (telomers) in these telomerization reactions. As shown in Table 9.5, alkyl mercaptans are effective chain transfer agents for the polymerization of styrene.

The hydrogen atom is abstracted from many telogens, including the phenolic hydrogen of phenol and the hydrogen of mercaptans. However,

TABLE 9.5 Chain Transfer Constants of Solvents to Styrene in Free-Radical Chain Polymerization at 60°C

Transfer agent	$C_S \times 10^4$
Acetic acid	2.0
Benzene	0.01
Butyl alcohol	0.06
tert-Butyl alcohol	6.7
Butyl disulfide	0.24
Carbon tetrabromide	18,000
Carbon tetrachloride	84
Chloroform	0.5
O-Chlorophenol	6.0
2,6-ditert-Butylphenol	49
1-Dodecanethiol	148,000
Hexane	0.9
N,N-Dimethylaniline	12
1-Naphthalenethiol	1500
1-Octanethiol	190,000
p-Methoxyphenol	260
Phenol	8.1
Triethylamine	1.4
Toluene	0.105
Water	0

the hydrogen on the α carbon atom is abstracted from carboxylic acids, and the hydroxyl group is abstracted from alkanols. Halogens are abstracted from many halogen compounds, such as carbon tetrabromide.

It is important to note that the new free-radical produced by chain transfer may or may not initiate another polymer chain formation, depending on its activity. Retarders, chain stoppers, and many antioxidants produce new free radicals with low polymerization activity.

9.4 POLYMERIZATION TECHNIQUES

Many monomers such as styrene, acrylonitrile, and vinyl chloride are toxic, and the polymerization reaction is highly exothermic. Hence, precautions must be taken to minimize exposure to these compounds and to control the temperature of the polymerization reaction. The principal methods are bulk, solution, and emulsion polymerization. Each has characteristic advantages and disadvantages.

Bulk polymerization of a liquid monomer such as methyl methacrylate is relatively simple in the absence of oxygen when small bottles or test tubes are used. As shown by the following equation, one may heat this monomer in the presence of an initiator and obtain a clear plastic, shaped like the container, but a little smaller because of shrinkage. Most monomers shrink during polymerization, and thus the density of the polymers is greater than that of the monomers. Polymethyl methacrylate (PMMA), as an atactic amorphous polymer, is sold under the tradenames of Lucite and Plexiglas.

$$\underset{\text{Free radical}}{R\cdot} + n\underset{\text{Methyl methacrylate}}{\mathrm{CH_2{=}C(CH_3)(C{=}O)OCH_3}} \xrightarrow{\Delta} R\underset{\text{Polymethyl methacrylate}}{\left(\mathrm{-CH_2-C(CH_3)(C{=}O\,OCH_3)-}\right)_n} \tag{9.30}$$

The rate of polymerization of liquid monomers such as methyl methacrylate may be followed by monitoring the change in volume by dilatometry or the increase in viscosity. The latter has essentially no effect on rate of polymerization or molecular weight unless it is relatively high. When the viscosity is high, the termination reaction is hindered, since the macroradicals are unable to diffuse readily in the viscous medium. In contrast, the monomer may diffuse quite readily and high molecular weight macroradicals are produced as the result of propagation in the absence of termination.

This autoacceleration, called the Norris-Trommsdorff, or gel effect, causes the formation of unusually high molecular weight polymers. The additional heat of polymerization may be dissipated in a small test tube, but special design of equipment is necessary for large-scale bulk (mass, or bulk) polymerizations. Fortunately, monomers such as methyl methacrylate may be polymerized without difficulty in sheets up to 5 cm in thickness either in static or continuous systems. The very high molecular weight product, produced because of increased viscosity which results in autoacceleration, is advantageous for cast plastics, but not for those that must be molded or extruded.

It is standard practice to polymerize liquid monomers with agitation in appropriate vessels as long as the system is liquid. In some instances, the unreacted monomer is removed by distillation and recycled. In most cases, the polymerization is continued in special equipment in which the viscous material is forced through extruder-like equipment under controlled temperature conditions. The product is polydisperse, i.e., it consists of a polymer with a broad distribution of molecular weights.

As shown in the following equation, ethyl acrylate may be polymerized by a free radical process. Polyethyl acrylate does not have a pendant methyl group on the α-carbon atom like polymethyl methacrylate, and it has a lower T_g and is flexible at room temperature. Polyacrylates with larger alkyl groups have lower T_g values and are more soluble in hydrocarbon solvents. However, the value of T_g increases when more than 10 carbon atoms are present in the alkyl group because of side-chain crystallization.

$$R\cdot + nCH_2{=}CH(COOC_2H_5) \longrightarrow R\!\left(\!-CH_2-CH(COOC_2H_5)-\right)_n \tag{9.31}$$

Ethyl acrylate　　Polyethyl acrylate

Water-insoluble monomers such as vinyl chloride may be polymerized as suspended droplets (10-1000 nm in diameter) in a process called suspension (pearl) polymerization. Coalescing of the droplets is prevented by use of small amounts of water-soluble polymers, such as polyvinyl alcohol. The suspension process is characterized by good heat control and ease of removal of the discreet polymer particles.

Since polyvinyl chloride (PVC) is insoluble in its monomer (VCM), it precipitates as formed in the droplets. This is actually advantageous, since it permits ready removal of any residual carcinogenic monomer from the solid beads by stripping under reduced pressure.

PVC, which is produced at an annual rate of 2.62 million tons, is characterized by good resistance to flame and corrosives. While the rigid product is used for some articles in which flexibility is not required, most PVC is plasticized or flexibilized by the addition of relatively large amounts of a compatible high-boiling liquid plasticizer such as dioctyl or didecyl phthalate. The equation for the polymerization of vinyl chloride is shown below:

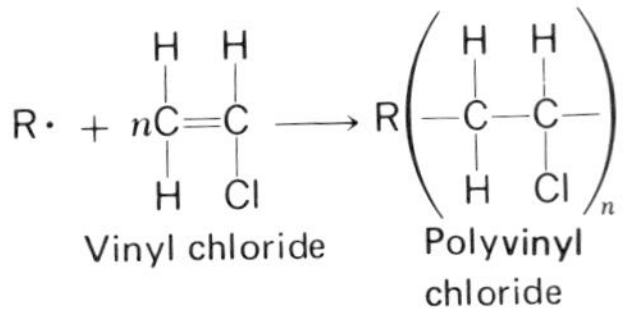

$$\mathrm{R}\cdot + n\underset{\substack{|\\ \mathrm{H}}}{\overset{\substack{\mathrm{H}\\ |}}{\mathrm{C}}}=\underset{\substack{|\\ \mathrm{Cl}}}{\overset{\substack{\mathrm{H}\\ |}}{\mathrm{C}}} \longrightarrow \mathrm{R}\left(-\underset{\substack{|\\ \mathrm{H}}}{\overset{\substack{\mathrm{H}\\ |}}{\mathrm{C}}}-\underset{\substack{|\\ \mathrm{Cl}}}{\overset{\substack{\mathrm{H}\\ |}}{\mathrm{C}}}-\right)_n \tag{9.32}$$

Vinyl chloride Polyvinyl chloride

Monomers may also be polymerized in solution using good or poor solvents for homogeneous and heterogeneous systems, respectively. Solvents with low chain-transfer constants should be used whenever possible to minimize reduction in molecular weight. While telogens do decrease molecular weight, the latter and the rate of polymerization are independent of the polarity of the solvent in homogeneous solution systems.

Polyvinyl acetate (PVAc) may be produced by the polymerization of vinyl acetate in the presence of an initiator in a solution such as benzene. The viscosity of the solution continues to increase until the reaction is complete, but the concentration of the solution is usually too dilute to exhibit autoacceleration because of the gel effect. The solution may be used as prepared, the solvent may be stripped off, or the polymer may be recovered by pouring the solution into an agitated poor solvent, such as ethanol.

PVAc is used in adhesives and coatings, and may be hydrolyzed to produce water-soluble polyvinyl alcohol (PVA). The latter, which is produced at an annual rate of 56,000 tons, may be reacted with butyraldehyde to produce polyvinyl butyraldehyde (PVB) (used as the inner lining in safety glass). The equations for the production of these polymers are as follows:

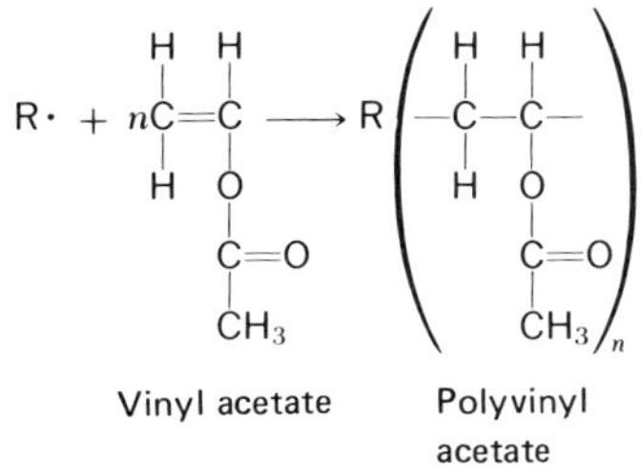

$$\mathrm{R}\cdot + n\underset{\substack{|\\ \mathrm{H}}}{\overset{\substack{\mathrm{H}\\ |}}{\mathrm{C}}}=\underset{\substack{|\\ \mathrm{O}\\ |\\ \mathrm{C=O}\\ |\\ \mathrm{CH_3}}}{\overset{\substack{\mathrm{H}\\ |}}{\mathrm{C}}} \longrightarrow \mathrm{R}\left(-\underset{\substack{|\\ \mathrm{H}}}{\overset{\substack{\mathrm{H}\\ |}}{\mathrm{C}}}-\underset{\substack{|\\ \mathrm{O}\\ |\\ \mathrm{C=O}\\ |\\ \mathrm{CH_3}}}{\overset{\substack{\mathrm{H}\\ |}}{\mathrm{C}}}-\right)_n$$

Vinyl acetate Polyvinyl acetate

(9.33)

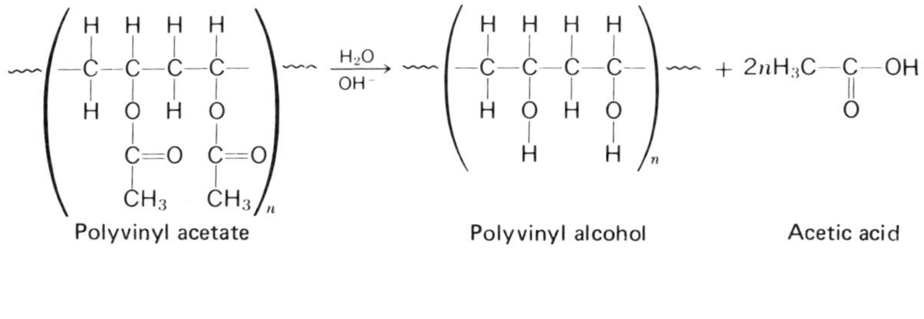

$$\sim\left(-\underset{\substack{|\\ \mathrm{H}}}{\overset{\substack{\mathrm{H}\\ |}}{\mathrm{C}}}-\underset{\substack{|\\ \mathrm{O}\\ |\\ \mathrm{C=O}\\ |\\ \mathrm{CH_3}}}{\overset{\substack{\mathrm{H}\\ |}}{\mathrm{C}}}-\underset{\substack{|\\ \mathrm{H}}}{\overset{\substack{\mathrm{H}\\ |}}{\mathrm{C}}}-\underset{\substack{|\\ \mathrm{O}\\ |\\ \mathrm{C=O}\\ |\\ \mathrm{CH_3}}}{\overset{\substack{\mathrm{H}\\ |}}{\mathrm{C}}}-\right)_n\sim \xrightarrow[\mathrm{OH^-}]{\mathrm{H_2O}} \sim\left(-\underset{\substack{|\\ \mathrm{H}}}{\overset{\substack{\mathrm{H}\\ |}}{\mathrm{C}}}-\underset{\substack{|\\ \mathrm{O}\\ |\\ \mathrm{H}}}{\overset{\substack{\mathrm{H}\\ |}}{\mathrm{C}}}-\underset{\substack{|\\ \mathrm{H}}}{\overset{\substack{\mathrm{H}\\ |}}{\mathrm{C}}}-\underset{\substack{|\\ \mathrm{O}\\ |\\ \mathrm{H}}}{\overset{\substack{\mathrm{H}\\ |}}{\mathrm{C}}}-\right)_n\sim + 2n\mathrm{H_3C}-\underset{\substack{\|\\ \mathrm{O}}}{\mathrm{C}}-\mathrm{OH}$$

Polyvinyl acetate Polyvinyl alcohol Acetic acid

$$\sim\left(\begin{array}{c}-CH_2-CH(OH)-CH_2-CH(OH)-\end{array}\right)_n\sim + nH_3C(CH_2)_2CHO \longrightarrow \sim\left(-CH_2-CH(O)-CH_2-CH(O)- \text{ bridged by } H-C-(CH_2)_2CH_3\right)_n\sim$$

Polyvinyl alcohol Butyraldehyde Polyvinyl butyral

(9.33 cont.)

When a monomer such as acrylonitrile is polymerized in a poor solvent such as benzene, macroradicals precipitate as they are formed. Since these are "living polymers," the polymerization continues as more acrylonitrile diffuses into the precipitated particles. This heterogeneous solution type of polymerization has been called precipitation polymerization. Acrylic fibers (Acrilan; produced at an annual rate of 339,000 tons) are based on polyacrylonitrile (PAN).

Since the acrylonitrile is carcinogenic, precautions must be taken to avoid contact with this monomer. The latter must not be present in high concentrations in acrylic fibers or plastics. It is of interest to note that polyacylonitrile forms a heat-resistant ladder polymer when heated at elevated temperatures. The equations for these reactions are as follows:

$$R\cdot + nH_2C{=}CH(CN) \longrightarrow R\left(-CH_2-CH(CN)-\right)_n$$

Acrylonitrile Polyacrylonitrile

$$\sim CH_2-CH(C{\equiv}N)-CH_2-CH(C{\equiv}N)-CH_2-CH(C{\equiv}N)\sim \xrightarrow{\Delta} \text{(cyclized ladder: C=N ring units)} \xrightarrow{O_2} \text{(aromatized ladder)} \qquad (9.34)$$

Polyacrylonitrile Ladder polymers

The black ladder polymer produced by pyrolysis of PAN is sometimes called black nylon or fiber AF. Polyacrylonitrile is a hydrogen-bonded polymer with a high solubility parameter value, on the order of 15 H, and hence is soluble only in polar solvents such as N,N-dimethylformamide (DMF).

Many water-insoluble vinyl monomers may also be polymerized by the emulsion polymerization technique. This technique, which differs from suspension polymerization in the size of the suspended particles and in the mechanism, is widely used for the production of many commercial plastics and elastomers. While the particles in the suspension range from 10 to 1000 nm, those in the emulsion process range from 0.05 to 5 nm. The small beads produced in the suspension process may be separated by filtering, but the latex produced in emulsion polymerization is a stable system in which the charged particles cannot be removed by ordinary separation procedures.

Since relatively stable macroradicals are produced in the emulsion process, the termination rate is decreased and a high molecular weight product is produced at a rapid rate. It is customary to use a water-soluble initiator such as potassium persulfate, and an anionic surfactant such as sodium stearate and to stir the aqueous mixture of monomer, initiator, and surfactant in the absence of oxygen at 40 to 70°C.

A typical recipe for emulsion polymerization includes 100 g of monomer, such as styrene, 180 g of water, 5 g of sodium stearate, and 0.5 g of potassium persulfate. When the concentration of soap exceeds the critical micelle concentration (CMC), these molecules are present as micelles in which the hydrophilic carboxylic acid ends are oriented toward the water-micelle interface, and the lyophilic hydrocarbon ends are oriented toward the center of the micelle. The micelles are present as spheres with a diameter of 5 to 10 nm when the soap concentration is less than 2%. However, with the higher concentrations customarily used, the micelles resemble aggregates of rods which are 100 to 300 nm in length.

As shown in Fig. 9.3, the water-insoluble monomer is attracted to the lyophilic ends in the micelles, and this causes the micelles to swell. The number of swollen micelles per milliliter of water is on the order of 10^{18}. However, at the initial stages of polymerization (phase I), most of the monomer is present as globules which resemble those observed in suspension polymerization.

Since the initiation of polymerization takes place in the aqueous phase, essentially no polymerization takes place in the globules. Thus, they serve primarily as a reservoir of monomer supplied to the micelles to replace the monomer converted to polymer. The number of droplets per milliliter of water is on the order of 10^{11}. Hence, since there are 10 million times as many micelles as droplets, the chance of initiation of monomer in a droplet is very, very small.

As shown in the following equations, the persulfate ion undergoes homolytic cleavage to produce two sulfate ion radicals. These serve as initiators for the few water-soluble monomer molecules present in the aqueous phase.

$$S_2O_8^{--} \longrightarrow 2SO_4\cdot^{-} \qquad (9.35)$$

Persulfate ion — Sulfate ion radical

$$SO_4\cdot^- + \underset{H}{\overset{H}{C}}{=}\underset{C_6H_5}{\overset{H}{C}} \longrightarrow O{=}\underset{O}{\overset{^-O}{S}}{-}O{-}\underset{H}{\overset{H}{C}}{-}\underset{C_6H_5}{\overset{H}{C}}\cdot \qquad (9.35\ \text{cont.})$$

Sulfate ion radical   Styrene dissolved in water   Styrene radical

According to a theory proposed by Harkins and refined by Smith and Ewart, the first stages of propagation in an emulsion system also take place in the aqueous phase to produce a more lyophilic surface-active oligoradical, as shown below in (9.36).

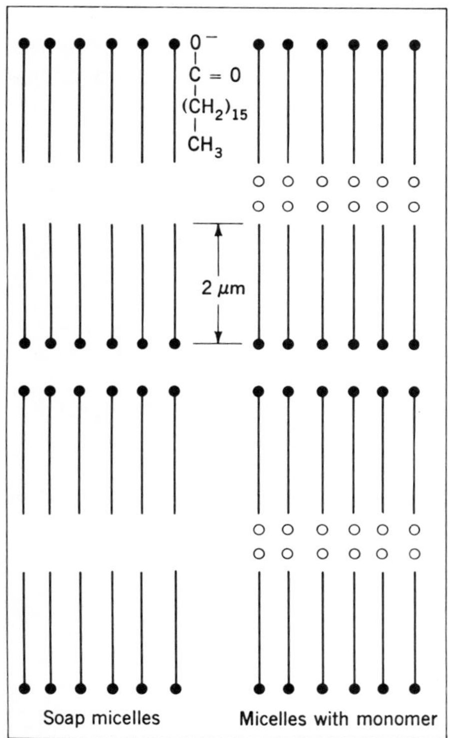

FIGURE 9.3 Micelles swollen with solubilized styrene monomer. (From Introduction to Polymer Chemistry by R. Seymour, McGraw-Hill, New York, 1971. Used with permission of McGraw-Hill Book Company.)

$$^{-}SO_4-\underset{H}{\overset{H}{C}}-\underset{C_6H_5}{\overset{H}{C}}\cdot + nH_2C=\underset{C_6H_5}{\overset{H}{C}} \xrightarrow{k_p} {}^{-}SO_4\left[\underset{H}{\overset{H}{C}}-\underset{C_6H_5}{\overset{H}{C}}\right]_n\underset{H}{\overset{H}{C}}-\underset{C_6H_5}{\overset{H}{C}}\cdot \tag{9.36}$$

Styrene radical Styrene Oligoradical

When the $\overline{DP}$ of the styrene oligoradical is 3 to 5, its solubility is much like that of styrene, and it migrates to the swollen micelle where propagation continues with the styrene molecules already present. According to accepted theories, each micelle can accommodate only one free radical, and until a second one enters and terminates the propagation reaction by coupling, propagation continues to take place in the micelles. From a statistical point of view, only one-half of the micelles (N/2) will contain growing chains at any one time. It should also be noted that since propagation occurs in the micelles, the rate of polymerization will be proportional to the number of micelles present; i.e., the rate is proportional to the soap concentration.

As the micelles grow by absorption of more monomer and formation of polymer, they become relatively large particles which absorb soap from micelles that have not been inoculated or stung by oligoradicals. Thus, in stage II, when about 20% of the monomer has been converted to polymer, the micelles disappear and are replaced by larger, but fewer monomer-polymer particles.

Polymerization continues in stage II, and monomer continues to be supplied to the particles by the droplets in the aqueous phase. These droplets disappear when about 30% of the monomer has been converted to polymer. Polymerization continues in stage III after about a 60% conversion, but all monomer must now be supplied to the macroradicals by a diffusion process within the micelles.

As shown below, the rate of initiation in the aqueous phase of emulsion polymerization is the same as that described for other free-radical chain initiations.

$$R_d = k_d[S_2O_8^{2-}] \tag{9.37}$$

$$R_i = k_i[SO_4\cdot^-][H_2C=\underset{C_6H_5}{\overset{H}{C}}] = 2k_d f [S_2O_8^{2-}] \tag{9.38}$$

The rate of propagation in the micelles is similar to that described for other free-radical chain propagations, but since the free-radical concentration is equal to the number of active micelles, the value of N/2 is used instead of [M·]. Thus, as shown by the following equation, the rate of propagation is dependent on the number of micelles present.

$$R_p = k_p[M][M\cdot] = k_p[M]\frac{N}{2} \qquad (9.39)$$

The rate of production of free radicals at 50°C is about 10^{13}/ml sec^{-1}. Thus, since there are 100,000 micelles for every free radical produced in a second, inoculation of any of the 10^{18} micelles per milliliter is infrequent. Hence, since propagation is a very fast reaction, long chains are produced before termination by coupling takes place as the result of the entrance of a new oligoradical in the active micelle. As shown by the following equation, the degree of polymerization is also proportional to the number of active micelles (N/2).

$$\overline{DP} = \frac{R_p}{R_i} = \frac{k_p}{R_i}[M]\frac{N}{2} \qquad (9.40)$$

The rate of polymerization in emulsion systems may be increased by the addition of reducing agents such as iron(II) salts. The presence of high molecular weight polymers is advantageous when the latex is used directly as a coating, adhesive, or film. However, the high molecular weight solid polymer obtained when the emulsion is coagulated may make subsequent processing difficult. This difficulty is overcome by the addition of chain transfer agents, such as dodecyl mercaptan (1-dodecanethiol).

In addition to LDPE, PS, PVC, PMMA, PVAc, and PAN, many other commercial polymers are produced by free-radical chain-reaction polymerization. Among these are the polyfluorocarbons, polyvinylidene chloride, neoprene elastomer, and SBR rubber. The latter, which is a copolymer of butadiene (75) and styrene (25), will be discussed in Chap. 10.

Polytetrafluoroethylene (Teflon, PTFE) was discovered accidentally in 1938 by Plunkett who found a solid in his cylinder of gaseous tetrafluoroethylene. As shown by the following structural formula, PTFE contains no hydrogen atoms. Because of the stability of the carbon-fluorine bond, the closeness of the carbon atoms to each other, the crowding by the fluorine atoms, and the regularity in its structure, PTFE has outstanding resistance to heat. It is a crystalline polymer which does not melt below a temperature of 327°C. Teflon is one of the most expensive polymers with extensive commercial use. At least some of its high cost is due to difficulty in its processability.

The processibility of this type of polyfluorocarbon is improved by replacing one of the eight fluorine atoms by a trifluoromethyl group. The product, called FEP or Viton, is a copolymer of tetrafluoroethylene and hexafluoropropylene. Polytrifluoromonochloroethylene (CTFE, Kel F) in which one fluorine atom has been replaced by a chlorine atom has a less regular structure than FEP and is also more easily processed.

Polyvinylidene fluoride (Kynar) and polyvinyl fluoride (Tedlar) are also more readily processable, and less resistant to solvents and corrosives than PTFE. The former has piezoelectric properties, i.e., it generates electric current when compressed. Polymers and copolymers of vinylidene chloride (PVDC, Saran) are used as film (Saran Wrap).

$$\left(\begin{array}{cc} F & F \\ | & | \\ C - & C \\ | & | \\ F & F \end{array}\right)_n$$

PTFE

$$\left(\begin{array}{cccc} F & F & F & CF_3 \\ | & | & | & | \\ C - & C - & C - & C \\ | & | & | & | \\ F & F & F & F \end{array}\right)_n$$

FEP

$$\left(\begin{array}{cc} F & F \\ | & | \\ C - & C \\ | & | \\ F & Cl \end{array}\right)_n$$

CTFE

$$\left(\begin{array}{cc} H & F \\ | & | \\ C - & C \\ | & | \\ H & F \end{array}\right)_n$$

Polyvinylidene fluoride

$$\left(\begin{array}{cc} H & Cl \\ | & | \\ C - & C \\ | & | \\ H & Cl \end{array}\right)_n$$

PVDC

TABLE 9.6 Production of Homopolymers in the U.S.A. by Free-Radical Chain Polymerization in 1978 (thousands of metric tons)

Thermoplastics	
Low-density polyethylene (LDPE)	3186
Polyvinyl chloride	2617
Polystyrene	1741
Polyvinyl alcohol, from PVAc	56
Total thermoplastics	7600
Elastomers	
Neoprene	126
Fibers	
Acrylic fibers (PAN)	339
Total polymers	8165

Production data for commercial polymers produced by free-radical chain polymerizations are shown in Table 9.6.

SUMMARY

1. Peroxides, such as benzoyl peroxide, and diazo compounds, such as azo-bis-isobutyronitrile, are readily homolytically cleaved by heat or ultraviolet light to produce free radicals, which serve as initiators for chain-reaction polymerization. Each initiator has its characteristic half-life. Their decomposition into free radicals may be accelerated by heat or by reducing agents.

2. The rate of initiation of free-radical chain polymerization, which is the rate-controlling step, is proportional to the product of the concentrations of the free radical (R·) and the monomer.

3. The rate of propagation is proportional to the concentrations of the monomer and the macroradicals. The additional stability of the macroradical with the functional group or the terminal carbon favors the head-to-tail configuration.

4. Termination of propagating macroradicals may take place by coupling or disproportionation. The kinetic chain length ν is equal to $\overline{DP}$ for the latter and $\overline{DP}/2$ for the former. The rate of termination is proportional to the square of the concentration of macroradicals.

5. The degree of polymerization $\overline{DP}$ is inversely proportional to the square root of the concentration of initiator and decreases as temperature increases.

6. Since growing chains continue to propagate until a high molecular weight product is formed, the concentration of monomer decreases steadily and approaches zero at the end of the reaction. At all times, prior to the end of the polymerization, the composition of the system consists of monomer and high molecular weight polymers.

7. Polymerization will not take place above the characteristic ceiling temperature.

8. Chain transfer, in which the macroradical abstracts a weakly bonded atom, causes branching when chain transfer with polymer occurs. Chain transfer with solvent or some other additive results in a dead polymer and a new free radical. If the latter does not serve as an initiator for further propagation, it is called a retarder or inhibitor.

9. The efficiency of a chain transfer agent (chain transfer constant) is the slope of the line when $1/\overline{DP}$ is plotted against [S]/[M] when S is the solvent or telogen.

10. Vinyl monomers may be polymerized without other additives, except free radicals in bulk polymerization. When the monomer is polymerized while suspended in a stirred aqueous medium, the process is called suspension, or pearl, polymerization. Polymerization may also take place in good or poor solvents. In the former case, the viscosity continues to increase, and in the latter, the macroradicals precipitate.

11. When the system is viscous, the termination step is hindered but propagation continues. Thus, this so-called Trommsdorff or gel effect produces high molecular weight polymers.

12. Monomers may also be polymerized by a water-soluble initiator while dispersed, by agitation, in a concentrated soap solution. In this emulsion polymerization process, initiation takes place in the aqueous phase and propagation takes place in the soap micelles. Since the growing macroradicals are not terminated until a new free radical enters the micelle, high molecular weight products are obtained in a relatively short time.

13. The rate of polymerization and the degree of polymerization in the emulsion process are proportional to the number of activated micelles.

14. The polyfluorocarbons are resistant to heat, solvents, and corrosives. The resistance is greatest in the regularly structured polytetrafluoroethylene and decreases as the geometry is upset by substitution of larger or smaller groups for the fluorine atoms.

15. Low-density polyethylene, polyvinyl chloride, polystyrene, and neoprene are made in large quantities by free-radical chain polymerization. Over 8 million tons of homopolymers are produced annually in the United States by this mechanism.

GLOSSARY

AIBN: Abbreviation for 2,2'-azo-bis-isobutyronitrile.

Acrilan: Tradename for fibers based on polymers of acrylonitrile (PAN).

backbiting: The hydrogen atom abstraction that occurs when a chain end of a macroradical doubles back on itself to form a more stable hexagonal conformation.

bimolecular reaction: A reaction involving two reactants.

BPO: Abbreviation for benzoyl peroxide.

branch point: The point on the polymer chain where additional chain extension takes place to produce a branch.

bulk polymerization: The polymerization of monomer without added solvents or water.

[ ]: Concentration.

C_S: Chain transfer constant.

ceiling temperature (T_c): A characteristic temperature above which polymerization does not take place and polymers decompose.

chain stopper: A chain transfer agent that produces inactive free radicals.

chain transfer: A process in which a free radical abstracts an atom or group of atoms from a solvent, telogen, or polymer.

chain transfer constant (C_S): The ratio of cessation or termination of transfer to the rate of propagation.

CMC: Critical micelle concentration.

critical micelle concentration: The minimum concentration of soap in water that will produce micelles.

dead polymer: A polymer in which chain growth has been terminated.

dilatometer: An instrument which measures changes in volume.

disproportionation: A process by which termination takes place as the result of chain transfer between two macroradicals to yield dead polymers, one of which has an ethylenic end group.

DMF: Abbreviation for N,N-dimethylformamide.

E_a: Activation energy.

f: The efficiency factor in the decomposition of initiators.

FEP: A copolymer of tetrafluoroethylene and hexafluoropropylene.

first-order reaction: A reaction in which the rate is proportional to the concentration of the reactant to the first power.

half-life time ($t_{1/2}$): The time required for half the reactants to be consumed in a first-order reaction.

heterolytic cleavage: A cleavage of a covalent bond or ion pairs which leaves the two electrons on one of the atoms. The products are a carbonium ion and a carbanion, or a cation and an anion.

homogeneous cleavage: A cleavage of a covalent bond which leaves one of the two electrons on each atom. The products are free radicals.

homopolymer: A polymer made up of only one repeating unit, in contrast to a copolymer, which is made up of more than one repeating units.

I: Initiator.

k_d: Decay constant or rate of decomposition constant.

Kel F: Tradename for TFE.

kinetic chain length: The length of the polymer chain (DP) initiated by one free radical:

$$\nu = \frac{R_p}{R_i} = \frac{R_p}{R_t}$$

Kynar: Tradename for polyvinylidene fluoride.

latex: A stable dispersion of a polymer in water.

M: Monomer.

M·: A monomer radical or a macroradical.

macroradicals: Electron-deficient polymers, i.e., those having a free radical present on the chain.

Mayo equation:

$$\frac{1}{\overline{DP}} = \frac{1}{\overline{DP}_0} + C_s \frac{[S]}{[M]}$$

micelles: Ordered groups of soap molecules in water.

N: The number of active micelles present.

nm: Nanometers (1×10^{-9} m).

ν: Symbol for the kinetic chain length.

Norris-Trommsdorff effect: Same as Trommsdorff effect.

oligoradical: A low molecular weight macroradical.

PAN: Polyacrylonitrile.

piezoelectric: The conversion of mechanical force such as pressure into electrical energy.

plasticizer: A high-boiling compatible liquid which lowers the T_g and flexibilizes a stiff polymer like PVC.

PMMA: Polymethyl methacrylate.

ppm: Parts per million.

PS: Polystyrene.

PTFE: Polytetrafluoroethylene.

PVA: Polyvinyl alcohol.

PVAc: Polyvinyl acetate.

PBC: Polyvinyl butyral.

PVDC: Polyvinylidene chloride.

R: Rate of reaction.

R·: A free radical.

retarder: An additive which acts as a chain transfer agent to produce less active free radicals.

RM·: A macroradical.

S: Solvent or telogen.

S: Styrene.

Saran: Tradename for polymers of vinylidene chloride.

SBR: A rubbery copolymer of styrene and butadiene.

stage I: The first stage in emulsion polymerization when up to 20% of the monomer is being polymerized.

stage II: The intermediate stage in emulsion polymerization when 20 to 60% of the monomer is being polymerized at a steady rate.

stage III: The last stage in emulsion polymerization when the last 40% of monomer is being polymerized.

suspension polymerization: A process in which liquid monomers are polymerized as liquid droplets suspended in water.

t: Time.

T_c: Ceiling temperature.

TBP: tert-Butyl peroxide.

Tedlar: Tradename for polyvinyl fluoride.

telogen: An additive that readily undergoes chain transfer with a macroradical.

telomer: A low molecular weight polymer resulting from chain transfer of a macroradical with a telogen.

telomerization: The process in which telomers are produced by chain transfer reactions.

TFE: Polytrifluoromonochloroethylene.

Trommsdorff effect: The decrease in termination rate in viscous media which results in higher molecular weight polymers.

vinyl group:

$$H_2C{=}C(H)(X)$$

where X may be R, X, $\overset{\displaystyle O}{\overset{\|}{C}}$—OR, OR, etc.

Viton: Tradename for FEP.

EXERCISES

1. Use a slanted line to show the cleavage of (a) boron trifluoride-water, (b) sodamide, and (c) AIBN in cationic, anionic, and free-radical initiations, respectively.
2. Which type of chain-reaction polymerization is most likely to terminate by coupling?
3. If an initiator has a half-life of 4 hr, what percentage of this initiator will remain after 12 hr?
4. If some head-to-head configuration is detected in a polymer chain known to propagate by head-to-tail addition, what type of termination has occurred?
5. Which is the better way to increase polymer production rates: (a) increasing the temperature or (b) increasing the initiator concentration?
6. Name three widely used thermoplastics produced by free-radical chain polymerization.
7. What effect does the increase of polarity of the solvent have on free-radical polymerization rates in solution?
8. Show the repeating units for (a) PS, (b) PVC, and (c) PMMA.
9. Can you think of any advantage of the Trommsdorff effect?
10. What is the limiting step in free-radical chain polymerization?
11. In general, which is more rapid: (a) free-radical chain reaction or (b) step-reaction polymerization?
12. If one obtained a yield of 10% polymer after 10 min of polymerizing styrene by a free-radical mechanism, what would be the composition of the other 90%?
13. Why is $t_{1/2}$ for all first-order reactions equal to $0.693/k_d$?

14. How could you follow the rate of decomposition of AIBN without measuring the rate of polymerization?

15. What is the usual value for the energy of activation of free-radical initiator?

16. What is the advantage of producing free radicals by use of ultraviolet radiation?

17. Which is the better catalyst for the polymerization of styrene? (a) AIBN or (b) BPO?

18. If [M·] is equal to 1×10^{-11} mol/liter under steady-state conditions, what will [M·] equal after (a) 30, (b) 60, and (c) 90 min?

19. In general, what is the activation energy in free-radical chain propagation of polymer chains?

20. What is the relationship of the rate of propagation to the concentration of initiators [I]?

21. When chain transfer with solvent occurs, what effect does this have on $\overline{DP}$?

22. Name a plasticizer for PVC.

23. What monomer is used to produce PVA?

24. How can you reconcile the two different equations for R_i:$R_i \propto [R\cdot]$ and $R_i \propto 2[I]$?

25. Does k_p increase or decrease when $\overline{DP}$ goes from 10 to 10^4?

26. Why is ethylene more readily polymerized by free-radical chain polymerization than isobutylene?

27. What is the termination mechanism in free-radical polymerization if $\overline{DP} = \nu$?

28. The value of ν increases as the polymerization temperature of a specific monomer is increased. What does this tell you about the termination process?

29. In general, what is the activation energy of termination?

30. Why wouldn't you recommend the use of poly-α-methylstyrene for a handle of a cooking utensil?

31. When backbiting occurs, a long branch forms at the branch point. Why is this called "short-chain branching"?

32. Which would you expect to have the higher chain transfer constant: (a) carbon tetrafluoride or (b) carbon tetrachloride?

33. While the addition of dodecyl mercaptan to styrene causes a reduction in $\overline{DP}$, the rate of polymerization is essentially unchanged. Explain.

34. Would it be safe to polymerize styrene by bulk polymerization in a 55-gal drum?

35. How do the kinetics of polymerization differ in the bulk and suspension polymerization methods?

36. Since the monomers are carcinogenic, should the polymerization of styrene, acrylonitrile, and vinyl chloride be banned?

37. What happens when a filament of polyacrylonitrile is pyrolyzed?

38. Why doesn't polymerization take place in the droplets, instead of in the micelles in emulsion polymerization?

39. Why doesn't initiation occur in the micelles in emulsion polymerization?

40. What would happen if one added a small amount of an inhibitor to styrene before bulk polymerization?

41. What would be the effect on the rate of polymerization if one used AIBN as the initiator and an amount of soap that was less than CMC in emulsion polymerization?

42. Why is the T_g of PTFE higher than that of FEP?

43. Why does an increase in soap concentration increase the $\overline{DP}$ and R_p of emulsion polymerization?

44. Which will have the higher specific gravity: (a) PVC or (b) PVDC?

BIBLIOGRAPHY

Albright, L. F. (1974): Processes for Major-Addition-Type Plastics and Their Monomers, McGraw-Hill, New York.

Allen, P. E. M., and Patrick, C. R. (1900): Kinetics and mechanisms of polymerization reactions, Makromol. Chem., 47:154.

Bailey, W. J. (1972): Macromolecular Synthesis, John Wiley, New York.

Bamford, C. H., Barb, W. G., Jenkins, A. D., Onyon, P. F. (1958): Kinetics of Vinyl Polymerization by Radical Mechanisms, Butterworths, London.

Barrett, K. E. J. (1975): Dispersion Polymerization in Organic Media, John Wiley, New York.

Bawn, C. E. H. (1972): Macromolecular Science, University Park Press, Baltimore.

Bevington, J. C. (1961): Radical Polymerization, Academic, New York.

Billmeyer, F. W. (1962): Textbook of Polymer Science, Wiley Interscience, New York.

Blackley, D. C. (1975): Emulsion Polymerization, Halsted, New York.

Boundy, R. H., and Boyer, R. F. (1952): Styrene, Reinhold, New York.

Bovey, F. A., Kolthoff, I. M., Medalia, A. I., Meehan, E. J. (1955): Emulsion Polymerization, Interscience, New York.

Brandrup, J., and Immergut, E. H. (1975): Polymer Handbook, John Wiley, New York.

Burnett, G. M. (1954): Mechanism of Polymer Reactions, John Wiley, New York.

Dalin, M. A., and Gingold, K. (1971): Acrylonitrile, Technomic Publication Co., Westport, Connecticut.

Dole, M. (1972): The Radiation Chemistry of Macromolecules, Academic, New York.

DuBois, H., and John, F. W. (1974): Plastics, Van Nostrand-Reinhold, New York.

Duck, E. W. (1974): Plastics and Rubber, Philosophical Library, New York.

Fawcett, E. W., Gibson, R. O., et al. (1937): British Patent 471,590, September 6, 1937.

Gaylord, N. G., and Mark, H. F. (1958): Linear and Stereoaddition Polymers, Interscience, New York.

Ham, G. E. (1967): Vinyl Polymerization, Vol. I, New York.

Harkins, W. D. (1947; 1950): Emulsion polymerization, J. Am. Chem. Soc., 69:1429; J. Polymer Sci., 5:217.

Harper, C. A. (1975): Handbook of Plastics and Elastomers, McGraw-Hill.

Hay, J. M. (1974): Reactive Free Radicals, Academic, New York.

Horn, M. B. (1960): Acrylic Resins, Reinhold, New York.

Huyser, E. S. (1972): Methods in Free Radical Chemistry, Dekker, New York.

Jenkins, A. D. (1972): Polymer Science, American Elsevier, New York.

Kresser, T. O. J. (1966): Polyethylene, Reinhold, New York.

Martin, L. F. (1974): Organic Peroxide Technology, Noyer Data Corp., Park Ridge, New Jersey.

Matthews, G. (1971): Vinyl Chloride and Vinyl Acetate Polymers, Butterworths, London.

Mayo, F. R. (1943): Chain transfer, J. Am. Chem. Soc., 65:2324.

Miles, D. C., and Briston, J. H. (1965): Polymer Technology, Chemical Publishing Company, New York.

Moore, W. R. (1963): An Introduction to Polymer Chemistry, Aldine, Chicago.

Nass, L. I. (1976): Encyclopedia of PVC, Dekker, New York.

Odian, G. (1970): Principles of Polymerization, Chap. 3, McGraw-Hill, New York.

Parker, D. B. V. (1975): Polymer Chemistry, Applied Science Publishers, Essex, England.

Penn, W. S. (1962): PVC Technology, MacLaren and Sons, London.

Piirma, I., and Gardon, J. L. (1976): Emulsion polymerization, ACS Symposium Series No. 24, American Chemical Society, Washington, D.C.

Plunkett, R. J. (1941): Polytetrafluoroethylene, U.S. Patent 2,230,654, February 4, 1941.

Raff, R. A. V., and Allison, J. B. (1964): Polyethylene, Wiley Interscience, New York.

Renfrew, A., and Morgan, P. (1960): Polyethylene—The Technology and Uses of Ethylene Polymers, Iliffe Books, London.

Riddle, E. H. (1961): Monomeric Acrylic Esters, Reinhold, New York.

Rodriquez, F. (1970): Principles of Polymer Systems, Chap. 5, McGraw-Hill, New York.

Roff, W. J., and Scott, J. R. (1972): Handbook of Common Polymers, CRC Press, Cleveland, Ohio.

Rudner, M. A. (1958): Fluorocarbons, Reinhold, New York.

Schildknecht, C. E. (ed.) (1956): Polymer Processes, Interscience, New York.

Seymour, R. B. (1971): Introduction to Polymer Chemistry, Chap. 6, McGraw-Hill, New York.

——. (1975): Modern Plastics Technology, Chaps. 8, 9, 10, Reston Publishing, Reston, Virginia.

Seymour, R. B., and Patel, V. (1973): Chain transfer, J. Macromol. Sci. Chem., 7(4):961.

Seymour, R. B., Sosa, J. M., Patel, V. (1971): Chain transfer, J. Paint Technol., 43(563):45.

Sittig, M. (1976): Polyolefin Production Processes, Noyes Data Corp., Park Ridge, New Jersey.

Small, P. A. (1975): Long Chain Branching in Polymers, Springer-Verlag, New York.

Smith, W. M. (1958): Vinyl Resins, Reinhold, New York.

Smith, W. V., and Ewart, R. H. (1948): Emulsion polymerization, J. Chem. Phys., 16:592.

Sorenson, W. R., and Campbell, T. W. (1968): Preparative Methods of Polymer Chemistry, 2nd ed., Wiley Interscience, New York.

Starks, C. (1975): Free Radical Telomerization, Academic, New York.

Stille, J. K. (1962): Introduction to Polymer Chemistry, John Wiley, New York.

Teach, W. C., and Kiessling, G. C. (1963): Polystyrene, 2nd ed., Reinhold, New York.

Topchiev, A. V., and Krentsel, B. A. (1962): Polyolefins, Pergamon, New York.

Treloar, L. R. G., and Archenhold, W. F. (1975): Introduction to Polymer Science, Wykeham Publishers, London.

Trommsdorff, E., Kohle, H., Lagally, P. (1948): Viscous polymerization, Makromol. Chem., 1:169.

Vollmert, B. (1973): Polymer Chemistry, Chap. 2, Springer-Verlag, New York.

Wall, F. A. (1972): Fluoropolymers, Wiley Interscience, New York.

Walling, C. (1957): Free Radicals in Solution, John Wiley, New York.

Willbecker, E. L. (1974): Macromolecular Synthesis, John Wiley, New York.

Williams, D. J. (1971): Polymer Science and Engineering, Chap. 4, Prentice-Hall, Englewood Cliffs, New Jersey.

Yokum, R. H., and Nyquist, E. G. (1974): Functional Monomers: Their Preparation Polymerization and Application, Dekker, New York.

10

Copolymerization

While the mechanism of copolymerization is similar to that discussed for the polymerization of one reactant (homopolymerization), the reactivities of monomers may differ when more than one is present in the feed. Copolymers may be produced by step-reaction or by chain-reaction polymerization. It is important to note that if the reactant species are M_1 and M_2, the composition of the copolymer is not a mixture or blend of $[M_1]_n + [M_2]_n$.

Most naturally occurring polymers are largely homopolymers, but both proteins and nucleic acids are copolymers. While many synthetic polymers are homopolymers, the most widely used synthetic rubber (SBR) is a copolymer of styrene (S) and butadiene (B). A widely used plastic (ABS) is a copolymer or blend of polymers of acrylonitrile, butadiene, and styrene. A special fiber called Spandex is a block copolymer of a stiff polyurethane and a flexible polyester.

Copolymers may be alternating copolymers, in which there is a regular order of M_1 and M_2 in the chain, i.e., $(M_1M_2)_n$; random copolymers, in which the sequences of M_1 and M_2 are arranged in a random fashion, i.e., $M_1M_1M_2M_1M_2M_2 \cdots$; block copolymers, in which there are long sequences of the same repeating unit in the chain, i.e., $(M_1)_n(M_2)_n$; or graft copolymers, in which the chain extensions of the second monomer are as branches, i.e.,

$$\begin{array}{l} + \\ M_1 \\ M_1—(M_2)_{\overline{n}}— \\ M_1 \\ M_1 \\ +_m \end{array}$$

It is interesting to note that block copolymers may be produced from one monomer only if the arrangements around the chiral carbon atom change sequentially. The copolymers in which the tacticity of the monomers in each sequence differs are called stereoblock copolymers.

10.1 KINETICS OF COPOLYMERIZATION

Because of a difference in the reactivity of the monomers, expressed as reactivity ratios (r), the composition of the copolymer (n) may be different from that of the reactant mixture or feed (x). When x equals n, the product is said to be an azeotropic copolymer.

In the early 1930s, Nobel laureate Staudinger analyzed the product obtained from the copolymerization of equimolar quantities of vinyl chloride (VCM) and vinyl acetate (VAc). He found that the first product produced was high in VCM, but as the composition of the reactant mixture changed because of a depletion of VCM, the product was higher in VAc. This phenomenon is called the composition drift.

Wall showed that n was equal to rx when the reactivity ratio r was equal to the ratio of the propagation rate constants. Thus, r was the slope of the line obtained when the ratio of monomers in the copolymer (M_1/M_2) was plotted against the ratio of monomers in the feed (m_1/m_2). The Wall equation shown below is not a general equation.

$$n = \frac{M_1}{M_2} = r\,\frac{m_1}{m_2} = rx \tag{10.1}$$

The copolymer equation that is now generally accepted was developed in the late 1930s by a group of investigators including Wall, Dostal, Lewis, Alfrey, Simha, and Mayo. These workers considered the four possible chain extension reactions when M_1 and M_2 were present in the feed. As shown below, two of these equations are homopolymerizations or self-propagating steps, and the other two are heteropolymerizations or cross-propagating steps. The ratio of the propagating rate constants are expressed as monomer reactivity ratios, where $r_1 = k_{11}/k_{12}$ and $r_2 = k_{22}/k_{21}$. $M_1\cdot$ and $M_2\cdot$ are used as symbols for the macroradicals with M_1 and M_2 terminal groups, respectively.

$$M_1\cdot + M_1 \xrightarrow{k_{11}} M_1M_1\cdot \tag{10.2}$$

$$M_1\cdot + M_2 \xrightarrow{k_{12}} M_1M_2\cdot \tag{10.3}$$

$$M_2\cdot + M_2 \xrightarrow{k_{22}} M_2M_2\cdot \tag{10.4}$$

$$M_2\cdot + M_1 \xrightarrow{k_{21}} M_2M_1\cdot \tag{10.5}$$

Experimentally it is found that the specific rate constants for the reaction steps described above are essentially independent of chain length, with the rate of monomer addition primarily dependent only on the adding monomer unit and the growing end. Thus, the four copolymerizations between two comonomers can be described using only four equations.

The rate of consumption of M_1 and M_2 in the feed or reactant mixture during the early stages of the reaction can be then described by the following equations:

$$\text{Disappearance of } M_1\text{:} \quad \frac{-d[M_1]}{dt} = k_{11}[M_1\cdot][M_1] + k_{21}[M_2\cdot][M_1] \qquad (10.6)$$

$$\text{Disappearance of } M_2\text{:} \quad \frac{-d[M_2]}{dt} = k_{22}[M_2\cdot][M_2] + k_{12}[M_1\cdot][M_2] \qquad (10.7)$$

Since it is experimentally observed that the number of growing chains remains approximately constant throughout the duration of most copolymerizations, the change in the rate of monomer consumption, $d[M\cdot]/dt$, is zero, permitting (10.6) and (10.7) to be equated to zero. Solving for $M\cdot$ gives

$$[M_1\cdot] = \frac{k_{21}[M_2\cdot][M_1]}{k_{12}[M_2]} \qquad (10.8)$$

Therefore, the ratio of disappearance of monomers M_1/M_2 is described by

$$\frac{d[M_1]}{d[M_2]} = \frac{[M_1]}{[M_2]}\left(\frac{k_{11}[M_1\cdot] + k_{21}[M_2\cdot]}{k_{12}[M_1\cdot] + k_{22}[M_2\cdot]}\right) \qquad (10.9)$$

Then, since the reactivity ratios $r_1 = k_{11}/k_{12}$ and $r_2 = k_{22}/k_{21}$, one may substitute r_1 and r_2 and obtain the copolymer equations.

$$n = \frac{d[M_1]}{d[M_2]} = \frac{[M_1]}{[M_2]}\left(\frac{r_1[M_1] + [M_2]}{[M_1] + r_2[M_2]}\right)$$

or (10.10)

$$n = \frac{d[M_1]}{d[M_2]} = \frac{r_1([M_1]/[M_2]) + 1}{r_2([M_2]/[M_1]) + 1} = \frac{r_1 x + 1}{r_2/x + 1}$$

The copolymer equation (10.10) may be used to show the effect of the composition of the feed (x) on the composition of the copolymer (n). While the values of these two parameters are equal in azeotropic copolymerization, they are different in most copolymerizations. Hence, it is customary to make up for this difference in reactivity ratios by adding monomers continuously to the feed in order to produce copolymers of uniform composition.

For example, from Table 10.1, the reactivity ratios for butadiene and styrene are $r_1 = 1.39$ and $r_2 = 0.78$, respectively. Since the rate of consumption of butadiene (M_1) is faster than that of styrene (M_2), the composition of the feed (x) would change rapidly if butadiene were not added to prevent a change in its composition, i.e., composition drift.

As shown by the following equation, an equimolar ratio of butadiene and styrene would produce a butadiene-rich copolymer in which there would be four molecules of butadiene to every three molecules of styrene in the polymer chain.

$$n = \frac{r_1 x + 1}{(r_2/x) + 1} = \frac{1.39(1) + 1}{(0.78/1) + 1} = \frac{2.39}{1.78} = 1.34 \qquad (10.11)$$

The reactivity ratios may be determined by an analysis of the change in composition of the feed during the very early stages of polymerization. Typical free-radical chain copolymerization reactivity ratios are listed in Table 10.1.

If the reactivity ratio for r_1, shown in Table 10.1, is greater than 1, then monomer M_1 tends to produce homopolymers, or block copolymers. Preference for reaction with the unlike monomer occurs when r_1 is less than 1. When both r_1 and r_2 are approximately equal to 1, the conditions are said to be ideal, and a random (not alternating) copolymer is produced, in accordance with the Wall equation. Thus, a perfectly random copolymer (ideal copolymer) would be produced when chlorotrifluoroethylene is copolymerized with tetrafluoroethylene.

When r_1 and r_2 are approximately equal to zero, as is the case with the copolymerization of maleic anhydride and styrene, an alternating copolymer is produced. In general, there will be a tendency toward alternation when the product of r_1r_2 approaches zero. In contrast, if the values of r_1 and r_2 are similar and the product r_1r_2 approaches 1, the tendency will be to produce random copolymers. The value of r_1r_2 for most copolymerizations is in between 1 and 0, and thus this value may be used with discretion for estimating the extent of randomness in a copolymer.

In the absence of steric or polar restrictions, the assumptions used in the development of the copolymerization equation are valid. Temperature conditions below T_c and the polarity of solvents have little effect on free-radical copolymerization. However, steric effects can be important. For example, as shown by the data in Table 10.1, styrene should tend to produce an alternating copolymer with fumaronitrile However, since there is not enough space for the fumaronitrile mer (M_1) in alternating sequences, it is

TABLE 10.1 Typical Free-Radical Chain Copolymerization Reactivity Ratios at 60°C[a]

M_1	M_2	r_1	r_2	r_1r_2
Acrylamide	Acrylic acid	1.38	0.36	0.5
	Methyl acrylate	1.30	0.05	0.07
	Vinylidene chloride	4.9	0.15	0.74
Acrylic acid	Acrylonitrile (50°C)	1.15	0.35	0.40
	Styrene	0.25	0.15	0.04
	Vinyl acetate (70°C)	2	0.1	0.2
Acrylonitrile	Butadiene	0.25	0.33	0.08
	Ethyl acrylate (50°C)	1.17	0.67	0.78
	Maleic anhydride	6	0	0
	Methyl methacrylate	0.13	1.16	0.15
	Styrene	0.04	0.41	0.16
	Vinyl acetate	4.05	0.06	0.24
	Vinyl chloride	3.28	0.02	0.07
Butadiene	Methyl methacrylate	0.70	0.32	0.22
	Styrene	1.39	0.78	1.08
Chlorotrifluoroethylene	Tetrafluoroethylene	1.0	1.0	1.0
Isoprene	Styrene	1.98	0.44	0.87
Maleic anhydride	Methyl acrylate	0	2.5	0
	Methyl methacrylate	0.03	3.5	0.11
	Styrene	0	0.02	0
	Vinyl acetate (70°C)	0.003	0.055	0.0002
Methyl acrylate	Acrylonitrile	0.67	1.26	0.84
	Styrene	0.18	0.75	0.14
	Vinyl acetate	9.0	0.1	0.90
	Vinyl chloride	5	0	0
Methyl isopropenyl ketone	Styrene (80°C)	0.66	0.32	0.21
Methyl methacrylate	Styrene	0.50	0.50	0.25
	Vinyl acetate	20	0.015	0.30
	Vinyl chloride	12.5	0	0
α-Methylstyrene	Maleic anhydride	0.038	0.08	0.003
	Styrene	0.38	2.3	0.87
Styrene	p-Chlorostyrene	0.74	1.025	0.76
	Fumaronitrile	0.23	0.01	0.002
	p-Methoxystyrene	1.16	0.82	0.95
	Vinyl acetate	55	0.01	0.55
	Vinyl chloride	17	0.02	0.34
	2-Vinylpyridine	0.56	0.9	0.50
Vinyl acetate	Vinyl chloride	0.23	1.68	0.39
	Vinyl laurate	1.4	0.7	0.98
Vinyl chloride	Diethyl maleate	0.77	0.009	0.007
	Vinylidene chloride	0.3	3.2	0.96
N-Vinylpyrrolidone	Styrene (50°C)	0.045	15.7	0.71

[a] Data from Polymer Handbook. Temperatures other than 60°C shown in parentheses.

necessary that two styrene mers (M_2) be in the chain after each regular alternating sequence, i.e., —$M_1M_2M_2M_1M_2M_2M_1M_2$—.

While 1,2-disubstituted vinyl monomers are not readily polymerized, they may form alternating copolymers. For example, stilbene and maleic anhydride produce an alternating copolymer but have little tendency to form homopolymers. It is now believed that a charge transfer complex is the active species in alternating copolymerization.

The formation of these charge transfer complexes is enhanced by the presence of salts such as zinc chloride. These complexes can be detected at low temperatures by ultraviolet or nuclear magnetic resonance spectrometry. Since the equilibrium constants for the formation of these charge complexes decrease as the temperature increases, random, instead of alternating copolymers, may be produced at elevated temperatures.

The resonance stability of the macroradical is an important factor in free-radical propagation. Thus, a conjugated monomer such as styrene is at least 30 times as apt to form a resonance-stabilized macroradical as vinyl acetate resulting in a copolymer rich in styrene. Providing there is not excessive steric hindrance, a 1,1-disubstituted ethylene monomer will polymerize more readily than the unsubstituted vinyl monomer.

Strongly electrophilic or nucleophilic monomers will polymerize exclusively by anionic or cationic mechanisms. However, monomers such as styrene or methyl methacrylate, which are neither strongly electrophilic or nucleophilic, will polymerize by ionic and free-radical chain polymerization mechanisms. As shown in Table 10.1, the values of r_1 and r_2 for these monomers are identical in free-radical chain polymerization. Thus, the formation of a random copolymer would be anticipated when equimolar quantities of these two monomers are present in the feed.

In contrast, the reactivity ratios for styrene and methyl methacrylate are $r_1 = 0.12$ and $r_2 = 26.4$ in an anionic system. Thus, a copolymer rich in methyl methacrylate would be predicted. However, since $r_1 = 10.5$ and $r_2 = 0.1$ in cationic systems, the reverse would be true.

Butyl rubber is a random copolymer prepared by the cationic copolymerization of isobutylene ($r_1 = 2.5$) and isoprene ($r_2 = 0.4$) at -100°C. The elastomeric copolymer of ethylene and propylene is prepared with a homogeneous Zeigler-Natta catalyst in chlorobenzene using $VO(OR)_3$ as the catalyst and $(C_2H_5)_2AlCl$ as the cocatalyst. In this case, r_1r_2 is approximately 1, so the product tends to be a random copolymer. It is customery to add a diene monomer so that the product may be cured through cross linking of the double bonds in the copolymer (EPDM).

The contrast between anionic, cationic, and free-radical methods of addition polymerization is clearly illustrated by the results of copolymerization utilizing the three modes of initiation. The composition of initial copolymer formed from a feed of styrene and methyl methacrylate is shown in Fig. 10.1. Such results illustrate the variations of reactivities and copolymer composition that are possible from employing the different initiation

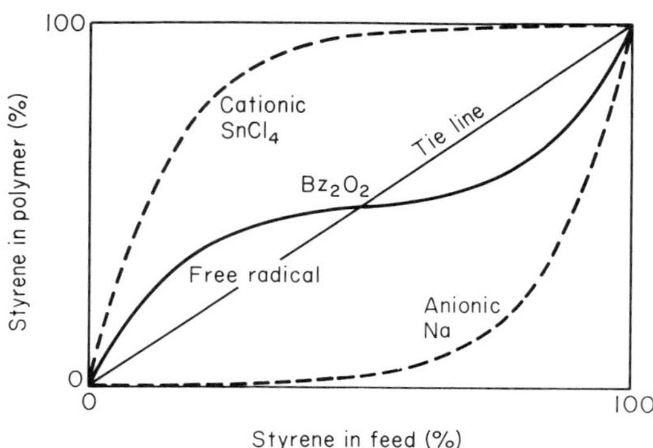

FIGURE 10.1 Instantaneous copolymer composition as a function of monomer composition and initiator employed for the comonomer system of styrene and methyl methacylate utilizing different modes of initiation. [Y. Landler, Comptes Rendus, 230:539 (1950). With permission of the Academie des Sciences, Paris, France. D. Pepper, Chem. Soc. Q. Rev., 8:88 (1954). With permission of The Chemical Society (Great Britain).]

modes. The free-radical "tie-line" resides near the middle since free-radical polymerizations are less dependent on the electronic nature of the comonomers relative to the ionic modes of chain propagation.

10.2 THE Q-e SCHEME

A useful scheme for predicting r_1 and r_2 values for free-radical copolymerizations was proposed by Alfrey and Price in 1947. The Alfrey-Price Q-e scheme is similar to the Hammett equation, but unlike in that it is not limited to substituted aromatic compounds. In the semiempirical Q-e scheme, the reactivities or resonance effects of the monomers and macroradicals are evaluated empirically by Q and P values, respectively. The polar properties of both monomers and macroradicals are designated by arbitrary e values.

Thus, as shown in Table 10.2, Q_1 and Q_2 are related to the reactivity and e_1 and e_2 are related to the polarity of monomers M_1 and M_2, respectively. Styrene, with Q and e values of 1.00 and -0.80, is used as the comparative standard. Higher Q values indicate greater resonance stability or reactivity, and higher e values (less negative) indicate greater electron-withdrawing power of the α substituents on the vinyl monomer.

Thus, as shown in Table 10.2, butadiene and isoprene with higher Q values are more reactive than styrene. Likewise, acrylonitrile and maleic anhydride with positive e values are more polar than styrene. While the Q-e scheme neglects steric factors, it is a useful guide when data for r_1

TABLE 10.2 Typical Q and e Values for Monomers[a]

Monomers	Q	e
Benzyl methacrylate	3.64	0.36
Methacrylic acid	2.34	0.65
2-Fluoro-1,3-butadiene	2.08	-0.43
p-Cyanostyrene	1.86	-0.21
p-Nitrostyrene	1.63	0.39
2,5-Dichlorostyrene	1.60	0.09
Methacrylamide	1.46	2.24
p-Methoxystyrene	1.36	-1.11
2-Vinylpyridine	1.30	-0.50
p-Methylstyrene	1.27	-0.98
2-Vinylnaphthalene	1.25	-0.38
Isopropyl methacrylate	1.20	-0.15
Methacrylonitrile	1.12	0.81
p-Bromostyrene	1.04	-0.32
Styrene	1.00	-0.80
m-Methylstyrene	0.91	-0.72
n-Amyl methacrylate	0.82	-0.32
Methyl methacrylate	0.74	0.40
Acrylonitrile	0.60	1.20
Methyl acrylate	0.42	0.60
Vinylidene chloride	0.23	0.36
Vinyl chloride	0.044	0.20
Vinyl acetate	0.026	-0.22

[a] Data from Polymer Handbook.

and r_2 are not available. The Alfrey Price equation, in which P_1 relates to macroradical $M_1\cdot$, Q_2 relates to monomer M_2, and e_1 and e_2 relate to polarity, is shown below.

$$k_{11} = P_1Q_1e^{-e_1^2}$$

$$k_{12} = P_1Q_2e^{-e_1e_2}$$

therefore,

$$r_1 = \frac{k_{11}}{k_{12}} = \frac{Q_1}{Q_2}e^{-e_1(e_1-e_2)} \qquad (10.12)$$

$$k_{22} = P_2Q_2e^{-e_2^2}$$

$$k_{21} = P_2Q_1e^{-e_1e_2}$$

$$r_2 = \frac{k_{22}}{k_{21}} = \frac{Q_2}{Q_1}e^{-e_2(e_2-e_1)}$$

$$r_1r_2 = e^{-(e_1-e_2)^2} \quad \text{or} \quad r_1r_2 = \text{exponential} -(e_1-e_2)^2 \qquad (10.13)$$

It is important to note that while the reactivity is related to resonance stability of the macroradical $M_1\cdot$, the composition of the copolymer is related to the relative polarity of the two monomers M_1 and M_2.

10.3 COMMERCIAL COPOLYMERS

One of the first commercial copolymers was the copolymer of vinyl chloride (87%) and vinyl acetate (13%) (Vinylite VYHH) which was introduced in 1928. As shown in Table 10.1, the r_1 value for vinyl acetate is 0.23 and r_2 for vinyl chloride is 1.68. Hence, a 4:1 molar ratio of VCM to VAc in the feed produced VYHH as the initial copolymer, and it was necessary to continue to add the monomers in the correct proportions in order to obtain the same composition throughout the polymerization.

Because the presence of vinyl acetate mers disrupted the regular structure of PVC, the copolymer was more flexible and more soluble than the homopolymer. A copolymer of vinyl chloride and vinyl isobutyl ether

(Vinoflex) has been produced in Germany and a copolymer of vinyl chloride and acrylonitrile (Vinyon, Dynel) has been used as a fiber in the United States. Copolymers of styrene and acrylonitrile are classified as high-performance or engineering plastics.

Copolymers of vinyl chloride and vinylidene chloride were introduced in the 1930s. The copolymer with a high vinyl chloride content was used as a plastic film (Pliovic) and the copolymer with a high vinylidene chloride content has been used as a film and filament (Saran). Three-component copolymers of vinyl chloride, vinyl acetate, and maleic anhydride have superior adhesive properties because of the polar anhydride groups present on the polymer chain.

Copolymers of ethylene and methacrylic acid (ionomers) also have good adhesive properties and transparency. When salts such as those of zinc, lithium, or sodium are added to these ionomers, they act like thermosetting plastics at room temperature but are readily molded since the ion pairs dissociate at processing temperatures.

Polybutadiene, produced in emulsion polymerization, is not useful as an elastomer. However, the copolymers with styrene (SBR) and acrylonitrile (Buna-N) are widely used as elastomers. Over 7 million tons of SBR was produced in the United States in 1979.

While most fibers are homopolymers, polyacrylonitrile fibers cannot be readily dyed. However, this difficulty is overcome when acrylonitrile is copolymerized with a small amount of acrylic acid, acrylamide, vinylpyridine, or vinylpyrrolidone. The dyability of polypropylene fibers is improved by graft copolymerization with vinylpyrrolidone.

10.4 BLOCK COPOLYMERS

While block copolymers do not occur naturally, synthetic block copolymers have been prepared by all known polymerization techniques. Block copolymers consisting of long sequences of mers are produced inadvertently when heveà rubber is milled with other polymers or when mixtures of different polyesters or mixtures of polyesters and polyamides are melted.

The first commercial block copolymer was a surfactant (Pluronics) prepared by the addition of propylene oxide to polycarbanions of ethylene oxide. While neither water-soluble polyethylene oxide nor water-insoluble polypropylene oxide exhibits surface activity, the ABA block copolymer consisting of hydrophilic and lyophilic segments, shown below, is an excellent surfactant.

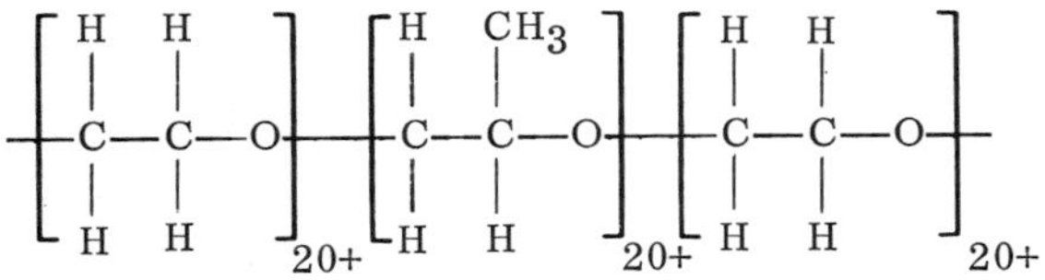

$$-\left[\begin{array}{ccccc} H & & H & & \\ | & & | & & \\ C & - & C & - & O \\ | & & | & & \\ H & & H & & \end{array}\right]_{20+}\!\!-\left[\begin{array}{ccccc} H & & CH_3 & & \\ | & & | & & \\ C & - & C & - & O \\ | & & | & & \\ H & & H & & \end{array}\right]_{20+}\!\!-\left[\begin{array}{ccccc} H & & H & & \\ | & & | & & \\ C & - & C & - & O \\ | & & | & & \\ H & & H & & \end{array}\right]_{20+}\!\!-$$

An ABA copolymer of ethylene oxide and propylene oxide

Elastomeric polyurethane fibers consisting of at least 85% segmented polyurethane, which are commercially available under the generic name of Spandex, are block copolymers. As shown by the following equation, these fibers, as well as some thermoplastic elastomers (TPE), are prepared by the reaction of a stiff polymeric diisocyanate with a flexible polymeric diol. Polyethers with terminal hydroxyl groups are used for the production of flexible polyurethane foams. TPE (Hytrel) is a block copolymer of a polyether and a polyester.

$$\underset{\substack{\text{Flexible}\\\text{polyester or}\\\text{polyether}}}{HO\sim\sim OH} + \underset{\text{Diisocyanate}}{O{=}C{=}N{-}R{-}N{=}C{=}O} \longrightarrow \underset{\text{Flexible block copolymer}}{-\overset{\overset{}{}}{\underset{\underset{O}{\|}}{C}}-\overset{H}{\overset{|}{N}}-R-\overset{H}{\overset{|}{N}}-\underset{\underset{O}{\|}}{C}-O\sim\sim} \qquad (10.14)$$

ABA block copolymers of dimethylsiloxane(A)-diphenylsiloxane(B)-dimethylsiloxane(C) are synthesized by the sequential polymerization of reactants such as hexamethylcyclotrisiloxane and hexaphenylcyclotrisiloxane in the presence of an initiator such as dilithiodiphenylsilanolate and a promotor such as tetrahydrofuran. As given in the following structure, ABCCBA siloxane block copolymers may be prepared in the same way.

$$-\!\!\left[OSi(C_6H_5)_2\right]_n\!\left[OSi(C_6H_5)(CH_3)\right]_n\!\left[OSi(CH_3)_2\right]_n\!-OSi(C_6H_5)_2O-\!\left[Si(CH_3)_2O\right]_n\!\left[Si(C_6H_5)(CH_3)O\right]_n\!\left[Si(C_6H_5)_2O\right]_n\!-$$

A B C C B A

As shown in the following equation, linear polysilarylenesiloxanes are prepared by the condensation of silphenylenesiloxanes, such as p-bis(dimethylhydroxysilyl)benzene and polydimethylsiloxane in the presence of n-hexylamine-2-ethylhexoate.

Other siloxane block copolymers have been made from polysiloxanes and polyalkylene ethers, polysiloxanes and polyarylene ethers and polysiloxanes and polyvinyl compounds. The latter are obtained by the coupling of polysiloxanes with polycarbanions of vinyl monomers such as styrene, α-methylstyrene, and isoprene. The chemistry of silicones is discussed in Chap. 11.

$$HO-\underset{CH_3}{\overset{CH_3}{Si}}-C_6H_4-\underset{CH_3}{\overset{CH_3}{Si}}-OH + HO\left[-\underset{CH_3}{\overset{CH_3}{Si}}-\right]_n O-H \longrightarrow \left[-\underset{CH_3}{\overset{CH_3}{Si}}-C_6H_4-\underset{CH_3}{\overset{CH_3}{Si}}-O-\right]_m\left[-\underset{CH_3}{\overset{CH_3}{Si}}-O-\right]_n \tag{10.15}$$

Block copolymers with segments or domains of random length have been produced by the mechanical or ultrasonic degradation of a mixture of two or more polymers such as hevea rubber and polymethyl methacrylate (Heveaplus). As shown by the following general equation, the products should have different properties than mixtures of the separate polymers, since segments of more than one polymer are present in the new chain.

$$M_{1_n}M_1\cdot + M_{2_n}M_2\cdot \longrightarrow M_{1_{n+1}}-M_{2_{n+1}} \tag{10.16}$$

Macroradical from elastomer molecule; Macroradical from plastic molecule; Block copolymer

The impact resistance of polypropylene has been increased by the preparation of block copolymers (polyallomers) with small segments of polyethylene. These polyallomers, and those with larger domains of polyethylene, are produced by Ziegler-Natta polymerization. Block copolymers have also been prepared from the same polymer with domains of different tacticity and with different configurations. For example, block copolymers with domains formed by the 1,2 and 1,3 polymerization of 4-methylpentene have been reported.

The most widely used chain-reaction block copolymers are those prepared by the addition of a new monomer to a macroanion. The latter have been called "living polymers" by Szwarc. AB and an ABA "block" copolymer called Solprene and Kraton, respectively, are produced by the addition of butadiene to styryl macroanions. As shown by the following equation, a more complex block copolymer is produced by the hydrogenation of poly-(styrene-b-butadiene-b)styrene. The product is actually a saturated copolymer block of styrene (A), butene (B), and styrene (A).

Block copolymers have been prepared by free-radical chain polymerization by introducing free-radical ends, by the cleavage of weak links such as peroxy links, by using polyperoxides, such as phthaloyl polyperoxide as initiators, by introducing an active group by telomerization, or by using a

$$-\!\!\left[CH_2-CH(C_6H_5)\right]_n\!\!-\!\!\left[CH_2-CH=CH-CH_2\right]_n\!\!-\!\!\left[CH_2-CH(C_6H_5)\right]_n\!\!-$$

$$-\!\!\left[CH_2-CH(C_6H_5)\right]_n\!\!-\!\!\left[CH_2-CH_2-CH_2-CH_2\right]_n\!\!-\!\!\left[CH_2-CH(C_6H_5)\right]_n\!\!-$$

complex compound such as azobiscyanopentanoic acid as the initiator. When only one of the isopropyl groups in diisopropylbenzene is oxidized to form the peroxide, this monofunctional initiator will produce a polymer which may be oxidized to produce a new isopropyl peroxide which can cause chain extension with a new monomer.

The stable macroradicals produced in heterogeneous solution polymerization or those formed in viscous homogeneous solutions may be used to produce a wide variety of block copolymers. These systems must be oxygen free and the new vinyl monomer must be able to diffuse into the macroradical. This diffusion is related to the difference in the solubility parameters between the new monomer and the macroradical. When this value is less than 3H, diffusion will take place. The rate of diffusion is inversely related to the difference in solubility parameters ($\Delta\delta$) between the monomer and macroradical.

It is of interest to note that while acrylonitrile (δ = 10.8 H) will diffuse into acrylonitrile macroradicals (δ = 12.5+ H), styrene (δ = 9.2 H) will not diffuse into these macroradicals. However, acrylonitrile will diffuse into styryl macroradicals (δ = 9.2 H) so that block copolymers of styrene and acrylonitrile are readily produced. Likewise, charge transfer complexes of styrene and acrylonitrile and styrene and maleic anhydride will diffuse into acrylonitrile macroradicals.

When soluble organic initiators are used in emulsion polymerization in the absence of droplets, initiation takes place in the micelles and stable macroradicals are produced. Block copolymers may be formed by the addition of a second monomer after all the primary radicals have been used up.

10.5 GRAFT COPOLYMERS

Since the major difference between block and graft copolymers is the position of chain extension, much of the information on block copolymerization may be applied to graft copolymers. The chain extensions in the latter are at branch points along the chain. Of course, branch polymers are typically homograft polymers.

Graft copolymers of nylon, protein, cellulose, or starch or copolymers of vinyl alcohol may be prepared by the reaction of ethylene oxide with these polymers. Graft copolymers are also produced when styrene is polymerized by Lewis acids in the presence of poly-p-methoxystyrene. The Merrifield synthesis of polypeptides is also based on graft copolymers formed from chloromethylated polystyrene.

Isobutylene and butadiene will also form cationic graft copolymers with chloromethylated polystyrene. Styrene has been grafted onto chlorinated butyl rubber and PVC in the presence of Lewis acids. The latter reaction is shown in (10.17).

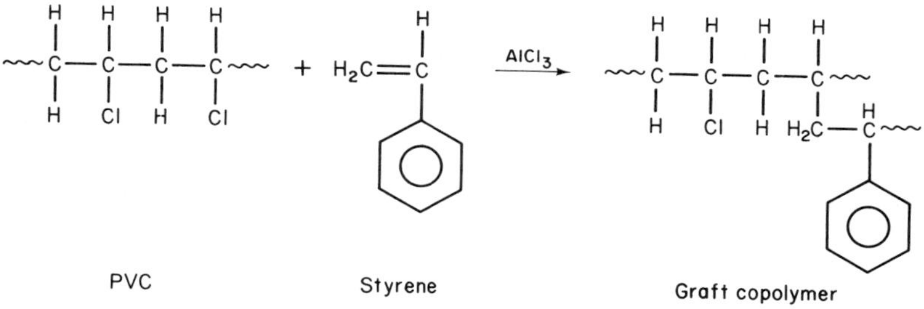

$$\sim CH_2-CHCl-CH_2-CHCl\sim + H_2C{=}CH(C_6H_5) \xrightarrow{AlCl_3} \sim CH_2-CHCl-CH_2-CH(CH_2-CH(C_6H_5)\sim)\sim$$

PVC — Styrene — Graft copolymer

(10.17)

As shown in (10.18), acrylonitrile graft copolymers of poly-p-chlorostyrene may be produced by anionic polymerization techniques.

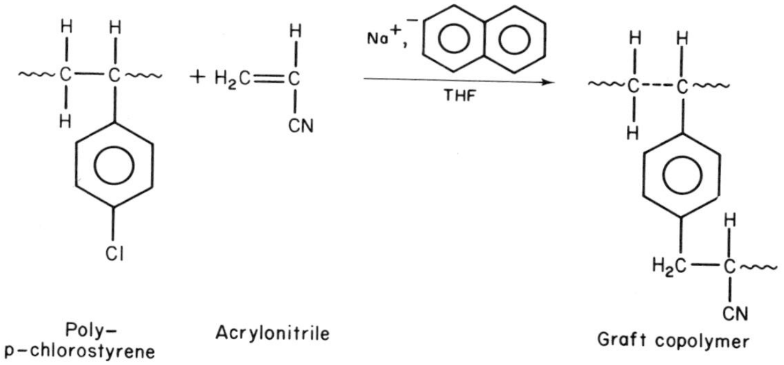

$$\sim CH_2-CH(C_6H_4Cl)\sim + H_2C{=}CH(CN) \xrightarrow[THF]{Na^+,\ \text{naphthalene}^-} \sim CH_2-CH(C_6H_4-CH_2-CH(CN)\sim)\sim$$

Poly-p-chlorostyrene — Acrylonitrile — Graft copolymer

(10.18)

As shown in (10.19), graft copolymers are also produced from the reaction of vinyl compounds and unsaturated polymers in the presence of Ziegler-Natta catalysts.

$$\sim\!\!\sim CH_2{-}CH{=}CH{-}CH_2 \sim\!\!\sim \; + \; CH_2{=}CH(CH_3) \xrightarrow[TiCl_3]{Al(H)(C_2H_5)_2} \sim\!\!\sim CH_2{-}CH(CH_2{-}CH(CH_3)\sim\!\!\sim){-}CH_2{-}CH_2 \sim\!\!\sim \qquad (10.19)$$

Polybutadiene Propylene Graft copolymer

Graft copolymers of many polymers have been prepared by irradiation with visible light in the presence of a photosensitizer or ionization radiation and a vinyl monomer. While the normal procedure involves direct radiation of the mixture of polymer and monomer, better results are obtained when the polymer is preradiated. High-energy radiation often causes cross linking.

The most widely used graft copolymer is the styrene-unsaturated polyester copolymer. The latter, which is usually reinforced by fibrous glass, is prepared by the free-radical chain polymerization of a styrene solution of an unsaturated polyester. Since oxygen inhibits the polymerization, it is preferable to polymerize in an oxygen-free atmosphere. As is the case with many other graft copolymers, considerable homopolymer is also produced. The general reaction is shown by (10.20).

$$\sim\!\!\sim O{-}C({=}O){-}CH{=}CH{-}C({=}O){-}O{-}(CH_2)_2 \sim\!\!\sim \; + \; CH_2{=}CH(C_6H_5) \xrightarrow{R\cdot}$$

Unsaturated polyester Styrene

$$\sim\!\!\sim O{-}C({=}O){-}CH(CH_2{-}CH(C_6H_5)\sim\!\!\sim){-}CH_2{-}C({=}O){-}O{-}(CH_2)_2 \sim\!\!\sim \qquad (10.20)$$

Polyester plastic

High-impact polystyrene (HIP) and some ABS copolymers may be produced by the free-radical chain polymerization of styrene in the presence of an unsaturated elastomer. While AIBN is a useful initiator for the polymerization of vinyl monomers, including styrene, it is not a satisfactory grafting initiator presumably because of the higher resonance stability of

$$\begin{array}{l}(CH_3)_2C\cdot \\ \qquad\quad | \\ \qquad\quad CN\end{array}$$

as compared to $C_6H_5COO\cdot$ or $C_6H_5\cdot$ from benzoyl peroxide. AIBN is not used as an initiator for styrene with unsaturated polyesters for the same reason.

The graft copolymers of acrylamide and cellulose or starch are of particular interest. These products, which are usually produced in the presence of cerium(IV) ions have potential use as water absorbents and in enhanced oil recovery systems. The graft copolymers with acrylic acid or the hydrolyzed graft copolymers with acrylonitrile have exceptionally good water absorbency.

10.6 GENERAL INFORMATION ON BLOCK AND GRAFT COPOLYMERS

Unlike mixtures which may be separated, these copolymers, which cannot be separated into components, may consist of sequences of polymers with diverse properties. For example, block or graft copolymers of styrene and methacrylic acid are soluble in both polar and nonpolar solvents. The acrylic acid chains are extended in the former but are coiled in nonpolar solvents. Each segment of the chain or each long branch exhibits its own characteristic properties. Thus, the copolymer will not only exhibit different conformations in solvents but will have characteristic glass transition temperatures.

Elastomeric fibers and thermoplastic elastomers have been produced by controlling the size and flexibility of the domains in block and graft copolymers. These techniques have opened up new fields for the tailor-making of functional polymers.

ABS copolymers, based on a wide variety of formulations, are produced at an annual rate of over 400,000 tons. Some of these high-performance plastics are graft copolymers but most are empirically developed blends of polystyrene and nitrile rubber [poly(butadiene-co-acrylonitrile)].

10.7 POLYMER BLENDS

The inherent brittleness of polystyrene has been overcome to some extent by the production of copolymers and by the blending of polystyrene with elastomers such as hevea rubber, SBR, or copolymers of butadiene and acrylonitrile. These polyblends, which are sometimes called polymer alloys, are usually incompatible mixtures of two or more polymers.

The toughness of high-impact polystyrene (HIP) is dependent on a dispersion of flexible elastomer molecules in a rigid polystyrene matrix. These blends may be made by mixing solutions or lattices of the components and by melt-mixing a mixture of the finely divided polymers.

ABS alloys with PVC, polyurethane (PU), and polycarbonate (PC) are widely used. The processing difficulties of polyphenylene oxide (PPO) are lessened by blending with polystyrene (PS). Elastomers and thermoplastic elastomers (TPE) have been used to flexibilize polyolefins and nylons. Many useful blends have also been developed empirically because of material shortages or the need to meet unusual specifications. For example, the use of blends of natural, synthetic, and reclaimed elastomers and thermoplastics is standard practice in the rubber industry.

SUMMARY

1. Unlike homopolymers, which consist of chains with identical repeating units, copolymers are macromolecules with more than one repeating unit in the same molecule. These repeating units may be randomly arranged or they may alternate in the chain. Block copolymers are linear polymers which consist of long sequences of repeating units in the chain, and graft copolymers are branch polymers in which the branches consist of sequences of repeating units which differ from those in the backbone.

2. In the special case of azeotropic copolymerization, the composition of the copolymer is identical to that of the feed. However, copolymer compositions usually differ because of the difference in reactivity ratios or rates at which the different monomers add to macroradicals with similar end groups. The composition of the copolymer may be estimated from the copolymer equation

$$n = \frac{r_1 x + 1}{(r_2/x) + 1}$$

where n and x are the molar ratios of the monomer in the copolymer and feed, respectively, and r_1 and r_2 are the reactivity ratios.

3. The product of the reactivity ratios $r_1 r_2$ may be used to estimate the relative randomness of the copolymer. When $r_1 r_2 \simeq 1$, the copolymer arrangement is random, and when $r_1 r_2 \simeq 0$, the arrangement is alternating. The latter is the result of the homopolymerization of charge transfer complexes which are unstable at elevated temperatures.

4. Strongly electrophilic or nucleophilic monomers will polymerize exclusively by anionic and cationic mechanisms. Those like styrene and

methyl methacrylate, which are neither strong electrophiles or nucleophiles, also polymerize by free-radical mechanisms. Since these two monomers also polymerize by ionic mechanisms, the reactivity ratios for all three systems may be compared.

5. The Q-e scheme, in which Q is related to reactivity and e to polarity, may be used to predict reactivity ratios:

$$r_1 = \frac{k_{11}}{k_{12}} = \frac{Q_1}{Q_2} e^{-e_1(e_1 - e_2)}$$

Styrene, which is assigned a Q value of 1.00 and an e value of -0.80, is used as the comparative reference for determining Q-e values for other monomers.

6. The principal copolymers are SBR, butyl rubber, poly(vinyl chloride-co-vinyl acetate), Saran, ionomers, and Acrilan fibers.

7. Block and graft copolymers differ from mixtures but have the properties of each component. Thus, block copolymers may be used as thermoplastic elastomers and graft copolymers with a flexible backbone may be used for high-impact plastics.

8. Block and graft copolymers may be produced by step-reaction polymerization and by chain-reaction polymerization.

9. The principal block copolymers are thermoplastic elastomers and elastic fibers. The principal graft copolymers are ABS, HIP, polyester plastics, and grafted starch and cellulose.

GLOSSARY

AB: A block copolymer with two sequences of mers.

ABA: A block copolymer with three sequences of mers in the order shown.

ABS: A three-component copolymer of acrylonitrile, butadiene, and styrene.

AIBN: Azobisisobutyronitrile.

alternating copolymer: An ordered copolymer in which every other building unit is different $(-M_1M_2-)_n$.

azeotropic copolymer: One in which the composition is the same as that of the feed.

block copolymer: A copolymer consisting of long sequences or runs of one mer followed by long sequences of another mer $(M_1)_2(M_2)_n$.

buna-N: An elastomeric copolymer of butadiene and acrylonitrile.

buna-S: An elastomeric copolymer of butadiene and styrene.

butyl rubber: An elastomeric copolymer of isobutylene and isoprene.

charge transfer complex: A complex consisting of an electron donor (D) and an electron acceptor (A) in which an electron has been transferred from D to A, i.e., (D^+, A^-).

composition drift: The change in composition of a copolymer that occurs as copolymerization takes place with monomers of different reactivities.

copolymer: A macromolecule consisting of more than one type of building unit or mer.

copolymer equation

$$n = \frac{d[M_1]}{d[M_2]} = \frac{r_1x + 1}{(r_2/x) + 1}$$

$\Delta\delta$: Difference in solubility parameters.

domains: Sequences in block copolymers.

Dynel: Tradename for a copolymer of vinyl chloride and acrylonitrile.

e: Polarity of monomers.

EPDM: Abbreviation for a curable (vulcanizable) copolymer of ethylene and propylene.

graft copolymer: A branched copolymer in which the backbone and the branches consist of different mers.

GRS: A name used for SBR during World War II.

Heveaplus: Tradename for block copolymers of methyl methacrylate and hevea rubber.

HIP: High-impact polystyrene.

homopolymer: A macromolecule consisting of only one type of building unit or mer.

Hytrel: Tradename for a commercial TPE.

ideal copolymer: A random copolymer, $r_1 = r_2$ and $r_1r_2 = 1$.

ionomer: Generic name for copolymers of ethylene and methacrylic acid.

k_{11}: Rate constant for the addition of M_1 to $M_1\cdot$.

Kraton: Tradename for an ABA block copolymer of styrene and butadiene.

living polymers: A name used by Szwarc for macrocarbanions.

$M_1\cdot$: A macroradical with a chain end of M_1.

$M_2\cdot$: A macroradical with a chain end of M_2.

n: The molar ratio of mers M_1 and M_2 in a copolymer chain, i.e., M_1/M_2.

P: Reactivity or resonance effect of monomers.

Pliovic: Tradename for copolymers of vinyl chloride and vinylidene chloride.

Pluronics: Tradename for block copolymers of ethylene oxide and propylene oxide.

polyallomers: Block copolymers of ethylene and propylene.

polyester plastic: A name used to describe polymers produced by the polymerization of a solution of an unsaturated polyester in styrene.

Q: Reactivity or resonance effect of monomers.

Q-e scheme: A semiempirical method for predicting reactivity ratios.

r: Reactivity ratios.

r_1: k_{11}/k_{12}.

r_2: k_{22}/k_{21}.

r_1r_2: The product of the reactivity ratios which predict the extent of randomness in a copolymer chain. When r_1 and r_2 are similar and their product equals 1, the macromolecule is an ideal random copolymer.

random copolymer: A copolymer in which there is no definite order for the sequence of the different mers or building blocks ($-M_1M_2M_1M_1M_2M_1M_2M_2-$).

reactivity ratio (r): The relative reactivity of one monomer compared to another monomer.

Saran: Tradename for copolymers of vinylidene chloride and vinyl chloride.

SBR: The elastomeric copolymer of styrene and butadiene.

siloxane: $\left[O-SiR_2-O \right]_n$

Solprene: Tradename for an AB block copolymer of styrene and butadiene.

Spandex: An elastic fiber consisting of a block copolymer of polyurethanes and polyesters.

TPE: Thermoplastic elastomer.

Vinoflex: Tradename for copolymers of vinyl chloride and vinyl isobutyl ether.

Vinylite: Tradename for copolymers of vinyl chloride and vinyl acetate.

Vinyon: Tradename for copolymers of vinyl chloride and acrylonitrile.

Wall equation: The predecessor to the copolymer equation.

x: Symbol for the molar ratio of monomers in the feed, i.e., $[M_1]/[M_2]$.

EXERCISES

1. Draw representative structures for (a) homopolymers, (b) alternating copolymers, (c) random copolymers, (d) AB block copolymers, and (e) graft copolymers of styrene and acrylonitrile.
2. If equimolar quantities of M_1 and M_2 are used in an azeotropic copolymerization, what is the composition of the feed after 50% of the copolymer has formed?
3. Define r_1 and r_2 in terms of rate constants.
4. Do the r_1 and r_2 values increase or decrease during copolymerization?
5. What is the effect of temperature on r_1 and r_2?
6. What will be the composition of copolymers produced in the first part of the polymerization of equimolar quantities of vinylidene chloride and vinyl chloride?
7. What monomer may be polymerized by anionic, cationic, and free-radical chain techniques?
8. Which chain polymerization technique would you select to polymerize (a) isobutylene, (b) acrylonitrile, and (c) propylene?
9. If $r_1 r_2 \simeq 0$, what type of copolymer would be formed?
10. Show a structure for an ABA block copolymer.
11. What is the value of $r_1 r_2$ for an ideal random copolymer?
12. Which would polymerize more readily, (a) H(Cl)C=C(Cl)H [cis: H above each C, Cl below each C] or (b) H₂C=CCl₂ [H and H on the left carbon, Cl and Cl on the right carbon]?
13. An equimolar mixture of styrene and maleic anhydride in decalin produces an alternating copolymer at 60°C and a random copolymer at 140°C; explain.
14. What is the composition of the first copolymer chains produced by the copolymerization of equimolar quantities of styrene and methyl methacrylate in (a) free-radical, (b) cationic, and (c) anionic copolymerization?
15. What is the composition of the first copolymer butyl rubber chains produced from equimolar quantities of the two monomers?
16. What is the composition of the first copolymer butyl rubber chains produced from a feed containing 9 mol of isobutylene and 1 mol of isoprene?
17. How would you assure the production of butyl rubber of uniform composition in question 16?

18. Which would be more reactive in free-radical polymerization (a) p-methylstyrene, or (b) m-methylstyrene?
19. What is the composition of the first polymer chains produced by the copolymerization of equimolar quantities of vinyl chloride and vinyl acetate?
20. What are the advantages, if any, of the vinyl chloride-vinyl acetate copolymer over PVC?
21. Why are ionomers superior to LDPE?
22. What is the difference between buna-S, GRS, and SBR?
23. What do the acrylonitrile comonomers, acrylic acid, acrylamide, vinylpyridine, and vinylpyrrolidone, have in common?
24. Which sequence in the ABA block copolymer of ethylene oxide and propylene oxide is lyophilic?
25. What is the advantage of TPE, if any, over hevea rubber?
26. What is the advantage, if any, of the hydrogenated ABA block copolymer of styrene-butadiene-styrene?
27. What product is obtained if 1.5 mol of styrene is copolymerized with 1 mol of maleic anhydride in benzene?
28. What precautions must be taken when making articles such as boats from fibrous glass-reinforced polyester plastics?
29. Are so-called polyester plastics cross-linked?
30. How could you use graft copolymerization techniques to reduce the water solubility of starch?
31. What is the end group when azobiscyanopentanoic acid is used as an initiator?

BIBLIOGRAPHY

Aggarwal, S. L. (1970): Block Copolymers, Plenum, New York.

Alfrey, Jr., T., Bohrer, J. J., Mark, H. (1952): Copolymerization, Interscience, New York.

Allpert, D. C., and Jones, W. H. (1973): Block Copolymers, Halsted, New York.

Arthur, J. C. (1970): Graft polymerization onto polysaccharides. In Advances in Macromolecular Chemistry, Vol. 2 (W. M. Pasika, ed.), Academic, New York.

Barrett, K. E. J. (1975): Dispersion Polymerization in Organic Media, John Wiley, New York.

Basdekis, C. H. (1964): ABS Plastics, Reinhold, New York.

Battaerd, H. A. J., and Tregear, G. W. (1967): Graft Copolymers, John Wiley, New York.

Brandrup, J., and Immergut, E. H. (1975): Polymer Handbook, John Wiley, New York.

Bruins, P. F. (1976): Unsaturated Polyester Technology, Gordon and Breach, New York.

Burk, J. J., and Weiss, V. (1973): Block and Graft Copolymers, Syracuse University Press, Syracuse, New York.

Burlant, W. J., and Hoffman, A. S. (1960): Block and Graft Copolymers, Reinhold, New York.

Casale, A., and Porter, R. S. (1975): Mechanical Synthesis of Block and Graft Copolymers, Springer-Verlag, New York.

Ceresa, R. J. (1962): Block and Graft Copolymers, Butterworths, London.

———. (1976): Block and Graft Copolymerization, Vol. 2, John Wiley, New York.

Coleman, D. (1959): Block step reaction copolymers, J. Polymer Sci., 14:15.

Cooper, W., Vaughan, G., Miller, S., Fielden, M. (1959): Rubber-methyl methacrylate graft copolymers, J. Polymer Sci., 34:651.

Cowie, J. M. G. (1974): Polymers: Chemistry and Physics of Modern Materials, Intext Educational Publishers, New York.

Dole, M. (1972): The Radiation Chemistry of Macromolecules, Academic New York.

Dostal, H. (1936): A basis for the reaction kinetics of mixed polymerization, Monatsh. Chem., 69:424-426.

Ellinger, L. P. (1968): Charge transfer polymerization. In Advances in Macromolecular Chemistry, Vol. 1 (W. M. Pasika, ed.), Academic, New York.

Ester, G. M., Cooper, S. L., Tobolsky, A. B. (1970): Block copolymers, Rev. Macromol. Chem., 5-2:167.

Gaylord, N. G. (1958): Block copolymers, SPE J., 14(1):31.

Haas, H. C., Kamath, P. M., Schuler, N. W. (1957): Cationic graft copolymers, J. Polymer Sci., 24:85.

Hahn, W., and Lechtenbohmer, H. (1955): Polyisopropyl styrene, Makromol. Chem., 16:50.

Hicks, E. M. (1963): Polyether-urethane block copolymers, Am. Dyestuff Rep., 52:18.

Hixon, H. F., and Goldberg, E. P. (1976): Polymer Grafts in Biochemistry, Dekker, New York.

Holliday, L. (1975): Ionic Polymers, Halsted, New York.

Ham, G. E. (1964): Copolymerization, Interscience, New York.

———. (1967): Vinyl Polymerization, Dekker, New York.

Houtz, R. C., and Adkins, H. (1933): Graft copolymers, J. Amer. Chem. Soc., 55:1609.

Jalbert, R. L., and Smejkal, J. P. (1976): Polymer blends, Mod. Plastics, 53(10A):108.

Legge, N. R., Holden, G., Davison, S., DeLaMare, H. E. (1975): Chemistry and technology of block copolymers. In Applied Polymer Science (J. K. Craver and R. W. Tess, eds.), Organic Coatings and Plastics Div., ACS, Washington, D.C.

Lenz, R. W. (1967): Organic Chemistry of Synthetic High Polymers, Wiley Interscience, New York.

Lunsted, L. G. (1931): Block copolymer surfactants, J. Amer. Oil Chem. Soc., 28:294.

Mano, E. B., and Coutino, F. M. B. (1975): Grafting on Polyamides, Springer-Verlag, New York.

Marvel, C. S. (1959): An Introduction to the Organic Chemistry of High Polymers, John Wiley, New York.

Seymour, R. B., and Cooper, S. L. (1973): Step reaction block copolymers, Macromolecules, 6(1):48.

Seymour, R. B., and Stahl, G. A. (1975): Block copolymers of styrene, Appl. Polymer Sci. Symp., 26:249.

———. (1976): Block copolymers of vinyl acetate, J. Polymer Sci., 14:2545.

Seymour, R. B., Stahl, G. A., Owen, D. R., Wood, H. (1975): Block copolymers of methyl methacrylate, Adv. Chem., 142:309.

Stevens, M. P. (1975): Polymer Chemistry, Addison-Wesley, Reading, Massachusetts.

Swarc, M. (1956): Block copolymerization with living polymers, Nature, 178:1168.

Urwin, J. R. (1958): Diisopropylbenzenemonohydroperoxide initiated polymers, J. Polymer Sci., 27:580.

Vaughn, T., Jackson, D., Lundsted, L. (1952): Polyalkylene oxide block copolymers, J. Amer. Oil Chemists Soc., 29:240.

Vermillion, J. L. (1967): Polyallomers, Mod. Plastics, 45(1A):187.

Vollmert, B. (1973): Polymer Chemistry, Springer-Verlag, New York.

Wall, F. T. (1944): The structure of copolymers, II, J. Amer. Chem. Soc., 66:2050-2057.

Walling, C. (1957): Free Radicals in Solution, John Wiley, New York.

Walrath, R. L., Reyes, Z., Russell, C. R. (1962): Graft copolymers of wheat starch. In Polymerization and Polycondensation Processes (R. F. Gould, ed.), American Chemical Society, Washington, D.C.

Welson, J. E. (1975): Radiation Chemistry of Monomers, Polymers and Plastics, Dekker, New York.

Wessling, R. A. (1974): Polyvinylidene Chloride, Gordon and Breach, New York.

Williams, D. J. (1971): Polymer science and engineering, Chap. 5, Prentice Hall, Englewood Cliffs, New Jersey.

11

Inorganic Polymers

Widely used materials such as glass, hydraulic cements, and many minerals are inorganic polymers, but because of their complex nature little is known about their polymeric structure. The chemistry of polyalkylene sulfides, nucleic acids, ionomers, and polysiloxanes is better understood. These have been discussed in preceding chapters, and of these only the polysiloxanes will be discussed in this chapter. Other inorganic polymers of interest which will also be discussed are phosphazenes, sulfur nitride polymers, carborane polymers, organometallic polymers, and coordination polymers.

11.1 POLYSILOXANES (SILICONES)

Unlike the relatively strong carbon-carbon bonds in catenated chains, the silicon-silicon bond in polysilanes is relatively weak. The tin-tin bonds in stannanes and the germanium-germanium bonds in germanes are even weaker. Thus, while the highest $\overline{DP}$ for silanes is 10, the $\overline{DP}$ values for other non-carbon members of the carbon group are even less. Hence, these products are not of interest as polymers.

In general, bonds between dissimilar atoms are more stable; hence, the silicon-carbon (58 kcal/mol) and silicon-oxygen (89 kcal/mol) are much stronger than the silicon-silicon (30 kcal/mol) bonds. The bond strength is increased when the pendant hydroxyl groups are replaced by alkyl groups. Compounds with SiOSi linkages are called siloxanes and their polymers are polysiloxanes. However, these were incorrectly named silicones by Kipping in the 1920s, and this name continues to be used almost universally.

The production of silicate glass is believed to be a transcondensation of the siloxane linkages in silica in the presence of calcium and sodium oxides. Thus, some calcium and sodium silicates are produced in glass making, but the siloxane backbone remains intact. A comparable polysilicic acid is produced when silicon tetrachloride is hydrolyzed, as shown in the following equation:

$$n\,ClSi(Cl)_2Cl \xrightarrow{4nH_2O} n\left[HO-\underset{OH}{\overset{OH}{Si}}-OH\right] \longrightarrow \left[-O-\underset{OH}{\overset{OH}{Si}}-O-\right]_n \quad (11.1)$$

Silicon tetrachloride — Silicic acid — Polysilicic acid

The polysilicic acid condenses further to produce a cross-linked gel. This cross linking may be prevented by replacing the hydroxyl groups in silicic acid by alkyl groups. Thus, Ladenburg prepared the first silicone polymer in the nineteenth century by the hydrolysis of diethyldiethoxysilane. Kipping recognized that these siloxanes were produced by the hydrolysis of dialkyldichlorosilanes in the early 1940s. In both cases, two of the hydroxyl groups shown in the formula for silicic acid in (11.1) were replaced by alkyl groups.

The instability of silicones is overcome by capping the hydroxyl end groups with a monofunctional trialkylchlorosilane or trialkylalkoxysilane. The monoalkyltrichlorosilane is used as a trifunctional cross-linking agent for silicones. The step reaction for the production of silicones from dialkyldichlorosilanes is similar to that shown for polysilicic acid. Because of the ease of formation of six- and eight-membered rings, there are many "wasted loop" side reactions.

Fortunately, the cyclic siloxanes may be removed by distillation and reused in the feed. Silicone oligomers are used as lubricants and antifoaming agents. Bouncing putty is produced when polydimethylsiloxanes with capped ends are heated with boric acid. Silicone oils are prepared in the presence of hexamethyldisiloxane which produces trimethylsiloxyl capped ends. The viscosity of silicone oils is controlled by the ratio of hexamethyldisiloxane to the dimethyldimethoxysilane used.

Since polymerization of alkoxy- or chlorosilanes takes place in the presence of water, one-package systems are used as room temperature curing (vulcanizing) silicone elastomers (RTV). Linear silicones may also be cured by free-radical reactions. Cross linking is also promoted by bubbling oxygen through silicone solutions in order to oxidize the alkyl groups and thus form oxygen linkages between chains. (Siloxane block copolymers are described in Chap. 10.)

The characteristic resistance of silicones to elevated temperatures is related to the heat-stable siloxane backbone. The lubricity and water repellancy are related to the pendant lyophilic alkyl groups which encase the abrasive backbone.

11.2 PHOSPHONITRILIC POLYMERS (POLYPHOSPHAZENES)

Phosphonitrilic polymers have been known for centuries but since they lacked resistance to water, they were not of interest as commercial polymers. However, when the pendant chlorine groups are replaced by fluorine atoms, amino, alkoxy, or phenoxy groups, these polymers are much more resistant to moisture. Phosphonitrile fluoroelastomers (PNF-200) are useful throughout a temperature range of -56 to 180°C.

As shown in the following equation, phosphazenes are produced by the thermal cleavage of a cyclic trimer obtained from the reaction of phosphorus pentachloride and ammonium chloride. Similar reactions occur when the chloro group is replaced by fluoro, bromo, or isothiocyano groups.

$$PCl_5 + NH_4Cl \xrightarrow{170°C} HCl + (NPCl_2)_3 \xrightarrow[\text{ROH, RCOOH, Na}]{\text{catalyst}} \left(-\underset{Cl}{\overset{Cl}{P}}=N- \right)_n \quad (11.2)$$

Phosphorus pentachloride; Hexachlorocyclotriphosphazene; Polyphosphonitrilic chloride

As shown by the following equations, amorphous elastomers are obtained when phosphazene is refluxed with nucleophiles, such as sodium trifluoroethoxide or sodium cresylate, and secondary amines. Copolymers are produced when mixtures of reactants are employed.

$$\left[-N=\underset{Cl}{\overset{Cl}{P}}- \right]_n + 2n\,NaOCH_2CF_3 \xrightarrow[-2nNaCl]{\Delta} \left[-N=\underset{OCH_2CF_3}{\overset{OCH_2CF_3}{P}}- \right]_n \quad (11.3)$$

$$\left[-N=\underset{Cl}{\overset{Cl}{P}}- \right]_n + 2n\,NaO-C_6H_4-CH_3 \xrightarrow[(-2_nNaCl)]{\Delta} \left[-N=\underset{O-C_6H_4-CH_3}{\overset{O-C_6H_4-CH_3}{P}}- \right]_n \quad (11.4)$$

$$\left[-N{=}\overset{\displaystyle Cl}{\underset{\displaystyle Cl}{\overset{|}{\underset{|}{P}}}}- \right]_n + 2n\ HNRR' \xrightarrow{\Delta} \left[-N{=}\overset{\displaystyle NRR'}{\underset{\displaystyle NRR'}{\overset{|}{\underset{|}{P}}}}- \right]_n \tag{11.5}$$

Difunctional reactants such as dihydroxybenzenes (hydroquinone) produce cross-linked phosphazenes. Fibers may be made from polyphosphates and sheets may be pressed from polymeric black phosphorus. The latter is a semiconductor which reverts to white or red phosphorus when heated.

11.3 CARBORANE POLYMERS

A polyborazole has been prepared by heating the cyclic trimer obtained by reacting ammonia and borane. However, attempts to produce useful polymers from carboranes have been more successful. Copolymers of siloxane and carborane are temperature-resistant elastomers that have been marketed under the tradename of Dexsil. Carborane polymers are obtained by heating the carborane obtained from the reaction of decarborane and acetylene.

$$H_3N + B_2H_6 \longrightarrow H_3NBH_3 \xrightarrow[\Delta]{-H_2} (HBNH)_3 \xrightarrow{\Delta} (\text{polyborazole})_n \tag{11.6}$$

11.4 FERROCENE POLYMERS

As a result of the discovery of ferrocene by Kealy and Pauson in 1951, many attempts have been made to produce polymers from metallocenes, such as di-π-cyclopentadienyl metal compounds $[(\pi{-}C_5H_5)_2Fe]$. In some of these, such as polyvinyl ferrocene, the ferrocene is the pendant group as shown by the following equation. In spite of the presence of these heat-resistant pendant groups, the heat resistance of polyvinyl ferrocene is similar to that of HDPE.

Other high-cost ferrocene polymers, such as polyferrocenylene, contain intralinear ferrocenylene groups. As shown by the following equation, these soluble polymers with $\overline{DP}$ values of up to 7000 are prepared by the free-radical polymerization of molten ferrocene.

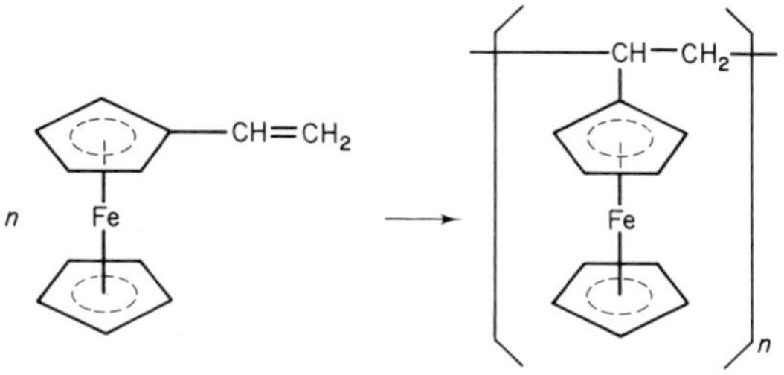

$$n\ \text{Vinylferrocene} \longrightarrow \text{Polyvinylferrocene}\ \left[-CH-CH_2-\right]_n \tag{11.7}$$

Vinylferrocene Polyvinylferrocene

$$n\ \text{Ferrocene} \xrightarrow[(-RH)]{R\cdot} H-\left[\ \right]_n-H \tag{11.8}$$

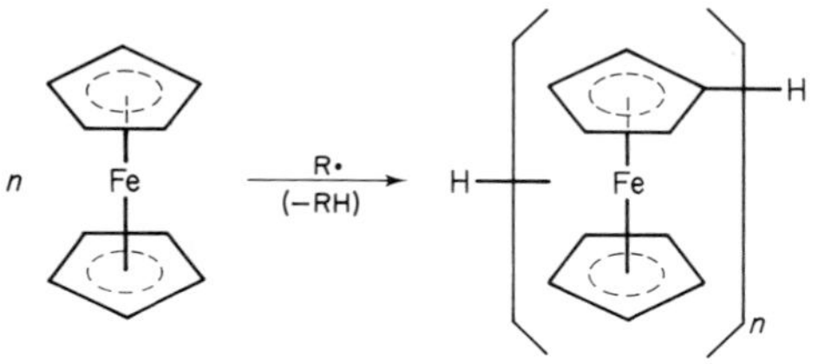

Ferrocene Polyferrocenylene

11.5 OTHER ORGANOMETALLIC POLYMERS

The number of already produced and potentially producible organometallic polymers (OMP) is quite large, offering one of the true frontiers for future synthesis, characterization, and application research.

Synthesis falls into two major classifications—vinyl polymers derived from metal-containing pendant groups (emphasized by groups such as Pittman's)

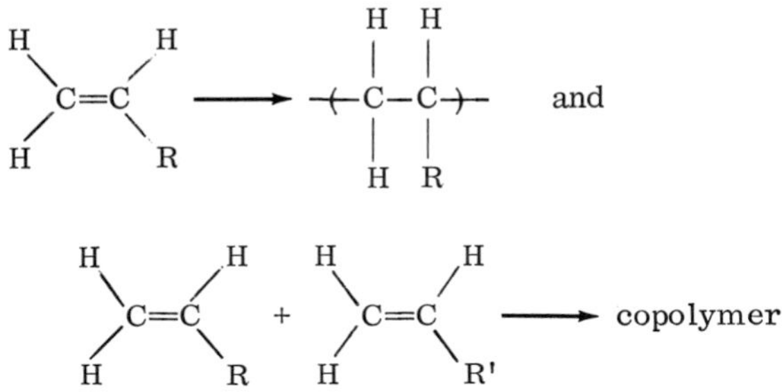

$$H_2C{=}CHR \longrightarrow -\!\!\left(-CH_2-CHR-\right)\!\!-\quad \text{and}$$

$$H_2C{=}CHR + H_2C{=}CHR' \longrightarrow \text{copolymer} \tag{11.9}$$

where R and/or R' has a metal-containing moiety, and condensation polymers (emphasized by groups such as Carraher's) derived from condensations and additions analogous to those employed for polyester and polyamide synthesis

$$H{-}A{-}H + X{-}M{-}X \longrightarrow {-}\!(A{-}M)\!{-} \quad (11.10)$$

where HAH can be diols, thiols, dioximes, hydrazines, diamines, diamidoximes, diacids, and mixed Lewis base function groups, and where X—M—X can contain metals such as Ti, Zr, Hf, Si, Ge, Sn, Pb, Mn, Co, Fe, U, Pt, As, Sb, and Bi.

Industrial applications have just begun in a number of areas including adhesives, flame retarders, and anchored metal catalysis; in medical applications as controlled delivery agents; and in electrical applications.

The formation of water-insoluble uranyl polymers, including polyesters, is proposed as a method of uranium control and purification since the natural water-soluble form of uranium is as the uranyl ion.

$$^{\ominus}O{-}\overset{O}{\overset{\|}{C}}{-}R{-}\overset{O}{\overset{\|}{C}}{-}O^{\ominus} + [(H_2O)(OH_2)UO_2]^{2+} \longrightarrow {-}\!(C(O)_2UO_2(OH_2)(H_2O)(O)_2C{-}R)\!{-}$$

Uranyl ion — Uranyl polyester

(11.11)

Many of the organometallic polymers are semiconductors with bulk specific resistivities in the range of 10^3 to 10^{12} ohm cm suitable for specific semiconductor activities. Further, some exhibit interesting photoproperties. Some polymers degrade on heating to give metal oxides with the process suitable for the homogeneous doping of other polymers and matrices with metal sites.

$$-\!\!\left[CH_2{-}CH(C_6H_5Cr(CO)_3)\right]\!\!- \xrightarrow{\Delta} Cr_2O_3 + \text{other products} \quad (11.12)$$

Platinum-containing polymers have been shown to be active against polio type I virus in HeLa cells at low concentrations, and at higher (but still acceptable) concentrations they are toxic to the HeLa human cancer cells themselves.

$$-\!\!\left(PtCl_2{-}NH_2{-}R{-}NH_2\right)_n\!\!-$$

Platinum polyamine

Polymers containing tin are typically antibacterial and antifungal. The use of tin-containing polymers in the formulation of antifouling paints for sea-going ships is increasing because many are effective in the control of barnacle formation on ship hulls. Cotton and polyethyleneimine, modified with certain organometallic tins, exhibit antifungal activity with the tin present in the ppm to ppb region.

$$-\!\!\left(\!\!-\underset{\displaystyle H}{\overset{\displaystyle H}{\underset{|}{\overset{|}{C}}}}-\underset{\displaystyle H}{\overset{\displaystyle H}{\underset{|}{\overset{|}{C}}}}-\overset{\displaystyle H}{\overset{|}{N}}-\!\!\right)_{\!n} + R_3SnCl \longrightarrow -\!\!\left(\!\!-\underset{\displaystyle H}{\overset{\displaystyle H}{\underset{|}{\overset{|}{C}}}}-\underset{\displaystyle H}{\overset{\displaystyle H}{\underset{|}{\overset{|}{C}}}}-\underset{SnR_3}{\underset{|}{N}}-\!\!\right)_{\!n} \tag{11.13}$$

A number of titanium, tin, and other metal-containing polymers form fibers on mechanical agitation reminiscent of metal wisker formation.

Several organometallic polymers offer outstanding high-temperature stabilities showing over 80% weight retention to 1000°C.

Because of the general high cost of the organometallics and increasing shortage of many metals, most applications of organometallic polymers will have to be where only minute quantities are involved.

11.6 COORDINATION POLYMERS

Small coordination molecules are characterized by unusually good thermal stability, but coordination polymers are seldom more stable and are less readily processed than classic organic polymers. The synthesis of these inorganic-organic polymers requires the use of higher multifunctional reactants in place of the classic ligands used to produce small coordination molecules. Thus, as shown by the following equation, a phthalocyanine polymer is produced when copper metal is heated with tetracyanoethylene.

$$2n\,(NC)_2C{=}C(CN)_2 + n\,Cu \xrightarrow{\Delta\Delta} [\text{Cu phthalocyanine}]_n \tag{11.14}$$

Tetracyanoethylene + Copper　　　Phthalocyanine polymer

Advantage of the instability of coordination polymers has been taken in the preparation of agricultural controlled-release compositions. For example, as shown by the following equation, a polymer which degrades slowly to yield 2,4-dichlorophenoxyacetic acid (2,4-D) may be synthesized from 2,4-D and iron(III) ions in the presence of aliphatic aldehydes.

$$3nC_6H_3Cl_2CH_2COO^- \quad + \quad nFe^{3+} \xrightarrow{RCHO}$$

2,4-D Iron(III) ion

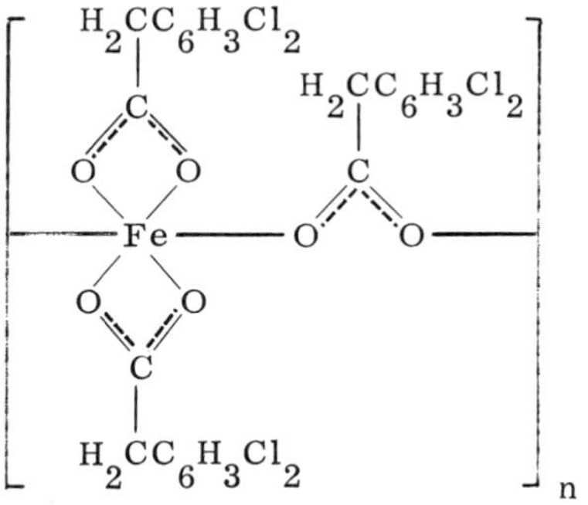

$$\left[-Fe(O_2CCH_2C_6H_3Cl_2)_2-O-C(CH_2C_6H_3Cl_2)=O- \right]_n \qquad (11.15)$$

Polymers coordinated with hexacoordinating metal atoms such as titanium may be produced by ligand exchange or by the reaction of a metallic ester such as tetrabutyl titanate and a bis(β-diketone), as shown in the following equation:

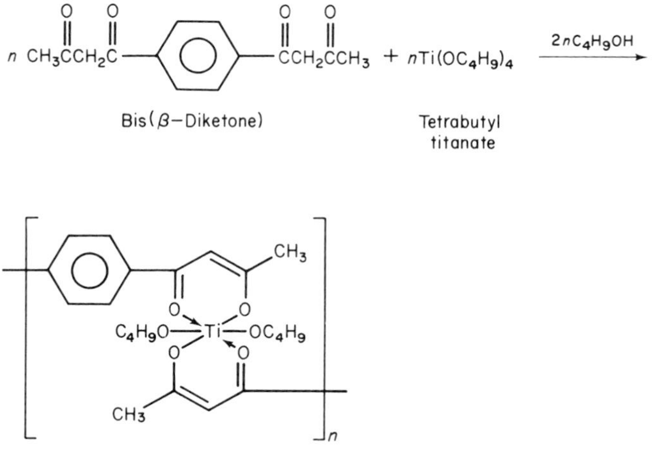

$$n\ CH_3\overset{O}{\overset{\|}{C}}CH_2\overset{O}{\overset{\|}{C}}-C_6H_4-\overset{O}{\overset{\|}{C}}CH_2\overset{O}{\overset{\|}{C}}CH_3 + nTi(OC_4H_9)_4 \xrightarrow{2nC_4H_9OH}$$

Bis(β-Diketone) Tetrabutyl titanate

$$\left[-C_6H_4-\text{(diketonate)}-Ti(OC_4H_9)_2-\text{(diketonate, } CH_3)- \right]_n \qquad (11.16)$$

Titanium coordination polymer

Polymeric chelates may also be prepared from vinyl polymers which have potential complexing pendant groups. For example, as shown by the following structure, complexes of metal ions (M), such as zinc, cadmium, cooper, nickel, cobalt, and iron, may be formed with polyvinyl macrocyclic polyethers (crown ethers) such as poly-4'-vinylbenzo-18-crown-6.

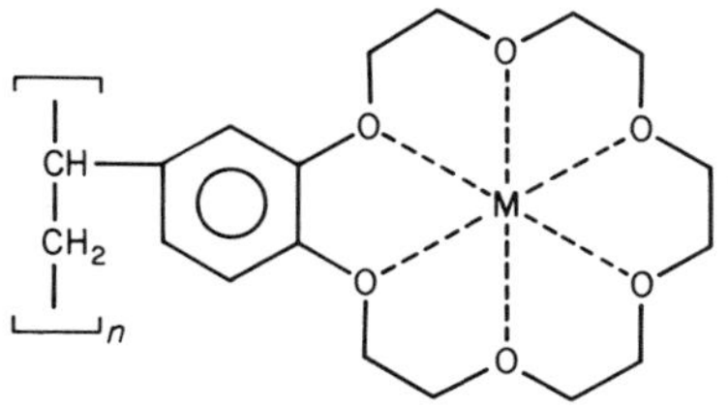

CH — CH$_2$ — n ; O O O M O O O

11.7 OTHER INORGANIC POLYMERS

As shown by the following equation, polycarboxylates (halatopolymers) may be produced by the reaction of metallic chlorides and sodium salts of dicarboxylic acids.

$$nMCl_2 + nNaOOCRCOONa \xrightarrow{-2nNaCl} -[-MOOCRCOO-]_n- \qquad (11.17)$$

Metallic chloride — Sodium salt of a dicarboxylic acid — Halatopolymer

Amorphous sulfur is an interesting unstable elastomer produced by quenching polymeric molten sulfur in cold water. Selenium polymers have also been described. Fibrous polymers, which are hydrolyzed by water, have been produced by heating aluminum sulfide with silicon dioxide, as shown by the following equation.

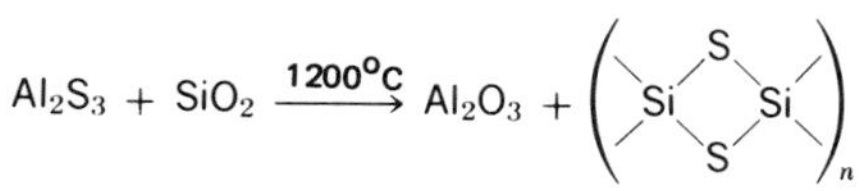

$$Al_2S_3 + SiO_2 \xrightarrow{1200^\circ C} Al_2O_3 + \left(\text{Si}\langle^{S}_{S}\rangle\text{Si} \right)_n \qquad (11.18)$$

Sulfur nitride polymers [$(SN)_n$], which have optical and electrical properties similar to metals, were synthesized in 1910. These crystalline polymers, which are superconductive at 0.25 K, may be produced by the room-temperature solid-state polymerization of the dimer (S_2N_2). Amorphous polymers are also obtained from the tetramer.

A dark, blue-black, amorphous paramagnetic form of polysulfur nitride may be produced by quenching the gaseous tetramer in liquid nitrogen. The tetramer is produced when the polymer is heated at 145°C. Golden metallic films of polysulfur nitride are obtained when the gaseous tetramer is condensed on a glass surface at room temperature. Films of bromine-containing derivatives of polysulfur nitride are superconductors at 0.31 K.

$$S_4N_4 \xrightarrow{300^\circ C} (-S-N=)_{4n} + nSOF_4 + nNH_3 \longrightarrow \left(-\overset{O}{\underset{F}{S}}-N=\right)_n \qquad (11.19)$$

Silicones, phosphazenes, and ionomers like glass and hydraulic cements are good examples of useful inorganic polymers. Technology for the last two is old, but new science and technology have been developed for the first three. In spite of the many difficulties involved in the production of other stable inorganic polymers, it can be predicted that many new ones will be developed and produced in the future.

SUMMARY

1. Naturally occurring silicates, such as asbestos and synthetic silicates like Portland cement and glass, are well known but their chemistry is not well understood. However, the chemistry of the production of polysilicic acid is similar to that of glass. Both are polysiloxanes and both tend to cross link.

2. The characteristic cross linking of polysilicic acid may be prevented by replacing two of the hydroxyl groups by alkyl groups. The lack of stability of these polysiloxanes may be overcome by capping the hydroxyl end groups with monofunctional chlorosilanes. Trifunctional trichloroalkylsilanes serve as cross-linking agents.

3. Relatively stable phosphazene elastomers, that are useful throughout a temperature range of -56 to -180°C, are produced by the thermal cleavage of the phosphazene cyclic trimer and replacement of the pendant chloro groups by fluoro, phenoxy, or amino groups.

4. Polycarboranes may be produced by the reaction of a borane such as decarborane and acetylene. Copolymers of carboranes and siloxanes are temperature-resistant elastomers.

5. Ferrocene polymers, in which the ferrocene is the pendant group, as in polyvinyl ferrocene and those in which the ferrocenylene is in the backbone, have been prepared.

6. Coordination polymers have been prepared using many different metals and various polydentates, but none of these is particularly stable at elevated temperatures.

7. Polymers of sulfur nitride decompose into tetramers when heated at 145°C, and interesting polymers with electrical conductivity are obtained when the gaseous tetramer is cooled.

8. The number and variety of organometallic polymers and potential applications for organometallic polymers are great. Due to the high cost of many of the metal-containing reactants, uses will probably be limited to applications employing minute quantities of the polymers.

GLOSSARY

amorphous: Noncrystalline.

borazoles: Molecules made up of boron and nitrogen atoms.

capping: Protecting the end groups.

carboranes: Molecules made up of carbon and boron atoms.

coordination polymers: Polymers based on coordination complexes.

crown ethers: Cyclic ethers shaped like a crown and numbered according to ring size and number of oxygen atoms. Thus, 18-crown-6 signifies 18 atoms in the ring, 6 of which are oxygen atoms.

Dexsil: Tradename for copolymers of carborane and siloxane.

ferrocene: A sandwichlike molecule of cyclopentadiene and iron.

halatopolymers: Polycarboxylates produced by the reaction of metallic chlorides and sodium salts of dicarboxylic acids.

hydraulic cement: A composition like Portland cement, which sets or polymerizes when water is added.

inorganic polymers: Those containing elements other than typically carbon, nitrogen, and oxygen in their backbone or pendant groups.

M: Any metal.

metallocenes: Sandwichlike molecules of cyclopentadiene and metals.

OMP: Organometallic polymer.

PNF: Poly(phosphonitrilic fluorides).

polyphosphazenes: Phosphonitrilic polymers.

polyphosphonitrile: Polymer with the repeating unit $+\!\!\!-\overset{|}{\underset{|}{P}}\!=\!N\!-\!\!\!+$.

RTV: Room-temperature vulcanization.

SN: Sulfur nitride.

silanes: A homologous series, like the alkanes, based on silicon instead of carbon.

EXERCISES

1. What properties of glass correspond to those of organic polymers?
2. How could you produce a more stable germanium polymer?
3. What is meant by "lost loops" in the production of silicones?
4. How could you produce a silicone with a low $\overline{DP}$?
5. What would you estimate the solubility parameters of silicones to be?
6. Sodium silicate is water soluble (water glass), but silicones are water repellants. Can you explain this difference?
7. How could you polymerize an aqueous solution of sodium silicate?
8. How could you explain the good temperature resistance of silicones?
9. Show the repeating unit for polydiethylsiloxane.
10. What are the reactants used to make phosphazenes?
11. Why would you predict that the chloro groups in phosphonitrilic polymers would be attacked by water?
12. Which phosphazene would be more flexible—one made by a reaction of polyphosphonitrilic chloride with (a) sodium trifluoroethoxide or (b) sodium trifluorobutoxide?
13. Show the structure of borazole.
14. Why isn't polyvinyl ferrocene stable at high temperatures?
15. Since tin-containing organometallic polymers are used in marine antifouling coatings, what would you predict about their water resistance?
16. In addition to high cost, name another disadvantage of coordination polymers.
17. What would you predict about the electrical conductivity of halatopolymers?
18. How can you detect the formation of polymers when sulfur is heated?
19. Why is the amorphous polymer of sulfur stable at low temperatures?
20. What is the ceiling temperature of sulfur nitride polymers?

BIBLIOGRAPHY

Allcock, H. R. (1972): Phosphorus-Nitrogen Compounds, Academic, New York.

Andrianov, K. A. (1965): Metallorganic Polymers, Wiley Interscience, New York.

Beasley, M. L., and Collins, R. L. (1970): Controlled release polymeric herbicides, Science, 169:769.

Baughman, R. H., Chance, R. R., Marshall, J. (1976): Sulfur nitride polymers, J. Chem. Phys., 64(5):1869.

Carraher, C. E. (1977): Organometallic polymers, Coatings and Plastics Preprints, 37(1):59.

Carraher, C. E., and Reese, D. R. (1977): Lead polyesters, Coatings and Plastics Preprints, 37(1):162.

Carraher, C. E., Sheats, J., Pittman, C. U. (eds.) (1978): Organometallic Polymers, Academic, New York.

Coates, G. E. (1956): Organometallic Compounds, John Wiley, New York.

Colin, E. (1960): Organosilicon Compounds, Academic, New York.

Davies, A. G., Harrison, P. G., Palan, P. R. (1967): Stannoxanes, J. Organomet. Chem., 10(3):33.

Economy, J., Mason, J. H., Wohrer, L. C. (1970): Halatopolymers, J. Polym. Sci., A-1, 8:223.

Fordham, S. (1961): Silicones, Philosophical Library, New York.

Gerrard, W. (1961): The Organic Chemistry of Boron, Academic, New York.

Gimblett, F. G. R. (1963): Inorganic Polymer Chemistry, Butterworths, London.

———. (1963): Inorganic Polymers, Blackwell Scientific, Oxford.

Grimes, R. N. (1970): Carboranes, Academic, New York.

Hunter, D. V. (1963): Inorganic Polymers, John Wiley, New York.

Katon, J. E. (1968): Organic Semiconducting Polymers, Dekker, New York.

Kipping, F. S. (1927): Silicones, J. Chem. Soc., 130:104.

Kopolov, S., Hoganosch, T. E., Smid, J. (1973): Coordination complexes of polyvinyl macrocyclic polyethers, Macromolecules, 6:133.

Kunin, R. (1958): Ion Exchange Resins, Wiley Interscience, New York.

Ladenburg, A. (1872): Silicones, Ann. Chem., 164:300.

Lappert, M. F., and Leigh, G. J. (1962): Developments in Inorganic Polymer Chemistry, American Elsevier, New York.

MacDiarmid, A. G., Heeger, A. J., Garito, A. F. (1977): Polymeric sulfur nitride, Coatings and Plastics Reprints, 37(1):419.

McGregor, R. R. (1956): Silicones and Their Uses, McGraw-Hill, New York.

Moedritzer, K., and Van Wazer, J. F. (1965): Germanium compounds, Polymer Preprints, 6(2):1140.

Neuse, E. W. (1968): Ferrocene polymers. In Advances in Macromolecular Chemistry, Vol. 1 (W. M. Pasika, ed.), Academic, New York.

Neuse, E. W., and Rosenberg, H. (1970): Metallocene Polymers, Dekker, New York.

O'Driscoll, K. R. (1964): The Nature and Chemistry of High Polymers, Chap. 3, Reinhold, New York.

Parker, G. M. (1965): Inorganic polymers, Polymer Preprints, 6(2):1165.

Petrov, A. D., Mitonov, F., et al. (1968): Synthesis of Organosilicon Monomers, Plenum, New York.

Rochow, E. G. (1951): An Introduction to the Chemistry of the Silicones, Wiley Interscience, New York.

Salahub, D. R., and Messmer, R. P. (1976): Sulfur nitride polymers, J. Chem. Phys., 64(5):2034.

Seymour, R. B. (1971): Introduction to Polymer Chemistry, Chap. 8, McGraw-Hill, New York.

Singler, R. E., and Hagnauer, G. L. (1977): Polyphosphazenes, Coatings and Plastics Preprints, 37(1):516.

Singler, R. E., Schneider, N. S., Hagnauer, G. L. (1975): Phosphazenes, Polym. Eng. Sci., 15(5):321.

Slocum, D. W., and Siegel, A. (1977): Ferrocene polymers, Coatings and Plastics Preprints, 37(1):64.

Stevens, M. P. (1975): Polymer Chemistry, An Introduction, Chap. 13, Addison-Wesley, Reading, Massachusetts.

Stone, F. G. A., and Graham, W. A. G. (1962): Inorganic Polymers, Academic Press, Inc., New York, 1962.

Thames, S. F., and Bufkin, B. G. (1975): Silicon resins. In Applied Polymer Science (J. K. Craver and R. W. Tess, eds.), Organic Coatings and Plastics Chemistry Div., American Chemical Society, Washington, D.C.

Van Wazer, J. R. (1965): Inorganic polymer chemistry, Coatings and Plastics Preprints, 25(2):275.

———. (1965): Inorganic polymer chemistry, Polymer Preprints, 6(2): 1887.

West, R. (ed.) (1968): Organosilicon Chemistry, Plenum, New York.

Yeager, W. L., and Castelli, V. J. (1977): Tin containing organometallic polymers, Coatings and Plastics Preprints, 37(1):185.

12

Fillers and Reinforcements for Polymers

Some films, fibers, and plastics are used as unfilled polymers, but the strength and cost of most elastomers and plastic composites are dependent on the presence of appropriate fillers or reinforcements. Some rubber articles such as crepe rubber shoe soles, rubber bands, inner tubes, and balloons are unfilled. However, the tread stock in pneumatic tires would not be serviceable without the addition of carbon black or amorphous silica. For example, addition of these fillers increases the tensile strength of SBR from 100 to 4000 psi. Likewise, most high-performance plastics are composites of polymers reinforced by fibrous glass.

12.1 THEORY OF THE EFFECT OF FILLERS

Many naturally occurring functional materials, such as wood, bone, and feathers, are composites consisting of a continuous resinous phase and a discontinuous phase. The first synthetic plastics such as celluloid and Bakelite were also composites. Wood flour was used to reinforce the pioneer phenolic resins and is still used today for the same purpose.

According to the American Society for Testing and Materials standard ASTM-D-883, a filler is a relatively inert material added to a plastic to modify its strength, permanence, working properties, or other qualities or to lower costs, while a reinforced plastic is one with some strength properties greatly superior to those of the base resin resulting from the presence of high-strength fillers embedded in the composition. According to ASTM, plastic laminates are the most common and strongest type of reinforced plastics.

According to one widely accepted definition, fillers are comminuted spherical or spheroidal solids. Glass beads which meet the requirements of this definition are used to reduce mold wear and to improve the quality of molded parts. The word extender, sometimes used for fillers, is not always appropriate since some fillers are more expensive than the resin.

Current theories describing the action of spherical fillers in polymers are based on the Einstein equation shown below. Einstein showed that the viscosity of a viscous Newtonian fluid (η_0) was increased when small, rigid, noninteracting spheres were suspended in the liquid. According to the Einstein equation, the viscosity of the mixture (η) is related to the fractional volume (c) occupied by the spheres, and η is independent of the size of the spheres or the polarity of the liquid.

$$\eta = \eta_0 (1 + 2.5c) \tag{12.1}$$

Providing that c is less than 0.1, good agreement with the Einstein equation is noted when glass spheres are suspended in ethylene glycol. Maximum packing of spheres (c = 90%) is attained when the composition equals 40% each of 20 and 325 mesh and 10% each of 35 and 100 mesh spheres.

The Einstein equation has been modified by including a hydrodynamic or crowding factor (β) which is equal to 1.35 and 1.91 for closely packed and loosely packed spheres, respectively. The modified Mooney equation shown below resembles the Einstein equation when $\beta = 0$.

$$\eta = \eta_0 \frac{2.5c}{1 - \beta c} \tag{12.2}$$

Many other empirical modifications of the Einstein equation have been made to predict actual viscosities of resinous composites. Since the modulus (M) is related to viscosity, these empirical equations like the Einstein-Guth-Gold (EGG) equation, may be used to predict changes in modulus when spherical fillers are added.

$$M = M_0 (1 + 2.5c - 14.1c^2) \tag{12.3}$$

Since carbon black and amorphous silica tend to form clusters of spheres (graping effect), an additional modification of the Einstein equation has been made to account for the nonspherical shape or aspect ratio (l/D). This factor (f) is equal to the ratio of the length (l) to the diameter (D) of nonspherical particles:

$$\eta = \eta_0 (1 + 0.67fc + 1.62f^2c^2) \tag{12.4}$$

It is generally recognized that the segmental mobility of a polymer is reduced by the presence of a filler. Small particles with a diameter of less than 10 mm increase the cross-linked density and active fillers increase the glass transition temperature (T_g) of the composite.

The high strength of composites is dependent on strong van der Waals interfacial forces. The latter are enhanced by the presence of polar functional groups on the polymer and by the treatment of filler surfaces with silanes, titanates, or other surface-active agents. Composites have been produced from almost every available polymer using almost every conceivable comminuted material as a filler.

12.2 FILLERS

Among the naturally occurring filler materials are cellulosics, such as wood flour, α-cellulose, shell flour, starch, and proteinaceous fillers such as soybean residues. Approximately 40,000 tons of cellulosic fillers are used annually by the American polymer industry. Wood flour, which is produced by the attrition grinding of wood wastes, is used as a filler for phenolic resins, dark-colored urea resins, polyolefins, and PVC. Shell flour, which lacks the fibrous structure of wood flour, has been made by grinding walnut and peanut shells. It is used as a replacement for wood flour.

α-Cellulose, which is more fibrous than wood flour, is used as a filler for urea and melamine plastics. Melamine dishware is a laminated structure consisting of molded resin-impregnated paper. Presumably, the formaldehyde in these thermosetting resins reacts with the hydroxyl groups in cellulose to produce a more compatible composite. Starch and soybean derivatives are biodegradable, and the rate of disintegration of resin composites may be controlled by the amount of these fillers present.

As was discussed in Chap. 10, many incompatible polymers are added to increase the impact resistance of other polymers such as polystyrene. Other comminuted resins such as silicones or polyfluorocarbons are added to increase the lubricity of other plastics. For example, a hot melt dispersion of polytetrafluoroethylene in polyphenylene sulfide is used as a coating for antistick cookware.

Since cellulose acetate butyrate is compatible with uncured polyester resins, but incompatible with the cured resin, it is added to the premix to reduce shrinkage during curing. Finely divided polyethylene, which is also incompatible with polyester resins, is added to reduce surface roughness in the so-called low profile resin technique.

Carbon black, which was produced by the smoke impingement process by the Chinese over a thousand years ago, is now the most widely used filler for polymers. Much of the 1.5 million tons produced annually in the United States is used for the reinforcement of elastomers. The most widely used carbon black is furnace carbon black. The particle size of the latter is about 0.08mm. Its hardness on the Mohs' scale is less than 1.

Carbon-filled polymers, especially those made from acetylene black, are fair conductors of heat and electricity. Polymers with fair conductivity have also been obtained by embedding carbon black in the surfaces of nylon or polyester filament reinforcements. The resistance of polyolefins to ultraviolet radiation is also improved by the incorporation of carbon black.

While glass spheres are classified as nonreinforcing fillers, the addition of 40 g of these spheres to 60 g of nylon-66 increases the flexural modulus, compressive strength, and melt index. The tensile strength, impact strength, creep resistance, and elongation of these composites are less than those of the unfilled nylon-66. A greater increase in flexural modulus is noted when the glass surface is altered by surface-active agents.

Milled glass fibers, multicellular glass nodules, and glass flakes have also been used as fillers. When added to resins, hollow glass and carbon spheres, called microballoons or microspheres, produce syntactic foams with varying specific gravities depending on the ratio of filler to resin. Superior high-performance composites are obtained when glass or graphite fibers are used as the additives.

Conductive composites are obtained when powdered metal fillers or metal-plated fillers are added to resins. These composites have been used to produce forming tools for the aircraft industry. Powdered lead-filled polyolefin composites have been used as shields for neutron and γ radiation. Zinc-filled plastics have been used as sacrificial composite electrodes, and magnetizable composites have been obtained by the incorporation of powdered aluminum-nickel alloys or barium ferrite.

Zinc oxide, which has a hardness of 2.5 on the Mohs' scale, is used to a large extent as an active filler in rubber and as a weatherability improver in polyolefins and polyesters. Anatase and rutile titanium dioxide are used as white pigments and as weatherability improvers in many polymers. Ground barites ($BaSO_4$) yield X-ray opaque plastics with controlled density.

The addition of finely divided calcined alumina, corundum, or silicon carbide produces abrasive composites. However, alumina trihydrate (ATH) which has a Mohs' hardness of less than 3, serves as a flame-retardant filler in plastics. Zirconia, zirconium silicate, and iron oxide, which have specific gravities greater than 4.5, are used to produce plastics with controlled densities.

Calcium carbonate, which has a Mohs' hardness of 3, is available both as ground natural limestone and as synthetic chalk. This filler is widely used in paints, plastics, and elastomers. The volume relationship of calcium carbonate to resin or the pigment volume required to fill voids in the resin composite is called the pigment-volume-concentration (PVC). The critical PVC (CPVC) is the minimum required to satisfy the resin demand.

In contrast to the cubically shaped, naturally occurring calcium carbonate filler, the synthetic product produced by the addition of carbon dioxide to a slurry of calcium hydroxide is acicular, or needle shaped. Calcium carbonate is used at an annual rate of 700 million tons as a filler in PVC, polyolefins, polyurethane foams, and in epoxy and phenolic resins (see Table 12.1).

TABLE 12.1 Types of Fillers for Polymers

- I. Organic materials
  - A. Cellulosic products
    - 1. Wood products
      - a. Kraft paper
      - b. Chips
      - c. Coarse flour
      - d. Ground flour
        - (1) Softwood flour
        - (2) Hardwood flour
        - (3) Shell flour
    - 2. Comminuted cellulose products
      - a. Chopped paper
      - b. Diced resin board
      - c. Crepe paper
      - d. Pulp preforms
    - 3. Fibers
      - a. α-Cellulose
      - b. Pulp preforms
      - c. Cotton flock
      - d. Textile byproducts
      - e. Jute
      - f. Sisal
      - g. Rayon
  - B. Lignin-type products
    - 1. Ground bark
    - 2. Processed lignin
  - C. Synthetic fibers
    - 1. Polyamides (nylon)
    - 2. Polyesters (Dacron)
    - 3. Polyacrylonitrile (Orlon, Acrilan)
  - D. Carbon
    - 1. Carbon black
      - a. Channel black
      - b. Furnace black
    - 2. Ground petroleum coke
    - 3. Graphite filaments
    - 4. Graphite whiskers
- II. Inorganic materials
  - A. Silica products
    - 1. Minerals
      - a. Sand
      - b. Quartz
      - c. Tripoli
      - d. Diatomaceous earth
    - 2. Synthetic materials
      - a. Wet-processed silica
      - b. Pyrogenic silica
      - c. Silica aerogel
  - B. Silicates
    - 1. Minerals
      - a. Asbestos
        - (1) Chrysotile
        - (2) Amosite
        - (3) Anthophyllite
        - (4) Crocidolite
        - (5) Tremolite
        - (6) Actinolite
      - b. Kaolinite (China clay)
      - c. Mica
      - d. Nepheline syenite
      - e. Talc
      - f. Wollastonite
    - 2. Synthetic products
      - a. Calcium silicate
      - b. Aluminum silicate
  - C. Glass
    - 1. Glass flakes
    - 2. Solid glass spheres
    - 3. Hollow glass spheres
    - 4. Milled fibers
    - 5. Fibrous glass
      - a. Filament
      - b. Rovings
      - c. Woven roving
      - d. Yarn
      - e. Mat
      - f. Fabric
  - D. Metals
  - E. Boron filaments
  - F. Metallic oxides
    - 1. Ground material
      - a. Zinc oxide
      - b. Alumina
      - c. Magnesia
      - d. Titania
    - 2. Whiskers
      - a. Aluminum oxide (sapphire)
      - b. Beryllium oxide
      - c. Magnesium oxide
      - d. Thorium oxide
      - e. Zirconium oxide
  - G. Calcium carbonate
    - 1. Chalk
    - 2. Limestone
    - 3. Precipitated calcium carbonate
  - H. Polyfluorocarbons
  - I. Other fillers
    - 1. Whiskers (nonoxide)
      - a. Aluminum nitride
      - b. Beryllium carbide
      - c. Boron carbide
      - d. Silicon carbide
      - e. Silicon nitride
      - f. Tungsten carbide
    - 2. Barium ferrite
    - 3. Barium sulfate

Silica, which has a specific gravity of 2.6, is used as naturally occurring and synthetic amorphous silica, as well as in the form of large crystalline particulates such as sand and quartz.

Diatomaceous earth, also called infusorial earth, fossil flour, and Fuller's earth, is a finely divided amorphous silica consisting of the skeletons of diatoms. This filler has a Mohs' hardness of less than 1.5 in contrast to sharp silica sand which has a value of 7. Diatomaceous earth is used to prevent rolls of film from sticking to itself (antiblocking) and to increase the compressive strength of polyurethane foams. Tripoli, or rotten stone, is porous silica formed by the decomposition of sandstone.

Pyrogenic, or fumed, silica is a finely divided filler obtained by heating silicon tetrachloride in an atmosphere of hydrogen and oxygen. This filler is used as a thixotrope to increase the viscosity of liquid resins. Finely divided silicas are also produced by the acidifaction of sodium silicate solutions and by the evaporation of alcoholic solutions of silicic acid.

Sharp silica sand is used as a filler in resinous cement mortars. Reactive silica ash produced by burning rice hulls and a lamellar filler, novaculite, from the novaculite uplift in Arkansas, are also used as silica fillers in polymers.

Hydrated finely divided silicas which contain surface silanol groups are used for the reinforcement of elastomers. Extreme care must be taken in handling silica to prevent silicosis. Approximately 25 million tons of silica fillers are used annually by the polymer industry.

Both naturally occurring and synthetic silicates are also widely used as fillers. Hydrated aluminum silicate, or kaolin, has a specific gravity of 2.6 and a hardness value of 2.5 on the Mohs' scale. Kaolin and other clays may be dissolved in sulfuric acid and regenerated by the addition of sodium silicate. Clays are used as fillers in synthetic paper, rubber, and bituminous products.

Mica, which has a specific gravity of 2.8 and a Mohs' hardness value of 3, is a naturally occurring lamellar or platelike filler with an aspect ratio below 30. However, much higher aspect ratios are obtained by ultrasonic delamination.

Talc is a naturally occurring fibrouslike hydrated magnesium silicate with a Mohs' hardness of 1 and a specific gravity of 2.4. Since talc-filled polypropylene is much more resistant to heat than PP, it is used in automotive accessories subject to high temperatures. Over 40 million tons of talc are used annually as fillers.

Nepheline syenite, a naturally occurring sodium potassium aluminum silicate filler, and wallastonite, an acicular calcium metasilicate filler, are used for the reinforcement of many plastics. Fibers from molten rock or slag (PMF) are also used for reinforcing polymers.

Asbestos is a naturally occurring magnesium silicate which in spite of its toxicity has been used for over 250 years as a flame-resistant fiber. Approximately 180 million tons of asbestos are used annually as an additive for polymers.

12.3 REINFORCEMENTS

According to the ASTM definition, fillers are relatively inert while reinforcements improve the properties of plastics. Actually, few fillers are used that do not improve properties, but reinforcing fibers produce dramatic improvements in the physical properties of the composites. Many fibrous reinforcements are available, but most theories have been developed as a result of investigations of fibrous glass, which is the most widely used reinforcement for polymers.

That filaments could be produced from molten glass was known for centuries, but fibrous glass was not produced commercially until the mid 1930s. Unlike the previously cited isotropic filler-resin composites, the stress in a fibrous glass-reinforced composite is concentrated at the fiber ends. Therefore, providing the strength of the fiber is greater than that of the resin, the properties of the composite are anisotropic and dependent on the direction of the stress.

The transverse modulus (M_T) and many other properties of a long fiber-resin composite may be estimated from the law of mixtures. The longitudinal modulus (M_L) may be estimated from the Kelly Tyson equation shown below; the longitudinal modulus is proportional to the sum of the fiber modulus (M_F) and the resin matrix modulus (M_M). Each modulus is based on the fractional volume (c). The constant k is equal to 1 for parallel continuous filaments and decreases for more randomly arranged shorter filaments.

$$M_L = kM_Fc_F + M_Mc_M \tag{12.5}$$

Since the contribution of resin matrix is small in a strong composite, the second term in the Kelly Tyson equation may be disregarded. Thus, the longitudinal modulus is dependent on the reinforcement modulus, which is independent of the diameter of the reinforcing fiber. The full length of filament reinforcement is utilized in filament-wound and pultruded composites. In each case, the impregnated resin becomes part of the finished composite.

While unsuccessful attempts were made to use cotton threads as reinforcements, the first successful reinforcements were with fibrous glass. The latter may be spun from low-cost soda lime, type E, or type C glass. In the spinning process, filaments are produced by passing the molten glass through orifices in the bushings.

In addition to the filament winding and pultrusion processes, chopped fibrous glass may be used as a reinforcement for spraying resin-impregnated chopped strand and for bulk molding compounds (BMC) and sheet molding compounds (SMC). The latter is the most widely used form of molded fibrous glass resin composite.

In many processes, such as SMC, the fibers are not continuous. When they are longer than the critical length (l_c), it is necessary to modify the first term in the Kelly Tyson equation by multiplying by a factor $(l - l_c)/2$ in which l is equal to the actual fiber length. The constant k approaches 0.5 for two-directionally oriented fibers.

Fibrous glass-reinforced resinous composites were introduced in 1940 and their use has increased steadily since then. Their use was originally confined to thermosetting resins, but fibrous glass-reinforced thermoplastics such as nylon are now important composites. Over 500,000 tons of fibrous glass-reinforced composites are produced annually in the United States.

Short, randomly oriented glass fibers and those from nylon, aramides, polyvinyl alcohol, polyacrylonitrile, and polyesters have been used successfully in the preparation of strong composites. Since these organic fibers crystallize, they serve as nucleating agents when used to reinforce crystallizable polymers such as polypropylene.

Polyester resin-impregnated fibrous glass roving or mat is used for SMC and BMC, respectively. The former is used like a molding powder and the latter is hot pressed in the shape of the desired object, such as one-half of a suitcase. Chopped fibrous glass roving may be impregnated with resin and sprayed, and glass mats may be impregnated with resin just prior to curing.

The strongest composites are made from continuous filaments impregnated with resin before curing. These continuous filaments are wound around a mandrel in the filament winding process and gathered together and forced through an orifice in the pultrusion molding process.

The first continuous filaments were rayon, and these as well as polyacrylonitrile fibers have been pyrolyzed to produce graphite fiber. High-modulus reinforcing filaments have also been produced by the deposition of boron atoms from boron trichloride vapors on tungsten or graphite filaments.

Small single crystals, such as potassium titanate, are being used at an annual rate of over 10,000 tons for the reinforcement of nylon and other thermoplastics. These PMRN composites are replacing die-cast metals in many applications. Another microfiber, sodium hydroxycarbonate (called Dawsonite), also improves the physical properties and flame resistance of many polymers. Many other single crystals, called whiskers, such as alumina, chromia, and boron carbide, have been used for making high-performance composites.

12.4 COUPLING AGENTS

The first commercial glass filaments were protected from breakage by a starch sizing which was removed before use in resin composites. Since polyvinyl acetate sizing, now in use, is more compatible with resins, it does not have to be removed from the glass surface. However, the interfacial attraction between fibrous glass and resins is poor, and strong composites require the use of coupling agents to increase the interfacial bond between the resin and reinforcing agent.

The original coupling agents, which were called promotors, were used to assure a good bond between rubber and the carbon black filler. The first commercial promotors were N-4-dinitroso-N-methylaniline and N-(2-methyl-2-nitropropyl)-4-nitrosoaniline. Presumably, coupling took place between carbon black and the N-nitroso group and between the elastomer and the p-nitroso group.

These promotors increased the tensile strength, modulus, and bound rubber content of rubber. While natural rubber is soluble in benzene, it becomes less soluble when carbon black or amorphous silica is added. The insoluble mixture of filler and rubber is called bound rubber.

The original promotors or coupling agents for fibrous glass and polyester resins were silanes. It is assumed that the trimethoxy groups in a coupling agent such as γ-mercaptopropyltrimethoxysilane couple with the silanol groups on the surface of fibrous glass and that the mercapto groups couple with the polymer.

Many silane and titanate coupling agents have been developed for the treatment of different reinforcing agents and fillers used with specific polymers. While it is the custom to treat the surface of the filler, coupling may also occur when the silane or titanate derivative is added to the resin or the mixture of resin and filler.

It is believed that the continuous resin matrix in a composite transfers applied stress to the reinforcing discontinuous phase through the interface between the two components. This interfacial attraction is often weakened in the presence of moisture, but a strong interfacial bond is maintained when coupling agents are used.

The interfacial bond between calcium carbonate fillers and resins has been improved by surface treatment with stearic acid. The bond between silica and resins has been strengthened by the addition of O-hydroxybenzyl alcohol or ethylene glycol.

Titanate coupling agents such as triisostearyl isopropyl titanate (TTS) are effective in reducing energy requirements for processing mixtures of fillers and resins. It has been proposed that monoalkyl titanates form titanium oxide monomolecular layers on the filler surface and modify the surface energy so that the viscosity of the resin-filler mixture is reduced.

Thus, ferric oxide loadings as high as 90% in nylon-66 and calcium carbonate loadings of 70% in polypropylene (PP) are possible when appropriate titanates are added. The melt flow of the filled PP is similar to that of the unfilled polymer, but the impact strength of the composite is much higher than that of PP itself.

SUMMARY

1. According to Einstein's equation, spherical fillers of any size increase the viscosity of a fluid in accordance with the partial volume of the

filler. The Einstein equation, which relates to moduli of composites, has been modified to account for filler aggregates and nonspherically shaped fillers.

2. Many comminuted materials, such as wood flour, shell flour, α-cellulose, starch, synthetic polymers, carbon black, glass spheres and flakes, powdered metals, metallic oxides, calcium carbonate, silica, mica, talc, clay, and asbestos, have been used as fillers in polymers.

3. When added to polymers, fibrous reinforcements are much more effective than spherical fillers in improving strength properties. The most widely used reinforcing fiber is fibrous glass. Its effect and that of other reinforcing fibers is dependent on fiber length and the interfacial bond between it and the continuous resin matrix.

4. Fibrous glass may be used in the form of resin-impregnated mat or roving in the SMC and BMC processes, respectively. Resin-impregnated glass filament may be wound on a mandrel or forced through an orifice and cured in the filament-winding and pultrusion processes, respectively.

5. Many sophisticated reinforcements based on graphite fibers, aramide fibers, boron-coated tungsten, and single crystals, such as those of potassium titanate and sapphire, have been used as the discontinuous phase in high-performance composites.

6. The interfacial bond between the resin and fibrous glass, as well as other fillers, may be improved by surface treatment with surface-active agents such as silanes and titanates. These coupling agents not only improve physical properties of the composite but are effective in reducing the energy required in processing.

GLOSSARY

acicular: Needle shaped.

α-Cellulose: Cellulose insoluble in 17.5% NaOH.

anisotropic: Properties vary with direction.

aramide: Nylon produced from aromatic reactants.

asbestos: Fibrous magnesium silicate.

aspect ratio: Ratio of length to diameter of particles.

ASTM: American Society for Testing and Materials.

ATH: Alumina trihydrate.

barites: Barium sulfate.

β: Hydrodynamic or crowding factor.

blocking: The sticking of sheets of film to each other.

BMC: Bulk molding compound; resin-impregnated short bundles of fibers.

bound rubber: Rubber adsorbed on carbon black which is insoluble in benzene.

c: Fractional volume occupied by a filler.

carbon black: Finely divided carbon made by the incomplete combustion of hydrocarbons.

comminuted: Finely divided.

composite: A filled or reinforced plastic.

continuous phase: The resin in a composite.

coupling agents: Products such as silanes or organic titanates which improve the interfacial bond between filler and resin.

CPVC: Critical pigment volume concentration.

D: diameter.

diatomaceous earth: Siliceous skeletons of diatoms.

discontinuous phase: The discrete filler additive in a composite.

EGG: Einstein-Guth-Gold equation: $M = M_0(1 + 2.5c + 14.1c^2)$.

Einstein equation: $\eta = \eta_0(1 + 2.5c)$.

η: Coefficient of viscosity of a mixture of a solid and liquid.

η_0: Coefficient of viscosity of a liquid.

extender: A term sometimes applied to an inexpensive filler.

f: Aspect ratio (l/D).

Fiberglas: Tradename for fibrous glass.

fibrous filler: One in which the aspect ratio is at least 150:1.

fibrous glass: Filaments made from molten glass.

filament winding: A process in which resin-impregnated continuous filaments are wound on a mandrel and the composite is cured.

filler: Usually a relatively inert material used as the discontinuous phase of a resinous composite.

Fuller's earth: Diatomaceous earth.

graphite fibers: Fibers made by the pyrolysis of polyacrylonitrile fibers.

isotropic: Identical properties in all directions.

kaolin: Clay.

Kelly Tyson equation: $M_L = kM_FC_F + M_MC_M$.

l_c: Critical fiber length.

lamellar: Sheetlike.

laminate: A composite consisting of layers adhered by a resin.

low profile resins: Finely divided incompatible resins that make a rough surface smooth.

lubricity: Slipperiness.

M: Modulus of a composite.

M_0: Modulus of an unfilled resin.

M_F: Modulus of a fiber.

M_L: Longitudinal modulus.

M_M: Modulus of resin matrix.

M_T: Transverse modulus.

mesh size: Size of screens used to classify finely divided solids.

mica: Naturally occurring lamellar silicate.

microballoons: Hollow glass spheres.

microspheres: Hollow carbon spheres.

Mohs' scale: A scale of hardness from 1 for talc to 10 for diamonds.

Mooney equation: $\eta = \eta_0 (2.5c/1 - \beta c)$.

novaculite: Finely ground quartzite rock.

PMRN: Composites reinforced by potassium titanate.

PP: Polypropylene.

promotor: Coupling agent.

pultrusion: A process in which bundles of resin-impregnated filaments are passed through an orifice and cured.

PVC: Pigment volume concentration.

reinforced plastic: A composite whose additional strength is dependent on a fibrous additive.

roving: A bundle of untwisted strands.

silanes: Silicon compounds corresponding to alkanes.

silanol group: SiOH.

SMC: Sheet molding compound: resin-impregnated mat.

strand: A bundle of filaments.

syenite: Igneous rock similar to feldspar.

syntactic foam: Composite of resin and hollow spheres.

talc: Naturally occurring hydrated magnesium silicate.

thixotrope: An additive which yields thixotropic liquids.

tripoli: Rotten stone; porous decomposed sandstone.

TTS: Triisostearylisopropyl titanate.

type C glass: Acid-resistant glass.

type E glass: Electrical grade glass.

van der Waals forces: Intermolecular attractions.

wallastonite: Acicular calcium metasilicate.

whiskers: Single crystals used as reinforcements.

wood flour: Attrition-ground, slightly fibrous wood particles.

EXERCISES

1. Name three unfilled polymers.
2. What is the continuous phase in wood?
3. What filler is used in Bakelite?
4. Name three laminated plastics.
5. How would you change a glass sphere from an extender to a reinforcing filler?
6. If one stirs a 5-ml volume of glass beads in 1 liter of glycerol, which will have the higher viscosity, small or large beads?
7. When used in equal volume, which will have the higher viscosity (a) a suspension of loosely packed spheres, or (b) a suspension of tightly packed spheres?
8. Why is the segmental mobility of a polymer reduced by the presence of a filler?
9. What effect does a filler have on T_g?
10. Which would yield the stronger composite: (a) peanut shell flour or (b) wood flour?
11. What is the advantage and disadvantage, if any, of α-cellulose over wood flour?

12. What filler is used in decorative laminates such as Formica table tops?
13. Which is the filler (discontinuous phase) and which is the resin (continuous phase) in a cookware coating produced from (a) polytetrafluoroethylene (Teflon) and (b) polyphenylene sulfide (Ryton)?
14. Would finely divided polystyrene make a good low-profile resin for reinforced polyesters?
15. How would you make a conductive syntactic foam?
16. Which would be stronger: a chair made from (a) polypropylene or one of equal weight made from (b) cellular polypropylene?
17. What advantage would a barium ferrite-filled PVC strip have over an iron magnet?
18. How would you make X-ray opaque PVC?
19. How would you make an abrasive foam from polyurethane?
20. How could you explain the flame retardant qualities of ATH?
21. How would you explain the improvement in strength of composites with stearic acid-treated calcium carbonate?
22. How could you justify the high cost of pyrogenic silica?
23. In what elastomer would hydrated silica be most effective as a filler?
24. Why is a good interfacial bond between the filler surface and the resin essential?
25. Providing the volumes of the fibers are similar, which will yield the stronger composite: fibers with small or large cross sections?
26. How would you make a strong, corrosion-resistant pipe?
27. What is the advantage of BMC and SMC over hand lay-up techniques such as those used in boat building?
28. What technique would you use to incorporate large amounts of filler (e.g., 70% calcium carbonate) in a resin?

BIBLIOGRAPHY

Briston, J. H., Katan, L. L., Broutman, L. J. (1974): Composite Materials—Fracture and Fatigue, Academic, New York.

Broutman, L. J., and Krock, R. H. (1974): Composite Materials, Academic, New York.

Buttery, D. N. (1960): Plasticizers, 2nd ed., Franklin Publishing, Palisades, New Jersey.

Darby, J. R., and Sears, J. K. (1975): Plasticizers, Chap. 42. In Applied Polymer Science (J. K. Craven and R. W. Tess, eds.), Organic Coatings and Plastics Chemistry Div. of ACS, Washington, D.C.

Deanin, R. C., and Schott, N. R. (1974): Fillers and Reinforcements, Advances in Chemistry Series 134, American Chemical Society, Washington, D.C.

Delmonte, J. (1961): Metal-Filled Plastics, Reinhold, New York.

Donnet, J. B., and Volt, A. (1976): Carbon Black, Physics, Chemistry and Elastomer Reinforcement, Dekker, New York.

Dumond, T. C. (1954): Shell Molding and Shell Mold Casting, Reinhold, New York.

Frissell, W. J. (1967): Fillers. In Encyclopedia of Polymer Science and Technology, Vol. 6 (H. F. Mark, N. G. Gaylord, and N. M. Bikales, eds.), Wiley Interscience, New York.

Gaylord, M. W. (1974): Reinforced Plastics, Cahners, Boston.

Guth, E. J. (1945): Filler vs. modulus, J. Appl. Phys., 16:20.

Huke, D. W. (1951): Introduction to Natural and Synthetic Rubbers, Chap. 5, Chemical Publishing, New York.

Katz, H. S., and Milewski, J. (1978): Handbook of Plastic Fillers and Reinforcements, Van Nostrand-Reinholt, New York.

Kinna, M. A., and Warfield, R. W. (1966): Filament winding, Polymer Eng. Sci., 6:41.

Kraus, G. (1965): Reinforcement of Elastomers, Wiley Interscience, New York.

Langley, M. (1973): Carbon Fibers in Engineering, McGraw-Hill, New York.

Lubin, G. (1969): Handbook of Fiberglass and Advanced Plastics Composites, Van Nostrand-Reinhold, New York.

Manson, J. H., and Sperling, L. H. (1975): Polymer Blends and Composites, Plenum, New York.

Monte, S. J. (1976): Non-silane coupling agents, Modern Plastics, 53(10A):161.

Morgan, P. (1957): Glass Reinforced Plastics, 2nd ed., Philosophical Library, New York.

Nielson, L. E. (1974): Mechanical Properties of Polymers and Composites, Dekker, New York.

Norman, R. H. (1970): Conductive Rubbers and Plastics, American Elsevier, New York.

——. (1973): Conductive Rubber and Plastics, Palmerton, New York.

Oleesky, S. S., and Mohr, J. J. (1964): Handbook of Reinforced Plastics, Reinhold, New York.

Parrott, N. J. (1973): Fiber Reinforced Materials Technology, Van Nostrand-Reinhold, New York.

Platzer, N. A. (1975): Copolymers, Polyblends, and Composites, American Chemical Society, Washington, D.C.

Plueddemann, E. P. (1974): Composite Materials, Academic, New York.

Ranney, M. W. (1976): Coupling agents, Modern Plastics, 53(10A):160.

——. (1977): Reinforced Plastics and Elastomers, Noyes Data Corp., Park Ridge, New Jersey.

Riley, M. (1955): Plastics Tooling, Reinhold, New York.

Rosato, D. V., and Grove, C. S. (1964): Filament Winding, John Wiley, New York.

Salkend, M. J., and Holister, G. S. (1973): Applications of Composite Materials, American Society for Testing Materials, Philadelphia.

Scala, E. (1973): Composite Materials for Combined Functions, Hayden, Rochelle Park, New Jersey.

Seymour, R. B. (1975): Plastics composites. In Polymer Plastics Technology and Engineering (L. Natureman, ed.), Dekker, New York.

——. (1976): Additives for plastics-fillers and reinforcements, Plastics Engineering, 32(8):29.

——. (1976): Fibrous reinforcements, Modern Plastics, 53(10A):169.

——. (1976): Fillers for plastics, Modern Plastics, 53(10A):172.

——. (1976): The role of fillers and reinforcements in plastics technology, Polym. Plast. Technol. Eng., 7(1):49.

Svalbonas, G. S., and Gustman, G. (1973): Analysis of Structural Composite Materials, Dekker, New York.

Titow, W. V., and Lanham, B. J. (1975): Reinforced Thermoplastics, John Wiley, New York.

Winding, C. C., and Hiatt, G. D. (1961): Polymeric Materials, McGraw-Hill, New York.

Zettlemoyer, A. C., and Chessick, J. J. (1964): Wettability by heats of immersion. In Contact Angle, Wettability and Adhesion (R. F. Gould, ed.), Chap. 5, American Chemical Society, Washington, D.C.

13

Plasticizers, Stabilizers, Flame Retardants, and Other Additives

While the modulus of polymers is usually increased by the addition of fillers and reinforcements, it may be decreased by the addition of moderate amounts of plasticizers. Other essential additives such as antioxidants, heat stabilizers, ultraviolet stabilizers, and flame retardants may reduce the modulus and other physical properties. Thus, it may be necessary to add reinforcing agents to counteract the weakening effect of some other additives. Nevertheless, additives are essential functional ingredients of polymers, and whenever possible, each should be used in optimum amounts for the attainment of high-quality products.

13.1 PLASTICIZERS

According to the ASTM-D-883 definition, a plasticizer is a material incorporated in a plastic to increase its workability and flexibility or distensibility. The addition of a plasticizer may lower the melt viscosity, elastic modulus, and glass transition temperature (T_g) of a plastic. Thus, the utility of cellulose nitrate (CN) produced by Schönbein in 1846 was limited until Parkes added castor oil to CN in 1865 and Hyatt added camphor to plasticize CN in 1870. Another plasticizer, tricresyl phosphate (TCP), was used to replace part of the camphor and reduce the flammability of celluloid in 1910.

Waldo Semon patented the use of tricresyl phosphate as a plasticizer for PVC in 1933. This was later replaced by the less toxic di-2-ethylhexyl phthalate (DOP) which is now the most widely used plasticizer. The annual worldwide production of plasticizers is 3.2 million tons, and the U.S. production is in excess of 1 million tons. In fact, plasticizers are major components of a number of polymer-containing products. For instance automobile safety glass is typically composed mainly of polyvinyl butyral and about 30% plasticizer.

The effect of plasticizers may be explained by the lubricity, gel, and free volume theories. The first states that the plasticizer acts as an internal lubricant and permits the polymer chains to slip by each other. The gel theory, which is applicable to amorphous polymers, assumes that a polymer such as PVC has many intermolecular attractions which are weakened by the presence of a plasticizer such as DOP. It is assumed that the addition of a plasticizer increases the free volume of a polymer and that the free volume is identical for all polymers at T_g.

Since plasticizers are essentially nonvolatile solvents, compatibility requires that the difference in the solubility parameter of the plasticizer and polymer ($\Delta\delta$) be less than 1.8H (see Table 13.1). It is of interest to note that δ for PVC is 9.66 H and for DOP is 8.85 H. Thus, $\Delta\delta = 0.81$ H for this widely used plasticizer-resin system. When present in small

TABLE 13.1 Solubility Parameters of Typical Plasticizers

Plasticizer	δ Solubility parameter (H)
Parafinic oils	7.5
Dioctyl phthalate	7.9
Dibutoxyethyl phthalate	8.0
Tricresyl phosphate	8.4
Dioctyl sebacate	8.6
Triphenyl phosphate	8.6
Chlorinated biphenyl (Arochlor 1248)	8.8
Dihexyl phthalate	8.9
Hydrogenated terphenyl (HB-40)	9.0
Dibutyl sebacate	9.2
Dibutyl phthalate	9.3
Dipropyl phthalate	9.7
Diethyl phthalate	10.0
Dimethyl phthalate	10.7
Santicizer 8	11.9
Glycerol	16.5

amounts, all plasticizers act as antiplasticizers, i.e., they increase the hardness and decrease the elongation of polymers.

Inefficient plasticizers require relatively large amounts of these additives to overcome the initial antiplasticization. However, good plasticizers such as DOP change from antiplasticizers to plasticizers when less than 10% of the plasticizer is added to PVC.

The development of plasticizers has been plagued with toxicity problems. Thus, the use of highly toxic polychlorinated biphenyls (PCB) has been discontinued. Phthalic acid esters, such as DOP, may be extracted by blood stored in plasticized PVC blood bags and tubing. These aromatic esters are also distilled from PVC upholstery in closed automobiles in hot weather. These problems have been solved by using oligomeric polyesters as nonmigrating plasticizers, instead of DOP.

Many copolymers, such as poly(vinyl chloride-co-vinyl acetate) are internally plasticized because of the flexibilization brought about by the change in structure of the polymer chain. In contrast, DOP and others are said to be external plasticizers. The presence of bulky groups on the polymer chain increases segmental motion. Thus, the flexibility increases as the size of the pendant group increases. However, linear bulky groups with more than 10 carbon atoms will reduce flexibility because of side-chain crystallization when the groups are regularly spaced.

Water is a widely utilized plasticizer in nature permitting flexibility of much of the human body as well as the "bendability" of flowers, leaves, tree branches, and so on. Fats and many proteins also act as plasticizers in animals.

Plasticizer containment still remains a major problem, particularly for periods of extended use. For instance, most plastic floor tiles become brittle with extended use, mainly due to the leaching out of plasticizer. This is becoming overcome through many routes including surface treatment of polymer product surfaces effecting less porous surface features and use of branched polymers which can act as plasticizers to themselves. Being polymers themselves, the highly branched polymers are slow to leach because of physical entanglements within the total polymer matrix.

13.2 ANTIOXIDANTS

Polymers such as polypropylene (PP) are not usable outdoors without appropriate stabilizers, because of the presence of readily removable hydrogen atoms on the tertiary carbon atoms. PP and many other polymers (RH) are attacked during processing or outdoor use in the absence of stabilizers because of a chain degradation reaction, as shown in the following equations.

By initiation $$\underset{\text{Polymer}}{\text{R—H}} \longrightarrow \underset{\text{Polymer}}{\text{R}\cdot}\ \underset{\text{Free radical}}{+\ \text{H}\cdot} \tag{13.1}$$

propagation:

$$\underset{\text{Free radical}}{R\cdot} + \underset{\text{Oxygen}}{O_2} \longrightarrow \underset{\text{Peroxy free radical}}{ROO\cdot}$$

$$\underset{\text{Peroxy free radical}}{ROO\cdot} + \underset{\text{Polymer}}{R{:}H} \longrightarrow \underset{\text{Dead polymer}}{ROOH} + \underset{\text{Free radical}}{R\cdot} \qquad (13.2)$$

termination:

$$R\cdot + R\cdot \longrightarrow \underset{\text{Dead polymer}}{R{:}R}$$

$$R\cdot + ROO\cdot \longrightarrow \underset{\text{Dead polymer}}{ROOR} \qquad (13.3)$$

$$ROO\cdot + ROO\cdot \longrightarrow \underset{\text{Dead polymer}}{ROOR} + O_2$$

The rate of the free-radical chain reactions shown above is accelerated by the presence of heavy metals, such as cobalt(II) ions, as shown in (13.4).

$$\begin{aligned} ROOH + Co^{2+} &\longrightarrow Co^{3+} + RO\cdot + OH^- \\ ROOH + Co^{3+} &\longrightarrow ROO\cdot + H^+ + Co^{2+} \end{aligned} \qquad (13.4)$$

In contrast, the rate of chain-reaction degradation is retarded by the presence of small amounts of antioxidants. Naturally occurring antioxidants are present in many plants, including hevea rubber trees. The first synthetic antioxidants were synthesized independently by Caldwell and by Winkelman and Gray by the condensation of aromatic amines with aliphatic aldehydes. While unpurified commercial products such as phenyl-β-naphthylamine are toxic, they are still used as antioxidants for rubber tires.

Many naturally occurring antioxidants are derivatives of phenol and hindered phenols, such as di-tert-butyl-para-cresol. As shown by the following equation, the antioxidant acts as a chain-transfer agent to produce a dead polymer and a stable free radical that does not initiate chain-radical degradation. However, the phenoxy free radical may react with other free radicals to produce a quinone derivative.

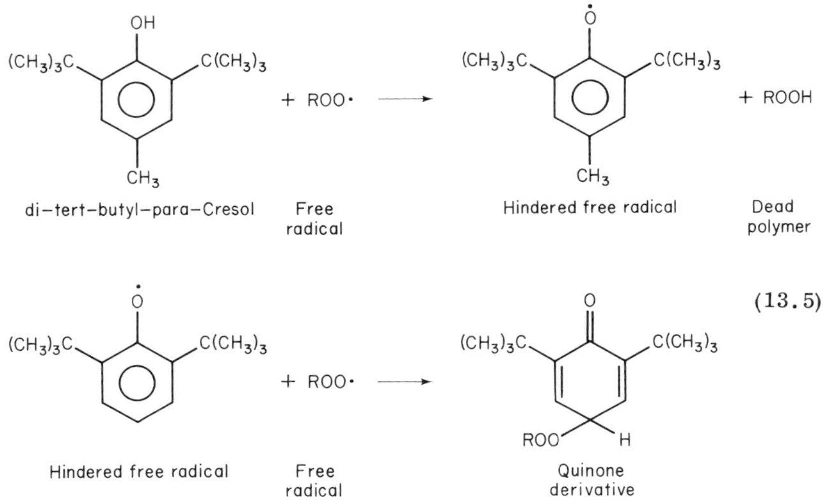

(CH3)3C / OH / C(CH3)3 / CH3 — di-tert-butyl-para-Cresol + ROO· (Free radical) ⟶ (CH3)3C / Ȯ / C(CH3)3 / CH3 — Hindered free radical + ROOH (Dead polymer)

(CH3)3C / Ȯ / C(CH3)3 — Hindered free radical + ROO· (Free radical) ⟶ (CH3)3C / O / C(CH3)3 / ROO / H — Quinone derivative

(13.5)

Since carbon black has many free electrons, it may be added to polymers such as polyolefins to retard free-radical degradation of the polymer. It is customary to add small amounts of other antioxidants, such as aliphatic thiols or disulfides, to enhance the stabilization by a so-called synergistic effect. The latter term is used to explain the more effective stabilization by a mixture of antioxidants. Over 3000 tons of antioxidants are used annually by the polymer industry in the United States.

13.3 HEAT STABILIZERS

In addition to the free-radical chain degradation described for polyolefins, another type of degradation (dehydrohalogenation) also occurs with chlorine-containing polymers such as PVC. As shown by the following equation, when heated, PVC may lose hydrogen chloride and form a chromophoric conjugated polyene structure. Since the allyl chlorides produced are very unstable, the degradation continues as an unzipping type of chain reaction.

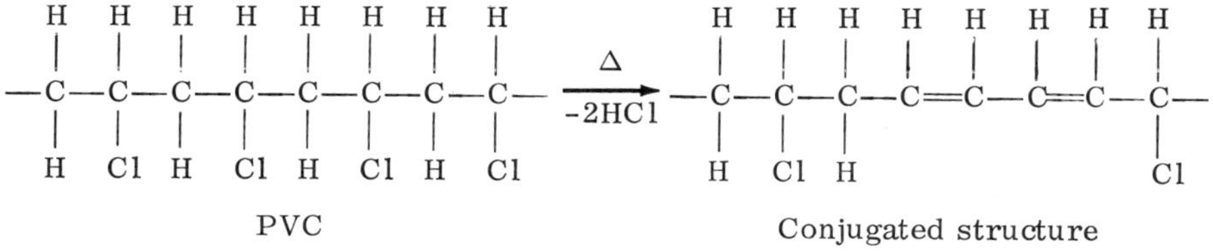

$$-\underset{H}{\overset{H}{C}}-\underset{Cl}{\overset{H}{C}}-\underset{H}{\overset{H}{C}}-\underset{Cl}{\overset{H}{C}}-\underset{H}{\overset{H}{C}}-\underset{Cl}{\overset{H}{C}}-\underset{H}{\overset{H}{C}}-\underset{Cl}{\overset{H}{C}}- \xrightarrow[-2HCl]{\Delta} -\underset{H}{\overset{H}{C}}-\underset{Cl}{\overset{H}{C}}-\underset{H}{\overset{H}{C}}-\overset{H}{C}=\overset{H}{C}-\overset{H}{C}=\overset{H}{C}-\underset{Cl}{\overset{H}{C}}-$$

PVC Conjugated structure

(13.6)

This type of degradation is accelerated in the presence of iron salts, oxygen, and hydrogen chloride. Toxic lead and barium and cadmium salts act as scavengers for hydrogen chloride and may be used as heat stabilizers in some applications, such as wire coating. Mixtures of magnesium and calcium stearates are less toxic. In spite of their toxicity, alkyl tin mercaptides and alkyl tin derivatives of thio acids have also been used. Dioctyltin salts are less toxic and produce clear PVC films.

Organic phosphites, such as mixed aryl, alkyl phosphites or triphenyl phosphite, form complexes with free metallic ions and prevent the formation of insoluble metal chlorides. Less toxic, epoxidized, unsaturated oils such as soy bean oil act as HCl scavengers as shown in 13.7.

$$-\!\!\left(\underset{\substack{|\\ \text{H}}}{\text{C}}\overset{\text{O}}{\frown}\underset{\substack{|\\ \text{H}}}{\text{C}}\right)\!\!- \;+\; \text{HCl} \longrightarrow -\!\!\left(\underset{\substack{|\\ \text{H}}}{\overset{\substack{\text{HO}\\ |}}{\text{C}}}-\underset{\substack{|\\ \text{H}}}{\overset{\substack{\text{Cl}\\ |}}{\text{C}}}\right)\!\!- \qquad (13.7)$$

Epoxy group — Chlorohydrin derivative

13.4 ULTRAVIOLET STABILIZERS

While much of the sun's high-energy radiation is absorbed by the atmosphere, some radiation in the 280 to 400 nm (ultraviolet) range reaches the earth's surface. Since the energy of this radiation is 100 to 72 kcal, it is sufficiently strong to cleave covalent bonds and cause yellowing and embrittlement of organic polymers.

Polyethylene, PVC, polystyrene, polyesters, and polypropylene are degraded at wavelengths of 300, 310, 319, 325, and 370 nm, respectively. The bond energy required to cleave the tertiary carbon hydrogen bond in polypropylene is 90 kcal/mol, corresponding to a wavelength of 318 nm.

Since the effect of ultraviolet radiation on synthetic polymers is similar to its effect on the human skin, it is not surprising that ultraviolet stabilizers such as phenyl salicylate have been used for many years in suntanning lotions. As shown in (13.8), phenyl salicylate rearranges in the presence of high-energy radiation to form a 2,2'-dihydroxybenzophenone. The latter, and other 2-hydroxybenzophenones, act as energy-transfer agents, i.e., they absorb energy to form chelates which release energy at longer wavelengths by the formation of quinone derivatives.

Many commercial ultraviolet stabilizers have alkoxyl groups on carbon 4 on the phenyl group. 2-Alkoxybenzophenones and those with bulky groups on carbon 6 are not useful as stabilizers. Other ultraviolet stabilizers are benzotriazoles, such as 2-(2'-hydroxyphenyl) benzotriazole;

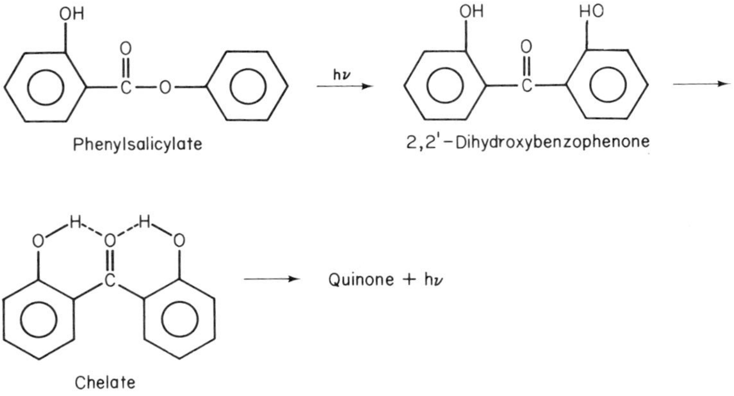

Phenylsalicylate $\xrightarrow{h\nu}$ 2,2'-Dihydroxybenzophenone $\longrightarrow$

Chelate $\longrightarrow$ Quinone + $h\nu$ (13.8)

substituted acrylonitriles, such as ethyl-2-cyano-3,3'-diphenyl acrylate; metallic complexes, such as nickel dibutyldithiocarbamate; and pigments, such as carbon black.

The metal complexes function as energy-transfer agents, free-radical scavengers, and decomposers of hydroperoxides. The pigments absorb UV radiation and act as screening agents. Over 100,000 tons of UV stabilizers are used annually by the U.S. polymer industry.

13.5 FLAME RETARDANTS

While some polymers such as PVC are not readily ignited, most organic polymers, like other carbonaceous materials, will burn at elevated temperatures, such as those present in burning buildings. Polyolefins, SBR, EPDM, and wood, of course, will support combustion when ignited with a match or some other source of flame. In addition to burning, thermoplastics such as polyester fibers will melt, and other plastics such as PVC, polyurethanes, and proteins, when ignited, will produce smoke and toxic gases such as CO, HCl, and HCN.

Since some polymers are used as shelter and clothing and in household furnishing, it is essential that they have good flame resistance. Combustion is a chain reaction that may be initiated and propagated by free radicals like the hydroxyl free radical. As shown in (13.9), hydroxyl radicals may be produced by the reaction of oxygen with macroalkyl radicals. Halogen radicals produced by the reaction of hydroxyl radicals with halides, such as HX, may serve as terminators for the chain reaction.

$$\sim RCH_2\cdot + O_2 \longrightarrow \sim RCHO + \cdot OH \qquad (13.9)$$

Macroalkyl radical	Oxygen	Dead polymer	Hydroxyl radical

$\cdot OH$	+	$\sim RCH_2H$	$\longrightarrow$	$\sim RCH_2\cdot$	+	HOH
Hydroxy radical		Polymer		Macroradical		Water

HX	+	$\cdot OH$	$\longrightarrow$	HOH	+	$X\cdot$
Hydrogen halide		Hydroxyl radical		Water		Halogen radical

(13.9 cont.)

$X\cdot$	+	$\sim RCH_2\cdot$	$\longrightarrow$	RCH_2X
Halogen radical		Macroradical		Dead polymer

13.6 FLAME-RETARDANT MECHANISMS

Since halogen and phosphorus radicals couple with free radicals produced in the combustion process and terminate the reaction, many flame retardants are halogen or phosphorus compounds. These may be additives, or external retardants, such as antimony oxide, and an organic bromide, or internal retardants, such as tetrabromophthalic anhydride, which yields a flame-resistant polyester. Over 100,000 tons of flame retardants are used annually in the United States.

Fuel, oxygen, and high temperature are essential for the combustion process. Thus, polyfluorocarbons, phosphazenes, and some composites have flame-retardant properties since they are not good fuels. Fillers such as alumina trihydrate (ATH) release water when heated, and hence reduce the temperature of the combustion reaction. Compounds such as sodium carbonate, which release carbon dioxide, shield the reactants from oxygen.

Char, formed in some combustion processes, also shields the reactants from oxygen and retards the outward diffusion of volatile combustible products. Aromatic polymers tend to char, and some phosphorus and boron compounds catalyze char formation.

Synergistic flame retardants such as a mixture of antimony trioxide and an organic bromo compound are much more effective than single flame retardants. Thus, while a polyester containing 11.5% tetrabromophthalic anhydride burned without charring at high temperatures, charring but no burning was noted when 5% antimony oxide was added.

Since combustion is subject to many variables, tests for flame retardancy may not predict flame resistance under unusual conditions. Thus, a disclaimer stating that flame-retardant tests do not predict performance in an actual fire must accompany all flame-retardant polymers. Flame retardants, like many other organic compounds, may be toxic or they may produce toxic gases when burned. Hence, extreme care must be exercised when using fabrics or other polymers treated with flame retardants.

13.7 COLORANTS

Color is a subjective phenomenon whose esthetic value has been recognized for centuries. Since it is dependent on the light source, the object, and the observer, color is not subject to direct measurement. Colorants which provide color in polymers may be soluble dyes or comminuted pigments.

Some polymeric objects, such as rubber tires, are black because of the presence of high proportions of carbon black filler. Many other products, including some paints, are white because of the presence of titanium dioxide, the most widely used inorganic pigment. Over 50,000 tons of colorants are used annually by the American polymer industry.

Pigments are classified as organic or inorganic. The former are brighter, less dense, and smaller in particle size than the more widely used, more opaque inorganic colorants. Iron oxides or ochers, available as yellow, red, black, brown, and tan, are the second most widely used pigments.

Other pigments, such as yellow lead chromate, molybdate orange, yellow cadmium pigments, and green zinc chromate, are toxic. Green zinc chromate is a blend of yellow lead chromate and iron blue—iron(II)ferrocyanide, or Prussian blue. Ultramarine blue is also widely used as a pigment.

Carbon black is the most widely used organic pigment, but phthalocyanine blues and greens are available in many different shades and are also widely used. Other organic pigments are the azo dyestuffs such as the pyrazolone reds, diarylide yellows, dianisidine orange and tolyl orange; quinacridone dyestuffs, such as quinacridone violet, magenta, and red; the red perylenes; acid and basic dyes, such as rhodamine red, and victoria blue; anthraquinones, such as flavanthrone yellow; dioxazines; such as carbazole violet; and isoindolines, available in the yellow and red range.

13.8 CURING AGENTS

The use of curing agents began with the serendipitous discovery of vulcanization of hevea rubber with sulfur by Charles Goodyear in 1838. The conversion of an A- or B-stage phenolic novolac resin with hexamethylenetetramine in the early 1900s was another relatively early example of the use of a curing (cross linking) agent. Organic accelerators, or catalysts, for the sulfur vulcanization of rubber were discovered by Oenslager in 1912. While these accelerators are not completely innocuous, they are less toxic than aniline, used previously to the discovery of accelerators. Sample accelerators are thiocarbanilide and 2-mercaptobenzothiazole (Captax).

Captax is used to the extent of 1% with hevea rubber and accounts for the major part of the 30,000 tons of accelerators used annually in the United States. Other accelerators, whose structional formulas are shown below, are 2-mercaptobenzothiazole sulfenamide (Santocure), used for the vulcanization of SBR, dithiocarbamates and thiuram disulfides. The last, called ultraaccelerators, catalyze the curing of rubber at moderate temperatures and may be used in the absence of sulfur.

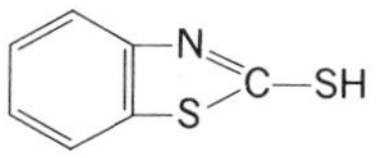

2-Mercaptobenzothiazole
(Captax)

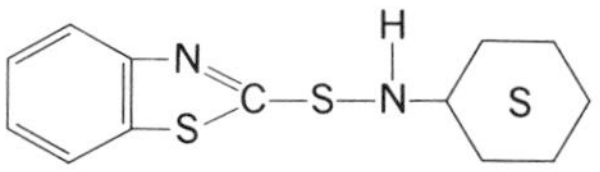

2-Mercaptobenzothiazole sulfenamide
(Santocure)

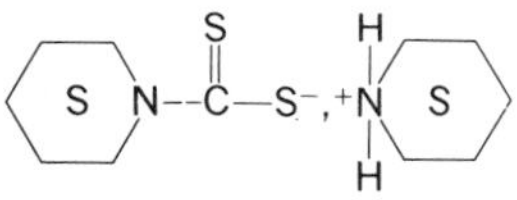

Piperidinium pentamethylene dithiocarbamate (pip-pip)

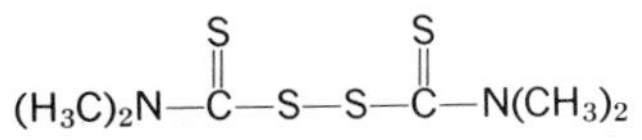

$(H_3C)_2N{-}C({=}S){-}S{-}S{-}C({=}S){-}N(CH_3)_2$

Tetramethyl thiuram disulfide
(Tuads)

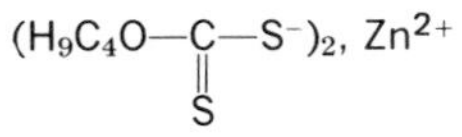

$(H_9C_4O{-}C({=}S){-}S^-)_2,\ Zn^{2+}$

Zinc butyl xanthate

Initators such as benzoyl peroxide are used not only for the initiation of chain-reaction polymerization but also for the curing of polyesters and for the grafting of styrene on elastomeric polymer chains. Peroxides such as 2,5-dimethyl-2,5-di(t-butylperoxy)hexyne-3 are used for cross linking HDPE. Since these compounds contain weak covalent bonds, precautions must be taken in their storage and use to prevent explosions. Free radicals for cross linking may also be produced by electrons, γ rays, or ultraviolet irradiation. The latter is more effective in the presence of additives such as the methyl ether of benzoin.

Unsaturated polymers such as alkyd resins may be cured or "dried" in the presence of oxygen, a salt of a heavy metal and an organic acid called a drier. The commonly used metals are cobalt, lead, and manganese, and the most common organic acids are linoleic, abietic, naphthenic, octoic, and tall oil fatty acids.

As shown in (13.10), oxygen is now believed to form a peroxide in the presence of a drier, yielding a macroradical capable of cross linking.

$$\underset{\text{Unsaturated oil}}{-\mathrm{CH{=}CH{-}CH_2{-}CH_2}-} + \mathrm{O_2} \longrightarrow \underset{\text{Peroxide}}{-\mathrm{CH{=}CH{-}CH(OOH){-}CH_2}-}$$

$$\underset{\text{Peroxide}}{-\mathrm{CH{=}CH{-}CH(OOH){-}CH_2}-} + \mathrm{Co^{2+}} \longrightarrow \mathrm{Co^{3+}} + \mathrm{OH^-} + \underset{\text{Macroradical}}{-\mathrm{CH{=}CH{-}CH(O\cdot){-}CH_2}-} \qquad (13.10)$$

13.9 MISCELLANEOUS ADDITIVES

Other polymer additives not previously discussed are antistatic agents, foaming agents, preservatives, and processing aids or lubricants.

Most polymers, except ionomers or metal-filled composites, are nonconductors which readily acquire an electrostatic charge during processing or subsequent handling. These charges, resulting from an excess or deficiency of electrons, may be counteracted by the use of air-ionizing bars during processing or by the addition of antistatic agents.

Antistatic agents may reduce the charge by acting as lubricants or they may provide a conductive path for the dissipation of the charge. Most antistats are hygroscopic and attract a thin film of water to the polymer surface. Internal antistats are admixed with the polymer, while external antistats are usually sprayed on the polymer surface. Some examples of antistatic agents are quaternary ammonium compounds, hydroxyalkylamines, organic phosphates, derivatives of polyhydric alcohols such as sorbitol, and glycol esters of fatty acids.

Cellular polymers not only provide insulation and resiliency but are usually stronger on a weight basis than solid polymers. Fluid polymers may be foamed by the addition of low-boiling liquids such as pentane or fluorocarbons, by blowing with compressed nitrogen gas, by mechanical heating, and by the addition of foaming agents. While some carbon dioxide is produced when polyurethanes are produced in the presence of moisture, auxiliary propellants are also added to the prepolymer mixture.

The most widely used foaming agents are nitrogen-producing compounds such as azobisformamide (ABFA). Other foaming agents, which decompose at various temperatures, are available. These may be used in extrusion, rotational molding, injection molding, and slush molding of plastisols. Plastisols consist of suspensions of polymer particles in a liquid plasticizer. These products, such as PVC plastisols, solidify when the temperature reaches a point at which the plasticizer penetrates the polymer particles.

While many unmodified synthetic polymers are not attacked by microorganisms, plasticizers and other additives, as well as naturally occurring cellulosics, starch, protein, and vegetable oil-based paints, are often subject to microbiologic deterioration. Preservatives are essential not only to prevent attack by microorganisms but also to prevent attack on rubber and PVC by rodents.

PVC is also subject to pink staining as a result of the diffusion of byproducts of attack by microorganisms. Quaternary ammonium carboxylates and tributyltin compounds are effective preservatives against pink staining. Other effective preservatives or biocides are esters of p-hydroxybenzoic acid, N-(trichloromethylthio)-4-phthalimide and bis(tri-n-butyltin) and bis(8-quinolinato) copper.

It is essential that polymers not stick to processing or fabricating equipment and that molded objects are readily removed from the mold. Processing aids prevent such sticking and may be viscosity depressants, such as ethoxylated fatty acids; slip agents, such as modified fatty acid esters; antiblocking or parting agents, such as polyvinyl alcohol; silicones; or polyfluorocarbons and mold-release agents, such as metallic stearates.

SUMMARY

1. Stiff polymers such as PVC may be flexibilized by the addition of a nonvolatile compatible liquid or solid which permits slippage of polymer chains and thus reduces the T_g and modulus of the polymer. Comparable effects may be accomplished by introducing randomness into the polymer by copolymerization.

2. The rate of degradation of polymers may be retarded by the addition of chain-transfer agents, called antioxidants, which produce inactive free radicals.

3. The rate of decomposition of polymers such as PVC at elevated temperatures may be decreased by the addition of heat stabilizers which

react with the decomposition products, like HCl. Soluble organic metal compounds, phosphites, and epoxides act as thermal stabilizers or scavengers for HCl.

4. The degradative effects of high-energy photolytic decomposition of polymers by ultraviolet radiation may be lessened by the addition of compounds such as 2-hydroxybenzophenones which serve as energy-transfer agents, i.e., they absorb radiation at low wavelength and reradiate it as lower energy at longer wavelengths.

5. Since fuel, oxygen, and high temperature are essential for the combustion of polymers, the removal of any one of these prerequisites will retard combustion. Thus, additives which when heated produce water or carbon dioxide are effective flame retardants.

6. The rapid combustion of organic polymers at elevated temperatures is also retarded by the presence of flame retardants which terminate the free-radical combustion reaction.

7. A wide variety of organic and inorganic pigments is used as additives to color polymers.

8. The rate of cross linking of natural rubber by sulfur is accelerated by catalysts like Captax which are called accelerators. Initiators like BPO which produce free radicals and heavy metal salts (driers) will also promote cross linking.

9. Antistats reduce the electrostatic charge on the surface of polymers.

10. Gas-producing additives are essential for the formation of cellular products.

11. Biocides are used as additives to prevent attack on polymers by microorganisms.

12. Lubricants serve as processing aids which prevent the sticking of polymers to metal surfaces during processing.

GLOSSARY

accelerator: A catalyst for the vulcanization of rubber.

antioxidant: An additive which retards the degradation of polymers.

antiplasticization: The hardening and stiffening effect observed when small amounts of a plasticizer are added to a polymer such as PVC.

antistat: An additive that reduces static charges on polymers.

biocide: An additive which retards attack by microorganisms.

Captax: 2-Mercaptobenzothiazole.

cellular polymers: Foams.

char: Carbonaceous residue produced by burning.

chelate: A cyclic complex resembling pincerlike claws.

CN: Cellulose nitrate.

colorant: A dye or pigment.

curing agent: An additive that causes cross linking.

$\Delta\delta$: Difference in solubility parameters.

dehydrohalogenation: Loss of HX.

DOP: di-2-Ethylhexyl phthalate.

drier: A catalyst which aids the reaction of polymers with oxygen.

drying: The cross linking of an unsaturated polymer chain.

energy-transfer agent: A molecule which absorbs high energy and reradiates it in the form of lower energy, i.e., longer wavelength.

flame retardant: An additive that increases the flame resistance of a polymer.

foaming agent: A gas producer.

free volume: Holes not occupied by polymer chains.

gel theory: The theory that assumes the presence of a pseudo 3-dimensional structure in PVC, and that the intermolecular attractions are weakened by the presence of a plasticizer.

h: Planck's constant.

HDPE: High density polyethylene.

heat stabilizers: Additives which retard the decomposition of polymers at elevated temperatures.

Hyatt, J. W.: The inventor of celluloid.

internal plasticization: The flexibilization resulting from the introduction of bulky groups in a polymer by copolymerization.

lubricity theory: The theory that explains plasticization on the basis of an increase in polymer chain slippage.

mold release agent: A lubricant which prevents the polymer from sticking to the mold cavity.

nm: Nanometer (1×10^{-9}m); 1 nm = 10 Å.

ν: Frequency.

ocher: An iron oxide pigment.

oligomeric polyesters: Low molecular weight polyesters.

PCB: Polychlorinated biphenyls.

pink staining: Discoloration of PVC resulting from attack by microorganisms.

plasticizer: A compatible nonvolatile liquid or solid which increases the flexibility of hard polymers.

plastisol: A suspension of finely divided polymer in a liquid plasticizer. The latter penetrates and plasticizes the polymer when heated.

PP: Polypropylene.

processing aid: A lubricant.

side-chain crystallization: A stiffening effect noted when long, regularly spaced bulky pendant groups are present on a polymer chain.

synergistic effect: The enhanced effect of a mixture of additives.

T_g: Glass transition temperature.

TCP: Tricresyl phosphate.

ultraaccelerator: A catalyst which cures rubber at low temperatures.

ultraviolet stabilizer: An additive that retards degradation caused by ultraviolet radiation.

UV: Ultraviolet.

vulcanization: Cross linking with heat and sulfur.

EXERCISES

1. Cellulose nitrate explodes when softened by heat. What would you add to permit processing at lower temperatures?
2. PVC was produced in the 1830s but not used until the 1930s. Why?
3. What is the source of "fog" on the inside of the windshield on pre-1976 automobiles?
4. Can you propose a mechanism for antiplasticization?
5. Why is plasticized PVC said to be toxic?
6. The T_g decreases progressively as the size of the alkoxy group increases from methyl to decyl in polyalkyl methacrylates, but then increases. Explain.
7. PP is now used in indoor/outdoor carpets. However, the first PP produced deteriorated rapidly when subjected to sunlight because of tertiary hydrogen atoms present. Explain.
8. Tests showed that crude phenyl-β-naphthylamine was a carcinogen, but the mice used for testing lived longer than normal when injected with di-tert-butyl-para-cresol. Explain.

9. Lead stearate is an effective thermal stabilizer for PVC, yet its use in PVC pipe is not permitted. Why?

10. When a PVC sheet fails in sunlight, it goes through a series of colors before becoming black. Explain.

11. What would be the advantage of using epoxidized soy bean oil as a stabilizer for PVC?

12. Why do PVC films deteriorate more rapidly when used outdoors?

13. Which of the following is more resistant to ultraviolet light: (a) polypropylene, (b) polyethylene, or (c) PVC?

14. Would 2-methoxybenzophenone be useful as an ultraviolet stabilizer?

15. Would 3,3'-dihydroxybenzophenone be useful as an ultraviolet stabilizer?

16. Polytetrafluoroethylene is considered to be noncombustible. Yet, two astronauts burned to death in a space capsule because of burning PTFE. Explain.

17. The disastrous effect of discarded burning cigarettes on polyurethane "stuffed" upholstery has been lessened by the use of a protective film of neoprene. Yet, disastrous fires have occurred, e.g., in jail cells. Explain.

18. The addition of "tris" as a retardant was required for children's sleeping garments by a government order in the early 1970. Nevertheless, the use of "tris" was discontinued in 1977. Why?

19. Antimony oxide is a good flame retardant in the presence of organic halogen compounds. Would you recommend it for textile applications?

20. Is a phosphazene elastomer flame resistant?

21. Cotton, wool, silk, flax, and wood, which are combustible, have been used for many centuries without flame retardants. Yet, synthetic polymers which are not any more combustible are banned unless flame retardants are added. Why?

22. Was carbon black always used as a reinforcing filler for tires?

23. How would you explain the different colors of ocher. ($Fe_2O_3 \cdot XH_2O$)?

24. What is the formula for Santocure?

25. How would you synthesize pip pip?

26. BPO is explosive. How would you store it?

27. Can you propose a better name for a drier?

28. What is the objection to the presence of static charges on polymer surfaces?

29. Explain how an internal antistat performs?
30. Why are foamed wire coatings preferred over solid coatings?
31. How would you design a foamed plastisol?
32. Why doesn't the liquid plasticizer penetrate a polymer particle such as PVC at ordinary temperatures?
33. Which would be more resistant to attack by microorganisms: (a) PVC or (b) plasticized PVC?
34. What naturally occurring fiber is more resistant to microbiologic attack than nylon?
35. Sometimes, molded plastics have opaque material called "bloom" on the surface. Explain.

BIBLIOGRAPHY

Abranoff, C. S. (1976): Ultraviolet stabilizers, Mod. Plast., 53(10A):222.

Benning, C. V. (1969): Plastic Foams, John Wiley, New York.

Bhatnger, V. (1973): Advances in Fire Retardants, Technomic Publishing Co., Westport, Connecticut.

Billmeyer, F. W. (1975): Color science, Chap. 18. In Applied Polymer Science (J. K. Craver and R. W. Tess, eds.), Organic Coatings and Plastics Chemistry Div. of ACS, Washington, D.C.

Boldus, L. R. (1976): Foaming agents, Mod. Plast., 53(10A):192.

Bruins, P. F. (1965): Plasticizer Technology, Vol. I, Reinhold, New York.

Buttrey, D. N. (1957): Plasticizers, Cleaver-Hume, London.

Byrne, R. E., Jr. (1969): Asbestos fibers, Mod. Plast., 46(10A):386.

Calvert, J. G., and Pitts, J. N. (1966): Photochemistry, John Wiley, New York.

Copp, J. (1976): Colorants, Mod. Plast., 53(10A):142.

Darby, J. R., and Sears, J. K. (1969): Plasticizers. In Encyclopedia of Polymer Science and Technology (H. F. Mark, N. G. Gaylord, and N. M. Bikales, eds.), Vol. 10, Wiley Interscience, New York.

DiBattisto, A. D. (1976): Antioxidants, Mod. Plast., 53(10A):138.

Doolittle, A. K. (1954): The Technology of Solvents and Plasticizers, John Wiley, New York.

Edwards, R. W. (1976): Antistatic agents, Mod. Plast., 53(10A):139.

Fisher, H. L. (1975): Accelerators. In Chemistry of Natural and Synthetic Rubber (M. Morton, ed.), Chap. 3, Reinhold, New York.

Garvey, B. S. (1959): Accelerators. In Introduction to Rubber Technology (M. Morton, ed.), Chap. 5, Reinhold, New York.

Gould, R. F. (ed.) (1965): Plasticization and Plasticizers Process, American Chemical Society, Washington, D.C.

Grassie, N. (1956): Chemistry of High Polymer Degradation Processes, Interscience, New York.

Hawkins, W. L. (1965): Oxidative degradation of high polymers. In Oxidation and Combustion Reviews, Vol. I (C. F. H. Tipper, ed.), Elsevier, Amsterdam.

Hilado, C. J. (1974): Flammability of Fabrics, Technomic Publishing Co., Westport, Connecticut.

———. (1974): Flammability of Solid Plastics, Technomic Publishing Co., Westport, Connecticut.

Holderried, J. A. (1969): Flame retardants, Mod. Plast., 46(10A):274.

Hopmeir, A. P., Greenstein, L. M., Petro, A. J. (1969): Pigments. In Encyclopedia of Polymer Science and Technology, Vol. 10 (H. F. Mark, N. G. Gaylord, and N. M. Bikales, eds.), Wiley Interscience, New York, pp. 157-216.

Ingold, K. U. (1961): Antioxidants, Chem. Rev., 61:653.

Jackson, W. J., and Caldwell, J. R. (1967): Antiplasticizers, J. Appl. Polymer Sci., 11(2):211, 227.

Johnson, K. (1976): Antistatic Compositions for Textiles and Plastics, Noyes Data Corp., Park Ridge, New Jersey.

Kan, R. O. (1966): Organic Photochemistry, McGraw-Hill, New York.

Koller, L. R. (1965): U.V. Radiation, 2nd ed., John Wiley, New York.

Kurgla, W. C., and Papa, A. J. (1973): Flame Retardancy of Polymeric Materials, Dekker, New York.

Lannon, D. A., and Hoskins, E. J. (1965): Effect of plasticisers, fillers, and other additives on physical properties, Chap. 7. In Physics of Plastics (P. D. Ritchie, ed.), Van Nostrand, Princeton, New Jersey.

Lewin, M., Atlas, S. M., Pearce, E. M. (1975): Flame Retardant Polymeric Materials, Plenum, New York.

Lundberg, W. O. (1961): Antioxidations and Antioxidants, Vol. I, Interscience, New York.

Maassen, G. C., Fawcett, R. J., Connell, W. R. (1965): Antioxidants. In Encyclopedia of Polymer Science and Technology, Vol. 2 (H. F. Mark, N. G. Gaylord, and N. M. Bikales, eds.), Wiley Interscience, New York, pp. 171-197.

Madorsky, S. L. (1964): Thermal Degradation of Organic Polymers, Wiley Interscience, New York.

Mellan, I. (1963): Industrial Plasticizers, MacMillan, New York.

Neiman, M. B. (1965): Aging and Stabilization of Polymers, Consultants Bureau, New York.

O'Connor, F. M. (1976): Processing aids, Mod. Plast., 53(10A):218.

Pastorino, R. L., and Lewis, R. N. (1976): Organic peroxides, Mod. Plast., 53(10A):202.

Patton, T. C. (1974): Pigment Handbook, Wiley Interscience, New York.

Pellen, M. (1856): Plasticizers, British Patent 2256,1856.

Powell, G. M., and Brister, J. E. (1900): Plastigels, U.S. Patent 2,427,507.

Preuss, H. P. (1970): Paint Additives, Noyes Data Corp., Park Ridge, New Jersey.

Ranney, M. W. (1974): Fire Resistant and Flame Retardant Polymers, Noyes Data Corp., Park Ridge, New Jersey.

Ritchie, P. D. (1970): Plasticizers, Stabilizers and Fillers, Butterworths, London.

Saltzman, M. (1975): Color pigments. Chap. 20 in Applied Polymer Science (J. K. Craver and R. W. Tess, eds.), Organic Coatings and Plastics Chemistry Division ACS, Washington, D.C.

Semon, W. L. (1936): Plastisol, U.S. Patent 2,188,396.

Seymour, R. B. (1971): Introduction to Polymer Chemistry, Chap. 11, McGraw-Hill, New York.

——. (1975): Modern Plastics Technology, Chap. 3, Reston Publishing, Reston, Virginia.

——. (1976): Additives for polymers. In Encyclopedia of Chemical Processing and Design, Vol. II (J. McKetta and W. A. Cunningham, eds.), Dekker, New York.

——. (1978): Additives for Plastics, Academic, New York.

Taylor, W., and Scott, K. A. C. (1976): Fire Performance and Testing of Plastics, Plastics and Rubber Institute, London.

Taylor, W., and Suhoza, R. (1976): Heat stabilizers, Mod. Plast., 53(10A):196.

Todd, W. D. (1956): Plastisols. In Polymer Processes, Chap. 14 (C. E. Schildknecht, ed.), Interscience, New York.

Underwriter Laboratories. (1975): Flammability Studies of Cellular Plastics and Other Building Materials, Underwriter Laboratories, Chicago.

Van Vonno, N. C. (1976): Lubricants, Mod. Plast., 53(10A):200.

Wallace, G. L. (1976): Plasticizers, Mod. Plast., 53(10A):210.

Webber, T. G. (1979): Coloring of Plastics, John Wiley, New York.

Weinberg, E. L. (1976): Preservatives, Mod. Plast., 53(10A):212.

Wymann, D. P. (1976): Flame retardants, Mod. Plast., 53(10A):186.

14

Reactions of Polymers

Synthesis and curing (cross linking) of polymers and telomerization are chemical reactions which have been discussed in previous chapters. Other reactions of polymers, such as hydrogenation, halogenation, cyclization, and degradation, will be described in this chapter. Providing the reaction sites are accessible to the reactants, reactions take place that are similar to classic organic chemical reactions. The rates of reactions of polymers may be enhanced by the presence of neighboring groups. This effect is called anchimeric assistance.

14.1 REACTIONS WITH POLYOLEFINS

Deuterated polyethylene could be produced from HDPE, but it is more readily produced by the polymerization of perdeuterated ethylene. The latter is prepared by the reduction of deuterated acetylene with chromium(II)sulfate in a dimethylformamide (DMF/H_2O) solution.

Polyethylene, like other alkane polymers, is resistant to chemical oxidation, but will burn in the presence of oxygen. The folds in crystalline polyethylene are less resistant to attack, and α,ω-dicarboxylic acids can be produced by the reaction of concentrated nitric acid on crystalline HDPE.

Polyolefins, like simple alkanes, may be chlorinated by chlorine at elevated temperatures or in the presence of ultraviolet light. This free-radical reaction produces HCl and chlorinated polyolefins (Tyrin), which are used as plasticizers and flame retardants. The commercial product is available with various percentages of chlorine. Since a tertiary hydrogen atom is more readily replaced than a secondary hydrogen, polypropylene is more readily chlorinated than HDPE. HDPE is readily converted to polytetrafluoroethylene by direct fluorination by fluorine.

Sulfochlorinated polyethylene (Hypalon) is obtained when a suspension of polyethylene in carbon tetrachloride is chlorinated by a mixture of chlorine and sulfur dioxide in pyridine. The commercial product, which contains 27.5% chlorine and 1.5% sulfur, is soluble in tetralin. It may be used as a coating which may be cured with sulfur and diphenylguanidine.

A chlorinated product called polyvinyl dichloride (PVDC) is obtained when PVC is chlorinated. Since the heat resistance of PVDC is superior to that of PVC, it is used for hot water piping systems.

Polyolefins may be cross linked by heating with peroxides such as di-tert-butyl peroxide or by irradiation. It is advantageous to cross link these polymers after they have been fabricated, as in wire coatings. The cross-linked products are less soluble and more resistant to heat than are the linear polyolefins.

Reactions comparable to those described for HDPE take place with many organic polymers. The pendant groups may also react with appropriate reactants.

14.2 REACTIONS OF POLYENES

Providing the ethylenic groups are accessible, the reactions of polyenes are similar to the classic reactions of alkenes. Thus, as demonstrated by Nobel laureate Hermann Staudinger, polyenes such as Hevea braziliensis may be hydrogenated, halogenated, hydrohalogenated, and cyclized. In his classic experiment in the early 1900s, Harries produced ozonides of rubber. Epoxides were also obtained by peroxidation.

The hydrogenation of H. braziliensis was investigated by Berthelot in 1869. The rate of this reaction with natural rubber, gutta percha, balata, or SBR may be followed by observing the changes in the glass transition temperature and the degree of crystallinity. The product obtained by the partial hydrogenation of polybutadiene (Hydropol) has been used as a wire coating.

$$\underset{\text{Polyene}}{\left(\mathrm{CH_2{-}C(CH_3){=}CH{-}CH_2} \right)_n} + \underset{\text{Hydrogen}}{\mathrm{H_2}} \xrightarrow{\text{Catalyst}} \underset{\text{Hydrogenated polyene}}{\left(\mathrm{CH_2{-}CH(CH_3){-}CH_2{-}CH_2} \right)_n} \tag{14.1}$$

A saturated ABA block copolymer (Kraton) is produced by the hydrogenation of the ABA block copolymer of styrene and butadiene.

$$-\!\!\left[\mathrm{CH_2}-\underset{\mathrm{C_6H_5}}{\mathrm{CH}}\right]_n\!\!-\!\!\left[\mathrm{CH_2}-\mathrm{CH}=\mathrm{CH}-\mathrm{CH_2}\right]_m\!\!-\!\!\left[\mathrm{CH_2}-\underset{\mathrm{C_6H_5}}{\mathrm{CH}}\right]_n\!\!- \xrightarrow[\text{cat.}]{H_2}$$

Block copolymer of butadiene

$$-\!\!\left[\mathrm{CH_2}-\underset{\mathrm{C_6H_5}}{\mathrm{CH}}\right]_n\!\!-\!\!\left[\mathrm{CH_2}-\mathrm{CH_2}-\mathrm{CH_2}-\mathrm{CH_2}\right]_m\!\!-\!\!\left[\mathrm{CH_2}-\underset{\mathrm{C_6H_5}}{\mathrm{CH}}\right]_n\!\!- \tag{14.2}$$

Block copolymer of styrene and butene

Chlorinated rubber (Tornesit or Parlon), which was produced by Traun in 1859, is available with varying amounts of chlorine and is used for the coating of concrete. While chlorinated NR is soluble in carbon tetrachloride, chlorinated SBR is insoluble, but both are soluble in benzene and chloroform.

$$\left(\mathrm{CH_2}-\underset{\mathrm{CH_3}}{\mathrm{C}}=\mathrm{CH}-\mathrm{CH_2}\right)_n + \mathrm{Cl_2} \longrightarrow \left(\mathrm{CH_2}-\overset{\mathrm{CH_3}}{\underset{\mathrm{Cl}}{\mathrm{C}}}-\underset{\mathrm{Cl}}{\mathrm{CH}}-\mathrm{CH_2}\right)_n \tag{14.3}$$

Hevea rubber — Chlorine — Chlorinated rubber

Hydrohalogenation of <u>H. braziliensis</u> proceeds by an ionic mechanism to yield a Markownikoff addition product with the halogen on the tertiary carbon atom. The principal use of rubber hydrochloride (Pliofilm) is as a packaging film. Some cyclization of the polymer also takes place during hydrohalogenation.

$$\left(\mathrm{CH_2}-\underset{\mathrm{CH_3}}{\mathrm{C}}=\mathrm{CH}-\mathrm{CH_2}\right)_n + \mathrm{HCl} \longrightarrow \left(\mathrm{CH_2}-\overset{\mathrm{CH_3}}{\underset{\mathrm{Cl}}{\mathrm{C}}}-\mathrm{CH_2}-\mathrm{CH_2}\right)_n \tag{14.4}$$

Hevea rubber — Hydrogen chloride — Rubber hydrochloride

Staudinger prepared cyclized polydienes by heating rubber hydrochloride with zinc dust. Commercial cyclized rubber (Thermoprene and Pliolite) has been produced by heating rubber with sulfuric acid or Lewis acids, respectively. These cyclized products or isomerized polymers, which are soluble plastics, are used as adhesives and coatings.

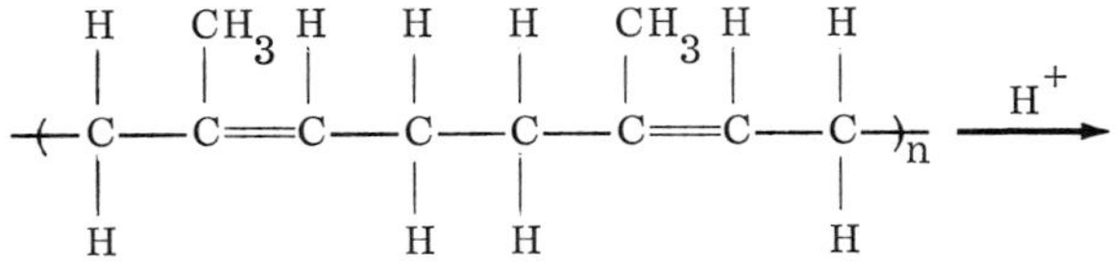

$$\mathrm{\left(CH_2-C(CH_3){=}CH-CH_2-CH_2-C(CH_3){=}CH-CH_2\right)_n \xrightarrow{H^+}}$$

Hevea rubber

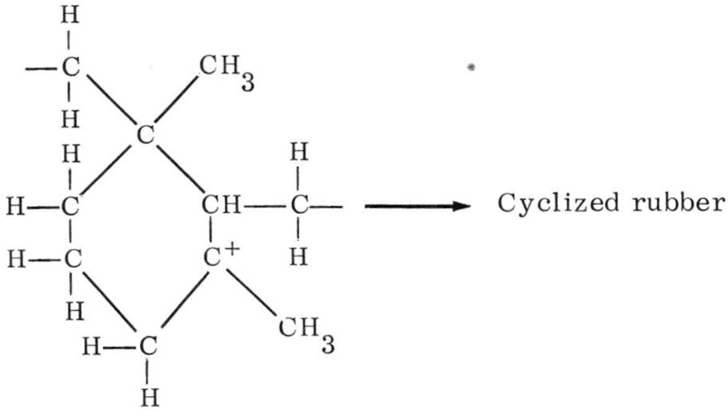

$$\text{(cyclic carbonium ion: } \mathrm{-CH_2-C(CH_3)<} \text{ ring of } \mathrm{CH_2, CH_2, CH_2, C^+(CH_3), CH-CH_2-} \text{)} \longrightarrow \text{Cyclized rubber} \tag{14.5}$$

Carbonium ion

Hydrogen peroxide or peracetic acid adds to polyenes such as hevea rubber or unsaturated vegetable oils to produce epoxidized polybutadiene (Oxiron) or epoxidized vegetable oils, respectively. These products react readily with water, alcohols, anhydrides, and amines.

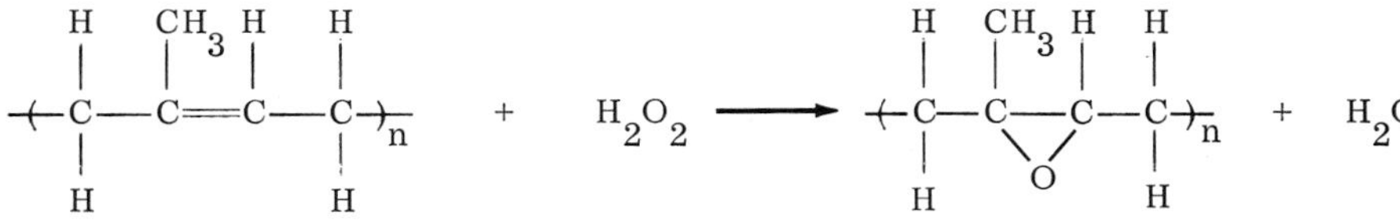

$$\mathrm{\left(CH_2-C(CH_3){=}CH-CH_2\right)_n + H_2O_2 \longrightarrow \left(CH_2-\overset{\diagdown O \diagup}{C(CH_3)-CH}-CH_2\right)_n + H_2O} \tag{14.6}$$

Hevea rubber — Hydrogen peroxide — Epoxidized polyene — Water

The reaction of ozone with polyenes yields ozonides which cleave to produce aldehydes in the presence of water and zinc dust. Since the ozonides are explosive, they are not usually isolated. As shown by the following equation, ozonolysis is used as a diagnostic procedure to locate the position of the double bonds in polyenes.

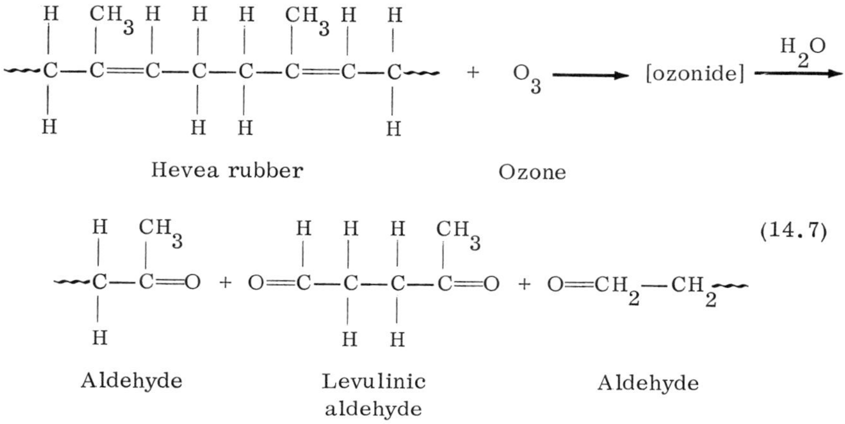

$$\sim\!\!\overset{\displaystyle H}{\underset{\displaystyle H}{\overset{|}{\underset{|}{C}}}}-\overset{\displaystyle CH_3}{\overset{|}{C}}=\overset{\displaystyle H}{\overset{|}{C}}-\overset{\displaystyle H}{\underset{\displaystyle H}{\overset{|}{\underset{|}{C}}}}-\overset{\displaystyle H}{\underset{\displaystyle H}{\overset{|}{\underset{|}{C}}}}-\overset{\displaystyle CH_3}{\overset{|}{C}}=\overset{\displaystyle H}{\overset{|}{C}}-\overset{\displaystyle H}{\underset{\displaystyle H}{\overset{|}{\underset{|}{C}}}}\!\!\sim \; + \; O_3 \longrightarrow [\text{ozonide}] \xrightarrow{H_2O}$$

Hevea rubber Ozone

$$\sim\!\!\overset{\displaystyle H}{\underset{\displaystyle H}{\overset{|}{\underset{|}{C}}}}-\overset{\displaystyle CH_3}{\overset{|}{C}}=O \; + \; O=\overset{\displaystyle H}{\overset{|}{C}}-\overset{\displaystyle H}{\underset{\displaystyle H}{\overset{|}{\underset{|}{C}}}}-\overset{\displaystyle H}{\underset{\displaystyle H}{\overset{|}{\underset{|}{C}}}}-\overset{\displaystyle CH_3}{\overset{|}{C}}=O \; + \; O=CH_2-CH_2\!\!\sim \qquad (14.7)$$

Aldehyde Levulinic aldehyde Aldehyde

14.3 REACTIONS OF ALIPHATIC PENDANT GROUPS

Esters such as polyvinyl acetate (PVAc) may be hydrolyzed to produce alcohols such as polyvinyl alcohol (PVA), which have the same $\overline{DP}$ as the ester. Thus, while the enol tautomer of acetaldehyde (vinyl alcohol) cannot be isolated, its water-soluble polymer can be obtained by the hydrolysis of any polyvinyl carboxylic acid ester. The solubility of the product in water is dependent on the extent of hydrolysis.

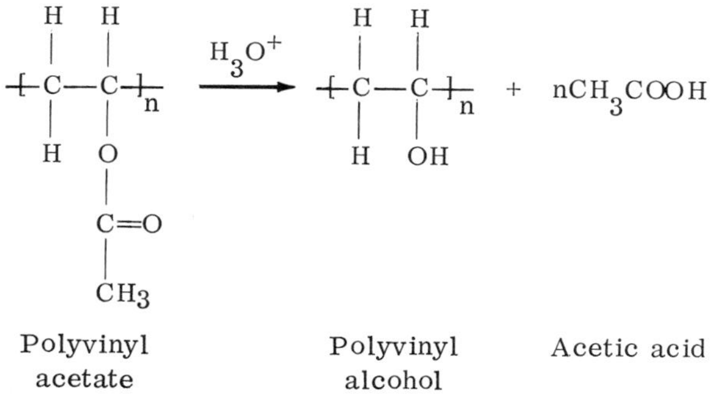

$$\left[\overset{\displaystyle H}{\underset{\displaystyle H}{\overset{|}{\underset{|}{C}}}}-\overset{\displaystyle H}{\underset{\displaystyle O-\overset{\displaystyle}{C}(=O)-CH_3}{\overset{|}{\underset{|}{C}}}}\right]_n \xrightarrow{H_3O^+} \left[\overset{\displaystyle H}{\underset{\displaystyle H}{\overset{|}{\underset{|}{C}}}}-\overset{\displaystyle H}{\underset{\displaystyle OH}{\overset{|}{\underset{|}{C}}}}\right]_n + nCH_3COOH \qquad (14.8)$$

Polyvinyl acetate Polyvinyl alcohol Acetic acid

The hydroxyl pendant groups in cellulose will form alkoxides with sodium hydroxide, and these alkoxides will produce ethers by the classic

Williamson reaction. Thus, Suida produced methylcellulose in 1905 by the reaction of soda cellulose and methyl sulfate.

Alkylcellulose may also be produced by the reaction of soda cellulose and alkyl chlorides. Since these alkoxy pendant groups reduce the hydrogen-bonding forces, the partially reacted products are water soluble. This solubility in water will decrease as the degree of substitution (DS) increases.

$$\underset{\text{Cellulose}}{\text{Cellulose—OH}} + \underset{\text{Sodium hydroxide}}{\text{NaOH}} + \underset{\text{Alkyl chloride}}{\text{RCl}} \longrightarrow \underset{\text{Cellulose ether}}{\text{Cellulose—OR}} + \underset{\text{Sodium chloride}}{\text{NaCl}} + \underset{\text{Water}}{H_2O} \quad (14.9)$$

Methylcellulose is widely used as a viscosity improver and thickener. Ethylcellulose is used as a melt coating. One of the most widely used cellulosic ethers is carboxymethylcellulose (CMC). This water-soluble cellulosic derivative is produced by the reaction of soda cellulose and chloroacetic acid.

CMC, with a DS of 0.5 to 0.8, is used in detergents and as a textile sizing agent. Products with higher DS are used as thickeners and in drilling mud formulations. Aluminum or chromium ions will produce insoluble gels.

$$\underset{\text{Cellulose}}{\text{Cellulose—OH}} + \underset{\text{Sodium hydroxide}}{\text{NaOH}} + \underset{\text{Sodium salt of chloroacetic acid}}{ClCH_2COONa} \longrightarrow \underset{\text{CMC}}{\text{Cellulose—}OCH_2COONa} + \underset{\text{Sodium chloride}}{\text{NaCl}} + \underset{\text{Water}}{H_2O} \quad (14.10)$$

Water-soluble sodium cellulose xanthate, with a DS of about 0.5, is produced by the room temperature reaction of carbon disulfide and soda cellulose. Since xanthic acids are unstable, the cellulose is readily regenerated by passing extrudates into an acid bath. Rayon and cellophane are produced from cellulose xanthate in the viscose process.

$$\text{Cellulose—OH} + \text{NaOH} + \text{CS}_2 \longrightarrow$$

Cellulose Sodium hydroxide Carbon disulfide

$$\text{Cellulose—O—}\overset{\overset{\displaystyle S}{\|}}{C}\text{—SNa} \xrightarrow{H_3O^+} \text{Cellulose—OH} \qquad (14.11)$$

Cellulose xanthate Regenerated cellulose

Hydroxyethylcellulose and hydroxypropylcellulose are obtained from the reaction of soda cellulose and ethylene oxide or propylene oxide, respectively. The former (Cellosize) is used as a water-soluble sizing agent and descaling agent in boiler water.

$$\text{Cellulose—OH} + \underset{\diagdown_{O}\diagup}{H_2C\text{——}CH_2} \longrightarrow \text{Cellulose—O—}\underset{H}{\overset{H}{\overset{|}{\underset{|}{C}}}}\text{—}\underset{H}{\overset{H}{\overset{|}{\underset{|}{C}}}}OH$$

Cellulose Ethylene oxide Hydroxyethylcellulose

(14.12)

Cyanoethylcellulose is produced by the reaction of soda cellulose and acrylonitrile. This derivative is more resistant to abrasion and biological attack than is cellulose. Cyanoethylcellulose and graft copolymers of acrylonitrile and cellulose may be hydrolyzed to yield products with excellent water absorbency characteristics.

$$\text{Cellulose—OH} + H_2C\text{=}\overset{\overset{\displaystyle H}{|}}{C}\text{—CN} \longrightarrow \text{Cellulose—O—}\underset{H}{\overset{H}{\overset{|}{\underset{|}{C}}}}\text{—}\underset{H}{\overset{H}{\overset{|}{\underset{|}{C}}}}\text{—CN}$$

Cellulose Acrylonitrile Cyanoethylcellulose

(14.13)

Cellulose nitrate (CN) (incorrectly called nitrocellulose) was one of the first synthetic plastics. The degree of substitution of CN is dependent on the concentration of the nitric acid used. The commercial product has a DS of about 2.0, corresponding to a nitrogen content of about 11%. Despite its flammability, CN plasticized by camphor is still used for personal accessories, toiletries, and industrial items. However, the principal use of CN is for coatings, in which the CN has a $\overline{DP}$ of 200 and a DS of about 2.0.

$$\underset{\text{Cellulose}}{\text{Cellulose—OH}} + \underset{\text{Nitric acid}}{HONO_2} \xrightarrow{H_2SO_4} \underset{\text{Cellulose nitrate}}{\text{Cellulose—}(ONO_2)} + \underset{\text{Water}}{H_2O} \tag{14.14}$$

Cellulose triacetate (DS 2.8) was originally prepared by Schutzenberger and Naudine in 1865 by the reaction of cellulose with acetic acid and acetic anhydride in the presence of sulfuric acid. This ester, which has an acetyl content of 43%, is soluble in chloroform or in mixtures of methylene chloride and ethanol. When plasticized by ethyl phthaloyl ethyl glycolate, it is used as a film and molding, and as an extrusion. The unplasticized cellulose triacetate is used as a specialty fiber.

$$\underset{\text{Cellulose}}{\text{Cellulose—}(OH)_3} + \underset{\text{Acetylation agents}}{\begin{matrix} H_3CCOOH \\ + \\ (H_3CCO)_2O \end{matrix}} \xrightarrow{H_2SO_4} \underset{\text{Cellulose triacetate}}{\text{Cellulose}\text{—}(OOCCH_3)_3} \tag{14.15}$$

Cellulose diacetate may be produced directly by the acylation of cellulose in a solution of dimethyl sulfoxide (DMSO) and formaldehyde, but this ester cannot be made directly from the acetylation of cellulose. The commercial product, which is also called secondary cellulose acetate ester, is produced by the partial saponification of cellulose triacetate.

Cellulose diacetate is widely used as extruded tape, in molded toys, electrical appliance housings, and sheet and blister packaging and fiber. Cellulose diacetate fiber, which is extruded from an acetone solution called "dope," is called acetate rayon.

$$\underset{\text{Cellulose triacetate}}{\text{Cellulose}\text{—}(OOCCH_3)_3} \xrightarrow{NaOH} \underset{\text{Cellulose diacetate}}{\text{Cellulose}\text{—}(OOCCH_3)_2} + \underset{\text{Sodium acetate}}{CH_3COONa} \tag{14.16}$$

Cellulose propionate and cellulose acetate butyrate are also available commercially. These esters, which are more readily processed and more resistant to moisture than CA, are used as sheets, tool handles, steering wheels, and for packaging.

Polyvinyl formal (PVF) and polyvinyl butyral (PVB) are produced by the reaction of polyvinyl alcohol with formaldehyde or butyraldehyde, respectively. PVF has been used as a wire coating, and PVB forms the inner layer of safety-glass windshields. These products contain residual acetate and hydroxyl pendant groups.

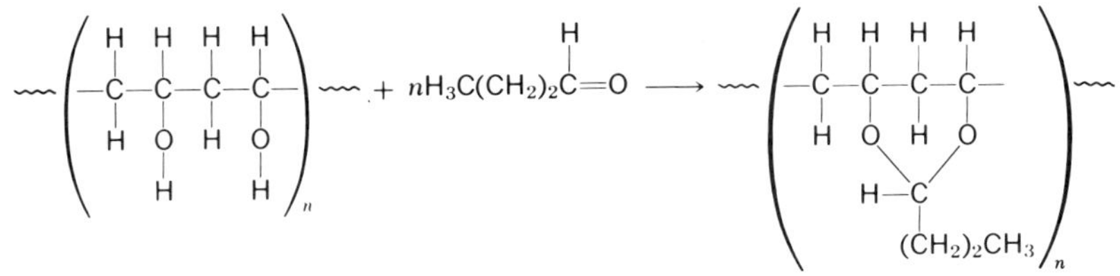

$$\sim\left(\begin{array}{cccc} H & H & H & H \\ | & | & | & | \\ -C- & C- & C- & C- \\ | & | & | & | \\ H & O & H & O \\ & | & & | \\ & H & & H \end{array}\right)_n\sim + nH_3C(CH_2)_2\overset{\overset{\displaystyle H}{|}}{C}{=}O \longrightarrow \sim\left(\begin{array}{cccc} H & H & H & H \\ | & | & | & | \\ -C- & C- & C- & C- \\ | & | & | & | \\ H & O & H & O \\ & \diagdown & & \diagup \\ & & H{-}C & \\ & & | & \\ & & (CH_2)_2CH_3 & \end{array}\right)_n\sim$$

Polyvinyl alcohol Butyraldehyde Polyvinyl butyral

(14.17)

Esters of polycarboxylic acids, nitriles, or amides may be hydrolyzed to produce polycarboxylic acids. Thus polyacrylonitrile, polyacrylamide, or polymethyl acrylate may be hydrolyzed to produce polyacrylic acid.

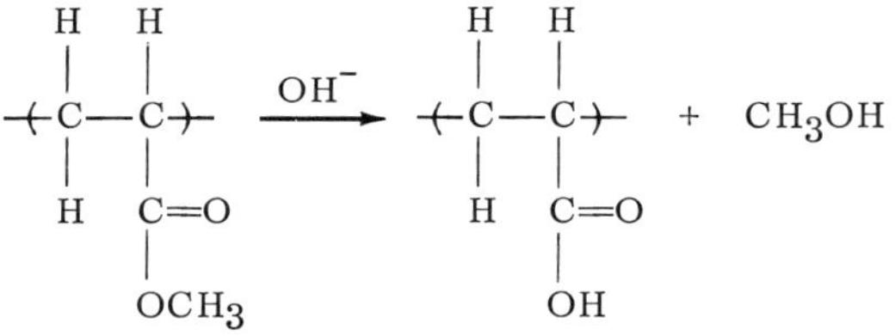

$$\begin{array}{cc} H & H \\ | & | \\ -\!\!(C & -C)\!\!- \\ | & | \\ H & C{=}O \\ & | \\ & OCH_3 \end{array} \xrightarrow{OH^-} \begin{array}{cc} H & H \\ | & | \\ -\!\!(C & -C)\!\!- \\ | & | \\ H & C{=}O \\ & | \\ & OH \end{array} + CH_3OH \qquad (14.18)$$

Polymethyl acrylate Polyacrylic acid Methanol

Polyacrylic acid and partially hydrolyzed polyacrylamide are used for the prevention of scale in water used for boilers and for flocculating agents in water purification. In the presence of aluminum ions, these polymeric acids produce flocs which remove impurities in water as they settle.

When heated, polymethacrylic acid loses water and forms a polymeric anhydride. The latter, as well as copolymers of maleic anhydride, such as styrene-maleic anhydride copolymers (SMA), undergo characteristic anhydride reactions with water, alcohols, and amines to produce acids, esters, and amides.

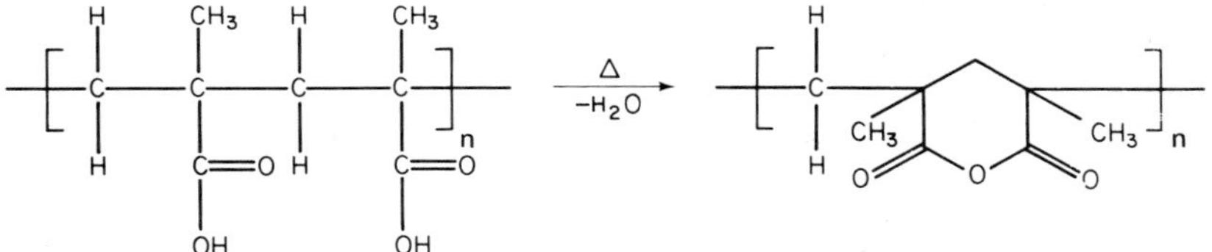

Polymethacrylic acid $\xrightarrow[-H_2O]{\Delta}$ Polymethacrylic anhydride

(14.19)

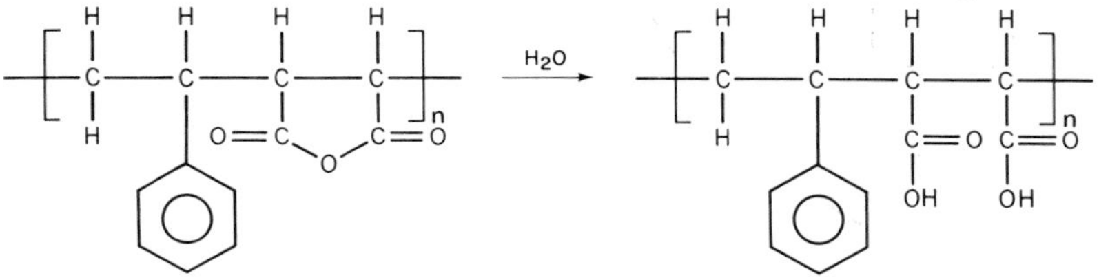

Styrene-maleic anhydride copolymers $\xrightarrow{H_2O}$ Styrene-maleic acid copolymers

(14.20)

When heated, polyacrylonitrile loses hydrogen cyanide and forms a ladder polymer with a qunizarine structure.

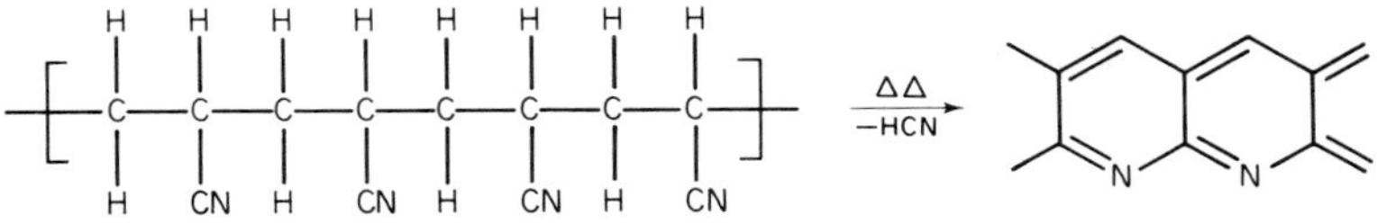

Polyacrylonitrile $\xrightarrow[-HCN]{\Delta\Delta}$ Ladder polymer

(14.21)

Polyvinyl amine is produced by the Hofmann degradation of polyacrylamide. Vinylamine, like vinyl alcohol, is unstable. Thus its polymer is prepared by an indirect reaction. Polyvinyl amine is soluble is aqueous acids.

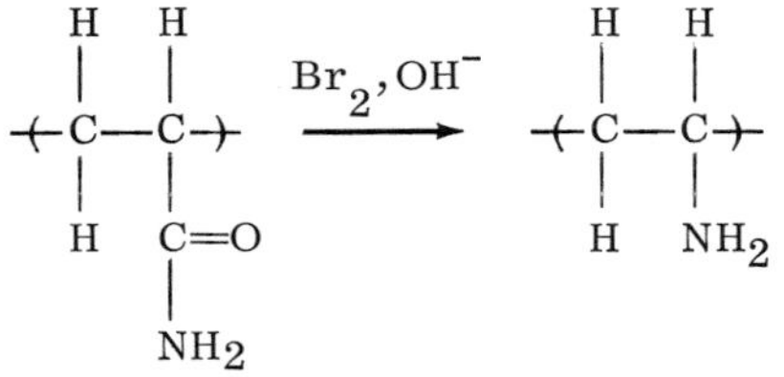

$$\text{Polyacrylamide} \xrightarrow{Br_2, OH^-} \text{Polyvinyl amine} \qquad (14.22)$$

14.4 REACTIONS OF AROMATIC PENDANT GROUPS

Polymers with aromatic pendant groups, such as polystyrene, undergo all the characteristic reactions of benzene, such as alkylation, halogenation, nitration, and sulfonation. Thus, oil-soluble polymers used as viscosity improvers in lubricating oils are obtained by the Friedel-Crafts reaction of polystyrene and unsaturated hydrocarbons such as cyclohexene. Polyvinyl cyclohexylbenzene is produced in the latter reaction.

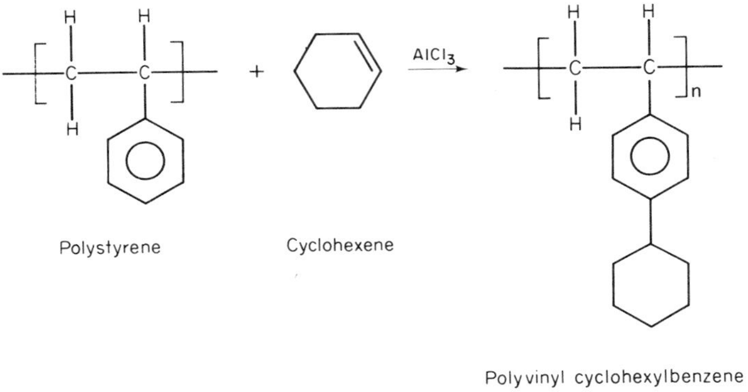

$AlCl_3$ (14.23)

Polystyrene Cyclohexene

Polyvinyl cyclohexylbenzene

In the presence of a Lewis acid, halogens such as chlorine react with polystyrene to produce chlorinated polystyrene. The latter has a higher softening point than polystyrene.

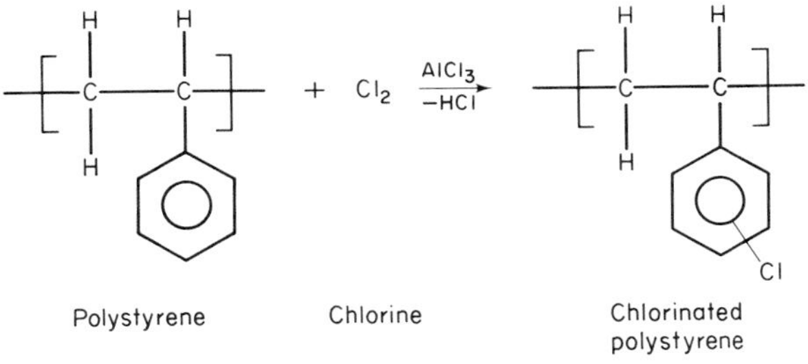

$+ Cl_2 \xrightarrow[-HCl]{AlCl_3}$ (14.24)

Polystyrene Chlorine Chlorinated polystyrene

Perfluoropolystyrene is produced by the reaction of fluorine and polystyrene. This reaction may also be run on the surface (topochemical) of polystyrene articles.

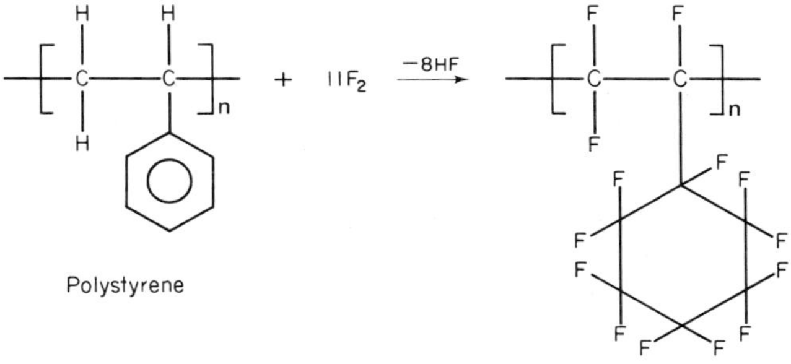

Polystyrene + $11F_2$ $\xrightarrow{-8HF}$ (14.25)

Polynitrostyrene is obtained by the nitration of polystyrene. The latter may be reduced to form polyaminostyrene. Polyaminostyrene may be diazotized to produce polymeric dyes.

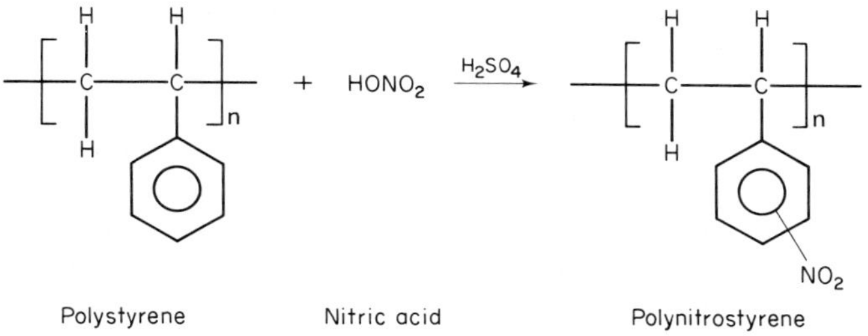

Polystyrene + $HONO_2$ (Nitric acid) $\xrightarrow{H_2SO_4}$ Polynitrostyrene (14.26)

Polystyrene and other aromatic polymers have been sulfonated by fuming sulfuric acid. Sulfonated cross-linked polystyrene has been used as an ion-exchange resin.

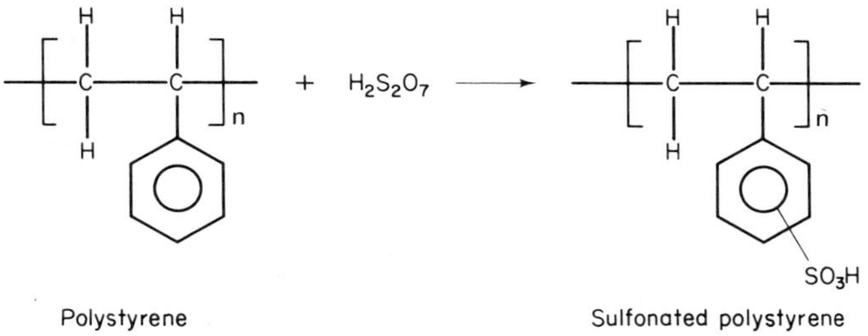

Polystyrene + $H_2S_2O_7$ $\longrightarrow$ Sulfonated polystyrene (14.27)

14.5 REACTIONS OF POLYAMIDES

Polyamides such as proteins or nylons may be reacted with ethylene oxide or formaldehyde. The latter serves as a cross-linking agent with proteins in embalming, leather production, and the stabilization of regenerated protein fibers.

14.6 POLYMERIZATION REACTIONS

The cross-linking of many thermosetting resins, such as novolac phenolic resins, takes place during the molding operation. Polymerization also occurs during the production of polyurethane (PU) foams and molded products. The latter are produced when liquid reactants are introduced in the injection molding press. One process is called liquid injection molding (LIM) and the other is called reaction injection molding (RIM). The latter has been used to mold automotive fascias, bumpers, and flexible fenders for automobiles.

14.7 DEGRADATION OF POLYMERS

In many chemical reactions with pendant groups, such as the hydrolysis of ester groups, the polymer is said to be degraded, but since the degree of polymerization is unchanged, the integrity of the polymer chain is maintained. However, the $\overline{DP}$ is decreased when chain-scission degradation occurs, and this type of degradation will be emphasized in this section.

Saturated linear polymers such as HDPE are resistant to degradation, but slow degradation will occur in the presence of oxygen, ultraviolet light, heat, and impurities. Since tertiary carbon atoms are more readily attacked, polypropylene is less resistant to degradation than HDPE. Unsaturated polymers are even less resistant to degradation as evidenced by the ozonolysis of hevea rubber and the degradation of dehydrohalogenated PVC.

The kinetics of random chain scission are essentially the reverse of those in stepwise propagation. Much information on this type of degradation has been obtained from studies of the acid-catalyzed homogeneous degradation of cellulose in which $\overline{DP}^{-1}$ increases with time. The initial degradation of polymeric hydrocarbons is usually the result of homolytic cleavage at weak points in the polymer chain. As shown in (14.28), the initial products are macroradicals.

$$\sim\!\!\underset{\underset{\displaystyle H}{|}}{\overset{\overset{\displaystyle H}{|}}{C}}-\underset{\underset{\displaystyle H}{|}}{\overset{\overset{\displaystyle H}{|}}{C}}\!\!\sim \xrightarrow{E} \sim\!\!\underset{\underset{\displaystyle H}{|}}{\overset{\overset{\displaystyle H}{|}}{C}}\cdot + \cdot\underset{\underset{\displaystyle H}{|}}{\overset{\overset{\displaystyle H}{|}}{C}}\!\!\sim \qquad (14.28)$$

Polymer Macroradicals

As shown in (14.29), hydroperoxides are formed in the presence of oxygen. These readily cleaved hydroperoxides also yield macroradicals.

$$\sim\!\underset{\textstyle H}{\overset{\textstyle H}{C}}\!-\!\underset{\textstyle CH_3}{\overset{\textstyle H}{C}}\!\sim + O_2 \longrightarrow \sim\!\underset{\textstyle H}{\overset{\textstyle H}{C}}\!-\!\underset{\textstyle CH_3}{\overset{\textstyle OOH}{C}}\!\sim \longrightarrow$$

Polymer Oxygen Hydroperoxide

$$\sim\!\underset{\textstyle H}{\overset{\textstyle H}{C}}\cdot + \cdot OH + \underset{\textstyle CH_3}{\overset{\textstyle O}{\overset{\|}{C}}}\!\sim \qquad (14.29)$$

Macro-radical Hydroxyl radical Ketone

Oxidizing acids such as concentrated nitric acid will also cause scission at weak links. This hypothesis is verified by the attack by nitric acid on the folds of polyethylene crystals to produce α,ω-dicarboxylic acids. Acids and alkalies will also hydrolyze ester and amide linkages in the polymer chain.

While most polymers undergo random chain scission, 1,1-disubstituted polymers, such as poly(methyl methacrylate) (PMMA), depolymerize or unzip quantitatively when heated above the ceiling temperature (T_c). In contrast, monosubstituted polymers such as polystyrene degrade by both depolymerization and random chain-scission reactions. Since higher temperatures favor the former, more than 85% styrene monomer is produced at 725°C.

Some degradation occurs when polymers are irradiated, but cross linking is the predominant reaction. Thus, thermoplastic coatings may be applied and cross-linked by radiation after application.

Today, major items related to the topic of polymer degradation involve degradation of polymers for potential reuse of the degradation products and degradation of polymers as a "garbage" material.

Polystyrene gives different thermal degradation products dependent on the exact degradation conditions. Under one set of conditions the major products are benzene, hydrogen, and ethylene, all three of which are usable chemical molecules.

$$\left[-CH_2-\underset{\textstyle C_6H_5}{CH}-\right]_n \xrightarrow{\Delta} H_2C=CH_2 + C_6H_6 + H_2 \qquad (14.30)$$

Polystyrene

A major problem in the burning of polymers containing halogens, such as polyvinyl chloride, is the emission of the hydrogen halide (e.g., hydrogen chloride) which is both quite dangerous to human and plant life and is the major problem in the deterioration of commercial incinerators. This problem will remain with us for some time since no reasonable solution has been thus far found.

$$\underset{\text{Polyvinyl chloride}}{\left(CH_2 - \underset{\underset{Cl}{|}}{CH} \right)_n} \xrightarrow{\Delta} \text{HCl plus other products} \tag{14.31}$$

14.8 RECENT TRENDS

Recent research trends related to the modification of polymers include modification of regenerable materials, direct chemical modification of commercially available polymers and use of polymers as catalysts. The first recognizes the need for use of regenerable materials in place of polymers based on essentially nonrenewable sources such as coal and other petroleum products (gas, oil, and others). Used regenerable materials include the celluloses, such as cotton, chiten, dextran, and sugars, with celluloses making up about one-third of all vegetable matter, and protein sources such as wool.

Chemical modifications of commercially available polymers often involve simply the recognition that functional groups contained within a polymer exhibit essentially the same types of chemical behaviors as if the functional group were contained within a smaller molecule. For instance, the esterification of polyvinyl alcohol with acid chlorides occurs in a fashion analogous to the esterification of typical smaller alcohols such as ethanol and ethylene glycol.

$$\underset{\text{Polyvinyl alcohol}}{\left(CH_2 - \underset{\underset{OH}{|}}{CH} \right)_n} + R - \overset{\overset{O}{\|}}{C} - Cl \longrightarrow \underset{\text{Ester}}{\left(CH_2 - \underset{\underset{\underset{\underset{\underset{R}{|}}{C=O}}{|}}{O}}{|}}{CH} \right)_n} \tag{14.32}$$

$$CH_3CH_2OH + R{-}\overset{\overset{\displaystyle O}{\|}}{C}{-}Cl \longrightarrow R{-}\overset{\overset{\displaystyle O}{\|}}{C}{-}O{-}CH_3$$

Ethanol Ester

$$HO{-}CH_2{-}CH_2{-}OH + Cl{-}\overset{\overset{\displaystyle O}{\|}}{C}{-}R{-}\overset{\overset{\displaystyle O}{\|}}{C}{-}Cl \longrightarrow \qquad (14.32\text{ cont.})$$

Ethylene glycol

$$\left(O{-}CH_2{-}CH_2{-}O{-}\overset{\overset{\displaystyle O}{\|}}{C}{-}R{-}\overset{\overset{\displaystyle O}{\|}}{C}\right)_n$$

Polyester

The use of polymers as catalysts may involve the chemical modification of the polymer with adjacent or neighboring side groups assisting in the catalysis event or may involve no real modification at all, such as in the case of anchored metal catalysts where the polymer mainly acts as a site for reaction without undergoing permanent chemical modification.

SUMMARY

1. In addition to the reactions occurring during synthesis, telomerization, and cross linking, polymers, like small molecules, may also react with selected reactants, providing the reaction sites are accessible.
2. Saturated polymeric hydrocarbons such as HDPE may be chlorinated, sulfochlorinated, or oxidized.
3. Polyenes such as hevea rubber may be hydrogenated, halogenated, hydrohalogenated, cyclized, epoxidized, and ozonized. While many of these plastics are used commercially, ozonide formation is also used to determine the position of double bonds in the polyene.
4. Pendant groups such as the ester groups in polyvinyl acetate may be hydrolyzed to yield polyvinyl alcohol. The latter and other polymeric alcohols, such as cellulose, undergo typical reactions of alcohols, such as the formation of ethers, xanthates, inorganic and organic esters, and acetals.
5. Esters, amides, or nitriles of polycarboxylic acids may be hydrolyzed to produce polycarboxylic acids. When heated, the latter form polymeric anhydrides which undergo typical reactions of anhydrides, such as hydrolysis, alcoholysis, and amidation. When heated, polyacrylonitrile

forms a dark ladder polymer. Polyamines are produced by the Hofmann degradation of polyamides.

6. Phenyl pendant groups such as those present in polystyrene undergo all the characteristic reactions of benzene, such as alkylation, halogenation, nitration, and sulfonation.

7. Degradation, in which the degree of polymerization is reduced, may occur by random chain scission, by depolymerization, or both. In the former reaction, which may occur in the presence of oxygen, ultraviolet light, heat, and impurities, tertiary carbon atoms are preferentially attacked. The latter is the preferred reaction for 1,1-disubstituted polymers such as PMMA.

GLOSSARY

acetate rayon: Cellulose diacetate.

anchimeric reactions: Those enhanced by the presence of neighboring groups.

cellophane: Regenerated cellulose sheet.

Cellosize: Tradename for hydroxyethylcellulose.

cellulose diacetate: Cellulose acetate with a DS of about 2.0.

cellulose triacetate: Cellulose acetate with a DS of about 3.0.

chain scission: Breaking of a polymer chain.

CMC: Carboxymethylcellulose.

CN: Cellulose nitrate.

curing: Cross linking to produce a network polymer.

cyclized rubber: Isomerized rubber containing cyclohexane rings.

deuterated polyethylene: One in which ^{1}H is replaced by ^{2}H.

1,1-disubstituted polymers:

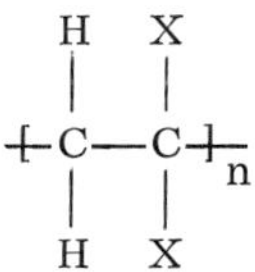

DMF: Dimethylformamide.

DMSO: Dimethylsulfoxide.

dope: Jargon for a solution of cellulose diacetate in acetone.

$\overline{\text{DP}}$: Average degree of polymerization.

DS: Degree of substitution.

fascias: Panels in the front and rear of an automobile.

halogenation: The reaction of a halogen such as chlorine with a molecule.

homolylic cleavage: Breaking of a covalent bond to produce two radicals.

hydrogenation: The addition of hydrogen to an unsaturated molecule.

Hydropol: Tradename for hydrogenated polybutadiene.

Hypalon: Tradename for sulfochlorinated polyethylene.

isomerization: Term often applied to cyclization reactions of polymers.

Kraton: Tradename for ABA block copolymer of styrene (A) and butadiene (B).

ladder polymer: One having a double-stranded backbone.

LIM: Liquid injection molding.

nitrocellulose: Incorrect name used for cellulose nitrate.

NR: *Hevea braziliensis*.

Oxiron: Tradename for epoxidized polybutadiene.

ozonolysis: The reaction of an unsaturated organic compound with ozone followed by cleavage with zinc and water.

Parlon: Tradename for chlorinated rubber.

perfluoropolystyrene: Polystyrene in which all hydrogen atoms have been replaced by fluorine.

Pliofilm: Tradename for rubber hydrochloride.

PMMA: Polymethyl methacrylate.

polyacrylamide:

$$\left[\begin{array}{cc} H & H \\ | & | \\ C - & C \\ | & | \\ H & C{=}O \\ & | \\ & NH_2 \end{array} \right]_n$$

polyacrylic acid:

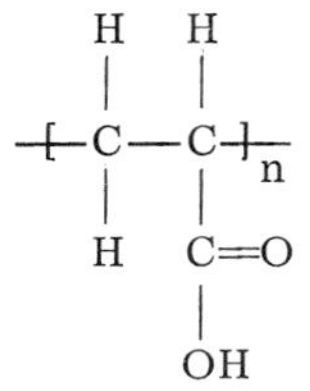

```
     H   H
     |   |
  -[-C---C-]-n
     |   |
     H   C=O
         |
         OH
```

polyvinyl acetate:

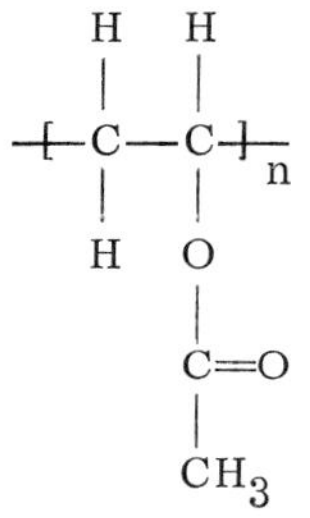

```
     H   H
     |   |
  -[-C---C-]-n
     |   |
     H   O
         |
         C=O
         |
         CH3
```

polyvinyl alcohol:

```
     H   H
     |   |
  -[-C---C-]-n
     |   |
     H   OH
```

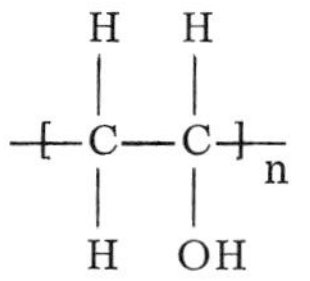

PU: Polyurethane.

PVA: Polyvinyl alcohol.

PVAc: Polyvinyl acetate.

PVB: Polyvinyl butyral.

PVDC: Polyvinyl dichloride (chlorinated PVC).

PVF: Polyvinyl formal.

rayon: Regenerated cellulose filaments.

RIM: Reaction injection molding.

SMA: Copolymer of styrene and maleic anhydride.

soda cellulose: The reaction product of cellulose and sodium hydroxide.

telomerization: Abstraction of an atom by a macroradical.

topochemical reactions: Reactions on the surface of a polymer.

Tornesit: Tradename for chlorinated rubber.

Tyrin: Tradename for chlorinated polyethylene.

viscose process: The production of regenerated cellulose from cellulose xanthate.

Williamson reaction: The reaction of an alkoxide and an alkyl chloride.

xanthate:

$$\mathrm{RO{-}\underset{\underset{S}{\|}}{C}{-}S^{-},\ Na^{+}.}$$

EXERCISES

1. What is the general mechanism for the curing of step-reaction polymers?
2. What is the general mechanism for the curing of unsaturated polymers?
3. Write the formula for perdeuterated polyethylene.
4. Explain why good yields of α,ω-dicarboxylic acids can be obtained by the reaction of concentrated nitric acid on crystalline HDPE.
5. Write the formula for diphenylguanidine.
6. How would you cross link a polyethylene coating after it is applied to a wire?
7. How would you prepare a block copolymer of styrene and an alternating copolymer of ethylene and propylene?
8. What is the difference between completely hydrogenated Hevea braziliensis and completely hydrogenated gutta percha?
9. Explain why the use of rubber hydrochloride film is limited.
10. Which would be more resistant to ozone: (a) H. braziliensis or (b) cyclized rubber?
11. Name a use for epoxidized vegetable oil.
12. What product would be produced by the ozonolysis of polybutadiene?
13. Write the structural formula for the polymeric hydrolytic products from (a) polyvinyl acetate and (b) polymethyl methacrylate.

14. Why is commercial methylcellulose more soluble in water than cellulose?
15. Why is CMC used in detergent formulations?
16. Propose a mechanism for the use of hydroxyethylcellulose or polyacrylic acid as a descaling agent.
17. What is the DS of cellulose nitrate when it is used as an explosive?
18. Why is the DS of cellulose triacetate only 2.8?
19. Which is more polar: (a) cellulose triacetate, or (b) cellulose diacetate?
20. Why is it not possible to prepare pure polyvinyl butyral?
21. Why is polyacrylic acid an effective flocculating agent?
22. Propose a use for pyrolyzed filaments of polyacrylonitrile.
23. What monomer would be obtained by the decomposition of PVA?
24. Which would be more resistant to nitric acid: (a) polystyrene or (b) perfluoropolystyrene?
25. What ions would be removed from water by sulfonated polystyrene: (a) cations or (b) anions?
26. What reaction occurs when tannic acid is added to proteins such as those present in cowhide?
27. What chain-reaction polymerization reactions take place in the molding operation?
28. Propose a procedure for recovering monomeric methyl methacrylate from scrap PMMA?
29. Which will produce the larger yield of monomer when heated at moderate temperatures: (a) polystyrene or (b) poly-α-methylstyrene?

BIBLIOGRAPHY

Bachman, G. B., Hellman, H., et al. (1947): Chlorinated polystyrene, J. Org. Chem., 12:108.

Bamford, C. H., and Tipper, C. F. H. (1975): Degradation of Polymers, Elsevier Scientific, Amsterdam.

Berthelot, P. E. M. (1869): Hydrogenation of rubber, Bull. Soc. Chem. France, 11:33.

Blazka, S. J., and Harwood, H. J. (1973): Reactions of polyaminostyrenes, Polymer Preprints, 16(1):633.

Bovey, F. A. (1958): The Effects of Ionizing Radiation on Natural and Synthetic High Polymers, Wiley Interscience, New York.

Carraher, C. E., and Tsuda, M. (Eds.) (1980): Modification of Polymers, ACS Symposium Series, New York.

Chapiro, A. (1962): Radiation Chemistry of Polymeric Systems, Wiley Interscience, New York.

Charlesby, A. (1960): Atomic Radiation and Polymers, Pergamon, New York.

Crowley, J. D. (1975): Cellulose esters. Chap. 56 in Applied Polymer Science (J. K. Craven and R. W. Tess, eds.), Organic Coatings and Plastics Chemistry, Div. of ACS, Washington, D.C.

Dannis, M. L., and Ramp, F. L. (1961): Poly(vinyl dichloride), U.S. Patent 2,996,486.

Dickstein, J., and Bouchard, R. (1964): Poly(vinyl alcohol). In Manufacture of Plastics, Vol. I (W. M. Smith, ed.), Chap. 5, Reinhold, New York.

Dole, M. (1973): The Radiation Chemistry of Macromolecules, Academic, New York.

Engelhard, G. A., and Day, H. H. (1859): Chlorinated Rubber, British Patent 2734.

Fettes, E. M. (ed.): (1964): Chemical Reactions of Polymers, Wiley Interscience, New York.

Geuskens, G. (1975): Degradation and Stabilization of Polymers, Halsted, New York.

Grassie, N. (1956): Chemistry of High Polymer Degradation Processes, Interscience, New York.

Grassie, N., and McNeill, I. C. (1958): Cyclization of polyacrylonitrile, J. Polymer Sci., 27:207.

Grot, W. G. F. (1972): Nafions, sulfonated fluorocarbons, Chem. Ing. Tech., 44:167.

Jamieson, D. R. (1976): Deuterated polyethylene, Coatings and Plastics Preprints, 36(2):793.

Keeley, F. W. (1959): Hypalon. In Introduction to Rubber Technology (M. Morton, ed.), Chap. 14, Reinhold, New York.

Kennedy, J. P., and Ichikawa, M. (1973): Phenylation of PVC, Polymer Preprints, 14(2):677.

Langton, H. M. (1951): Ester gums. In Synthetic Resins and Allied Plastics (R. S. Morrell, ed.), Chap. 8, Oxford University Press, London.

Leis, D. G. (1976): Reaction injection molding (RIM), Mod. Plast., 55(10A):346.

Lenz, R. W. (1967): Organic Chemistry of Synthetic High Polymers, Wiley Interscience, New York.

Litt, M., and Masuda, T. (1975): Sulfonated polystyrene, Polymer Preprints, 16(2):58.

Lundberg, W. O. (1961): Antioxidations and Antioxidants, Vol. I, Interscience, New York.

Madorsky, S. L. (1964): Thermal Degradation of Organic Polymers, Wiley Interscience, New York.

Martins, J. G., and Price, A. F. (1964): Poly(vinyl acetal). In Manufacture of Plastics, Vol. I (W. M. Smith, ed.), Chap. 6, Reinhold, New York.

McCaffery, E. M. (1970): Laboratory preparation for macromolecular chemistry. Experiment II in Cellulose Esters, McGraw-Hill, New York.

Miles, R. D. (1955): Cellulose Nitrate, Oliver & Boyd, London.

Moore, J. A. (1974): Reactions of Polymers, D. Reidal Publishing, Boston.

Neiman, M. B. (1965): Aging and Stabilization of Polymers, Consultants Bureau, New York.

Noshay, A., and Robeson, L. M. (1975): Sulfonated polystyrene, Polymer Preprints, 16(2):81.

Odian, G. (1970): Principles of Polymerization, McGraw-Hill, New York.

Pinner, S. H. (ed.) (1967): Weathering and Degradation of Plastics, Gordon and Breach, New York.

Platzer, N. (symposium chairman) (1967): Irradiation of polymers. In Advances in Chemistry Series (R. F. Gould, ed.), Vol. 66, American Chemical Society, Washington, D.C.

Powers, P. O. (1943): Synthetic Resins and Rubber, Part 5, John Wiley, New York.

Pummerer, R., and Burkhard, P. A. (1922): Hydrogenated rubber, Ber. Bunsenges. Phys. Chem., 55:3458.

Raave, A. (1967): Organic Chemistry of Macromolecules, Dekker, New York.

Ranby, B. G., and Rabek, J. (1974): Photodegradation, Photo-oxidation, and Photostabilization of Polymers, Wiley Interscience, New York.

Ranby, B. G., and Rydholm, S. A. (1956): Cellulose derivatives. In Polymer Processes (C. E. Schildknecht, ed.), Wiley Interscience, New York.

Reich, L., and Stivala, S. S. (1974): Elements of Polymer Degradation, McGraw-Hill, New York.

Scales, R. E. (1976): Cellulosis, Mod. Plast., 53(10A):21.

Seymour, R. B. (1971): Introduction tc Polymer Chemistry, Chap. 9, McGraw-Hill, New York.

———. (1975): Modern Plastics Technology, Chap. 14, Reston Publishing, Reston, Virginia.

Seymour, R. B., Branum, I., Hayward, R. W. (1949): Surface reactions of polymers, Ind. Eng. Chem., 41(7):1479, 1482.

Seymour, R. B., and Steiner, R. S. (1955): Plastics for Corrosion Resistant Applications, Reinhold, New York.

Starks, C. M. (1974): Free Radical Telomerization, Academic, New York.

Staudinger, H., and Geiger, E. (1926): Cyclized rubber, Helv. Chim. Acta, 9:549.

Stevens, M. P. (1975): Polymer Chemistry, An Introduction, Chap. 8, Addison-Wesley, Reading, Massachusetts.

Thies, H. R., and Clifford, A. M. (1934): Isomerized rubber, Ind. Eng. Chem., 26:123.

Titus, J. (1973): Environmentally Degradable Plastics, U.S. Department of Commerce, Springfield, Virginia.

Wentz, C. A., and Hooper, E. E. (1967): Telechelic polymers, Ind. Eng. Chem. Prod. Res. Develop., 6(4):209.

Wilson, J. E. (1975): Radiation Chemistry of Monomers, Polymers, and Plastics, Dekker, New York.

Wint, R. F., and Vanderslice, C. W. (1975): Cellulose derivatives. Chap. 57 in Applied Polymer Science (J. K. Craven and R. W. Tess, eds.), Organic Coatings and Plastics Chemistry Div. of ACS, Washington, D.C.

15

Synthesis of Reactants and Intermediates for Polymers

Many of the difunctional reactants used for the production of step-reaction polymers are standard organic chemicals. However, because the degree of polymerization ($\overline{DP}$) is dependent on high purity, these reactants must be at least 99% pure.

Impurities in vinyl monomer may reduce the degree of polymerization through telomerization reactions. Less active impurities may not affect the rate or degree of polymerization, but may be present as contaminants in the polymer.

15.1 REACTANTS FOR STEP-REACTION POLYMERIZATION

Adipic acid (hexanoic acid, 1,4-butanedicarboxylic acid), melting point 152°C is used for the production of nylon-66 and may be produced by the oxidation of cyclohexane using air or nitric acid, from furfural or from 1,3-butadiene. As shown by (15.1), cyclohexane is obtained by the Raney nickel-catalytic hydrogenation of benzene. Both the cyclohexanol and cyclohexanone produced by the cobalt(II)acetate-catalyzed air oxidation of cyclohexane are oxidized to adipic acid by heating with 50% nitric acid; 700,000 tons of adipic acid are produced annually in the United States.

$$\text{Benzene} \xrightarrow[\text{Ni}]{H_2} \text{Cyclohexane} \xrightarrow[\substack{140\text{-}180^\circ C \\ Co(OAc)_2}]{O_2} \text{Cyclohexanol} + \text{Cyclohexanone} \xrightarrow[75^\circ C]{50\%\ HNO_3} HO{-}\underset{\underset{O}{\|}}{C}{-}(CH_2)_4{-}\underset{\underset{O}{\|}}{C}{-}OH \ (\text{Adipic acid}) \tag{15.1}$$

As shown in (15.2), tetrahydrofuran (THF), which is obtained from furfural, may be carbonylated in the presence of nickel carbonyl-nickel iodide catalyst at a pressure of 2000 atm and at a temperature of 270°C. Furfural is a chemurgic product obtained by the steam-acid digestion of corn cobs, oat hulls, bagasse, or rice hulls.

$$\text{THF} + 2CO + H_2O \xrightarrow[Ni(CO_4)-NiI_2]{270^\circ C} HO-\underset{\underset{O}{\|}}{C}-(CH_2)_4-\underset{\underset{O}{\|}}{C}-OH \qquad (15.2)$$

Tetrahydro-furan; Adipic acid

Adiponitrile, melting point 295°, may be produced by the hydrodimerization of acrylonitrile or from 1,3-butadiene via 1,4-dicyanobutene-2.

$$2\,\underset{\underset{H}{|}}{\overset{\overset{H}{|}}{C}}=\overset{\overset{H}{|}}{C}-CN \xrightarrow{(H_2)} NC(CH_2)_4CN \xrightarrow{(H_2)} H_2N(CH_2)_6NH_2 \qquad (15.3)$$

Acrylonitrile; Adiponitrile; Hexamethylene-diamine

As shown in (15.3), hexamethylenediamine (1,6-diaminohexane), melting point 40°C, which is used for the production of nylon-66, is obtained by the liquid-phase catalytic hydrogenation of adiponitrile or adipamide. As shown in (15.4), the latter is obtained by the ammonation of adipic acid.

$$HO-\underset{\underset{O}{\|}}{C}-(CH_2)_4-\underset{\underset{O}{\|}}{C}-OH \xrightarrow[350^\circ C]{NH_3} H_2N-\underset{\underset{O}{\|}}{C}-(CH_2)_4-\underset{\underset{O}{\|}}{C}-NH_2 \xrightarrow[125^\circ C\ 600\ atm]{Co/Cu(H_2)} H_2N(CH_2)_6NH_2 \qquad (15.4)$$

Adipic acid; Adipamide; Hexamethylene-diamine

Sebacic acid (decanedioc acid, octane dicarboxylic acid), melting point 134°C, which has been used for the production of nylon-610, has been produced from 1,3-butadiene and by the dry distillation of castor oil (ricinolein) with sodium hydroxide at 250°C. The cleaveage of the ricinoleic acid produces 2-octanol (capryl alcohol) and the sodium salt of sebacic acid.

$$\text{Castor oil} \xrightarrow{OH^-} H_3C(CH_2)_5\underset{\underset{H}{|}{O}}{\overset{H}{\overset{|}{C}}}-CH_2-\overset{H}{\overset{|}{C}}=\overset{H}{\overset{|}{C}}-(CH_2)_7\overset{O}{\overset{\|}{C}}-OH \xrightarrow[\Delta,\ H_2O]{NaOH}$$

Ricinoleic acid

$$H_3C(CH_2)_5\underset{\underset{H}{|}{O}}{\overset{H}{\overset{|}{C}}}CH_3 + Na^+, {}^-O-\underset{O}{\underset{\|}{C}}-(CH_2)_8-\underset{O}{\underset{\|}{C}}-O^-, Na^+ + H_2 \qquad (15.5)$$

2-Octanol Sodium sebacate Hydrogen

Phthalic acid (1,2-benzene dicarboxylic acid), melting point 231°C, isophthalic acid (1,3-benzene dicarboxylic acid), melting point 347°C, and terephthalic acid (1,4-benzene dicarboxylic acid), melting point 300°C (sublimes), are made by the selective catalytic oxidation of the corresponding xylenes. Terephthalic acid may also be produced by the isomerization of its isomers by heating the potassium salts at 400°C in the presence of cadmium iodide.

Over 2 million tons of terephthalic acid are produced annually in the United States. Phthalic acid is converted to phthalic anhydride, melting point 131°C, when heated. This acid may also be produced by the classic oxidation of naphthalene and by the hydrolysis of terephthalonitrile.

$$\text{p-Xylene} \xrightarrow[360^oC]{V_2O_5(O_2)} \text{Terephthalic acid} \qquad \text{m-Xylene} \xrightarrow[360^oC]{V_2O_5(O_2)} \text{Isophthalic acid} \qquad (15.6)$$

$$\text{o-Xylene} \xrightarrow[360^oC]{V_2O_5(O_2)} \text{Phthalic acid} \xrightarrow{(-H_2O)} \text{Phthalic anhydride} \xleftarrow[360^oC]{V_2O_5(O_2)} \text{Naphthalene} \qquad (15.7)$$

Maleic anhydride (2,5-furandione, toxilic anhydride), melting point 60°C, is obtained as a byproduct (about 6%) in the production of phthalic anhydride, and by the vapor-phase oxidation of butylene or crotonaldehyde.

It is also obtained by the dehydration of malic acid and by the oxidation of benzene. Maleic anhydride is used for the production of unsaturated polyester resins. This reactant, like most reactants, including benzene, is fairly toxic.

$$\text{Benzene} \xrightarrow[450^\circ C]{V_2O_5(O_2)} \text{HC(COOH)=HC(COOH)} + 2CO_2 + 2H_2O \xrightarrow{\Delta} \text{Maleic anhydride} \qquad (15.8)$$

Benzene — Maleic acid — Maleic anhydride

2-Pyrrolidone, melting point 25°C, is a lactone which is used for the production of nylon-4. This reactant may be produced by reductive ammonation of maleic anhydride. ϵ-Caprolactam, melting point 69°C, which is used for the production of nylon-6, may be produced by the Beckman rearrangement of cyclohexanone oxime. The latter may be produced by the catalytic hydrogenation of nitrobenzene, the photolytic nitrosylation of cyclohexane, or the classic reaction of cyclohexanone and hydroxylamine. ϵ-Caprolactam is also produced by the nitrosylation of cyclohexane carboxylic acid. The latter is obtained by the hydrogenation of benzoic acid which is obtained by the oxidation of toluene.

$$\text{Cyclohexane} + NOCl + HCl \xrightarrow{h\nu} \text{Cyclohexanoneoxime hydrochloride (=NOH·HCl)} \qquad (15.9)$$

Cyclohexane — Nitrosyl chloride — Hydrogen chloride — Cyclohexanoneoxime hydrochloride

$$\text{Cyclohexane} \xrightarrow[160^\circ C,\ Co(OAc)_2]{O_2} \text{Cyclohexanone} \xrightarrow[HCl]{H_2NOH} \text{Cyclohexanoneoxime hydrochloride} \qquad (15.10)$$

Cyclohexane — Cyclohexanone — Cyclohexanoneoxime hydrochloride

$$\text{Cyclohexanoneoxime (=NOH)} \xrightarrow{H_2SO_4} \epsilon\text{-Caprolactam} \qquad (15.11)$$

Cyclohexanoneoxime — ϵ-Caprolactam

Ethylene oxide (oxirane), boiling point 11°C, used for the production of ethylene glycol and polyethylene oxide, is obtained by the catalytic oxidation of ethylene. Ethylene glycol, boiling point 197°C, used for the production of polyesters, is produced by the hydrolysis of ethylene oxide. Ethylene oxide and ethylene glycol are produced at an annual rate of 2 million tons and 1.5 million tons, respectively, in the United States.

$$\mathrm{H_2C{=}CH_2} \xrightarrow[\mathrm{H_2O}]{\mathrm{Cl_2}} \mathrm{HO{-}CH_2{-}CH_2{-}Cl} \xrightarrow{\mathrm{Ca(OH)_2}} \mathrm{H_2C{-}CH_2\ (\text{–O–ring})} \xrightarrow{\mathrm{H_2O}} \mathrm{HO{-}CH_2{-}CH_2{-}OH}$$

Ethylene glycol (15.12)

$$\mathrm{H_2C{=}CH_2} \xrightarrow[250^{\circ}\mathrm{C}]{\mathrm{(O_2)Ag}} \mathrm{H_2C{-}CH_2\ (\text{–O–ring})}$$

Ethylene Ethylene oxide

Propylene oxide is obtained by the oxidation of propylene in a similar manner.

Glycerol (glycerin), boiling point 290°C, used for the production of alkyds, is produced by the catalytic hydroxylation or the hypochlorination of allyl alcohol. The latter is produced by the reduction of acrolein, which is obtained by the oxidation of propylene.

$$\underset{\text{Propylene}}{\mathrm{H_2C{=}CH{-}CH_3}} \xrightarrow[400^{\circ}\mathrm{C}]{\mathrm{O_2}} \underset{\text{Acrolein}}{\mathrm{H_2C{=}CH{-}CH{=}O}} \xrightarrow[400^{\circ}\mathrm{C}]{\mathrm{Na_2ZnO_2}} \mathrm{H_2C{=}CH{-}CH_2{-}OH}$$

$$\mathrm{H_2C{=}CH{-}CH_2{-}OH} \xrightarrow{\mathrm{H_2O_2},\ \mathrm{WO_3},\ 65^{\circ}\mathrm{C}} \underset{\text{Glycerol}}{\mathrm{HO{-}CH_2{-}CH(OH){-}CH_2{-}OH}}$$

$$\mathrm{H_2C{=}CH{-}CH_2{-}OH} \xrightarrow{\mathrm{Cl_2},\ \mathrm{H_2O}} \underset{\text{Glycerol } \alpha\text{-chlorohydrin}}{\mathrm{Cl{-}CH_2{-}CH(OH){-}CH_2{-}OH}} \xrightarrow[\mathrm{NaOH}]{\mathrm{Na_2CO_3}} \underset{\text{Glycerol}}{\mathrm{HO{-}CH_2{-}CH(OH){-}CH_2{-}OH}} \quad (15.13)$$

Pentaerythritol, melting point 262°C, used in the production of alkyds, is produced by a crossed Cannizzaro reaction of the aldol condensation product of formaldehyde and acetaldehyde. The byproduct, calcium formate, serves as the major source of formic acid.

$$3H{-}\overset{H}{\overset{|}{C}}{=}O + H{-}\underset{H}{\underset{|}{\overset{H}{\overset{|}{C}}}}{-}\overset{H}{\overset{|}{C}}{=}O \xrightarrow{Ca(OH)_2} \left(HO{-}\underset{H}{\underset{|}{\overset{H}{\overset{|}{C}}}}\right)_3{-}C{-}\overset{H}{\overset{|}{C}}{=}O$$

Formaldehyde Acetaldehyde Trimethylol acetaldehyde

$$\left(HO{-}\underset{H}{\underset{|}{\overset{H}{\overset{|}{C}}}}\right)_3{-}C{-}\overset{H}{\overset{|}{C}}{=}O \xrightarrow[Ca(OH)_2]{H-\overset{H}{\overset{|}{C}}=O} \left(HO{-}\underset{H}{\underset{|}{\overset{H}{\overset{|}{C}}}}\right)_4{-}C + 0.5Ca(O{-}\underset{O}{\underset{\|}{C}}{-}H)_2 \tag{15.14}$$

Trimethylol acetaldehyde Pentaery thritol Calcium formate

2,4-Tolylene diisocyanate (TDI), used for the production of polyurethanes and polyureas, is obtained by the phosgenation of 2,4-tolylenediamine. Phosgene is obtained by the reaction of chlorine and carbon monoxide. TDI may also be produced by the catalytic liquid-phase reductive carbonylation of dinitrotoluene.

$$C_6H_3(CH_3)(NH_2)_2 + Cl{-}\underset{O}{\underset{\|}{C}}{-}Cl \longrightarrow C_6H_3(CH_3)(NCO)_2 \tag{15.15}$$

2, 4-Tolulenediamine Phosgene Tolulene diisocyanate

Formaldehyde, which is used for the production of phenolic and amino resins, is produced at an annual rate of 2 million tons by the catalytic hot-air oxidation of methanol. Hexamethylenetetramine (hexa), melting point 280°C, is produced by the condensation of ammonia and 30% aqueous formaldehyde (formalin).

$$6H_3C{-}OH \underset{cat.}{\overset{(O_2)}{\rightleftharpoons}} 6H_2 + 6H{-}\overset{H}{\overset{|}{C}}{=}O \xrightarrow{4NH_3} (CH_2)_6N_4 + 6H_2O \tag{15.16}$$

Methanol Formaldehyde Hexamethylenetetramine

While Dow continues to produce some of its phenol by the nucleophilic substitution of chlorine in chlorobenzene by the hydroxyl group, most synthetic phenol (carbolic acid, phenylic acid) is produced by the acidic decomposition of cumene hydroperoxide. The latter is obtained by the oxidation of cumene.

$$\text{Chlorobenzene } (C_6H_5Cl) \xrightarrow[\text{4500 psi}]{\text{NaOH, 360°C}} \text{Sodium phenoxide } (C_6H_5O^-, Na^+) \xrightarrow[-\text{NaCl}]{\text{HCl}} \text{Phenol } (C_6H_5OH) \tag{15.17}$$

$$\text{Benzene} \xrightarrow[H_3PO_4]{H_2C{=}CH{-}CH_3} \text{Cumene } (C_6H_5CH(CH_3)_2) \xrightarrow{(O_2)} \text{Cumene hydroperoxide } (C_6H_5C(CH_3)_2{-}O{-}O{-}H) \xrightarrow{H_2SO_4} \underset{\text{Acetone}}{H_3C{-}C({=}O){-}CH_3} + \underset{\text{Phenol}}{C_6H_5OH} \tag{15.18}$$

Some of the newer processes for synthesizing phenol are the dehydrogenation of cyclohexanol, the decarboxylation of benzoic acid, and the hydrogen peroxide hydroxylation of benzene. Phenol, melting point 45°C, which is used for production of phenol-formaldehyde resins, is produced at an annual rate of over 2 million tons.

Urea (carbamide), melting point 133°C, used for the production of urea-formaldehyde resins, is produced at an annual rate of 3.5 million tons by the in situ decomposition of ammonium carbamate at 5 atm pressure. The latter is obtained by the condensation of liquid ammonia and liquid carbon dioxide at a temperature of 200°C and at a pressure of 200 atm.

$$\underset{\text{Ammonia}}{2H_3N} + \underset{\text{Carbon dioxide}}{CO_2} \longrightarrow H_2N{-}C({=}O){-}ONH_4 \longrightarrow H_2O + \underset{\text{Urea}}{H_2N{-}C({=}O){-}NH_2} \tag{15.19}$$

Melamine (cyanuramide), melting point 354°C, is obtained by heating dicyanodiamide (dicy) at 209°C. The latter is obtained by heating cyanamide at 80°C. Melamine, which is used for the production of melamine-formaldehyde resins, is also obtained by heating urea.

$$CaCN_2 \xrightarrow{H_3O^+} H_2NCN \xrightarrow{80^\circ C} H_2N{-}\underset{\underset{NH}{\|}}{C}{-}\overset{\overset{H}{|}}{N}{-}CN \xrightarrow{209^\circ C} \text{Melamine (2,4,6-triamino-1,3,5-triazine, } C_3N_3(NH_2)_3) \tag{15.20}$$

Calcium cyanamide — Cyanamide — Dicyanodiamide — Melamine

$$6H_2N{-}\underset{\underset{O}{\|}}{C}{-}NH_2 \xrightarrow{\Delta} C_3N_3(NH_2)_3 + 6NH_3 + 3CO_2 \tag{15.21}$$

Urea — Melamine — Ammonia

Bisphenol A [(bis-4-hydroxyphenyl)dimethylmethane], melting point 153°C, used for the production of epoxy resins and polycarbonates, is obtained by the acidic condensation of phenol and acetone. In this reaction, the carbonium ion produced by the protonation of acetone attacks the phenol molecule at the para position to produce a quinoidal oxonium ion which loses water and rearranges to a p-isopropyl phenol carbonium ion. The water attacks another phenol molecule in the para position to produce a quinoidal structure which rearranges to bisphenol A.

$$2HO{-}C_6H_5 + O{=}C(CH_3)_2 \xrightarrow{(H_2SO_4)} HO{-}C_6H_4{-}\underset{\underset{CH_3}{|}}{\overset{\overset{CH_3}{|}}{C}}{-}C_6H_4{-}OH + H_2O \tag{15.22}$$

Phenol — Acetone — Bisphenol A — Water

Epichlorohydrin (chloropropylene oxide), boiling point 115°C, used for the production of epoxy resins, is obtained by the dehydrochlorination of glycerol α,β-dichlorohydrin (2,3-dichloro-1-propanol). The latter is produced by chlorohydrination of allyl chloride.

$$H_2C{=}\overset{\overset{H}{|}}{C}{-}CH_3 \xrightarrow[200^\circ C]{Cl_2} H_2C{=}\overset{\overset{H}{|}}{C}{-}\underset{\underset{H}{|}}{\overset{\overset{H}{|}}{C}}{-}Cl \xrightarrow{H_2O\ +\ Cl_2} H_2C{-}\underset{\underset{OH}{|}}{\overset{\overset{H}{|}}{C}}{-}\underset{\underset{Cl}{|}}{\overset{\overset{H}{|}}{C}}{-}\underset{\underset{H}{|}}{C}{-}Cl \xrightarrow{Ca(OH)_2} \underbrace{H_2C{-}\overset{\overset{H}{|}}{C}}_{O}{-}\underset{\underset{H}{|}}{\overset{\overset{H}{|}}{C}}{-}Cl \tag{15.23}$$

Propylene — Allyl chloride — Glycerol α,β-dichlorohydrin — Epichlorohydrin

Methyltrichlorosilane is readily produced by the Grignard reaction of silicon tetrachloride and methyl magnesium chloride. Dimethyldichlorosilane is obtained by the reaction of methylmagnesium chloride and methyltrichlorosilane. Since the silicon atom is less electronegative than carbon, chlorine is much more electronegative than silicon and is a good leaving group in nucleophilic substitution reactions.

$$H_3CMgCl + SiCl_4 \longrightarrow H_3CSiCl_3 + MgCl_2$$

Methylmagnesium chloride, Silicon tetrachloride, Methyltrichlorosilane, Magnesium chloride

(15.24)

$$H_3CMgCl + H_3CSiCl_3 \longrightarrow (H_3C)_2SiCl_2 + MgCl_2$$

Methylmagnesium chloride, Methyltrichlorosilane, Dimethyldichlorosilane, Magnesium chloride

(15.25)

15.2 SYNTHESIS OF VINYL MONOMERS

Styrene, boiling point 145°C, which is one of the most important aromatic compounds, is produced at an annual rate of 3 million tons by the catalytic vapor-phase dehydrogenation of ethylbenzene. As shown in (15.26), the latter is obtained by the Friedel-Crafts condensation of ethylene and benzene. Styrene can also be produced by the palladium acetate-catalyzed condensation of ethylene and benzene and by the dehydration of methyl phenyl carbinol obtained by the propylation of ethylbenzene hydroperoxide. Because of its toxicity, the concentration of styrene in the atmosphere must be limited to a few parts per million.

$$C_6H_6 + H_2C{=}CH_2 \xrightarrow{AlCl_3} C_6H_5C_2H_5 \xrightarrow{ZnO \text{ or } Fe_2O_3} C_6H_5CH{=}CH_2 + H_2 \qquad (15.26)$$

Benzene, Ethylene, Ethylbenzene, Styrene

Vinyl chloride (chloroethene, VCM), boiling point 14°C, which was formerly obtained from acetylene, is now produced at an annual rate of 2.6 million tons by the trans catalytic process in which chlorination of ethylene, oxychlorination of byproduct hydrogen chloride, and dehydrochlorination of ethylene dichloride take place in a single reactor.

$$\underset{\text{Ethylene}}{H_2C{=}CH_2} + 2HCl + 0.5O_2 \xrightarrow{Cu_2Cl_2,\ FeCl_3} H_2O + \underset{\text{Ethylene dichloride}}{H{-}CHCl{-}CHCl{-}H} \xrightarrow{\Delta} HCl + \underset{\text{Vinyl chloride}}{H{-}CH{=}CH{-}Cl} \tag{15.27}$$

Vinylidene chloride, boiling point 317°C, is produced by the pyrolysis of 1,1,2-trichloroethane at 400°C. Since both vinyl chloride and vinylidene chloride are carcinogenic, their concentrations in air must be kept to a few parts per million.

$$\underset{\text{1, 1, 2-Trichloroethane}}{Cl{-}CH_2{-}CHCl{-}Cl} \xrightarrow{400^{\circ}C} \underset{\text{Vinylidene chloride}}{H{-}CH{=}CCl{-}Cl} + HCl \tag{15.28}$$

Vinyl acetate, boiling point 72°C, which is produced annually at a rate of 670,000 tons, was formerly obtained by the catalytic acetylation of acetylene. However, as shown in (15.29), this monomer is now produced by the catalytic oxidative condensation of acetic acid and ethylene. Other vinyl esters may be obtained by the transesterification of vinyl acetate with higher boiling carboxylic acids.

$$\underset{\text{Ethylene}}{H_2C{=}CH_2} + \underset{\text{Acetic acid}}{H_3C{-}C({=}O){-}OH} \xrightarrow[\Delta,\ \text{cat.}]{O_2} \underset{\text{Vinyl acetate}}{HC(H){=}C(H){-}O{-}C({=}O){-}CH_3} \tag{15.29}$$

Acrylonitrile (vinyl cyanide), boiling point 70°C, is produced at an annual rate of 700,000 tons by the ammoxidation of propylene. Since this monomer is carcinogenic, considerable care must be taken to minimize exposure to acrylonitrile.

$$\underset{\text{Propylene}}{H{-}CH_2{-}CH{=}CH{-}H} + \underset{\text{Ammonia}}{NH_3} + 1.5O_2 \xrightarrow[BiP(Mo_3O_{10})_4]{300\text{-}540^{\circ}C} \underset{\text{Acrylonitrile}}{H_2C{=}CH{-}CN} + 3H_2O \tag{15.30}$$

Ethylene, boiling point -103.7°C; propylene, boiling point -47.7°C; and butylene, boiling point 6.9°C, are produced at annual rates of 10 million,

4.5 million, and 200,000 tons, respectively, by the vapor-phase cracking of light oil fractions of petroleum feedstocks or petroleum gases. The acetylenes, produced as byproducts, are selectively absorbed, and the monomers are obtained by fractional distillation.

Tetrafluoroethylene, boiling point -76.3°C, is obtained by the thermal dehydrochlorination of chlorodifluoromethane. The latter is produced by the reaction of chloroform and hydrogen fluoride.

$$\underset{\text{Hydrogen fluoride}}{HF} + \underset{\text{Chloroform}}{HCCl_3} \longrightarrow \underset{\text{Hydrogen chloride}}{HCl} + \underset{\text{Chlorodifluoromethane}}{HCClF_2} \tag{15.31}$$

$$\underset{\text{Chlorodifluoromethane}}{2\overset{H}{\overset{|}{C}}ClF_2} \xrightarrow[80^\circ]{\Delta} \underset{\text{Hydrogen chloride}}{2HCl} + \underset{\text{Tetrafluoroethylene}}{F_2C{=}CF_2} \tag{15.32}$$

Trifluoromonochloroethylene, boiling point -28°C, is obtained by the zinc metal dechlorination of trichlorotrifluoroethane. The latter is produced by the fluorination of hexachloroethane.

$$\underset{\text{Hexachloroethane}}{Cl_3{-}CCl_3} \xrightarrow{SbF_3{-}SbCl_3} \underset{\text{Trichlorotrifluoroethane}}{F_2\overset{Cl}{\overset{|}{C}}{-}\overset{F}{\overset{|}{C}}Cl_2} \longrightarrow \underset{\text{Trifluoromonochloroethylene}}{F_2C{=}\overset{F}{\overset{|}{C}}Cl} + \underset{\text{Zinc chloride}}{ZnCl_2} \tag{15.33}$$

Vinylidene fluoride, boiling point -84°C, is produced by the thermal dehydrochlorination of 1,1,1-monochlorodifluoroethane.

$$\underset{\text{1,1,1-Monochlorodifluoroethane}}{H\overset{H}{\underset{H}{C}}{-}\overset{F}{\underset{F}{C}}Cl} \xrightarrow{\Delta} \underset{\text{Vinylidene fluoride}}{H_2C{=}CF_2} + \underset{\text{Hydrogen chloride}}{HCl} \tag{15.34}$$

Vinyl fluoride, boiling point -72°C, may be obtained by the catalytic hydrofluorination of acetylene.

$$\underset{\text{Acetylene}}{HC{\equiv}CH} + \underset{\text{Hydrogen fluoride}}{HF} \xrightarrow{HgCl_2-BaCl_2} \underset{\text{Vinyl fluoride}}{H_2C{=}CHF} \qquad (15.35)$$

Vinyl ethyl ether, boiling point 35.5°C, is obtained by the ethanolysis of acetylene in the presence of potassium ethoxide.

$$\underset{\text{Acetylene}}{HC{\equiv}CH} + \underset{\text{Ethanol}}{H{-}CH_2{-}CH_2{-}OH} \xrightarrow[130\text{-}180^\circ C]{KOC_2H_5} \underset{\text{Vinyl ethyl ether}}{H_2C{=}CH{-}OC_2H_5} \qquad (15.36)$$

1,3-Butadiene, boiling point -4.4°C, which is used for the production of elastomers, is produced, at an annual rate of 1.5 million tons by the catalytic thermal cracking of butane and as a byproduct of other cracking reactions.

$$\underset{\text{Butane}}{H{-}CH_2{-}CH_2{-}CH_2{-}CH_2{-}H} \xrightarrow[Cr_2O_3-Al_2O_3]{600\text{-}700^\circ C} \underset{\text{1, 3-Butadiene}}{H_2C{=}CH{-}CH{=}CH_2} + \text{other products} \qquad (15.37)$$

Chloroprene, boiling point 59.9°C, used for the production of neoprene rubber, is obtained by the dehydrochlorination of dichlorobutene. The latter is produced by the chlorination of 1,3-butadiene.

$$\underset{\text{1,3-Butadiene}}{H_2C{=}CH{-}CH{=}CH_2} \xrightarrow{Cl_2} \underset{\text{Dichlorobutene}}{H_2C{-}CCl{-}CClH{-}CH{=}CH_2} \xrightarrow{\Delta} \underset{\text{Chloroprene}}{H_2C{=}CCl{-}CH{=}CH_2} \qquad (15.38)$$

Acrylic acid, boiling point 141°C, may be prepared by the catalytic oxidative carbonylation of ethylene or by heating formaldehyde and acetic acid in the presence of potassium hydroxide.

$$\underset{\text{Ethylene}}{H_2C{=}CH_2} + \underset{\text{Carbon monoxide}}{CO} + \underset{\text{Oxygen}}{\frac{1}{2}O_2} \xrightarrow[FeCl_3]{ThCl_2} \underset{\text{Acrylic acid}}{H_2C{=}CH{-}COOH} \qquad (15.39)$$

Methyl acrylate, boiling point 80°C, may be obtained by the addition of methanol to the reactants in the previous synthesis for acrylic acid or by the methanolysis of acrylonitrile.

$$\underset{\text{Acrylonitrile}}{H_2C{=}\overset{\overset{\displaystyle H}{|}}{C}{-}CN} + \underset{\text{Methanol}}{H_3COH} \xrightarrow{H_2O} \underset{\text{Methylacrylate}}{H_2C{=}\overset{\overset{\displaystyle H}{|}}{C}{-}\underset{\underset{\displaystyle O}{\|}}{C}{-}OCH_3} + \underset{\text{Ammonium ion}}{NH_4^+} \tag{15.40}$$

Methyl methacrylate, boiling point 101°C, may be prepared by the catalytic oxidative carbonylation of propylene in the presence of methanol.

$$\underset{\text{Propylene}}{H_2C{=}\overset{\overset{\displaystyle CH_3}{|}}{C}H} + \underset{\text{Carbon monoxide}}{CO} + \underset{\text{Oxygen}}{\frac{1}{2}O_2}$$

$$+ \underset{\text{Methanol}}{CH_3OH} \xrightarrow[FeCl_2]{ThCl_2} \underset{\text{Methyl methacrylate}}{H_2C{=}\overset{\overset{\displaystyle CH_3}{|}}{C}{-}\overset{\overset{\displaystyle O}{\|}}{C}{-}O{-}CH_3} \tag{15.41}$$

Other esters of acrylic and methacrylic acids may be prepared by transesterification with higher boiling alcohols.

15.3 SYNTHESIS OF FREE-RADICAL INITIATORS

Free-radical initiators are compounds containing covalent bonds that readily undergo homolytic cleavage to produce free radicals. The most widely used organic free-radical initiators are peroxides and azo compounds.

Benzoyl peroxide is produced when benzoyl chloride and sodium peroxide are stirred in water.

$$2\,C_6H_5{-}C(=O){-}Cl + Na_2O_2 \xrightarrow{-2NaCl} C_6H_5{-}C(=O){-}O{-}O{-}C(=O){-}C_6H_5 \qquad (15.42)$$

Benzoyl chloride — Sodium peroxide — Benzoyl peroxide

tert-Butyl hydroperoxide is produced by the acid-catalyzed addition of hydrogen peroxide to isobutylene. tert-Butyl peroxide is produced when tert-butyl hydroperoxide is added to isobutylene.

$$(CH_3)_2C{=}CH_2 + H_2O_2 \xrightarrow{H_2SO_4} (CH_3)_3COOH \qquad (15.43)$$

Isobutylene — Hydrogen peroxide — tert-Butyl hydroperoxide

$$(CH_3)_2C{=}CH_2 + (CH_3)_2COOH \xrightarrow{H_2SO_4} (CH_3)_3COOC(CH_3)_3 \qquad (15.44)$$

Isobutylene — tert-Butyl hydroperoxide — tert-Butyl peroxide

Dicumyl peroxide is produced by the air oxidation of cumene.

$$2\,C_6H_5{-}CH(CH_3)_2 + O_2 \longrightarrow C_6H_5{-}C(CH_3)_2{-}O{-}O{-}C(CH_3)_2{-}C_6H_5 \qquad (15.45)$$

Cumene — Oxygen — Dicumyl peroxide

All initiators are potentially explosive compounds and must be stored and handled with care. 2,2'-Azobisisobutyronitrile (AIBN, 2,2-dicyano-2,2-azopropane) is obtained from the reaction of acetone with potassium cyanide and hydrazine hydrochloride. As shown in (15.46), the reaction of potassium cyanide with hydrazine hydrochloride produces hydrogen cyanide and hydrazine. The latter reacts with acetone to form acetone dihydrazone which reacts with the former (HCN) to produce a substituted hydrazone which is then oxidized to AIBN by sodium hypochlorite. When methyl ethyl ketone is used in place of acetone, 2,2'-azobis-2-methylbutyronitrile is produced.

$$2KCN + Cl^-, {}^+H_3N{-}NH_3^+, Cl^- \xrightarrow[-KCl]{} 2HCN + H_2N{-}NH_2$$

Potassium cyanide | Hydrazine hydrochloride | Hydrogen cyanide | Hydrazine

$$(CH_3)_2C{=}O + H_2N{-}NH_2 \longrightarrow (CH_3)_2C{=}N{-}N{=}C(CH_3)_2$$

Acetone | Hydrazine | Acetone dihydrazone

$$(CH_3)_2C{=}N{-}N{=}C(CH_3)_2 + 2HCN \longrightarrow$$

Acetone dihydrazone | Hydrogen cyanide

$$(CH_3)_2C(CN){-}NH{-}NH{-}C(CN)(CH_3)_2 \qquad (15.46)$$

2,2'-Hydrazobisisobutyronitrile

$$(CH_3)_2C(CN){-}NH{-}NH{-}C(CN)(CH_3)_2 + NaOCl \xrightarrow[-NaCl]{-H_2O}$$

2,2'-Hydrazobisisobutyronitrile | Sodium hypochlorite

$$(CH_3)_2C(CN){-}N{=}N{-}C(CN)(CH_3)_2$$

AIBN

The physical constants of polymer reactants and monomers are listed in Tables 15.1 and 15.2. Data on initiators are listed in Chap. 8.

TABLE 15.1 Physical Properties of Polymer Reactants

COMPOUND	MELTING POINT, °C	BOILING POINT, °C	SPECIFIC GRAVITY	INDEX OF REFRACTION
Adipic acid	152	265^{10}	1.360^{25}_{4}	
Epichlorohydrin	−57	117^{756}	1.183^{25}_{25}	1.4397^{16}
Ethylene glycol	−15.6	198	1.113^{19}_{4}	1.4318^{20}
Ethylene oxide	−111.7	10.7	0.887^{7}_{4}	$1.3599^{8.4}$
Formaldehyde	−92	−21	0.815^{20}	
Furfural	−39	162	1.159^{20}_{4}	1.5261^{20}
Furfuryl alcohol	. . .	169.5^{752}	1.129^{25}_{4}	1.4852^{20}
Glycerol	18.2	290	1.261^{20}_{4}	1.4729^{20}
Hexamethylenediamine	42	204.5		
Maleic anhydride	60	202	1.5	
Melamine	354	. . .	1.5373^{25}	
Pentaerythritol	262	276^{30}		
Phenol	43	181.8^{8}	1.071^{25}_{4}	1.54^{45}
Phthalic acid (*o*)	231	. . .	1.593^{20}_{4}	
Isophthalic acid (*m*)	347			
Terephthalic acid (*p*)	300 *(s)*			
Phthalic anhydride	132	284.5	1.527^{4}	
Pyromellitic dianhydride	287	397–400	1.68	
Sebacic acid	135.5	294.5^{100}	1.207^{25}_{4}	1.42^{133}
Urea	132.7	. . .	1.335^{20}_{4}	

TABLE 15.2 Physical Properties of Monomers

COMPOUND	MELTING POINT, °C	BOILING POINT, °C	DENSITY	INDEX OF REFRACTION
Acrylamide	85	125^{25}	1.122^{30}	
Acrylic acid	12	141	1.0511^{20}	1.4224^{20}
Methyl acrylate	−75	80	0.953^{20}	1.3984^{20}
Acrylonitrile	−83.6	79	0.8060^{20}	1.393^{20}
1,3-Butadiene	−109	−4.4	0.6211^{20}	1.4292^{-25}
Chloroprene	. . .	59.4	0.9583^{20}	1.4583^{20}
Chlorotrifluoroethylene	−158	−28		
1-Butene	−185	−6.3	0.5951^{20}	1.3962^{20}
Isobutylene (2-methylpropene)	−141	−6.6	$0.6266^{-6.6}$	1.3814^{-25}
Ethylene	−169	−104	0.566^{-102}	1.363^{-100}
Tetrafluoroethylene	−142.5	−76.3	1.519^{20}	
Isoprene	−146	34	0.6806^{20}	1.4194^{20}
Methacrylic acid	15.5	161	1.0153^{20}	1.43143^{20}
Methyl methacrylate	−48	101	0.936^{20}	1.413^{20}
Methacrylonitrile	−36	90.3	0.7998^{20}	1.4007^{20}
Methyl isopropenyl ketone	−54	98	0.8550^{20}	1.4220^{20}
Propylene	−185	−48	0.5139^{-20}	
Styrene	−30.6	145.2	0.9090^{20}	1.54682^{20}
α-Methylstyrene	−23.2	163.4	0.9165^{10}	1.5386^{20}
Vinyl acetate	. . .	72.5	0.9338^{20}	1.3953^{20}
Vinyl chloride	−154	−14	0.99176^{-15}	1.398^{15}
Vinyl ethyl ether	−115	35	0.7589^{20}	1.3767^{20}
Vinyl fluoride	−161	−72		
Vinylidene chloride	−122	31.7	1.2129^{20}	1.4249^{20}
2-Vinylpyridine	. . .	80^{29}	0.9985^{0}	1.5494^{20}

SUMMARY

1. While all polymer reactants can be produced by classic reactions, new reactions have been developed for the industrial production of many of the reactants used in large quantities.

2. The natural products furfural (from oat hulls) and ricinoleic acid (from castor oil) are used to produce adipic and sebacic acid, respectively.

3. The isomers of phthalic acid are obtained by the catalytic oxidation of xylenes.

4. ϵ-Caprolactan is produced by the classic Beckman rearrangement of cyclohexanone oxine.

5. Ethylene and propylene oxides are produced by the catalytic oxidation of ethylene and propylene, respectively.

6. 2,4-Tolylene diisocyanate is produced by the phosgenation of 2,4-tolylenediamine.

7. Phenol is produced by the acidic decomposition of cumene hydroperoxide.

8. Urea is produced by the condensation of liquid ammonia and liquid carbon dioxide. Melamine is obtained by heating urea.

9. The alkylchlorosilanes are produced by the reaction of a Grignard reagent and silicon tetrachloride.

10. Styrene is produced by the catalytic dehydrogenation of ethylbenzene.

11. Vinyl chloride is produced by the oxychlorination process from ethylene and hydrogen chloride.

12. Vinyl acetate is produced by the oxidative condensation of acetic acid and ethylene.

13. Acrylonitrile is produced by the ammoxidation of propylene.

14. Ethylene, propylene, butylene, and butadiene are produced by cracking hydrocarbon feedstocks.

15. Fluorocarbon monomers are produced by the dehydrochlorination of chlorofluoro compounds.

16. Acrylic and methacrylic esters are produced by the oxidative carbonylation of ethylene and propylene, respectively.

17. Benzoyl peroxide is produced by the condensation of sodium peroxide and benzoyl peroxide. tert-Butyl peroxides are produced by the addition of hydrogen peroxide to isobutylene, and dicumyl peroxide is produced by the air oxidation of cumene.

18. 2,2'-Azobisisobutyronitrile is produced by the reaction of acetone with potassium cyanide and hydrazine hydrochloride.

19. Since many reactants and monomers are toxic and initiators are unstable compounds, extreme care must be exercised in their use.

GLOSSARY

AIBN: 2,2'-Azobisisobutyronitrile.

Cannizzaro reaction: An internal oxidation reduction reaction of aldehydes.

carbamide: Urea.

carcinogenic: Cancer producing.

chemurgic compound: One made from a plant source.

chloroprene: 2-Chloro-1,3-butadiene.

Friedel Crafts condensation: One that takes place in the presence of a Lewis acid, such as aluminum chloride.

Grignard reagent: RMgX.

isophthalic acid: The meta isomer.

Raney nickel: A porous nickel catalyst produced from a nickel-aluminum alloy.

TDI: 2,4-Tolulene diisocyanate.

terephthalic acid: The para isomer of the dicarboxylic acid of benzene.

THF: Tetrahydrofuran.

VCM: Vinyl chloride.

EXERCISES

1. Why are there so many methods for the preparation of adipic acid?
2. Write the equations for the industrial synthesis of the following:
   a. Adipic acid
   b. Hexamethylenediamine
   c. Sebacic acid
   d. Terephthalic acid
   e. Maleic anhydride
   f. ϵ-Caprolactan
   g. Ethylene oxide
   h. Glycerol
   i. Pentaerythritol
   j. TDI
   k. Hexamethylenetetramine
   l. Phenol

m. Urea
n. Melamine
o. Bisphenol A
p. Epichlorohydrin
q. Methyltrichlorosilane
r. Styrene
s. Vinyl chloride
t. Vinyl acetate
u. Acrylonitrile
v. Vinyl ethyl ether
w. Methyl methacrylate
x. Benzoyl peroxide
y. tert-Butyl peroxide
z. AIBN

3. Name a reactant or monomer produced by
   a. Grignard reaction
   b. Friedel-Crafts reaction
   c. Beckman rearrangement
   d. A chemurgic process
   e. A crossed Cannizzaro reaction

BIBLIOGRAPHY

Boundy, R. H., Boyer, R. F., Stroesser, S. M. (1965): Styrene, Its Polymer, Copolymers and Derivatives, Hafner, New York.

Braun, D., Cherdron, H., Kern, W. (1972): Techniques of Polymer Synthesis and Characterization, Wiley Interscience, New York.

Collins, E. A., Bares, J., Billmeyer, F. W. (1973): Experiments in Polymer Science, Chap. 3, Wiley Interscience, New York.

Deanin, R. D. (1974): New Industrial Polymers, ACS Symposium Series 4, Washington, D.C.

Frisch, K. C. (1972): Cyclic Monomers, John Wiley, New York.

Hulme, P., and Turner, P. (1968): Caprolactam, Chem. Eng., 75(7):82.

Landau, R., Brown, D., Saffer, A., Porcelli, J. V. (1968): Ethylene oxide, Chem. Eng. Prog., 64(3):27.

Leonard, E. C. (1970): Vinyl and Diene Monomers, Wiley Interscience, New York.

Long, R. (1967): The Production of Polymers and Plastics Intermediates from Petroleum, Plenum, New York.

Martin, L. F. (1974): Organic Peroxide Technology, Noyes Data Corp., Park Ridge, New Jersey.

Noller, C. R. (1965): Chemistry of Organic Compounds, 3d ed., W. B. Saunders, Philadelphia.

Pinner, S. H. (1961): A Practical Course in Polymer Chemistry, Pergamon, New York.

Sandler, S. R., and Karo, W. (1961): Polymer Synthesis, Academic, New York.

Saunders, K. J. (1973): Organic Polymer Chemistry, Halsted, New York.

Seymour, R. B. (1971): Introduction to Polymer Chemistry, Chap. 15, McGraw-Hill, New York.

———. (1976): New sources of monomers and polymers, Polymer Eng. Sci., 16(12):817.

Spitz, P. H. (1968): Vinyl chloride, Chem. Eng. Prog., 64(3):19.

Starks, C. M. (1974): Free Radical Telomerization, Academic, New York.

Stille, J. K. (1968): Industrial Organic Chemistry, Prentice-Hall, Englewood Cliffs, New Jersey.

Stille, J. K., and Campbell, T. W. (1972): Condensation Monomers, Wiley Interscience, New York.

Wessling, R. A. (1974): Polyvinylidene Chloride, Gordon and Breach, New York.

Williams, A. (1974): Furans, Synthesis, and Applications, Noyes Data Corp., Park Ridge, New Jersey.

Wolcock, J. W. (1961): Olefin production. In Introduction to Petroleum Chemicals (H. Steiner, ed.), Pergamon, New York.

Yokum, R. H., and Nyquist, E. B. (1974): Functional Monomers, Their Preparation, Polymerization and Application, Dekker, New York.

16

Polymer Technology

While much classic polymer technology was developed without the benefit of science, modern polymer technology and polymer science are closely associated. The technology of fibers, elastomers, coatings, and plastics is discussed in this chapter.

16.1 FIBERS

Since there are many natural fibers, much of this phase of polymer technology was developed before the twentieth century. Long, threadlike cells of animal and vegetable origin have been used for centuries for textiles, paper, brushes, and cordage. The animal protein fibers, namely, wool and silk, are no longer competitive with other fibers unless their production is subsidized. The vegetable cellulosic fibers, cotton, kapok, abaca, agave, flax, hemp, jute, kenaf, and ramie are still in use, but cotton is no longer the "king of fibers."

Regenerated proteins from casein (lanital), peanuts (ardil), soybeans (aralac), and zein (vicara) are used as specialty fibers, but cellulose ester and regenerated cellulose (rayon) are used in relatively large quantities. Cellulose triacetate fibers (Tricel) are produced by the acetylation of α-cellulose, and cellulose diacetate fiber (acetate rayon) is produced by the deacetylation of the triacetate. Further deacetylation (saponification) yields regenerated cellulose. (See Table 16.1 for the physical properties of typical fibers.)

Most regenerated cellulose (rayon) is produced by the viscose process in which an aqueous solution of the sodium salt of cellulose xanthate is precipitated in an acid solution. The relatively weak fibers produced by this wet spinning process are stretched in order to produce strong (high-tenacity) rayon. The annual production of acetate rayon and rayon in the United States is 225,000 tons and 357,000 tons, respectively.

TABLE 16.1 Physical Properties of Typical Fibers

Polymer	Tenacity (g/denier)	Tensile strength (kg cm^2)	Elongation (%)
Cellulose			
Cotton	2.1-6.3	3-9000	3-10
Rayon	1.5-2.4	2-3000	15-30
High-tenacity rayon	3.0-5.0	5-6000	9-20
Cellulose diacetate	1.1-1.4	1-1500	25-45
Cellulose triacetate	1.2-1.4	1-1500	25-40
Proteins			
Silk	218-5.2	3-6000	13-31
Wool	1.0-1.7	1-2000	20-50
Vicara	1.1-1.2	1-1000	30-35
Nylon-66	4.5-6.0	4-6000	26
Polyester	4.4-5.0	5-6000	19-23
Polyacrylonitrile	2.3-2.6	2-3000	20-28
Saran	1.1-2.9	1.5-4000	20-35
Polyurethane (Spandex)	0.7	630	575
Polypropylene	7.0	5600	25
Asbestos	1.3	2100	25
Glass	7.7	2100	3.0

While no truly synthetic fiber was produced before 1936, over 4 million tons of these important products are now produced annually. The leading fiber is polyethylene terephthalate (polyester, Dacron, Terylene, Kodel, Vycron) which is produced at an annual rate of 1.8 million tons by forcing the molten polymer through small holes in a spinneret in a process called melt spinning.

Nylon-66 and nylon-6 fibers are also produced by melt spinning molten polymers at an annual rate of over 1 million tons. Acrylic fibers (Acrilan, Orlon) are produced at an annual rate of over 325,000 tons by forcing a solution of acrylonitrile polymers in dimethylformamide (DMF) through spinnerets and evaporating the solvent from the filament. This process, which is also used for the production of cellulose acetate fiber, is called dry spinning.

Polyurethane (Perlon, Spandex), polypropylene, and polyethylene fibers are produced by melt spinning of molten polymers. The total annual polyolefin fiber production in the United States is about 330,000 tons. Polyurethane fibers are produced in large quantities in Germany but these are used as specialty fibers in the United States. Over 300,000 tons of these fibers are produced by the melt spinning process.

Filaments of thermoplastics such as polypropylene may also be produced by a fibrillation process in which strips of film are twisted and these fibrils are heated and stretched. In addition to the traditional spinning and weaving processes, textiles may be produced in the form of nonwoven textiles by the fiber-bonding process. Bonding results from the addition of thermoplastics or by admixing thermoplastic fibers with cotton or rayon fibers before bonding by heat.

16.2 ELASTOMERS

Prior to World War II, hevea rubber accounted for over 99% of all elastomers used, but synthetic elastomers account for more than 70% of all rubber used today. Natural rubber and many synthetic elastomers are available in latex form. The latex may be used, as such, for adhering carpet fibers or for dipped articles, such as gloves, but most of the latex is coagulated and the dried coagulant is used for the production of tires and mechanical goods.

Over 5 million tons of synthetic rubber are produced annually in the United States. The principal elastomer is the copolymer of butadiene (75%) and styrene (25%) (SBR), produced at an annual rate of over 3 million tons by the emulsion polymerization of butadiene and styrene. The copolymer of butadiene and acrylonitrile (Buna-N, Hycar) is also produced by the emulsion process at an annual rate of about 80,000 tons.

Likewise, neoprene is produced by the emulsion polymerization of chloroprene at an annual rate of 126,000 tons. Butyl rubber is produced by the cationic copolymerization of isobutylene (90) and isoprene (10) at an annual rate of 146,000 tons.

Polybutadiene, polyisoprene, and ethylene-propylene copolymer rubber (EPDM) are produced by anionic polymerization processes at annual rates of 444,000, 76,000, and 151,000 tons, respectively. One of the original synthetic elastomers (Thiokol), as well as polyfluorocarbon elastomers (Viton), silicone (Silastic), polyurethane (Adiprene), and phosphazenes are specialty elastomers. The physical properties of typical elastomers are shown in Table 16.2.

TABLE 16.2 Physical Properties of Typical Elastomers

	Pure gum vulcanizates		Carbon-black reinforced vulcanizates	
	Tensile strength (kg cm^{-2})	Elongation (%)	Tensile strength (kg cm^{-2})	Elongation (%)
Natural rubber	210	700	315	600
Styrene-butadiene rubber (SBR)	28	800	265	550
Acrylonitrile-butadiene rubber (NBR)	42	600	210	550
Polyacrylates (ABR)			175	400
Thiokol (ET)	21	300	85	400
Neoprene (CR)	245	800	245	700
Butyl rubber (IIR)	210	1,000	210	400
Polyisoprene (IR)	210	700	315	600
Ethylene-propylene rubber (EPM)				
Polyepichlorohydrin (CO)				
Polyfluorinated hydrocarbons (FPM)				
Silicone elastomers (SI)				
Polyurethane elastomers (AU)	350	600	420	500

16.3 FILMS, SHEETS, COATINGS, AND ADHESIVES

Films such as regenerated cellulose (cellophane) are produced by precipitating a polymeric solution after it has passed through a slit die. Some films, such as cellulose acetate, are cast from a solution of the polymer, but most films are produced by the extrusion process. Some relatively thick films and coextruded films are extruded through a flat slit die, but most thermoplastic film, such as polyethylene film, is produced by the air blowing of a warm extruded tube as it emerges from the circular die as shown in Fig. 16.1.

The most widely used films are LDPE, cellophane, PETP, PVC, cellulose acetate, polyfluorocarbons, nylons, polypropylene, polystyrene, and Saran. Films of UHMWPE, polyamides, and polytetrafluoroethylene are produced by skiving molded billets. The strength of many films, such as PETP, is improved by biaxial orientation.

Most of the thermoplastics used as films may also be extruded as relatively thick sheets. These sheets may also be produced by pressing a stack of film at elevated temperature (laminating) or by the calendering process. The latter consists of passing softened resin between two or more counterrotating rolls.

Wire is coated by passing the wire through a plastic extruder, but most substances are coated by polymers from solutions, emulsions, or hot powders. The classic brushing process has been replaced to a large extent by roll coating, spraying, and hot powder coating. The application of polymers from water dispersions to large objects, such as automobile frames, has been improved by electrodeposition of the polymer on the metal surface.

Because of the need to reduce environmental pollution, the trend is toward high solids coatings with a solvent-volume concentration of less than 20%. Plastisols, which are solvent free, consist of polymers, such as PVC, dispersed in liquid plasticizers, such as DOP. These plastisols may be coated on substrates and fused at 160°C.

While naturally occurring resins formerly dominated the adhesive resin field, they now account for less than 10% of the market. Elastomers, thermosets, and thermoplastics account for 35, 30, and 20% of the adhesive resins used, respectively. SBR, phenolic, and polyvinyl acetate are the principal resins used in this 3 billion dollar market.

Printing inks are highly filled solutions of resin. The classic printing inks were drying oil-based systems, but the trend is toward solvent-free ink in this 700 million dollar business.

The permeability to gases and the tearing strength of films are shown in Table 16.3.

16.4 POLYMERIC FOAMS

Prior to 1920, our only flexible foam was the natural sponge, but chemically foamed rubber and mechanically foamed rubber latex were introduced

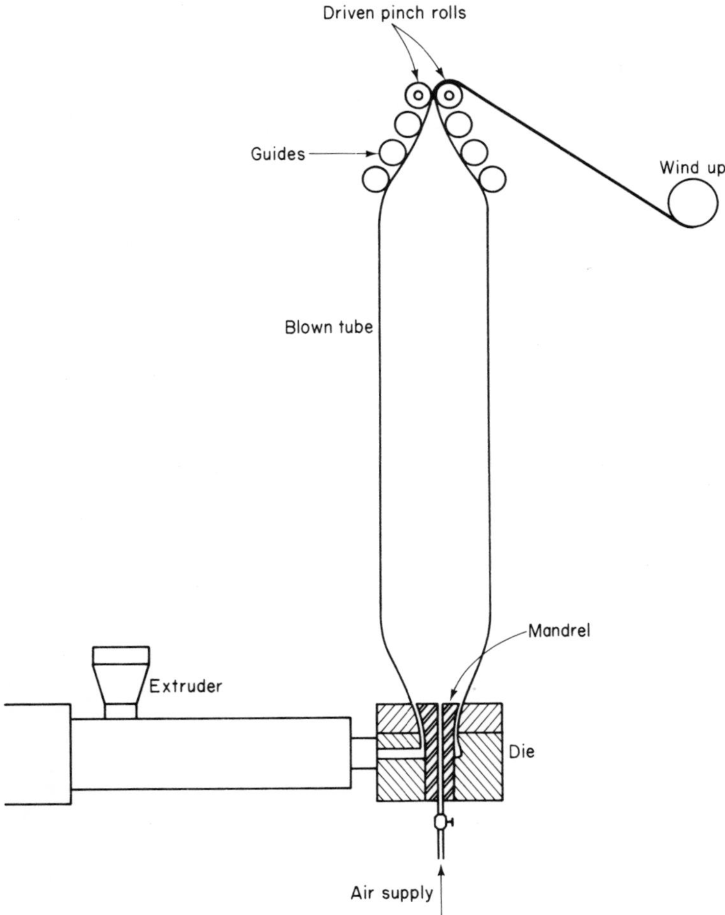

FIGURE 16.1 Film formation through extrusion. (N. Bikales, USP Extrusion and Other Plastics Operations, Wiley Interscience, 1971; with permission of J. Wiley & Sons, Publishers.)

TABLE 16.3 Permeability to Gases (cm/day/100 in.^{2}/mil at 25°C)

Polymer	MVT	CO_2	H_2	N_2	O_2	Initial tearing strength (g/mil)
Cellophane	0.4-134	0.4-0.6	1.2-2.2	0.5-1.6	0.2-5.0	2-20
Polyethylene (I)	1.0-1.5	2700	—	180	500	100-500
Polyethylene (III)	0.3	580	—	42	185	16-300
Rubber hydrochloride	—	288-13,500	—	—	38-2250	60-1600
Cellulose acetate	30-40	860-1000	835	30-40	117-150	1-2
Cellulose acetate butyrate	30-40	6000	—	250	950	5-10
Ethylcellulose	4.8-14.2	5000	—	600	2000	215-395
Plasticized polyvinyl chloride	4	100-3000	—	—	30-2000	60-1400
Saran	—	12	—	—	2.4	10-100
Polyvinyl alcohol	—	200	—	—	120	785-890
Polyethylene terephthalate	1.7-1.8	15-25	100	0.017-1.0	6.0-8.0	12-27
Polystyrene (oriented)	7.0-10.0	900	—	—	350	5.0
Polycarbonate	11.0	1075	1600	50	300	20-25
Polyurethane	45-75	465-1650	—	41-119	75-327	220-710
Nylon-66	3-6	9.1	—	0.35	5.0	—
Nylon-6	5.4-20	10-12	110	0.9	2.6	50-90
Polyvinyl fluoride	3.24	11.1	58	0.25	3	12-100

prior to World War II. These foams may consist of discrete unit cells (unicellular, closed cells) or they may be made up of interconnecting cells (multicellular, open cells), depending on the viscosity of the system at the time the blowing agent is introduced.

Unicellular foams are used for insulation, buoyancy, and flotation applications, while multicellular foams are used for upholstery and laminated textiles. Expanded polystyrene (Styrofoam), which is produced by the extrusion of polystyrene beads containing a volatile liquid, is used to produce low-density moldings such as foamed drinking cups and insulation board. The K volume for these products is on the order of 0.24 BTUH.

Foamed products are also produced from PVC, LDPE, urea resins, ABS, and polyurethane (PU). The last are versatile products which range from hard-rigid to soft-flexible. These are produced by the reaction of a polyol and a diisocyanate. Polyurethane planks are available in a wide variety of specific gravities.

The residual gases in many polymeric foams and their flammability is cause for concern. However, over 1.5 million tons of foamed plastic are produced annually, and this volume is increasing at an annual rate of about 10%.

16.5 REINFORCED PLASTICS

Many naturally occurring products such as wood are reinforced composites consisting of a resinous continuous phase and a fibrous discontinuous reinforcing stage. Laminates, consisting of alternate layers of phenolic resins and cloth, paper, or wood, were available prior to World War II, but reinforced plastics were not available until the 1940s.

Most modern reinforced plastics consist of unsaturated polyester resins reinforced by fibrous glass. Continuous untwisted glass strands, or rovings, may be used in the filament winding or pultrusion processes. Chopped fibrous glass strands and preformed glass mats are used for SMC, BMC, and hand layup composites.

Boron filaments, produced by the deposition of boron on tungsten wire, single crystals or whiskers of sapphire, or aluminum oxide and graphite, are used as more sophisticated reinforcements, and epoxy resins as well as thermoplastics are also used in place of unsaturated polyester resins.

While fibrous glass-reinforced polyester resins continue to be used at an annual rate in excess of about 900,000 tons, the generally accepted engineering composite of the future will probably be based on graphite-reinforced epoxy resins. These composites have specific tensile strength (based on unit weight) and specific modulus 400% greater than that of wood, aluminum, steel, or fibrous glass-epoxy resin composite. These sophisticated composites have coefficients of thermal expansion less than those of many other construction materials.

16.6 MOLDED PLASTICS

Most plastics are converted to finished products by molding or extrusion. Until recently, most thermosets were molded by compression in which the molding powder was heated under pressure in the die cavity of a mold. This labor-intensive process has been replaced to some extent by transfer and injection molding. In the former process, a preformed briquette is warmed by induction heating and forced under pressure through an orifice into a heated multicavity mold. The cured moldings are ejected when the two-pieced mold is reopened.

While an injection-molding press, such as shown in Fig. 16.2, may be used for molding thermosets, its principal use is for the rapid molding of over 3 million tons of thermoplastics annually. This press consists of a hopper (a) which feeds the molding powder to a heated cylinder (b) where the polymer is melted and forced forward by a reciprocating plunger (c). The molten material advances toward a spreader or torpedo into a cool, closed two-piece mold (d). The cooled plastic part is ejected when the mold opens, and then the cycle is repeated. As shown in Fig. 16.3, the molten plastic passes from the nozzle through a tapered sprue, a channel or runner, and a small gate into the cooled mold cavity. The plastic in the narrow gate section is readily broken off and the thermoplastic materials in the sprue, runner, and gate are ground and remolded.

Labor costs of molding thermosets can be reduced by use of injection-molding techniques. BMC and plastic foams may also be injection molded. Special techniques are often used with the latter to produce a solid, dense

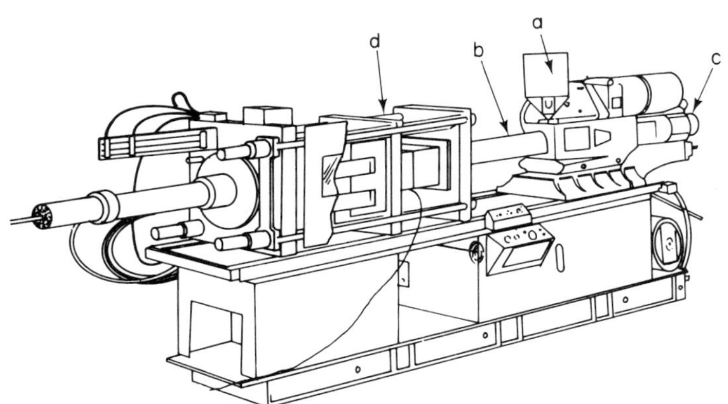

FIGURE 16.2 Cross-section of an injection molding press. (From Modern Plastics Technology by R. Seymour, 1975, Reston Publishing Co., Reston, Virginia. Used with permission of Reston Publishing Company.)

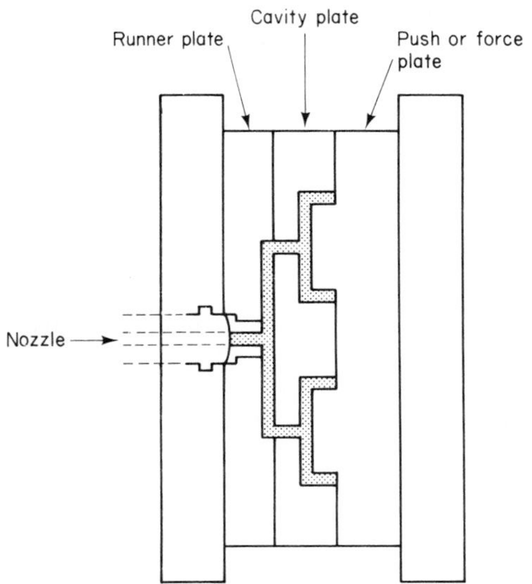

FIGURE 16.3 Injection mold in closed position (part d in Fig. 16.2). (Adapted from Modern Plastics Technology by R. Seymour, 1975, Reston Publishing Company, Reston, Virginia.)

surface. These structural foams, which are stronger than solid moldings on a weight basis, are used for furniture and similar complex objects.

As shown in Fig. 16.4, hollow plastic articles such as bottles are produced by a blow-molding process in which a heat-softened hollow plastic tube, or parison, is forced against the walls of the mold by air pressure in an automated process at a rapid rate. It is customary to cool the mold to increase the number of cycles per minute. Approximately 1 million tons of thermoplastics are used annually in the blow molding process.

As shown in Fig. 16.5, warm thermoplastic sheets may be forced into a mold by a plug in order to produce articles varying in size from briefcases to boats. The thermoforming process may be as simple as laying a warm plastic sheet over a male mold or it may be more sophisticated, such as the plug-assisted vacuum forming technique shown with biaxially oriented sheet. The principal object is to obtain a part with uniform thickness.

16.7 EXTRUSION

An extruder is an unusually versatile machine which, as shown in Fig. 16.6, accepts granulated thermoplastic in a hopper (c), plasticates the

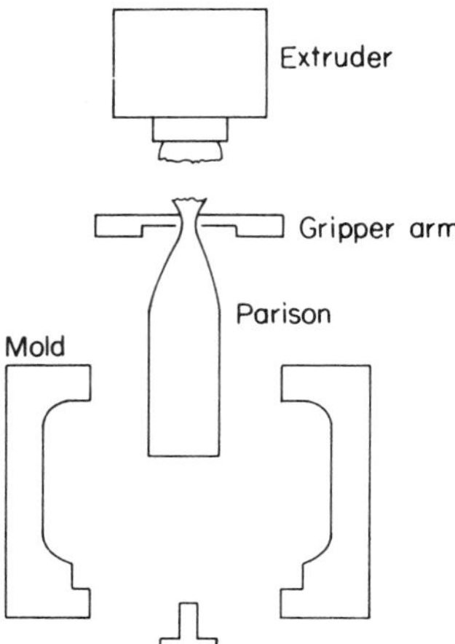

FIGURE 16.4 Sketch of extrusion blow molding scheme. (From Modern Plastics Technology by R. Seymour, 1975, Reston Publishing Co., Reston, Virginia. Used with permission of Reston Publishing Co.)

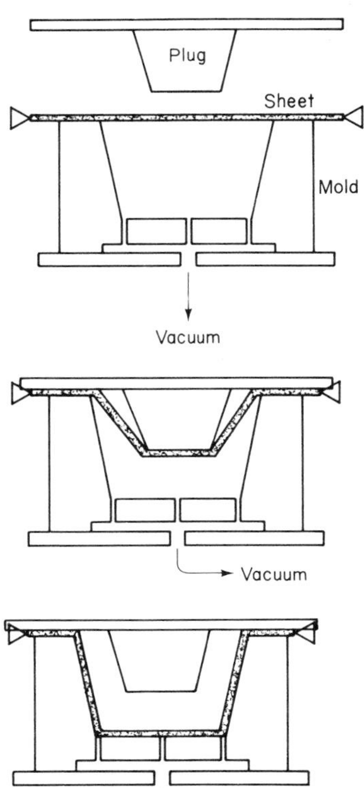

FIGURE 16.5 Steps in plug-assisted vacuum thermoforming. (Modern Plastics Encyclopedia, McGraw-Hill, New York, 1976-77; with permission of McGraw-Hill Publishers.)

TABLE 16.4 Properties of Molded Plastics

Polymer	Tensile strength (kg cm^{-2})	Flexural strength (kg cm^{-2})	Heat deflection point (@18.6 kg cm^{-2})	Dielectric constant (at 60 cycles)	Power factor (at 60 cycles)
Phenol formaldehyde resin	280	945	57		
Wood-flour filled	535	700	121	6.0	0.08
Glass-fiber filled	840	2100	232	7.1	0.05
Urea-formaldehyde, α-cellulose filled	630	980	135	8.0	0.04
Melamine-formaldehyde, α-cellulose filled	700	910		8.7	0.05
Alkyd resin glass-filled	490	1050	130	5.7	0.010
Allyl resin glass-filled	595	1050	232	4.4	0.03
Epoxy resin glass-filled	1400	2450	224	4.2	0.025
Polyethylene (type I) (LDPE)	112		38	2.3	0.0005
Polyethylene (type II) (HDPE)	315	70	49	2.3	0.0005
Polypropylene	343	490	57	2.4	0.0005
Ionomers	315		38 @ 4.6 kg cm^{-2}	2.4	0.002
Polystyrene	595	770	85	2.5	0.0002
Polymethyl methacrylate	770	1680	99	3.0	0.007
ABS copolymer	490	770	93	3.5	0.005
Polytetrafluoroethylene	245		60	2.1	0.0002
Cellulose acetate	385	630	66	5.5	0.05
Acetal resins	700	980	124	3.7	
Chlorinated polyether	420	350	93	3.1	0.01
Phenoxy resin	595	875	82	4.1	0.0012
Polycarbonate	630	945	135	3.0	0.0007
Polysulfone	700	1050	174	3.1	0.008
Polyphenylene oxide	770	1050	190	2.6	0.0003
Nylon-66 mineral filled	980	1000	166		
Polybutylene terephthalate	560	1000	66	3.29	
Polyimide	1190	1100	132	3.43	
Polymethylpentene	2800			2.12	0.00007
Polyphenylene sulfide	7000	14000	137		
Polyurethane	2800			6.0	0.03

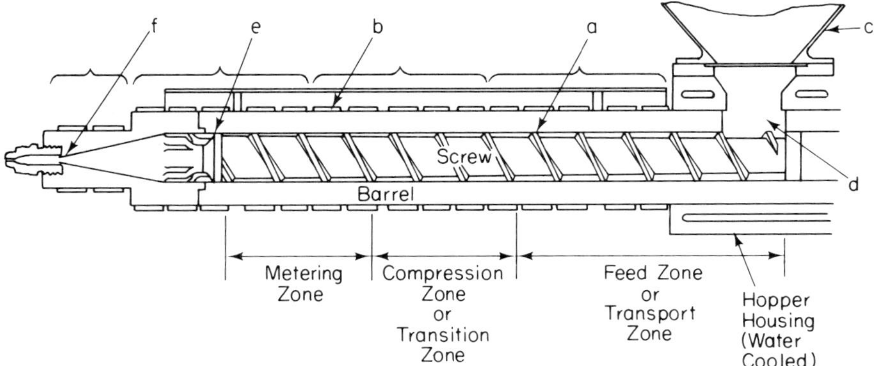

FIGURE 16.6 Sketch details of screw and extruder zones. (From Modern Plastics Technology by R. Seymour, 1975, Reston Publishing Co., Reston, Virginia. Used with permission of Reston Publishing Co.)

polymer, and forces it from the feed throat (d) through a die (f). The die may be circular for the production of rod or pipe, it may be flat for the production of sheet, or it may have any desired profile for the continuous production of almost any uniformly shaped product. The screw (a) advances the polymer through a heated cylinder (barrel) (b) to a breaker plate and protective screen pack (e) before it enters the die (f). As shown in Fig. 16.6, the extrusion process may be divided into a feed or transport zone, a compression or transition zone, and a metering zone. Over 1 million tons of extruded pipe are produced annually in the United States. The properties of molded or extruded plastic are summarized in Table 16.4.

SUMMARY

1. Synthetic fibers are produced by forcing a solution of polymer or a molten polymer through small holes in a spinneret. The extrudate from the solution may be precipitated in the wet spinning process or the solvent may be evaporated in the dry spinning process. The molten extrudate is cooled in the melt spinning process.

2. The most widely used elastomer (SBR) is obtained by coagulation of an emulsion of a copolymer of butadiene and styrene. In addition to being produced by the free-radical emulsion polymerization technique, elastomers are also produced by cationic copolymerization (butyl rubber) and by anionic polymerization (polybutadiene).

3. Films may be cast from melt or solution or extruded from a slit die, but most film is produced by air blowing a warm tubular extrudate and slitting the expanded tube.

4. Wire and paper may be coated by use of an extruder, but most coatings consist of solutions or aqueous dispersons of polymers. The trend in the coatings industry is toward lower concentrations of volatile organic solvents.

5. Polymeric foams may be produced by the mechanical frothing of a latex or by the use of gaseous propellants. The latter may be produced in situ in PU or added during processing.

6. Composites consisting of a reinforcing fiber and a resin have excellent strength properties. Graphite-epoxy resin composites are superior to many classic construction materials.

7. Thermosets may be compression molded by heating a prepolymer under pressure in a mold cavity. Thermoplastics are usually injection molded in a fast, automated process in which a granulated polymer is heat softened or plasticated in a barrel and forced into a closed cooled mold by a reciprocating ram. The molded part is ejected when the mold opens and the process is repeated.

8. Hollow articles such as bottles are produced by air blowing a heat-softened tube or parison into a two-component mold.

9. Articles like containers or boats may be produced by the thermoforming of plastic sheets.

10. Pipe and various profiles may be produced continuously by forcing heat-softened polymer through a die and cooling the extrudate.

GLOSSARY

abaca: A hemplike fiber from the Phillipines.

acetate rayon: Cellulose diacetate fibers.

Acrilan: Polyacrylonitrile-based fibers.

acrylic fibers: Those based on polyacrylonitrile.

Adiprene: PU elastomer.

agave: Fibers from the leaves of the desert century plant.

Aralac: Soybean fiber.

Ardil: Peanut fiber.

biaxial orientation: The process in which a film is stretched in two directions at right angles to each other.

BMC: Bulk-molding compound.

BTU: British thermal unit.

buna-N: Acrylonitrile-butadiene copolymer.

calender: A machine for making polymeric sheet, containing counter-rotating rolls.

casting: Production of film by evaporation of a polymeric solution.

cellophane: Regenerated cellulosic film.

charge: The amount of polymer used in each molding cycle.

coextruded film: One produced by the simultaneous extrusion of two or more polymers.

Dacron: Polyethylene terephthalate fiber.

DMF: Dimethylformamide.

draw: Depth of mold cavity.

dry spinning: Process for obtaining fiber by forcing a solution of a polymer through holes in a spinneret and evaporating the solvent from the extrudate.

elastomer: Rubber.

electrodeposition: The use of an electric charge to deposit polymer film or aqueous dispersion onto a metal substrate.

EPDM: Curable ethylene-propylene copolymer elastomer.

extrusion: A fabrication process in which a heat-softened polymer is forced continually by a screw through a die.

fibrillation: Process for producing fiber by heating and pulling twisted film strips.

filament: A continuous thread.

filament winding: Process in which filaments are dipped in a prepolymer, wound on a mandrel, and cured.

flax: The threadlike fiber from the flax plant.

gate: Thin sections of runner at the entrance of a mold cavity.

hemp: Fiber from plants of the nettle family.

hevea rubber: Hevea braziliensis, natural rubber.

Hycar: Buna-N elastomer.

jute: Plant fiber used for making burlap.

kapok: Seed fibers from the tropical silk tree.

kenaf: Cellulose fiber from the kenaf plant.

Kodel: Polyethylene terephthalate fiber.

K value: A measure of thermal conductivity in BTUs.

lamination: The plying of sheets.

Lanital: Casein fiber.

latex: A stable dispersion of a polymer in water.

mechanical goods: Industrial rubber products such as belts.

melt spinning: Process for obtaining fiber by forcing molten polymer through holes in a spinneret and cooling the filaments produced.

molding powder or compound: A premix of resin and other additives used as a molding resin.

multicellular: Open cells.

Neoprene: Polychloroprene.

nonwoven textiles: Sheet produced by binding fibers with a heated thermoplastic.

Orlon: Polyacrylonitrile-based fiber.

parison: A short plastic tube which is heated and expanded by air in the blow-molding process.

perlon: PU fibers.

PET: Polyethylene terephthalate.

phosphazene: Polyphosphonitrile elastomer.

plastisol: A dispersion of a polymer such as PVC in a liquid plasticizer.

printing ink: Highly pigmented coatings used in the printing of sheets.

PU: Polyurethane.

pultrusion: Process in which filaments are dipped in a prepolymer, passed through a die, and cured.

ramie: Fiber from an Asiatic plant.

rayon: Regenerated cellulosic fiber.

rovings: Multiple untwisted strands of filaments.

runner: Channel between the sprue and the mold cavity.

saponification: Alkaline hydrolysis.

SBR: Styrene-butadiene copolymer elastomer.

screen pack: A metal screen which prevents foreign material from reaching the die in an extruder.

silk: Natural protein fiber.

SMC: Sheet-molding compound.

spandex: Elastic PU fiber.

specific strength: Strength based on mass rather than area.

spinneret: A metal plate with many small, uniformly sized, minute holes.

sprue: Tapered orifice between nozzle and runner. This term is also applied to plastic material in the sprue.

structural foams: Polymeric foamed articles with a dense surface.

Styrofoam: Foamed polystyrene.

technology: Applied science.

tenacity: Fiber strength.

Terylene: Polyethylene terephthalate.

thermoforming: The shaping of a hot thermoplastic sheet.

Thiokol: Polyolefin sulfide elastomer.

transfer molding: A process in which a preheated briquette or preform is forced through an orifice into a heated mold cavity.

Tricel: Cellulose triacetate.

UHMWPE: Ultrahigh molecular weight polyethylene polymer.

unicellular: Closed cells.

Vicara: Zein fiber.

viscose process: Regeneration of cellulose fibers by precipitation of the sodium salt of cellulose xanthate in acid.

Viton: Polyfluorocarbon elastomer.

Vycron: Polyethylene terephthalate.

wet spinning: Obtaining fibers by precipitation of polymeric solutions.

wool: Natural protein fiber.

zein: Protein from maize (corn).

EXERCISES

1. Which is more important: (a) polymer science or (b) polymer technology?
2. Name three important natural fibers.
3. Name an important regenerated fiber.

4. Why is secondary cellulose acetate more widely used than the tertiary cellulose acetate?
5. What is the difference between rayon and cellophane?
6. Name three important synthetic fibers.
7. Name an elastomer produced by (a) cationic, (b) anionic, (c) free-radical, and (d) step-reaction polymerization techniques.
8. How is LDPE film produced?
9. Why is there a trend toward the use of less solvent in polymeric coatings?
10. What is meant by trade sales?
11. Why is a plastisol stable at room temperature?
12. How would you produce a unicellular foam?
13. Which is preferable for upholstery: (a) unicellular or (b) multicellular?
14. Why do nonflame retardant foams burn readily?
15. What reinforced plastic has been used as an automobile body?
16. Why is graphite-reinforced epoxy resin a good candidate for parts in future automobiles?
17. Why are molded thermoplastics used more than molded thermosets?
18. How could you increase the output of an injection molding press?
19. Why are structural foams used for complex furniture?
20. What are some of the advantages of a blow molded PET bottle?
21. Why would an article be thermoformed instead of molded?
22. What is the limit to the length of an extrudate such as PVC pipe?

BIBLIOGRAPHY

Akin, R. B. (1964): Acetal Resins, Reinhold, New York.

Allen, P. W. (1974): Natural Rubber and Synthetics, Palmerton, New York.

Bailey, F. E., Koleske, J. V. (1976): Polyethylene Oxide, Academic, New York.

Banow, A. (1974): Paints and Coatings Handbook, Structure Publishing, Farmington, Michigan.

Basdekas, C. H. (1964): ABS Plastics, Reinhold, New York.

Bateman, L. (ed.) (1963): The Chemistry and Physics of Rubber-Like Substances, John Wiley, New York.

Benning, C. J. (1969): Plastic Foams, John Wiley, New York.

Billmeyer, W. (1970): Textbook of Polymer Science, Part 5, Wiley Interscience, New York.

Bishop, R. B. (1971): Practical Polymerization of Styrene, Cahners Books, Boston.

Bloch, B., and Hastings, G. W. (1972): Plastic Materials in Surgery, Charles C. Thomas, Springfield, Illinois.

Boundy, R. H., and Boyer, R. F. (1952): Styrene, Its Polymers, Copolymers, and Derivatives, Reinhold, New York.

Brewer, G. E. (1973): Electrodeposition of Coatings, Advances in Chemistry Service, Washington, D.C.

Bruins, P. F. (1973): Basic Principles of Thermoforming, Society of Plastics Engineers, Greenwich, Connecticut.

——. (1976): Unsaturated Polyester Technology, Gordon and Breach, New York.

Brydson, J. A. (1966): Plastics Materials, Van Nostrand, Princeton.

Cagle, C. V. (1973): Handbook of Adhesive Bonding, McGraw-Hill, New York.

Carswell, T. S. (1947): Phenoplasts, Interscience, New York.

Casper, M. S. (1972): Synthetic Turf and Sporting Surface, Noyes Data Corp., Park Ridge, New Jersey.

Craver, J. K., and Tess, R. W. (1975): Applied Polymer Science, Organic Coatings and Plastic Chemistry Div. of ACS, Washington, D.C.

Crosby, E. G., and Kochis, S. N. (1974): Practical Guide to Plastic Applications, Cahners Books, Boston.

Deanin, R. D. (1974): New Industrial Polymers, American Chemical Society, Washington, D.C.

DeRenzo, D. J. (1974): Polymers in Lithography, Noyes Data Corp., Park Ridge, New Jersey.

Doyle, E. N. (1974): The Development of Polyurethane Products, McGraw-Hill, New York.

DuBois, J. H., and John, F. W. (1967): Plastics, Reinhold, New York.

———. (1974): Plastics, Van Nostrand-Reinhold, New York.

Duck, E. N. (1974): Plastics and Rubber, Philosophical Library, New York.

Economy, J. (1976): New and Specialty Fibers, John Wiley, New York.

Eisenman, G. (1975): Membranes, Dekker, New York.

Farnham, S. E. (1972): Guide to Thermoformed Plastic Packaging, Cahners Books, Boston.

Fisher, E. G. (1969): Extrusion of Plastics, John Wiley, New York.

Floyd, D. E. (1958): Polyamide Resins, Reinhold, New York.

Frisch, K. C., and Saunders, J. H. (1973): Plastic Foams, Dekker, New York.

Gaylord, N. W. (1974): Reinforced Plastics, Cahners Books, Boston.

Glanville, A. B. (1975): Plastic Engineers Data Book, Industrial Press, New York.

Golding, B. (1959): Polymers and Resins, Van Nostrand, Princeton.

Gould, D. T. (1959): Phenolic Resins, Reinhold, New York.

Griff, A. L. (1962): Plastics Extrusion Technology, Reinhold, New York.

Gross, S. (ed.) (1976): Materials (plastics), Mod. Plast., 53(10A):6.

Grzegorczyk, D., and Feineman, G. (1973): Handbook of Plastics in Electronics, Reston Publishing, Reston, Virginia.

Hearle, J. W. S., Grosberg, P., Backer, S. (1969): Structural Mechanics of Fibers, Yarns and Fabrics, Wiley Interscience, New York.

Hensen, J. H. T., and Whelan, A. (1974): Developments in PVC, Applied Science Pub., Barkind, England.

Herman, B. S. (1976): Adhesives, Noyes Data Corp., Park Ridge, New Jersey.

Herman, J. H. T., and Whelan, A. (1974): Developments in PVC, Applied Science Pub., Barkind, England.

Holiday, L. (1974): Ionic Polymer, Halsted, New York.

Horn, M. B. (1960): Acrylic Resins, Reinhold, New York.

Kohan, M. I. (1973): Nylon Plastic, Wiley Interscience, New York.

Kraus, G. (ed.) (1965): Reinforcement of Elastomers, Wiley Interscience, New York.

Kresser, T. O. J. (1960): Polypropylene, Reinhold, New York.

——. (1967): Polyethylene, Reinhold, New York.

Kromenthal, R. L., Oser, Z., Martin, E. (1975): Polymer in Medicine and Surgery, Plenum, New York.

Lane, R. I. (1974): Rigid Polyurethane Foam, Society of Plastic Engineers, Greenwich, Connecticut.

Lee, H. (1975): Adhesion Science and Technology, Plenum, New York.

Lee, H., and Neville, K. (1966): Handbook of Epoxy Resins, McGraw-Hill, New York.

Lenz, R. W., and Stein, R. S. (1973): Structure and Properties of Polymer Fibers, Plenum, New York.

Mark, H. F., Atlas, S. M., Cernia, E. (eds.) (1968): Man-Made Fibers, Science and Technology, Wiley Interscience, New York (Vol. 1, 1967, Vols. 2, 3, 1968).

Martens, C. R. (1961): Alkyd Resins, Reinhold, New York.

Martin, R. W. (1956): The Chemistry of Phenolic Resins, John Wiley, New York.

Mathews, G. (1971): Vinyl Chloride and Vinyl Acetate Polymers, Butterworths, London.

May, C. A., and Tanada, Y. (1973): Epoxy Resins, Dekker, New York.

McDermett, J. (1972): Industrial Membranes, Noyes Data Corp., Park Ridge, New Jersey.

McKelvey, J. M. (1962): Plastics Processing, John Wiley, New York.

Megson, N. J. L. (1958): Phenolic Resin Chemistry, Academic, New York.

Meltzer, Y. L. (1972): Water Soluble Polymers, Noyes Data Corp., Park Ridge, New Jersey.

Milby, R. V. (1973): Plastic Technology, McGraw-Hill, New York.

Miles, D. C., and Briston, J. L. (1965): Polymer Technology, Part 2, Chemical Publishing, New York.

Mohr, J. G. (1973): SPI Handbook of Reinforced Plastics, Van Nostrand-Reinhold, New York.

Moncrief, R. W. (1975): Man-Made Fibers, Halsted, New York.

Paist, W. D. (1958): Cellulosics, Reinhold, New York.

Parkyn, B., Lamb, F., Clifton, B. V. (1967): Polyesters, American Elsevier, New York.

Parrott, N. J. (1973): Fiber Reinforced Materials Technology, Van Nostrand-Reinhold, New York.

Patten, W. J. (1976): Plastics Technology, Reston Publishing, Reston, Virginia.

Penn, W. S. (1962): PVC Technology, Maclaren & Sons, London.

——. (1972): PVC Technology, John Wiley, New York.

Peterson, D. C. (1974): The OSHA Compliance Manual, Society of Plastic Engineers, Greenwich, Connecticut.

Plueddemann, E. P. (1974): Composite Materials, Academic, New York.

Pritchard, J. G. (1970): Polyvinyl Alcohol, Gordon and Breach, New York.

Raff, R. A. V. (ed.) (1967): Technical Progress in Plastics Industry, Washington State University, Pullman, Washington.

Randolph, A. F. (ed.) (1960): Plastics Engineering Handbook, Reinhold, New York.

Ravve, A. (1967): Organic Chemistry of Macromolecules, Dekker, New York.

Renner, E., and Samsonov, G. V. (1973): Protective Coatings on Metals, Plenum, New York.

Richardson, P. (1974): Introduction to Extrusion, Society of Plastic Engineers, Greenwich, Connecticut.

Richardson, T. A. (1975): Modern Industrial Plastics, Howard Sams & Co., Indianapolis, Indiana.

Robitshek, P., and Lewin, A. (1950): Phenolic Resins, Iliffe Books, London.

Rosato, D. V. (1976): Plastics Industry Safety Handbook, Cahners Books, Boston.

Rosato, D. V., and Grove, Jr., C. S. (1964): Filament Winding, Wiley Interscience, New York.

Rubin, I. I. (1972): Injection Molding, Theory and Practice, Wiley Interscience, New York.

Schildknecht, C. E. (1962): Vinyl and Related Polymers, John Wiley, New York.

Schultz, J. M. (1973): Polymer Material Science, Prentice-Hall, Englewood Cliffs, New Jersey.

Schnell, H. (1964): Chemistry and Physics of Polycarbonates, Wiley Interscience, New York.

Segal, C. K. (1967): High Temperature Polymers, Dekker, New York.

Seymour, R. B. (1972): Introduction to Polymer Chemistry, Chap. 14, McGraw-Hill, New York.

———. (1975): Modern Plastics Technology, Reston Publishing, Reston, Virginia.

Sittig, M. (1972): Polyamide Fiber Manufacture, Noyes Data Corp., Park Ridge, New Jersey.

Skeist, I. (1962): Handbook of Adhesives, Reinhold, New York.

———. (1974): Synthetic Water Soluble Polymers, Skeist Laboratories, Livingston, New Jersey.

Stille, J. K. (1962): Introduction of Polymer Chemistry, John Wiley, New York.

Summerville, S. (1972): Plastic Contact Lenses, Noyes Data Corp., Park Ridge, New Jersey.

Sweeting, O. J. (1969): The Science and Technology of Polymer Films, Vol. 1, John Wiley, New York.

Teach, W. C., and Kressling, G. C. (1960): Polystyrene, Reinhold, New York.

Titow, M. O., and Lanhan, B. J. (1975): Reinforced Thermoplastics, Halsted, New York.

Vale, C. P., and Taylor, W. G. K. (1964): Aminoplastics, Iliffe Books, London.

Vogl, O. (1967): Polyaldehydes, Dekker, New York.

Wall, L. A. (1972): Flurocopolymer, Wiley Interscience, New York.

Wein, C. I. (1975): Introduction to Injection Molding, Society of Plastic Engineers, Greenwich, Connecticut.

Wessling, R. A. (1977): Polyvinylidene Chloride, Gordon and Breach, New York.

Wheelan, M. A. (1974): Injection Molding of Rubber, Halsted, New York.

Whitby, G. S., Davis, C. C., Dunbrook, R. F. (eds.) (1954): Synthetic Rubber, John Wiley, New York.

Whitehouse, A. A. K., and Pritchett, E. G. K. (1955): Phenolic Resins, Plastics Inst. Monograph, London.

Williams, D. J. (1971): Polymer Science and Engineering, Prentice-Hall, Englewood Cliffs, New Jersey

Winding, C. C., and Hiatt, G. D. (1961): Polymeric Materials, Chaps. 7, 8, McGraw-Hill, New York.

Solutions

In the case of certain questions several answers may be appropriate. Also, the depth and breadth of an answer or answers to a question may vary depending on the preference of the student/teacher. Usually, a single answer is given in brief detail, indicating at least one direction of thought. Further, the answers to some questions are not specifically contained within the text. Answers to questions also may involve taking pieces of information acquired from several chapters. Thus, the questions are meant to encourage thinking, rationalization, and integration, and possibly an extra glance through a particular chapter. Ultimately, the questions are meant to act as a teaching/learning tool.

CHAPTER 1

1. This list could include paper, wood, nylon, polyester fibers, melamine dishware, polyethylene fibers, Teflon coated cooking utensils, starchy foods, meat, wool, hair, paint, etc.
2. A(1), B(1), C(2)
3. A. Polyethylene
   B. Bakelite
   C. Any protein, e.g., casein
4. c
5. b, c, d, e, f
6. e, f
7. b, c, d
8. Possibly, wait and see or live and learn.
9. Because polymer science is a relatively new science.
10. Approximately 100 percent.
11. 28002

12. Both are regenerated cellulose which differ in physical form. Rayon is a filament and cellophane is a sheet.

13. Since the novolac resin is produced by the condensation of phenol with a small amount of formaldehyde on the acid side, it has residual unreacted phenol functional groups and is more heat stable than the resole resin which is made using an excess of formaldehyde.

CHAPTER 2

1.

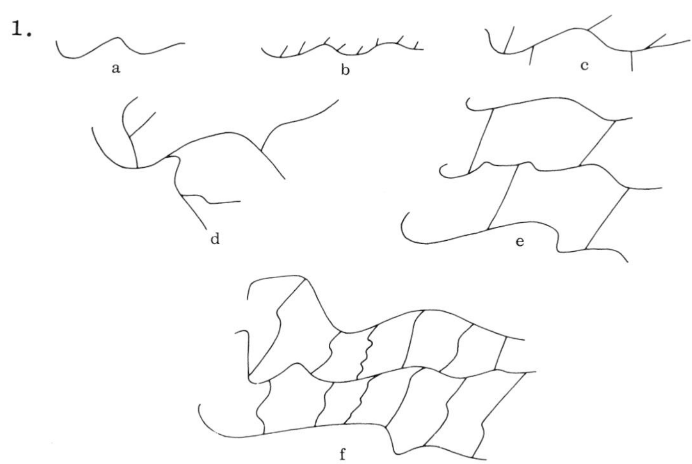

2. a. LDPE, b. LDPE.

3. a. 109.5°, b. 109.5°; zigzag chains characteristic of alkanes.

4. a. 503.5 nm, b. 503.5 nm.

5. d, g, i.

6. 999.

7.

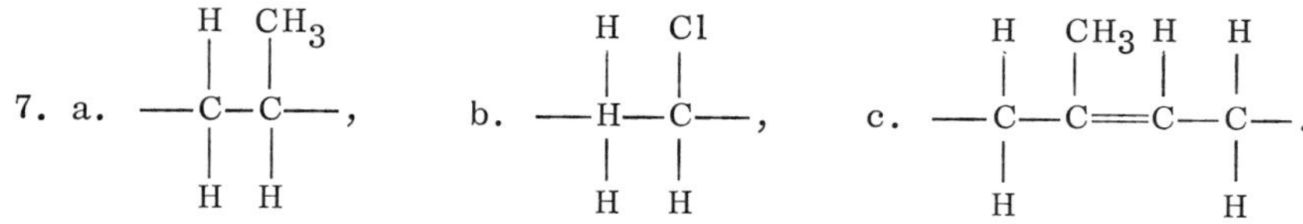

8. c.

9. d, e, f, g.

10. a.

11. a.

12. a.

13. a.

```
       H  H  H  H                      H  H  H  H
       |  |  |  |                      |  |  |  |
14. a. —C—C—C—C—                   b.  —C—C—C—C—
       |  |  |  |                      |  |  |  |
       H OH  H OH                      H OH OH  H
```

```
                Cl                      Cl    Cl
                |                       |     |
15. a. —C—C—C—C—                   b.  —C—C—C—C—
          |
          Cl
```

16.

```
       CH2                      CH2
  H2C        H            H            CH2

   H         H            H            H
        H                       H
```

17. a. HDPE, LDPE, hevea rubber, etc.
    b. PVC, etc.
    c. Nylon-66, cellulose, silk, etc.

18. b.

19. a.

20. a.

21. b.

22. a.

23. 378 nm.

24. a.

25. About 50%.

26. b.

27. Intramolecular hydrogen bonds.

28. a.

29. a.

30. a.
31. Add a nucleating agent to the melt and cool rapidly in a thin layer.
32. a.
33. b.

CHAPTER 3

1. Morphology is the study of shape, while rheology is the study of flow and deformation.
2. b, d.
3. G is the shear modulus.
4. c.
5. a. increase, b. decrease.
6. The slope or modulus would be greater for polystyrene.
7. a has a low modulus and high viscosity, therefore η/G will be large.
8. a, because its viscosity would decrease as the shear rate is increased.
9. b, since its Poisson's ratio is less than 0.5.
10. Both would have the same volume percent occupied by holes.
11. a, because of die swell.
12. At a temperature of 35°C above the T_g of polystyrene, i.e., at about 140°C.
13. a_1 and a_2 are related to the free volume.
14. The coefficient of viscosity (η) is equal to the ratio of the applied stress (s) to the applied velocity gradient $d\gamma/dt$.
15. Stress relaxation.
16. b.
17. One in which London forces are the predominant intermolecular attractions.
18. b.
19. Cohesive energy density is equal to the strength of the intermolecular forces between molecules, which is equal to the molar energy of vaporization per unit volume $\Delta E/V$.
20. b.

21. Higher.
22. $\Delta S = (\Delta H - \Delta G)/T$ at constant T.
23. A good solvent.
24. 0.
25. θ temperature.
26. b.
27. 547.6 cal cm^{-3}.
28. 0.
29. 1,000,000 g.
30. $\delta = 9.05$ H = [1.05(133 + 28 + 735)]/104.
31. M = 0.33, $(300\ M)^{1/2} = 10$ H.
32. The contribution of the polar group becomes less significant as the alkyl portion increases.
33. b. $\delta = 9.2$ H.
34. a. Benzene is a better solvent therefore the value of a is greater.
35. 0.
36. When $\alpha = 0$.
37. $\sqrt{\overline{r}^2}$ = the root mean square end-to-end distance of a polymer chain.
38. As shown in the Arrhenius equation $\log [\eta] = \log A + E/2.3RT$, $[\eta]$ is inversely related to T.
39. b. Less is extruded in the same time under identical conditions.

CHAPTER 4

1. b., c., d., e.
2. 50,000.
3. $\overline{M}_n = 1.57 \times 10^6$, $\overline{M}_w = 1.62 \times 10^6$.
4. a. 1, b. 2.0.
5. $\overline{M}_n$, $\overline{M}_v$, $\overline{M}_w$, $\overline{M}_z$.
6. b., c., d.
7. $[\eta] = K\overline{M}^a$.
8. GPC, ultracentrifugation.

9. d., e., f.
10. One is the reciprocal of the other.
11. 0.5.
12. 2 (end groups).
13. 2.0.
14. 2.25×10^8.
15. c.
16. A type of double extrapolation for the determination of $\overline{M}_w$ for high molecular weight polymers in which both the concentration and the angle of the incident beam are extrapolated to zero.
17. $\overline{M}_n$.
18. Because of higher vapor pressure, the solvent evaporates faster from a pure solvent than from a solution; an application of Raoult's law.
19. The melt viscosity is proportional to the molecular weight to the 3.4 power.
20. The extremely high molecular weight polymer is much tougher.
21. When the exponent a in the Mark-Houwink equation equals 1.
22. A nonsolvent whose solubility parameter differed from that of the polymer by at least 1.8 H.
23. a. VPO, b. membrane osmometry.
24. Small polymer molecules may pass through a semipermeable membrane.
25. b.
26. a.
27. Answer may vary. For a homodisperse sample, a is better if polymer drainage is important. For a long chained heterodisperse sample, b is a more accurate answer.
28. B is a constant related to the interaction of the solvent and the polymer.

CHAPTER 5

1. ASTM.
2. $TS = \frac{L}{A} = \frac{282 \text{ kg}}{1.25 \text{ cm} \times 0.32 \text{ cm}} = 705 \text{ kg cm}^{-2}$.
3. $FS = \frac{3PL}{2bd^2} = \frac{3(18.2 \text{ kg})(1.27 \text{ cm})}{2(1.27 \text{ cm})(3.2 \text{ cm})^2} = 8.53 \text{ kg cm}^{-2}$.

4. $CS = \frac{L}{A} = \frac{3500 \text{ kg}}{1.27 \text{ cm} \times 1.27 \text{ cm}} = 2170 \text{ kg cm}^{-2}$.

5. $\% El = \frac{\Delta l}{l} = \left(\frac{12 - 5}{5}\right)(100) = 140\%$.

6. $E = \frac{TS}{El} = \frac{705 \text{ kg cm}^{-2}}{0.026 \text{ cm/cm}} = 27{,}100 \text{ kg cm}^{-2}$.

7. Creep is slow-dimensional change in polymers resulting from irreversible chain slippage or segmental motion.

8. a. 0.5, b. 0.3.

9. Primarily reversible bond stretching and distortion of bond angles in the polymer chain.

10. Irreversible uncoiling and slippage of chains.

11. By relative areas under the curves.

12. Increase.

13. Decrease.

14. No. The former is tougher but this is not a linear relationship.

15. Because polymers, often being poor conductors, are so widely used in electrical applications.

16. a.

17. Because they are poor conductors of heat.

18. 18.60 kg cm^{-2}, 4.65 kg cm^{-2}.

19. Almost every organic compound will burn if the conditions are ideal for combustion. Tests such as the OI test are useful as comparative tests only.

20. a.

21. They change abruptly.

22. This is an area still in motion. Thus several answers can be properly presented.

23. 21 per propylene unit (3n-trans.-rot.).

24. about 190 to 800 μm.

25. a.

26. Preferably X-ray diffraction; nmr may also be used, etc.

27. DTA, DSC, TML, TBA, etc.

CHAPTER 6

1. Enzymes are present in the human digestive system for the hydrolysis of α linkages but not for β linkages in polysaccharides.
2. Cellobiose is a β glucoside while maltose is an α glucoside.
3. Because of the presence of intermolecular hydrogen bonds.
4. It is the same since there is an equilibrium between the α and β conformations of D-glucose.
5. a.—it is less soluble than b.
6. Three.
7. Secondary cellulose acetate.
8. It forms an amine salt.
9. a.
10. It contains carboxylic acid groups.
11. It is a polyamide.
12. Glycine, because it has no chiral carbon atom.
13. To the positive pole.
14. Collagen has strong intermolecular hydrogen bonds.
15. It should be a linear crystalline polymer, with strong intermolecular hydrogen bonds, and high tensile strength and modulus associated with a regular repeating structure.
16. b.
17. 16.
18. $\left(\!-\text{O}-\text{P}-\text{O}-\underset{}{\overset{\text{B}}{\overset{|}{\text{S}}}}-\!\right)$ where S = deoxyribose, S = sugar, B = base.
19. b.
20. Thymine.
21. The presence of bulky pendant groups and hydrogen bonding favors the helical arrangement.
22. TAATGCAGTA.
23. The maximum of 16 dinucleotides is not enough to direct the initiation, termination, and insertion of 20 amino acids in a protein chain; 64 trinucleotides is more than ample.
24. a. is trans and b. is a cis isomer of 1,4-polyisoprene.

25. 0.5.

26. Increase.

27. Contracts.

28. An elastomer is an amorphous polymer with a low T_g and low intermolecular forces which increases in entropy and crystallizes when stretched.

29. Guayule grows on arid soil in temperate areas and has a high content of natural rubber.

30. b.—isoprene is the monomer in the synthetic process and isopentenylpyrophosphate is the precessor in natural rubber.

31. It must be

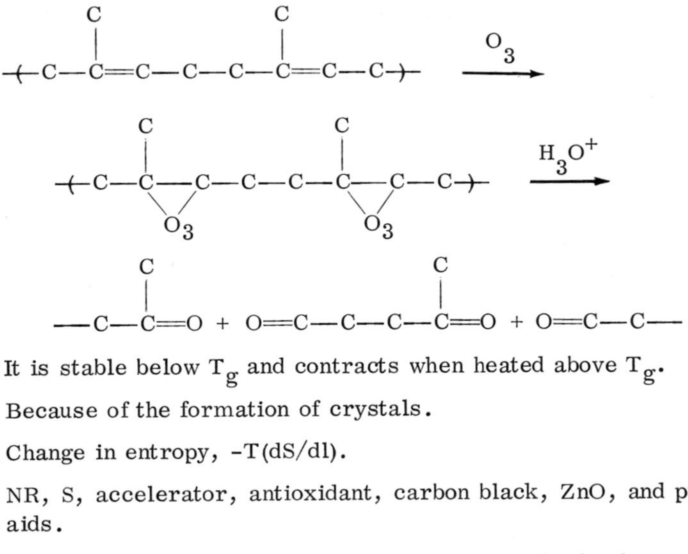

$$-\!\!(\!-C-\overset{\overset{\displaystyle C}{|}}{C}=C-C-C-\overset{\overset{\displaystyle C}{|}}{C}=C-C-\!)\!\!- \xrightarrow{O_3}$$

$$-\!\!(\!-C-\overset{\overset{\displaystyle C}{|}}{C}\underset{O_3}{\underbrace{\;-\;}}C-C-C-\overset{\overset{\displaystyle C}{|}}{C}\underset{O_3}{\underbrace{\;-\;}}C-C-\!)\!\!- \xrightarrow{H_3O^+}$$

$$-C-\overset{\overset{\displaystyle C}{|}}{C}=O + O=C-C-C-\overset{\overset{\displaystyle C}{|}}{C}=O + O=C-C-$$

32. It is stable below T_g and contracts when heated above T_g.

33. Because of the formation of crystals.

34. Change in entropy, $-T(dS/dl)$.

35. NR, S, accelerator, antioxidant, carbon black, ZnO, and processing aids.

36. It couples with the macroradical to produce a dead polymer.

37. They often cost more, are often contaminated, and are often inferior to synthetic products.

38. A polar solvent, since it is a polyol.

39. A hydrocarbon, since asphalt contains aliphatic cyclic hydrocarbons.

40. b.

41. At least 60 million tons.

42. Yes, casein is no longer used as a molding resin and, hence, the article may have value as a collectors item.

CHAPTER 7

1. b., c., e.
2. No. The polymer chains would probably be too flexible.
3. a.—less flexible.
4. 100,000.
5. $\log k = (-E_a/2.3RT) + \log A$. Therefore, the value of log k increases as the first term in the equation becomes less because of an increase in the value of T.
6. The dimer.
7. A trimer or a tetramer, since two dimer molecules may react, or a dimer may react with a molecule of the reactant.
8. Stretch the filament to permit the formation of more hydrogen bonds.
9. Polytetramethylene adipamide, or nylon-46.
10. a.—a stable six-membered ring could be formed.
11. a.
12. 1 hr.
13. b.
14. 9.
15. It would be a stiff linear high molecular weight polymer with strong hydrogen bonds.
16. 133.
17. 2.2.
18. 0.91.
19. 2.8.
20. a. would have better geometry.
21. It would be weak at the angle perpendicular to the stretch.
22. b.
23. a.—there would be more surface available for attack.
24. Produce it from a mixture of isomers or use a mixture of esters of p-hydroxybenzoic acid and p-hydroxyphenylacetic acid.
25. Increase the number of methylene groups, e.g., nylon-1212.

26. Reduce the number of methylene groups so that it would absorb more moisture.
27. a.—the amide is a stiffening group.
28. Because of the presence of bulky pendant groups.
29. b. is a ladder polymer.
30. Not particularly, since the polyamine reacts to produce a polyurea. However, other propellants are used commercially in foam production.
31. Use an excess of the glycol.
32. Increase the number of methylene groups in the reactant.
33. Because of the presence of phenylene stiffening groups.
34. Because of the presence of strong polar groups.
35. The precursor, furfural, is produced from waste corn cobs.
36. An average of one functional group on each phenol is unreacted in the A-stage resin. Hence, one must add formaldehyde to produce a cross-linked polymer.
37. No; resorcinol is trifunctional and very reactive.
38. Phenolic resins were developed before there was much information on polymer science. Those involved in an art have a tendency to create new terms to describe what they do not understand.
39. Most people prefer to use light-colored dinnerware.
40. All three.
41. a.—b. would be a branched chain.

CHAPTER 8

1. (a) A small amount of reactants, dimer, trimer, and oligomers, plus low molecular weight polymers. (b) High molecular weight polyisobutylene plus monomer.
2. A Lewis base-cocatalyst complex. Actually, the proton is the initiator.
3. A carbonium ion.
4. A macrocarbonium ion.
5. A gegenion.
6. a.
7. b.

8. The macroions have similar charges.

9. a.

10. b.

11. (a) HDPE or PP. (b) IR, EP, or butyl rubber (IIR). (c) PP.

12. a.

13. b.

14. a, b.

15. b, d, e.

16. b.

17. $\nu = \overline{DP}$.

18. Polyisobutylene.

19. $R_i = kC[M]$, where C equals [catalyst-cocatalyst complex].

20. Increases the rate.

21. No observable change.

22. a.

23. c, d.

24. A cation.

25. They are equal.

26. $\overline{DP} = R_p/R_t$.

27. (b) Many times higher.

28. 0%.

29. $\overline{DP}$ is independent of [C].

30. No: they are thermally unstable.

31. Cap the ends by esterification or copolymerize with dioxolane.

32. Because formaldehyde is produced in the decomposition which is the reverse of propagation.

33. No: this is above the ceiling temperature.

34. Polymerize in the presence of oxirane.

35. Add a water-soluble linear polymer such as polyethylene oxide.

36. Because of its regular structure.

37. It is a carcinogen.

38. CO_2.

39. Convert them to solid polymers by cationic chain polymerization using sulfuric acid as the initiator.

40. A carbanion.

41. Macrocarbanions.

42. Because they are stable macrocarbanions capable of further polymerization.

43. c.

44. Nylon-6.

45. 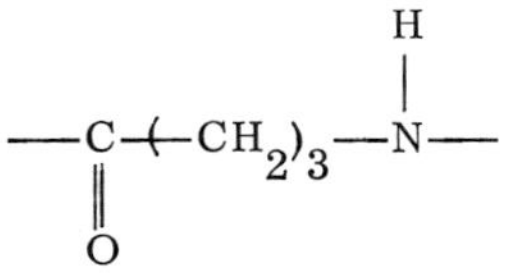 $$-\underset{\underset{O}{\|}}{C}-(CH_2)_3-\overset{\overset{H}{|}}{N}-$$

46. $TiCl_3$ and $(C_2H_5)_2AlCl$.

47. It yields atactic polymers.

48. The propagating species in anionic chain polymerization is a butyl-terminated macroanion. Propagation takes place by the addition of monomer units to the chain end of this anion. The propagating species in complex coordination catalyst polymerization is an active center with an alkyl group from the cocatalyst as the terminal group. Propagation takes place by the insertion of the monomer between the titanium atom and the carbon atom by way of a π complex.

49. Its very low specific gravity (0.83).

50.

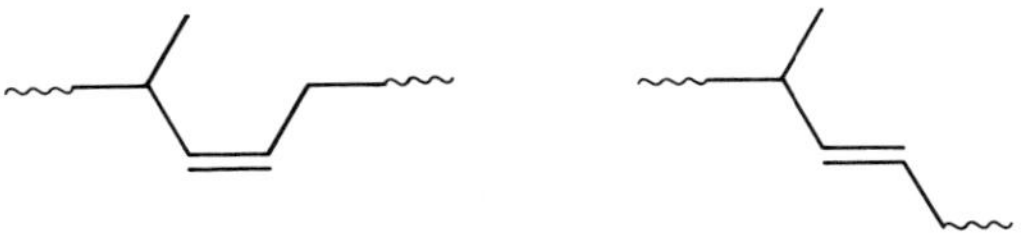

Cis

Trans

51. (a)

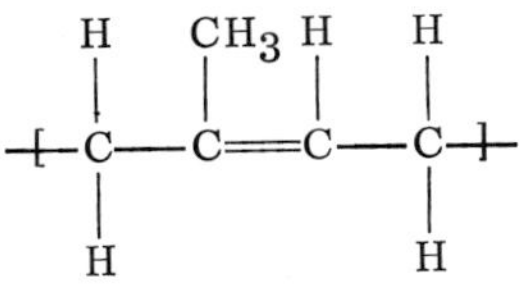

$$-\!\!\left[\underset{\underset{H}{|}}{\overset{\overset{H}{|}}{C}}-\overset{\overset{CH_3}{|}}{C}=\overset{\overset{H}{|}}{C}-\underset{\underset{H}{|}}{\overset{\overset{H}{|}}{C}}\right]\!\!-$$

(b)

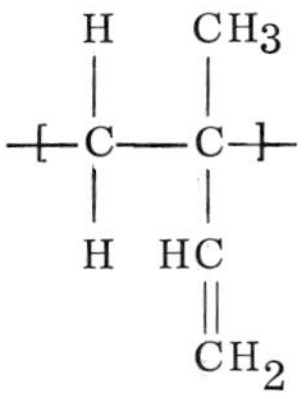

$$\begin{array}{c} \quad H \quad CH_3 \\ \quad | \quad\;\; | \\ -\!\!\!+\!C\!-\!\!-\!C\!+\!\!\!- \\ \quad | \quad\;\; | \\ \quad H \quad HC \\ \qquad\quad \| \\ \qquad\quad CH_2 \end{array}$$

52. A chromia catalyst supported on silica (Phillips catalyst).

53. cis-Polyisoprene.

54. Ethylene-propylene copolymer.

CHAPTER 9

1. (a) H/:BF_3OH. (b) Na/:NH_2. (c) $(H_3C)_2\!-\!\underset{\underset{CN}{|}}{C}\!-\!N\!\cdot\!/\!\!\cdot N\!-\!\underset{\underset{CN}{|}}{C}\!-\!(CH_3)_2$.

2. Free-radical chain polymerization.

3. 12.5%.

4. Coupling.

5. Neither, since both will reduce $\overline{DP}$.

6. LDPE, PVC, PS, etc.

7. None, provided the system is a homogeneous solution.

8. (a) (b) 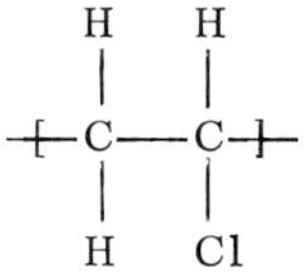 (c)

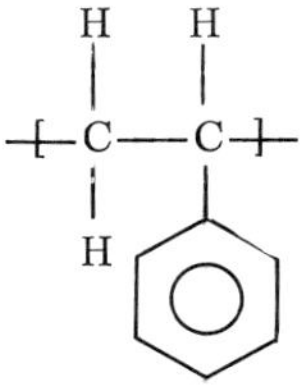

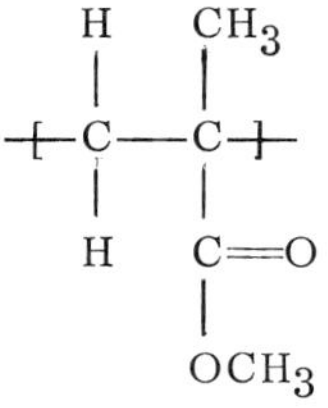

$$\begin{array}{c} H \quad H \\ | \quad\; | \\ -\!\!\!+\!C\!-\!\!-\!C\!+\!\!\!- \\ | \quad\; | \\ H \quad C_6H_5 \end{array} \qquad \begin{array}{c} H \quad H \\ | \quad\; | \\ -\!\!\!+\!C\!-\!\!-\!C\!+\!\!\!- \\ | \quad\; | \\ H \quad Cl \end{array} \qquad \begin{array}{c} H \quad CH_3 \\ | \quad\;\; | \\ -\!\!\!+\!C\!-\!\!-\!C\!+\!\!\!- \\ | \quad\;\; | \\ H \quad C\!=\!O \\ \qquad\; | \\ \qquad\; OCH_3 \end{array}$$

9. Since the rate of termination has decreased, more monomer may be added gradually to produce very high molecular weight polymers.

10. Initiation, which is governed by the rate of production of free radicals.

11. a.

12. Monomeric styrene.

13. ln 2 = 0.693.

14. Measure the volume of N_2 produced.

15. 40 ± 10 kcal/mol.

16. One may polymerize at low temperatures and also regulate the rate of production of free radicals.

17. Neither one is a catalyst; both are good initiators.

18. a, b, c = 1×10^{-11} mol/liter, assuming monomer is still present.

19. 5 ± 3 kcal mol^{-1}.

20. $R_p \propto [I]^{1/2}$.

21. $\overline{DP}$ decreases.

22. Dioctyl phthalate or other nonvolatile dialkyl phthalates.

23. Vinyl acetate. PVA is obtained by hydrolysis of PVAc.

24. The initiator produces 2R· by homolytic cleavage.

25. Neither; it remains unchanged.

26. Ethylene has no electron-donating groups and is less polar than isobutylene.

27. Disproportionation.

28. The termination mechanism at higher temperatures is disproportionation.

29. 4 to 10 kcal mol^{-1}.

30. T_c = 61°C. Therefore, poly(α-methylstyrene) would decompose when heated above 61°C.

31. The original 6-carbon chain segment is called the branch and it is relatively short compared to the new chain extension.

32. (b) The bond strength for C—Cl is less.

33. The $H(CH_2)_{12}S\cdot$ produced by chain transfer is an active free radical which initiates new chains.

34. No: the heat from the exothermic reaction might cause an explosion.

35. They are the same.

36. No, but one should avoid contact with the skin and ascertain that there is a minimal amount of monomer residue in the polymer.

37. It forms a ladder polymeric filament.

38. The droplets are relatively few in number, and the chances of an oligoradical entering them is extremely small.

39. The primary free radicals are water soluble.

40. The initial polymerization rate would be retarded.

41. The rate would be slower, and probably the polymerization would be by the suspension mechanism.

42. The structure of PTFE is regular. The large pendant group in FEP destroys this regularity.

43. Both $\overline{DP}$ and R_p are proportional to N/2 where N/2 is the number of active micelles.

44. (b) The additional chlorine on the repeating unit increases the specific gravity.

CHAPTER 10

1. (a)

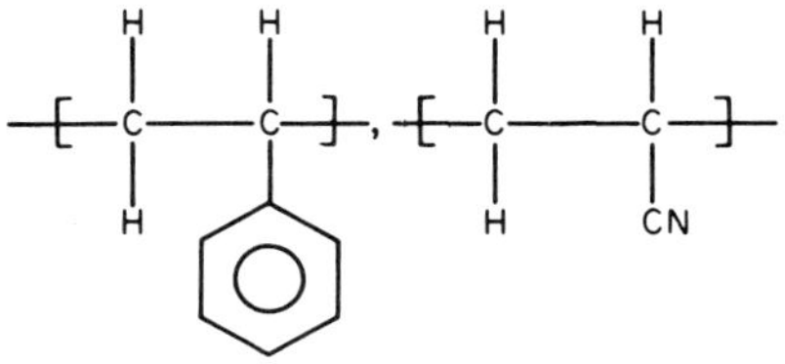

$-[-CH_2-CH(C_6H_5)-]-$, $-[-CH_2-CH(CN)-]-$

(b)

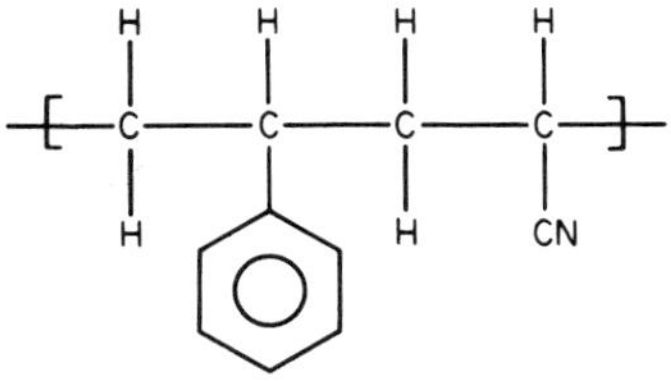

$-[-CH_2-CH(C_6H_5)-CH_2-CH(CN)-]-$

(c)

$-[-CH_2-CH(C_6H_5)-CH_2-CH(C_6H_5)-CH_2-CH(CN)-]-$

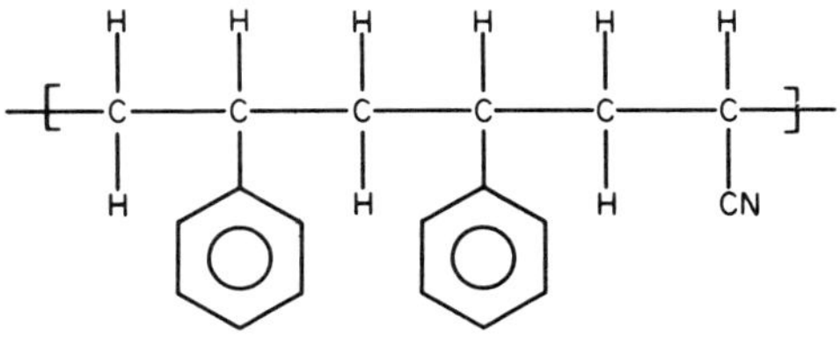

(d)

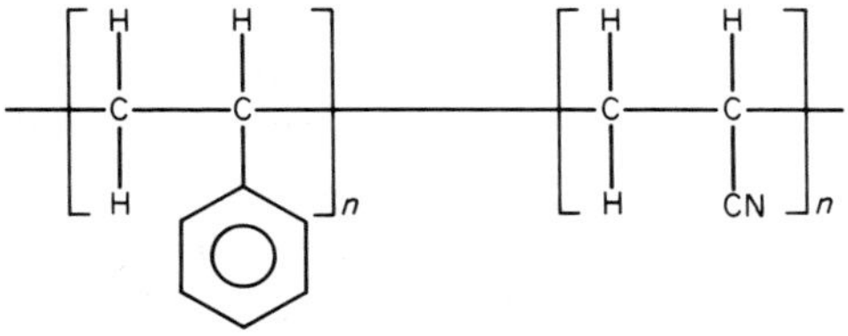

(e)

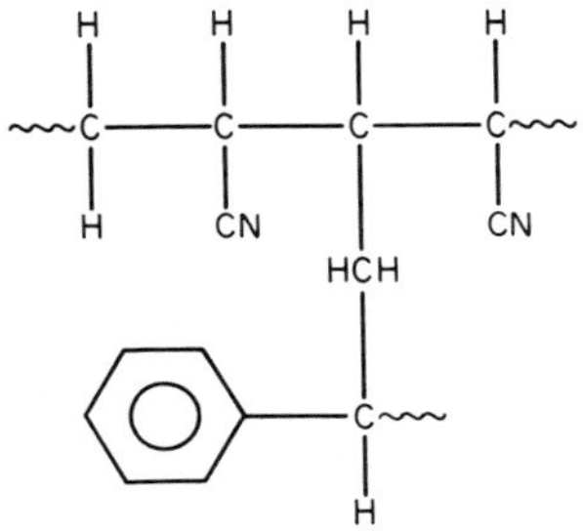

2. Equimolar.
3. $r_1 = k_{11}/k_{12}$, $r_2 = k_{22}/k_{21}$.
4. No: they are constant.
5. They vary in accordance with the Arrhenius equation.
6. Vinylidene chloride, 72%, vinyl chloride, 28%.
7. Styrene, etc.
8. (a) cationic, (b) anionic or free radical, (c) Ziegler-Natta.
9. Alternating.
10. $(M_1)_n(M_2)_n(M_1)_n$.
11. $r_1r_2 \simeq 1$.
12. b.
13. A charge transfer complex is present at the lower temperature.
14. (a) 50% of each. (b) 91% S and 9% MMA. (c) 94% MMA and 6% S.
15. Isobutylene, 71.4%, isoprene, 29.6%.
16. Isobutylene, 96%.
17. Add a mixture of monomers to maintain the original ratio of reactants.
18. (a) Q value is higher.

19. Vinyl chloride, 68%.
20. The presence of vinyl acetate mers in the chain breaks up the regularity characteristic of PVC so that the copolymer has a lower T_g, is more soluble in organic solvents, more flexible, and more readily processed.
21. The methacrylic acid mers present decrease the crystallinity and improve the toughness and adhesive properties. The salts act like cross-linked polymers at ordinary temperatures.
22. They are all essentially the same copolymers of butadiene and styrene.
23. They are all hydrophilic and aid dyeability.
24. B.
25. It produces a stable, molded, rubberlike product without vulcanization.
26. It is more weather resistant because of the absence of ethylenic groups.
27. An alternating copolymer is produced rapidly until the maleic anhydride is consumed. The styrene then forms a block copolymer on the SMA in a slower process.
28. Since styrene is flammable and toxic, its concentration in the atmosphere must be held to very low values, such as 1 PPM.
29. Yes: the styrene macroradicals on the grafts terminate by coupling.
30. Graft it with a lyophilic monomer such as styrene.
31. A carboxylic acid group.

CHAPTER 11

1. They are viscoelastic, have glass transition temperatures, and may be linear or cross-linked.
2. By introducing oxygen or nitrogen atoms in the chain, capping the ends, and introducing alkyl pendant groups.
3. The formation of cyclic compounds instead of linear polymers.
4. By using a mixture of monochloro- and dichloroalkylsilanes.
5. Like the alkyl pendant groups, 6 to 7 H.
6. The silanol groups in silicic acid are polar, but the alkyl groups in silicones are nonpolar.
7. Acidify it. The silicic acid will polymerize spontaneously.

8. Failure of polymers at elevated temperatures is usually due to the breaking of covalent bonds in the main polymer chain. The O—Si—O bonds are very strong.

9.

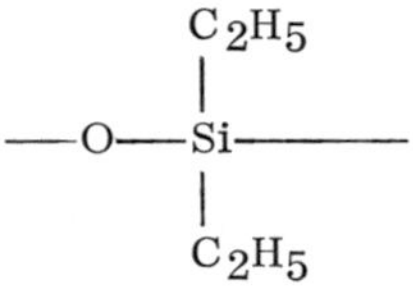

$$-O-\underset{\displaystyle C_2H_5}{\overset{\displaystyle C_2H_5}{\overset{|}{\underset{|}{Si}}}}-$$

10. Phosphorus pentachloride and ammonium chloride.

11. $PCl_5 + 4H_2O \longrightarrow H_3PO_4 + 5HCl$, therefore

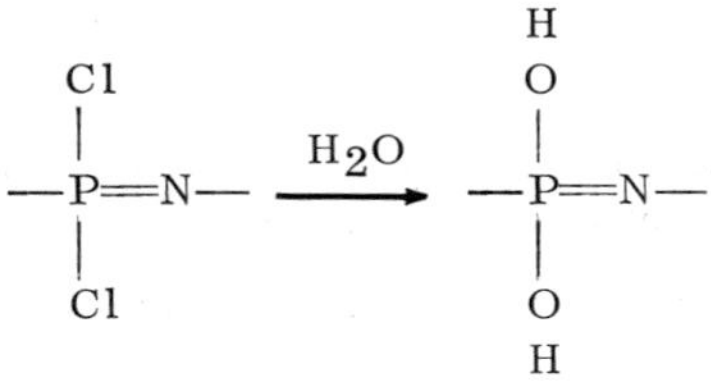

$$-\underset{\displaystyle Cl}{\overset{\displaystyle Cl}{\overset{|}{\underset{|}{P}}}}=N- \xrightarrow{H_2O} -\underset{\displaystyle \underset{H}{O}}{\overset{\displaystyle \overset{H}{O}}{\overset{|}{\underset{|}{P}}}}=N-$$

12. b.

13.

```
        H
        B
      /   \
   HN       NH
    |       |
   HB       BH
      \   /
        N
        H
```

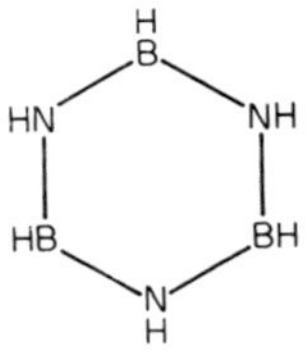

14. Its stability will depend to a large extent on the backbone, which is polyethylene.

15. They decompose slowly in water.

16. Often undefined with combinations of structures.

17. They should be fair conductors of electricity.

18. By the increase in viscosity of molten sulfur.

19. Because of decreased segmental motion which aids degradation.

20. Evidently below 145°C.

CHAPTER 12

1. For example, PMMA sheet, rubber bands, cellophane, clear polyethylene sheet, nylon filament, rayon.

2. Lignin.

3. Wood flour.

4. Formica table tops, plywood, fibrous glass-reinforced plastic boats, graphite-reinforced plastic golf shafts, etc.

5. Treat the surface with a silane or melt it and convert it into a fiber.

6. According to the Einstein equation, the viscosities will be equal.

7. a.

8. The intermolecular attractions impede the motion.

9. T_g increases.

10. b.

11. Advantages: more fibrous, less discoloration. Disadvantages: higher cost, more difficult to process because of bulk factor.

12. Wood flour below the surface and α-cellulose and paper near and at the surface.

13. b. continuous, a. discontinuous.

14. No: it is compatible with the resin.

15. Coat the hollow spheres with metal.

16. b.

17. Light weight and flexibility.

18. Fill it with $BaSO_4$.

19. Fill it with alumina, corrundum, or silicon carbide.

20. Water is evolved when it is heated. $Al_2O_3 \cdot 3H_2O \xrightarrow{\Delta} Al_2O_3 + 3H_2O\uparrow$

21. Probably the stearate groups replace the surface carbonate groups:

$$CaCO_3 + 2H(CH_2)_{16}COOH \longrightarrow Ca(OOC(CH_2)_{16}H)_2 + CO_2\uparrow + H_2O$$

22. It serves a purpose not fulfilled by less expensive silica.

23. Silicone rubber.

24. So that the applied stress on the softer resin can be transferred to the stronger filler.

25. According to the Kelly Tyson equation, the two composites should have equal strength.

26. Use the filament winding or pultrusion process with epoxy resin-coated filaments.

27. Convenience, uniformity, speed, reproducibility, and less exposure of the workers to volatile monomers.

28. Add a surface-active agent such as TTS to the resin-filler mixture.

CHAPTER 13

1. A plasticizer such as camphor or TCP.

2. PVC decomposes at processing temperatures; therefore, it was not useful until it was plasticized by TCP and later by DOP.

3. DOP volatilized from the PVC upholstery.

4. The stiffness of polymers such as PVC is due to intermolecular attractions. A small amount of plasticizer permits chain orientation which increases this attraction.

5. Because of the presence of residual toxic monomer and plasticizer.

6. As the size of bulky groups increases, T_g decreases. However, long pendant groups are attracted to each other and increase T_g.

7. Appropriate antioxidants were added.

8. Aging is believed to involve at least some free-radical processes. Antioxidants terminate this process, and hence the test animals live longer.

9. The water in lead-stabilized pipe might be contaminated with lead ions.

10. The diene group is a chromophoric group and the color will change as the number of these groups increase.

11. It is essentially nontoxic and also serves as a plasticizer.

12. Because most high-energy ultraviolet radiation is filtered out indoors.

13. b.

14. No.

15. No.

16. PTFE will not burn in air but will burn in the oxygen atmosphere used in the capsule at that time.

17. Unless flame retardants are added, polyurethane foam will burn at elevated temperatures. If the neoprene protective film is punctured, the polyurethane can be ignited.

18. Laboratory tests with mice showed "tris" to be a carcinogen.

19. Probably not because of its mild toxicity.

20. Yes.

21. This is a good question that is not answered from a technical viewpoint.

22. No: prior to 1910, it was patented by Goodyear and used as a colorant. A compounder made a mistake and used a 100-fold excess. This is called serendipity.

23. Different amounts of water of hydration.

24.

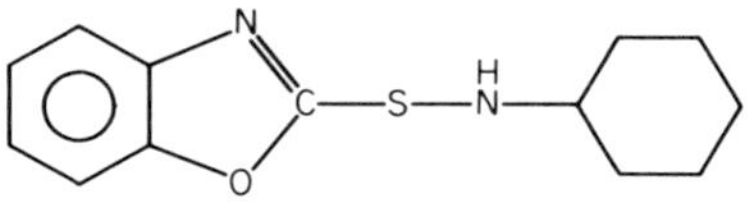

N

C—S—N(H)—

O

25. Add carbon disulfide to piperidine at room temperature.

26. Preferably in a solution. Otherwise, in individual nonmetal containers at moderate temperatures.

27. It is an initiator, but don't waste much time trying to change this or other erroneous terms.

28. They collect dust and may start fires, and can shock you severely.

29. It must migrate to the surface.

30. They are less expensive and more effective on a comparative weight basis.

31. Add a foaming agent that decomposes at the temperature used to convert the plastisol to a solid (150°C).

32. The particles are coated with a surfactant.

33. a.

34. None.

35. Bloom may be the result of the migration of lubricants to the surface.

CHAPTER 14

1. The reaction with functional groups.

2. Cross linking through double bonds.

3. $$\left[\begin{array}{cc} D & D \\ | & | \\ C - & C \\ | & | \\ D & D \end{array} \right]_n$$

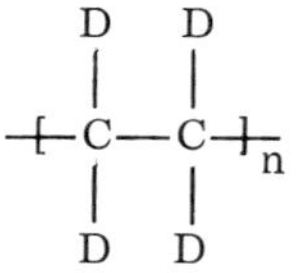

where D = ^2H.

4. The attack is on the folds of lamellar crystals of essentially uniform thickness.

5. $C_6H_5—NH—C(=NH)—NHC_6H_5$.

6. Expose it to high-energy radiation.

7. Hydrogenate the block copolymer of styrene and isoprene.

8. They are both alternating copolymers of propylene and ethylene.

9. It is more costly than LDPE.

10. (b) is a saturated polymer.

11. As an HCl scavenger in PVC.

12. Succinic aldehyde:

$$O{=}C(H)(CH_2)_2C(H){=}O$$

13. (a)

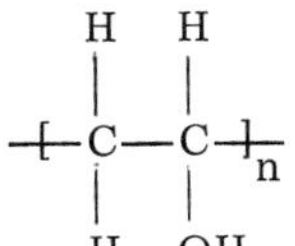

(b)

$$\left[CH_2—C(CH_3)(COOH) \right]_n$$

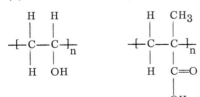

14. The introduction of a few methoxyl groups reduces the hydrogen-bonding forces so that the polymer with the remaining hydroxy groups will dissolve in water.

15. It forms a protective film around dirt particles and prevents their redeposition.

16. These water-soluble polymers coat the microscopic crystals of calcium carbonate as they form and prevent their growth.

17. The maximum, i.e., about 2.8.

18. All the hydroxyl groups are not accessible in the heterogeneous acetylation reaction.

19. (b) has more free hydroxyl groups.

20. There are residual acetyl groups in the reactant PVA, and the acetal formation requires two 1,3-hydroxyl groups.

21. It produces extremely large molecules when it forms salts with polyvalent cations such as Al^{3+}.

22. These so-called graphite fibers are used to reinforce resins such as epoxy resins.

23. None: any vinyl alcohol would rearrange to acetaldehyde.

24. b.

25. a.

26. The phenolic hydroxyl groups react with the protein and produce a cross-linked polymer.

27. The polymerization of styrene in the molding of unsaturated polyesters such as BMC or SMC.

28. Heat the polymer and condense the monomer produced by thermal depolymerization.

29. b.

CHAPTER 15

1. Because chemical engineers are always seeking a better and more economical source of this compound which is used on a large scale.

2. See the following equations:
   a. (15.1) or (15.2).
   b. (15.3) or (15.4).
   c. (15.5).
   d. (15.6).
   e. (15.8).
   f. (15.11).
   g. (15.12).
   h. (15.13).
   i. (15.14).
   j. (15.15).
   k. (15.16).
   l. (15.17) or (15.18).
   m. (15.19).
   n. (15.20) or (15.21).
   o. (15.22).
   p. (15.23).

q. (15.24) or (15.25).
r. (15.26).
s. (15.27).
t. (15.29).
u. (15.30).
v. (15.36).
w. (15.41).
x. (15.42).
y. (15.43) or (15.44).
z. (15.46).

3. (a) Silanes, (b) styrene (ethylbenzene), (c) ϵ-caprolactam, (d) adipic acid or sebacic acid, (e) pentaerythritol.

CHAPTER 16

1. They both are important and dependent on each other.
2. Cotton, wool, silk, hemp, jute, and so on.
3. Rayon, etc.
4. It is soluble in less expensive solvents, such as acetone.
5. They are both regenerated cellulose.
6. Polyester, nylon, acrylic fiber, polyurethane, polyolefins.
7. (a) Butyl rubber; (b) polybutadiene; (c) SBR, neoprene; and (d) silicone, polyurethane elastomer, Thiokol.
8. By air blowing an extruded tube.
9. For prevention of environmental pollution.
10. Over-the-counter sales.
11. The suspended polymer particles are coated by a surfactant.
12. Delay the blowing step until a viscous, strong, high molecular weight polymer is present.
13. b.
14. Because of the availability of large surface areas.
15. Fibrous glass-reinforced polyester resin in the Corvette.
16. It has a high specific modulus and low coefficient of expansion.
17. Most molded thermosets are molded by high-cost compression molding.
18. Lower the temperature of the mold cavity.

19. They have high specific strength, and once an intricate design has been incorporated in the die, the intricate design, such as that resembling hard wood carving, is reproduced at low cost.

20. Low cost, light weight, recyclable, nontoxic, and less hazardous than glass.

21. The molds are relatively inexpensive, and large articles can be produced readily by the thermoforming process.

22. The length is limited by the ability to store and transport the extrudate. Actually, pipe can be made in continuous lengths by extruding on the job site. Flexible pipe such as LDPE can be coiled.

Appendix A

Symbols

A_0 Original concentration

A Concentration at time T

Å Angstrom unit (10^{08} cm)

A Arbitrary constant

A Area

A Arrhenius constant

A Lewis acid

A· Antioxidant free radical

Ac Acetyl group

Ar Aryl group

AA Reactant (step reactions)

ABS Copolymer from acrylonitrile, butadiene, and styrene

AIBN 2,2'-Azo-bis-isobutyronitrile

ANSI American National Standards Institute (formerly American Standards Association)

AR Acrylate

ASTM American Society for Testing Materials

ATR Attenuated total reflectance spectroscopy

AU Polyurethane

AXF Polydiphenylethane

a Constant in the WLF equation

a Exponent

a_T Shift factor

B Virial constant

BPO Benzoyl peroxide

BSI British Standards Institute

BTU British thermal unit

b Arbitrary constant

bp Boiling point

C Arbitrary constant
C Catalyst-cocatalyst complex
C Celsius (centigrade)
C Concentration
C Degree of crystallinity
CA Cellulose acetate
CAB Cellulose acetate butyrate
CED Cohesive energy density
CMC Carboxymethyl cellulose
CN Cellulose nitrate
CO Polyepichlorohydrin
CPVC Critical pigment volume concentration
CR Neoprene
C_p Specific heat
C_s Chain transfer constant
c Velocity of light (3 × 10 cm/sec)
cal Calorie
cm Centimeter
cm^{-1} Reciprocal centimeter
cm^3 Cubic centimeter
co Copolymer
cp Chemically pure

D Debye units (dipole)
D Density
D Dextro
D Diameter
D Diffusion constant
DNA Deoxyribonucleic acid
$\overline{DP}$ Average degree of polymerization
DRS Dynamic reflectance spectroscopy
DS Degree of substitution
DSC Differential scanning calorimetry
DTA Differential thermal analysis
DWV Drain, waste, and vent pipe
d Density
d Dextro
d Diameter
d Total derivative (infinitesimal change)

E Energy of activation
E Energy content
E Energy of vaporization
E Young's modulus of elasticity

ECO	Epichlorohydrin elastomer
EEK	Accelerated test with sunlight at constant right angle
EGG	Einstein-Guth-Gold equation
EMMA	Equatorial mounting with mirrors (accelerated sunlight test)
EP	Epoxy resin
EPM	Poly(ethylene-co-propylene)
EPDM	Poly(ethylene-co-propylene) cross-linked
EPR	Electron paramagnetic resonance spectroscopy
ESR	Electron spin resonance spectroscopy
ET	Thiokol
ETA	Electrothermal analysis
e	Base of natural logarithms (2.718)
e	Exponential
e	Polarity factor (Alfrey-Price equation)
F	Fahrenheit
F	Mole fraction of monomers in copolymer
F	Stress (filled elastomers)
F_g	Fractional free volume (plasticizers)
FEP	Copolymer of tetrafluoroethylene and hexafluoropropylene
FPM	Polyfluorinated hydrocarbon
f	Aspect ratio
f	Efficiency factor (chain reactions)
f	Force
f	Functionality factor (step reactions)
f	Segmental friction factor
ft	Foot
G	Gauche conformation
G	Gibbs free energy
G	Modulus
G	Molar attraction constant (small)
GC	Gas chromatography
GPC	Gel permeation chromatography
GRS	Poly(butadiene-co-styrene)
g	Gauche conformation
g	Gram
g	Gravity
gr	Graft (copolymer)
H	Arbitrary constant
H	Enthalpy (heat content)
H	Hydrogen atom
H	Latent heat of transition

H	Magnetic field strength
H	Proportionality constant in light scattering
HIP	High impact polystyrene
h	Height
h	Planck's constant (6.625×10^{-27} erg-sec)
hp	Horsepower
hr	Hour
I	Initiator (chain reactions)
I	Intensity
I	Spin of nucleus
IIR	Butyl rubber
IR	Infrared
ISO	International Standards Organization
IUPAC	International Union of Pure and Applied Chemistry
i	Incident ray
in.	Inch
it	Isotactic
K	Arbitrary constant
K	Constant in Mark-Houwink equation
K	Kelvin
K	Kinetic constant in Avrami equation
K	Rate constant
K	Thermal-conductivity factor
k	Specific rate constant
kcal	Kilocalorie
kg	Kilogram
L	Length
L	Levo
LIM	Liquid injection molding
l	Length
l	Levo
l_c	Critical fiber length
ln	Natural logarithm
log	Logarithm (base 10)
M	Chain stiffener constant
M	Molecular weight
M	Monomer (chain reaction)
[M]	Monomer concentration
M	Quantum number
M·	Free-radical chain (Macroradical)

Me	Methyl radical
MF	Melamine-formaldehyde resin
MR	Molar refraction
MVT	Moisture vapor transmission
MWD	Molecular weight distribution
M	Modulus
M_F	Modulus of a fiber
M_L	Longitudinal fiber
M_M	Modulus of resin matrix
M_O	Modulus of an unfilled resin
M_T	Transverse modulus
$\overline{M}$	Average molecular weight
$\overline{M}_n$	Number average molecular weight
$\overline{M}_v$	Viscosity average molecular weight
$\overline{M}_w$	Weight average molecular weight
m	Consistency factor (power law)
m	Meta isomer
m	Meter
m	Mole fraction of reactants (copolymers)
m	Number of mers in polymer chain
ml	Milliliter
mp	Melting point
N	Nitrogen atom
N	Number of units or items
NBR	Poly(butadiene-co-acrylonitrile)
NMR (nmr)	Nuclear magnetic resonance spectroscopy
NR	Natural rubber
$\overline{N}_n$	Number average molecular weight
n	Index of flow (power law)
n	Index of refraction
n	Mole (step reactions) fraction
n	Normal (continuous chain, linear)
n	Number of mers in polymer chain
n	Numbers of theoretical plates
n	Ratio of mers in copolymer
nm	Nanometers
O	Oxygen atom
OI	Oxygen index
OMP	Organometallic polymer
o	Ortho isomer
oz	Ounce

P	Phosphorus atom
P	Polymer chain
P	Polymer radical
P	Pressure
P	Resonance-stability (Alfrey-Price equation)
PA	Polyamide (nylon)
PBI	Polybenzimidazole
PC	Polycarbonate
PCB	Polychlorinated biphenyls
PE	Polyethylene
PET	Polyethylene terephthalate
PF	Phenol-formaldehyde resin
PGC	Pyrolysis gas chromatography
PMMA	Polymethyl methacrylate
PMR	Protonmagnetic resonance spectroscopy
PNF	Polyphosphonitrilic fluorides
POM	Polyoxymethylene, polyformaldehyde, acetals
PP	Polypropylene
PS	Polystyrene
PTFE	Polytetrafluoroethylene
PU	Polyurethane
PVAc	Polyvinyl acetate
PVA	Polyvinyl alcohol
PVB	Polyvinyl butyral
PVC	Polyvinyl chloride
PVDC	Polyvinylidene chloride (Saran)
p	Para isomer
p	Pressure
p	Probability, fractional yield (Carothers)
p	Propagation
psi	Pounds per square inch
Q	Quantity of heat, rate of heat flow
Q	Resonance-stability factor (Alfrey-Price equation)
q	Electronic charge
R	Alkyl radical
R	Gas constant (1.986 cal/mole °K)
R	Rate (chain reactions)
R	Run number (copolymers)
R·	Free radical
RF	Radio frequency
RIM	Reaction injection molding
RNA	Ribonucleic acid

r	Distance between centers of charge of dipoles
r	Radius
r	Ratio of reactants (step reaction)
r	Reactivity ratio (copolymers)
r	Refracted ray
$\bar{r}$	Average end-to-end distance
S	Entropy
S	Radius of gyration
S	Sedimentation constant
S	Solvent
S	Sulfur atom
SAM	Poly(styrene-co-acrylonitrile)
SBR	Poly(butadiene-co-styrene) elastomer
SEM	Scanning electron microscopy
SI	Silicone
SMA	Copolymer of styrene and maleic anhydride
SMC	Sheet molding compound
SN	Sulfur nitride
SPE	Society of Plastics Engineers
SPI	The Society of the Plastics Industry
SR	Synthetic rubber
S_N	Nucleophilic substitution
s	Stress
st	Syndiotactic
T	Absolute temperature (°A or °K)
T	Tentative (ASTM)
T	Trans
TAPPI	Technical Association of the Pulp and Paper Industry
TDI	Tolylene diisocyanate
TGA	Thermal gravimetric analysis
TMMV	Threshold molecular weight value
TPE	Thermoplastic elastomer
TPX	Poly-4-methylpentene
T_c	Ceiling temperature
T_c	Cloud-point temperature
T_g	Glass transition temperature
T_m	Melting point
t	Termination (chain reaction)
t	Trans isomer
tit	Threodiisotactic
tst	Threosyndiotactic
tr	Transfer

UF	Urea-formaldehyde resin
UHMWPE	Ultra high molecular weight polyethylene polymer
UV (uv)	Ultraviolet
V	Volume
V_e	Elution volume
V_F	Fractional volume
WLF	Williams-Landel-Ferry equation
WS	Polyurethane
$\overline{W}_n$	Weight average molecular weight
w	Width
w	Work
X	Ratio of reactants (copolymer)
X	Substituent (vinyl monomer)
yd	Yard
z	Critical chain length
α	Carbon atom adjacent to a functional group
α	One configuration of an isomer
α	Branching coefficient
α	First in a series
α_F	Expansion coefficient
α_c	Critical value for incipient gelation
β	One configuration of an isomer
β	Second carbon atom away from a functional group
β	Second in a series
γ	Magnetogyric ratio (nmr)
γ	Hydrogen-bonding index (Lieberman)
γ	Strain
γ	Third carbon atom away from a functional group
Δ	Change
Δ	Heat
δ	Chemical shift (nmr)
δ	Expansion factor (solution process)
δ	Fourth carbon atom away from a functional group
δ	Solubility parameter (Hildebrand)
ϵ	Fifth carbon atom away from a functional group
η	Molar absorption coefficient
η	Viscosity
η_r	Reduced viscosity

η_{rel}	Relative viscosity
η_{sp}	Specific viscosity
$[\eta]$	Intrinsic viscosity (viscosity number)
Θ	Flory critical miscibility temperature at which polymer-solvent interaction is zero
θ	Angle of scattering
λ	Wavelength
λ	Distance from origin to vertices of tetrahedra in filler
μ	Dipole moment
μ	Measure of polymer-solvent interaction (Flory-Huggins)
μ	Micron (10^{-4} cm, 10^4 Å)
μ	Nuclear magnetic moment
ν	Average kinetic chain length of chain-reaction polymers
ν	Frequency (vibrations/sec)
ν	Kinetic chain length
π	A bond formed by the side-to-side overlap of two p_z orbitals which accounts for the high activity of vinyl monomers
π	Osmotic pressure
ρ	Density
Σ	Summation
σ	Sigma bonds
τ	Orientation relaxation or retardation time
τ	Relaxation time
τ	Turbidity or scattered flux
τ	Universal viscosity constant (Flory)
ϕ	Fractional volume
ϕ	Jump frequency in hole filling (solution)
ϕ	Related to viscosity in Herschel-Bulkley equation
ω	Last in a series (e.g., carbon farthest away from functional group)
χ	Thickness
[ ]	Concentration

Appendix B

Tradenames

Trade or brand name	Product	Manufacturer
Abafil	Reinforced ABS	Rexall Chemical Co.
Abalyn	Abietic acid derivative	Hercules, Inc.
Abcite	Plastic sheet	E.I. du Pont de Nemours & Co., Inc.
Abson	ABS polymers	B.F. Goodrich Chemical Co.
Acelon	Cellulose acetate	May & Baker Plastics Ltd.
Aclar	Polyfluorocarbon film	Allied Chemical Corp.
Acralen	Styrene-butadiene latex	Farbenfabriken Bayer AG
Acronal	Polyalkyl vinyl ether	General Aniline Film Corp.
Acrylacon	Fibrous-glass-reinforced polymers	Rexall Chemical Co.
Acrylafil	Reinforced polymers	Rexall Chemical Co.
Acrilan	Polyacrylonitrile	Chemstrand Co.
Acrylite	Polymethyl methacrylate	American Cyanamid Co.
Acryloid	Resins solutions	Rohm & Haas Co.
Acrysol	Thickeners	Rohm & Haas Co.
Actol	Polyethers	Allied Chemical Corp.

Trade or brand name	Product	Manufacturer
Adipol	Plasticizer	FMC Corp.
Adiprene	Urethane elastomers and prepolymer	E.I. du Pont de Nemours & Co., Inc.
Admex	Plasticizers	Ashland Chemical Co.
Advastab	Antistatic agents	Cincinnati Milacron Chemicals, Inc.
Aerodux	Resorcinol-formaldehyde resin	Ciba (A.R.L.) Ltd.
Afcoryl	ABS polymers	Pechiney-Saint-Gobain
Agerite series	Antioxidants	R.T. Vanderbilt Co., Inc.
Agro	Rayon fibers	Beaunit Mills Corp.
Alathon	Polyethylene	E.I. du Pont de Nemours & Co., Inc.
Albacar	Calcium carbonate filler	Pfizer Corp.
Albertols	Phenolic resins	Chemische Werke, Albert
Aldocryl	Acetal resin	Shell Chemical Co.
Alfane	Epoxy resin cement	The Atlas Mineral Products Co.
Algil	Styrene copolymer monofilament	Shawinigan Chemicals, Ltd.; also Polymer Corp.
Alkathene	Polyethylene resins	Imperial Chemical Industries Ltd.
Alkon	Acetal copolymer	Imperial Chemical Industries Ltd.; Celanese Corp. of America
Alkor	Furan resin cement	Atlas Minerals Products Co.
Alloprene	Chlorinated natural rubber	Imperial Chemical Industries Ltd.
Alsibronz	Wet ground muscovite mica	Franklin Mineral Products Co.
Alsilate	Clays	Freeport Kaolin Co.
Alsynite	Reinforced plastic panels	Reichhold Chemicals, Inc.

Trade or brand name	Product	Manufacturer
Amberlac	Modified alkyd resins	Rohm & Haas Co.
Amberol	Phenolic resins	Rohm & Haas Co.
Amberlite	Ion-exchange resins	Rohm & Haas Co.
Ameripol	Polyethylene	Goodrich-Gulf Chemicals, Inc.
Amerith	Cellulose nitrate	Celanese Corp. of America
Amilan	Nylon	Tojo Rayon Co.
Ampcoflex	Rigid polyvinyl chloride	Atlas Mineral Products Co.
Antarox	Low foaming wetting agent	GAF Corp.
Antiblaze	Organic phosphorus flame retardants	Mobil Chemical Co.
Antron	Nylon fiber	E.I. du Pont de Nemours & Co., Inc.
Aralac	Protein fiber	Imperial Chemical Industries Ltd.
Araldite	Epoxy resins	Ciba (A.R.L.) Ltd.
Ardil	Protein fiber	Imperial Chemical Industries Ltd.
Armite	Vulcanized fiber	Spaulding Fibre Co.
Arnel	Cellulose triacetate	Celanese Corp. of America
Arnite	Polyethylene terephthalate	Algemene Kuntstzijde Unie N.V.
Aroclor	Chlorinated polyphenyls	Monsanto Chemical Co.
Arofene	Phenolic resins	Ashland Chemical Co.
Aropol	Polyester resins	Ashland Chemical Co.
Arothane	Polyester resins	Ashland Chemical Co.
Astrel	Polyarylsulfone	3M Co.
Atlac	Polyester cast resin	ICI America Inc.
Atomite	Calcium carbonate	Thompson, Weinman & Co.
Avron	Rayon fiber	American Viscose Corp.
Azdel	Fibrous-glass-reinforced ABS copolymer sheet	Generic name

Trade or brand name	Product	Manufacturer
Azocel	Azodicarbonamide blowing agent	Fairmont Chemical Co.
Aztran	Poromeric sheet	B.F. Goodrich Chemical Co.
Bakelite	Phenol-formaldehyde	Union Carbide Chemicals Co.
Barden	Kaolin clay	Huber, J.M., Corp.
Barex	Barrier resin	Vistron Corp.
Baygal	Polyester for casting resins	Farbenfabriken Bayer AG
Baypren	Polychloroprene	Farbenfabriken Bayer AG
Beckacite	Modified phenolic	Reichhold Chemicals, Inc.; Beck, Koller & Co. Ltd.
Beckamine	Urea-formaldehyde	Reichhold Chemicals, Inc.; Beck, Koller & Co., Ltd.
Beckosol	Alkyd resins	Reichhold Chemicals, Inc.; Beck, Koller & Co., Ltd.
Beetle	Urea-formaldehyde resins	American Cyanamid Co.
Bemberg	Rayon fiber	Beaunit Mills Corp.
Bentone	Gelling agent	Kronos Titan GmbH
Benvic	Polyvinyl chloride	Solvay & Cie S.A.
Bexphane	Polypropylene	Bakelite Xylonite Ltd.
Blendex	ABS resin	Borg-Warner Corp.
Bolta Flex	Vinyl sheeting and film	General Tire & Rubber Co.
Boltaron	Plastic sheets	General Tire & Rubber Co.
Bonadur	Organic pigments	American Cyanamid Co.
Bondstrand	Filament wound fiber-glass reinforced plastics	Ameron Corrosion Control Div.
Borofil	Boron filaments	Texaco Corp.
Boronol	Polyolefins with boron	Allied Resinous Products, Inc.
Busan	Flame-retardant micro-biocide	Buckman Laboratories

Trade or brand name	Product	Manufacturer
Butacite	Polyvinyl acetal resins	E.I. du Pont de Nemours & Co., Inc.
Butakon	Butadiene copolymers	Imperial Chemical Industries, Ltd.
Butaprene	Styrene-butadiene elastomers	Firestone Tire & Rubber Co.
Butarez CTL	Telechelic butadiene polymer	Phillips Petroleum Co.
Buton	Butadiene-styrene resin	Enjay Chemical Co.
Bu-Tuf	Polybutene	Petrotex Chemical Corp.
Butvar	Polyvinyl butyral resin	Shawinigan Resins Corp.
Cab-O-Sil	Colloidal silica	Cabot Corp.
Cadco	Plastic rod, etc.	Cadillac Plastics
Cadon	Nylon filament	Chemstrand Corp.
Cadox	Organic peroxides	Cadet Chemical Corp.
Calwhite	Calcium carbonate	Georgia Marble Co.
Camel-Carb	Calcium carbonate	Harry T. Campbell Sons' Corp.
Capran	Nylon 6	Allied Chemical Corp.
Captax	Accelerator (2-mercapto-benzothiazole)	Goodyear Tire & Rubber Co.
Carbitol	Solvents	Union Carbide Corp.
Carboloy	Cemented carbides	General Electric Co.
Carbomastic	Epoxy coal tar coating	Carboline Co.
Carbopol	Water-soluble resins	B.F. Goodrich Chemical Co.
Carboset	Acrylic resins	B.F. Goodrich Chemical Co.
Carbospheres	Hollow carbon spheres	Versar, Inc.
Carbowax	Polyethylene glycols	Union Carbide Chemical Co.
Cariflex I	cis-1,4-Polyisoprene	Shell Chemical Co. Ltd.
Carina	Polyvinyl chloride	Shell Chemical Co. Ltd.

Trade or brand name	Product	Manufacturer
Carinex	Polystyrene	Shell Chemical Co. Ltd.
Carstab	Urethane foam catalysts	Cincinnati Milacron Chemicals, Inc.
Castethane	Castable polyurethanes	Upjohn Co.
Catalac	Phenol-formaldehyde resin	Catalin Ltd.
Celanar	Polyester film and sheeting	Celanese Plastics Co.
Celanex	Thermoplastic polyester	Celanese Plastics Co.
Celcon	Acetal copolymers	Celanese Plastics Co.
Celgard	Microporous polypropylene film	Celanese Plastics Co.
Celite	Diatomite filler	Johns-Manville Corp.
Cellofoam	Polystyrene foam board	United States Mineral Products, Co.
Cellosize	Hydroxyethyl cellulose	Union Carbide Corp.
Celluloid	Plasticized cellulose nitrate	Celanese Plastics Co.
Celogan	Blowing agents	Uniroyal, Inc.
Celramic	Glass nodules	Pittsburgh Corning Corp.
Cerex	Styrene copolymer	Monsanto Chemical Co.
Chemigum	Urethane elastomer	Goodyear Tire & Rubber Co.
Chem-o-sol	PVC plastisol	Chemical Products Co.
Chempro	Ion-exchange resin	Freeman Chem. Corp.
Chlorowax	Chlorinated paraffins	Diamond Alkali Co.
Cibanite	Aniline-formaldehyde resin	Ciba Products Co.
Cis-4	cis-1,4-polybutadiene	Phillips Petroleum Co.
Clarite	PVC stabilizers	National Lead Co.
Cobex	Polyvinyl chloride	Bakelite Xylonite Ltd.

Trade or brand name	Product	Manufacturer
Collodion	Solution of cellulose nitrate	Generic name
Coral rubber	cis-polyisoprene	Firestone Tire & Rubber Co.
Cordo	PVC foam and films	Ferro Corp.
Cordura	Regenerated cellulose	E.I. du Pont de Nemours & Co., Inc.
Corfam	Poromeric film	E.I. du Pont de Nemours & Co., Inc.
Corval	Rayon fiber	Courtaulds
Corvel	Plastic coating powders	The Polymer Corp.
Corvic	Vinyl polymers	Imperial Chemical Industries Ltd.
Covol	Polyvinyl alcohol	Corn Products Co.
Creslan	Acrylonitrile-acrylic ester copolymers	American Cyanamid Co.
Cronar	Polyethylene	E.I. du Pont de Nemours & Co., Inc.
Cryorap	Thermoplastic sheets and films	W. R. Grace & Co.
Cryovac	Polypropylene film	W. R. Grace & Co.
Crystalex	Acrylic resin	Rohm & Haas Co.
Crystalon	Rayon fiber	American Enka Corp.
Crystic	Polyester resins	Scott Bader Co.
Cumar	Coumarone-indene resins	Allied Chemical Corp.
Cyanaprene	Polyurethane	American Cyanamid Co.
Cyanolit	Cyanoacrylate adhesive	Leader, Denis, Ltd.
Cyasorb	Ultraviolet absorbers	American Cyanamid Co.
Cycloset	Cellulose acetate fiber	E.I. du Pont de Nemours & Co., Inc.
Cycolac	Acrylonitrile-butadiene-styrene copolymer	Borg-Warner Corp.

Trade or brand name	Product	Manufacturer
Cymac	Thermoplastic molding materials	American Cyanamid Co.
Cymel	Melamine molding compound	American Cyanamid Co.
Dabco	Triethylenediamine	Air Products Co.
Dacovin	Rigid polyvinyl chloride	Diamond Alkali Co.
Dacron	Polyester fiber	E.I. du Pont de Nemours & Co., Inc.
DAP	Diallyl phthalate monomer	FMC Corp.
Dapon	Diallyl phthalate pre-polymer	FMC Corp.
Daponite	Dapon-fabric laminates	FMC Corp.
Daran	Polyvinylidene chloride emulsion coatings	W. R. Grace & Co.
Darex	Styrene copolymer resin	W. R. Grace & Co.
Darvan	Polyvinylidene cyanide	Celanese Corp. of America
Darvic	Polyvinyl chloride	Imperial Chemical Industries, Ltd.
Daxad	Dispersing agents	W. R. Grace & Co.
Decanox	Organic peroxides	Wallace & Tiernan, Inc.
Deenax	Antioxidants	Enjay Chemical Co.
Delrin	Acetal polymer	E.I. du Pont de Nemours & Co., Inc.
Derakane	Polyester resin	Dow Chemical Co.
Derolite	Ion-exchange resin	Diamond Alkali Co.
Desmodur	Isocyanates for polyurethane foam	Farbenfabriken Bayer AG
Desmopan	Polyurethanes	Farbenfabriken Bayer AG
Desmophen	Polyesters and polyethers for polyurethanes	Farbenfabriken Bayer AG

Trade or brand name	Product	Manufacturer
Devran	Epoxy resins	Devoe & Reynolds Co.
Dexel	Cellulose acetate	British Celanese Ltd.
Dexsil	Polycarboranesiloxane	Olin Mathieson Corp.
Diakon	Polymethyl methacrylate	Imperial Chemical Industries Ltd.
Diall	Diallyl phthalate	Allied Chemical Corp.
Dicalite	Diatomaceous earth	Dicalite/Grefco, Inc.
Diene	Polybutadiene	Firestone Tire & Rubber Co.
Dimetcote	Protective coating	Americoat Corp.
Dion	Polyester resin	Diamond Alkali Co.
Doryl	Polydiphenyl oxide	Westinghouse Electric Corp.
Dowex	Ion-exchange resins	Dow Chemical Co.
Duco	Cellulose nitrate lacquers	E.I. du Pont de Nemours & Co., Inc.
Dulac	Lacquers	Sun Chemical Corp.
Dulux	Polymeric enamels	E.I. du Pont de Nemours & Co., Inc.
Duolite	Ion-exchange resin	Diamond Alkali Co.
Duralon	Furan molding resins	U.S. Stoneware Co.
Duramac	Alkyd resins	Commercial Solvents Corp.
Duraplex	Alkyd resins	Rohm & Haas Co.
Duraspan	Spandex fibers	Carr-Fulflex Corp.
Durethan	Nylon 6	Farbenfabriken Bayer AG
Durethan U	Polyurethanes	Farbenfabriken Bayer AG
Durethene	Polyethylene film	Sinclair-Koppers Co., Inc.
Durathon	Polybutylene resins	Witco Chemical Corp.
Durite	Phenolic resins	The Borden Co.
Dyal	Alkyd resins	Sherwin-Williams Co.
Dylan	Polyethylene resins	Sinclair-Koppers Co., Inc.

Trade or brand name	Product	Manufacturer
Dylel	ABS copolymer	Sinclair-Koppers Co., Inc.
Dylene	Polystyrene resins	ARCO Polymer, Inc.
Dylite	Expandable polystyrene	Sinclair-Koppers Co., Inc.
Dynafilm	Polypropylene film	U.S. Industrial Chemicals Co., Div., National Distillers & Chemical Corp.
Dynel	Modacrylic fiber	Union Carbide Corp.
Dyphene	Phenol-formaldehyde resins	Sherwin-Williams Co.
Dyphos	Stabilizer for polyvinyl chloride	National Lead Co.
Eccospheres	Hollow glass spheres	Emerson & Cummings, Inc.
Elastothane	Polyurethane elastomer	Thiokol Corp.
Elf	Carbon black	Cabot Corporation
El Rexene	Polyolefin resins	Rexall Chemical Co.
El Rey	Low-density polyethylene	Rexall Chemical Co.
Elvacet	Polyvinyl acetate emulsion	E.I. du Pont de Nemours & Co., Inc.
Elvacite	Acrylic resins	E.I. du Pont de Nemours & Co., Inc.
Elvanol	Polyvinyl alcohol resins	E.I. du Pont de Nemours & Co., Inc.
Elvax	Polyethylene-co-vinyl acetate	E.I. du Pont de Nemours & Co., Inc.
Enkalure	Nylon fiber	American Enka Corp.
Enrad	Preirradiated polyethylene	Enflo Corp.
Enrup	Thermosetting resin	United States Rubber Co.
Epibond	Epoxy adhesive resin	Furane Plastics, Inc.
Epicure	Curing agents for epoxy resins	Celanese Corp.
Epikote	Epoxy resins	Shell Chemical Co.

Trade or brand name	Product	Manufacturer
Epi-Rez	Epoxy cast resin	Celanese Corp.
Epocast	Epoxy resins	Furane Plastics, Inc.
Epocryl	Epoxy acrylate resin	Shell Chemical Co.
Epodite	Epoxy resins	Showa Highpolymer Co.
Epolene	Low-melt polyethylene	Eastman Chemical Products, Inc.
Epon	Epoxy resins	Shell Chemical Co.
Epotuf	Epoxy resins	Reichhold Chemical Co.
Epoxylite	Epoxy resins	Epoxylite Corp.
Escon	Polypropylene	Enjay Chemical Co.
Estane	Polyurethane resins	B.F. Goodrich Chemical Co.
Estron	Cellulose acetate filament	Eastman Chemical Products, Inc.
Ethocel	Ethyl cellulose	Dow Chemical Co.
Evenglo	Polystyrene	Sinclair-Koppers Co., Inc.
Exon	Polyvinyl chloride	Firestone Plastics
Extrel	Plastic films	Exxon Chemical Co. U.S.A.
Fabrifil	Chopped-rag fillers	Microfibers, Inc.
Fabrikoid	Pyroxylin-coated fabrics	E.I. du Pont de Nemours & Co., Inc.
Fibercast	Reinforced plastic pipe	Fibercast Co.
Fiberglas	Fibrous glass	Owens-Corning Fiberglas Corp.
Fiberite	Phenolic molding compounds	Fiberite Corp.
Filfrac	Cut cotton fiber	Rayon Processing Co. of Rhode Island
Firemaster	Fire retardants	Michigan Chemical Corp.
Firmex	Carbon black	Columbian Carbon Co.
Flakeglas	Glass flakes for reinforcements	Owens-Corning Fiberglas Corp.

Trade or brand name	Product	Manufacturer
Flectol	Amine-type antioxidants	Monsanto Co.
Flexol	Plasticizers	Union Carbide Chemical Co.
Floranier	Cellulose	Rayonier, Inc.
Fluon	Polytetrafluoroethylene	Imperial Chemical Industries, Ltd.
Fluon	PTFE powders and dispersions	Imperial Chemical Industries, Ltd.
Fluorel	Polyvinylidene fluoride	Minnesota Mining and Mfg. Co.
Fluorobestos	Asbestos-Teflon composite	Raybestos Manhattan, Inc.
Fluoron	Polychlorotrifluoro-ethylene	Stokes Molded Products
Fluoroplast	Polytetrafluoroethylene	U.S. Gasket Co.
Foamex	Polyvinyl formal	General Electric Co.
Formex	Polyvinyl acetal	General Electric Co.
Formica	Thermosetting laminates	Formica Corp.
Formrez	Liquid resins for urethane elastomers	Witco Chemical Co.
Formvar	Polyvinyl formal	Shawinigan Resins Corp.
Forticel	Cellulose propionate	Celanese Corp. of America
Fortiflex	Polyethylene	Celanese Plastics Co.
Fortisan	Saponified cellulose acetate	Celanese Corp. of America
Fortrel	Polyester fiber	Fiber Industries, Inc.
Fostacryl	Polystyrene-co-acrylonitrile	Foster Grant Co.
Fostalene	Plastic	Foster Grant Co.
Fostarene	Polystyrene	Foster Grant Co.
FPC	PVC resins compound	Firestone Tire & Rubber Co.
Freon	Blowing agents	E.I. du Pont de Nemours & Co., Inc.

Trade or brand name	Product	Manufacturer
Furnane	Epoxy and furan resins	Atlas Mineral Products Co.
Fyberoid	Fishpaper	Wilmington Fibre Specialty Co.
Fyrol	Flame retardants	Stauffer Chemical Co.
Galalith	Casein plastics	Generic name
Gama-Sperse	Calcium carbonate	Georgia Marble Co.
Gantrez	Polyvinyl ether-co-maleic anhydride	Dyestuff & Chemical Div., General Aniline & Film Corp.
Garan	Fibrous-glass roving	Johns-Manville Corp.
Garan Finish	Sizing for glass fibers	Johns-Manville Corp.
Garox	Organic peroxides	Ram Chemicals, Inc.
Gelva	Polyvinyl acetate	Shawinigan Resins Corp.
Gelvatex	Polyvinyl acetate emulsions	Shawinigan Resins Corp.
Gelvatol	Polyvinyl alcohol	Shawinigan Resins Corp.
Genaire	Poromeric film	General Tire & Rubber Co.
Genal	Thermosets	General Electric Co.
Genthane	Polyurethane elastomer	General Tire & Rubber Co.
Genetron	Fluorinated hydrocarbon monomers and polymers	Allied Chemical Co.
Gentro	Butadiene copolymer	General Tire & Rubber Co.
Geon	Polyvinyl chloride	B.F. Goodrich Chemical Co.
Glaskyd	Glass-reinforced alkyd resin	American Cyanamid Co.
Glufil	Shell flour	Agrashell Inc.
Glyptal	Alkyd coating	General Electric Co.
Grex	Polyethylene	W. R. Grace & Co.
Halar	Polyfluorocarbons	Allied Chemical Co.
Halex	Polyfluorocarbon	Allied Chemical Co.
Halon	Fluorochlorocarbon	Allied Chemical Co.

Trade or brand name	Product	Manufacturer
Halowax	Chlorinated naphthalene	Union Carbide Corp.
Harflex	Plasticizers	Wallace & Tiernan, Inc.
HB-40	Hydrogenated terphenyl	Monsanto Co.
Hercocel	Cellulose acetate	Hercules Powder Co.
Hercoflex	Phthalate plasticizers	Hercules Powder Co.
Hercolyn	Hydrogenated methyl abietate	Hercules Powder Co.
Hercose	Cellulose acetate-propionate	Hercules Powder Co.
Herculoid	Cellulose nitrate	Hercules Powder Co.
Herculon	Polypropylene	Hercules Powder Co.
Herox	Nylon	E.I. du Pont de Nemours & Co., Inc.
Het anhydride	Chlorendic anhydride	Hooker Chemical Corp.
Hetron	Fire-retardant polyester resins	Hooker Chemical Corp.
Heveaplus	Copolymer of methyl methacrylate and rubber	Generic name
Hexcel	Structural honeycomb	Hexcel Products, Inc.
H-film	Polyimide film	E.I. du Pont de Nemours & Co., Inc.
Hi-Blen	ABS polymers	Japanese Geon Co.
Hi-fax	High-density polyethylene	FMC Corp.; Hercules Powder Co.
Hipack	Polyethylene	Showa Highpolymer Co.
Hi-Sil	Amorphous silica	PPG Corp.
Hitalex	Polyethylene	Hitachi Chemical Co.
Hitanol	Phenol-formaldehyde resins	Hitachi Chemical Co.
Horse Head	Zinc oxide pigments	New Jersey Zinc Co.

Trade or brand name	Product	Manufacturer
Hostaflon C2	Polychlorotrifluoro-ethylene	Farbwerke Hoechst AG
Hostaflon TF	Polytetrafluoroethylene	Farbwerke Hoechst AG
Hostalen	Polyethylene	Farbwerke Hoechst AG
Hyamine	Cationic surfactants	Rohm & Haas Co.
Hycar	Butadiene acrylonitrile copolymer	B.F. Goodrich Chemical Co.
Hydraflex	Printing ink	Sun Chemical Corp.
Hydrocal	Gypsum	U.S. Gypsum Co.
Hydropol	Hydrogenated polybuta-diene	Phillips Petroleum Co.
Hylene	Organic isocyanates	E.I. du Pont de Nemours & Co., Inc.
Hypalon	Chlorosulfonated polyethylene	E.I. du Pont de Nemours & Co., Inc.
Igepal	Wetting agents	General Aniline & Film Corp.
Igepon	Surfactants, wetting agents	General Aniline & Film Corp.
Implex	Acrylic resins	Rohm & Haas Co.
Insurok	Phenol-formaldehyde molding compounds	The Richardson Co.
Intamix	Rigid PVC	Diamond Shamrock Corp.
Ionac	Ion-exchange resins	Permutit Co.
Ionol	Antioxidant	Shell Chemical Co.
Irganox	Antioxidants	Geigy Chemical Corp.
Irrathene	Irradiated polyethylene	General Electric Co.
Isofoam	Polyurethane foam resins	Isocyanate Products, Inc.
Isomid	Polyester-polyimide film magnet wire	Schenectady Chemicals, Inc.
Isonate	Diisocyanates	Upjohn Co.

Trade or brand name	Product	Manufacturer
Isonol	Propoxylated amines	Upjohn Co.
Iupilon	Polycarbonate	Mitsubishi Edogawa Chemical Co.
Jay-Flex	Plasticizers	Enjay Chemical Co.
Jet-Kote	Furane resin coatings	Furane Plastics, Inc.
Kadox	Zinc oxide	New Jersey Zinc Co.
Kalite	Precipitated calcium carbonate	Diamond Alkali Co.
Kalmac	Calcium carbonate	Georgia Marble Co.
Kaofill	Coating and filler clay	Thiele Kaolin Co.
Kapsol	Plasticizers	Ohio-Apex Div., FMC Corp.
Kapton	Polyimide	E.I. du Pont de Nemours & Co., Inc.
Kardel	Polystyrene film	Union Carbide Corp.
Kaurit	Urea-formaldehyde resins	Badische Anilin & Coda-Fabrik AG
Kel-F	Trifluorochloroethylene resins	Minnesota Mining & Mfg. Co.
Keltrol	Copolymers	Textron, Inc.
Kematal	Acetal copolymers	Imperial Chemical Industries, Ltd.
Kenflex	Hydrocarbon resins	Kenrich Petrochemicals, Inc.
Kessco	Plasticizers	Kessler Chemical Co., Inc.
Ketac	Ketone-aldehyde resin	American Cyanamid Co.
Kodacel	Cellulose acetate film	Eastman Chemical Products, Inc.
Kodaflex	Plasticizers	Eastman Chemical Products, Inc.
Kodel	Polyester fibers	Eastman Kodak Co.
Kollidon	Polyvinyl pyrrolidone	General Aniline & Film Corp.

Trade or brand name	Product	Manufacturer
Kolorbon	Rayon fiber	American Enka Corp.
Kopox	Epoxy resin	Koppers Co.
Korad	Acrylic film	Rohm & Haas & Co.
Korez	Phenolic resin cement	Atlas Mineral Products Company
Koroseal	Polyvinyl chloride	B.F. Goodrich Chemical Co.
Kosmos	Carbon black	United Carbon Co.
Kotol	Resin solutions	Uniroyal, Inc.
Kralac	ABS resins	Uniroyal, Inc.
Kralastic	ABS	Uniroyal, Inc.
Kralon	High-impact styrene and ABS resins	Uniroyal, Inc.
Kraton	Butadiene block copolymers	Shell Chemical Co.
Krene	Plasticized vinyl film	Union Carbide Corp.
K-Resin	Butadiene-styrene copolymer	Phillips Petroleum Co.
Kriston	Allyl ester casting resins	B.F. Goodrich Chemical Co.
Kroniflex	Phosphate ester plasticizer	FMC Corp.
Kronisol	Dibutoxyethyl phthalate	FMC Corp.
Kronitex	Tricresyl phosphate	FMC Corp.
Kronos	Titanium dioxide	Kronos Titan
Kronox	Plasticizer	FMC Corp.
Kurlon	Polyvinyl alcohol fibers	
Kydex	Acrylic-polyvinyl chloride sheet	Rohm & Haas Co.
Kylan	Chitin	
Kynar	Polyvinylidene fluoride	Pennwalt Chemicals Corp.

Trade or brand name	Product	Manufacturer
Laminac	Polyester resins	American Cyanamid Co.
Laurox	Polymerization catalysts	Akzo Chemie Nederland BV
Leguval	Polyester resins	Farbenfabriken Bayer AG
Lekutherm	Epoxy resins	Farbenfabriken Bayer AG
Lemac	Polyvinyl acetate	Borden Chemical Co.
Lemol	Polyvinyl alcohol	Borden Chemical Co.
Levapren	Ethylene-vinylacetate copolymers	Farbenfabriken Bayer AG
Lexan	Polycarbonate resin	General Electric Co.
Lindol	Phosphate plasticizers	Stauffer Chemical Co.
Lock Foam	Polyurethane foam	Nopco Chemical Co.
Lucidol	Benzoyl peroxide	Wallace and Tiernan, Inc.
Lucite	Polymethyl methacrylate	E.I. du Pont de Nemours & Co., Inc.
Ludox	Colloidal silica	E.I. du Pont de Nemours & Co., Inc.
Lumarith	Cellulose acetate	Celanese Corp. of America
Lumite	Saran filaments	Chicopee Manufacturing Co.
Luperco	Organic peroxides	Pennwalt Corp.
Luperox	Organic peroxides	Pennwalt Corp.
Lustran	Molding and extrusion resins	Monsanto Chemical Co.
Lustrex	Polystyrene	Monsanto Chemical Co.
Lutonal	Polyvinyl ethers	Badische Anilin & Soda-Fabrik AG
Lutrex	Polyvinyl acetate	Foster Grant Co.
Luvican	Polyvinyl carbazole	Badische Anilin & Soda-Fabrik AG
Lycra	Spandex fibers	E.I. du Pont de Nemours & Co., Inc.

Trade or brand name	Product	Manufacturer
Madurik	Melamine-formaldehyde resins	Casella Farbwerke Mainkur AG
Makrofol	Polycarbonate film	Naftone, Inc.
Makrolon	Polycarbonate	Farbenfabriken Bayer AG
Maranyl	Nylons	Imperial Chemical Industries Ltd.
Maraset	Epoxy resin	The Marblette Corp.
Marbon	Polystyrene and copolymers	Borg-Warner Corp.
Marlex	Polyolefin resins	Phillips Chemical Co.
Marvibond	Metal-plastics laminates	Uniroyal, Inc.
Marvinol	Polyvinyl chloride	Uniroyal, Inc.
Melan	Melamine resins	Hitachi Chemical Co., Ltd.
Melinex	Polyethylene terephthalate	Imperial Chemical Industries Ltd.
Melit	Melamine-formaldehyde resins	Societa Italiana Pesine
Melmac	Melamine molding materials	American Cyanamid Co.
Melurac	Melamine-urea resins	American Cyanamid Co.
Merlon	Polycarbonate	Mobay Chemical Co.
Methocel	Methylcellulose	Dow Chemical Co.
Micarta	Thermosetting laminates	Westinghouse Electric Corp.
Micronex	Carbon black	Columbian Carbon Co.
Microthene	Powdered polyethylene	U.S. Industrial Chemicals Co.
Minex	Aluminum silicate filler	American Nepheline Corp.
Minlon	Reinforced nylon	E.I. du Pont de Nemours & Co., Inc.
Modulene	Polyethylene resin	Muehlstein & Co.
Mogul	Carbon black	Cabot Corp.

Trade or brand name	Product	Manufacturer
Molplen	Polypropylene	Novamont Corp.
Moltopren	Polyurethane foam	Farbenfabriken Bayer AG
Mondur	Organic isocyanates	Mobay Chemical Co.
Montrek	Polyethylene imine	Dow Chemical Co.
Moplen	Polypropylene	Montecatini
Mowilith	Polyvinyl acetate	Farbwerke Hoechst AG
Mowiol	Polyvinyl alcohol	Farbwerke Hoechst AG
Mowital	Polyvinyl butyral	Farbwerke Hoechst AG
Multron	Polyesters	Mobay Chemical Co.
Mycalex	Inorganic molded plastics	Mycalex Corp. of America
Mylar	Polyester film	E.I. du Pont de Nemours & Co., Inc.
Nacconate	Organic diisocyanate	Allied Chemical Corp.
Nadic	Maleic anhydride	Allied Chemical Corp.
Nalgon	Plasticized polyvinyl chloride	Nalge Co.
Napryl	Polypropylene	Pechiney-Saint-Gobain
Natene	Polyethylene	Pechiney-Saint-Gobain
Natsyn	cis-1,4 Polyisoprene	Goodyear Tire & Rubber Co.
Naugahyde	Vinyl-coated fabric	U.S. Rubber Co.
Nebony	Petroleum hydrocarbon resin	Neville Chemical Co.
Neoprene	Polychloroprene	E.I. du Pont de Nemours & Co., Inc.
Neozone	Antioxidants	E.I. du Pont de Nemours & Co., Inc.
Nepoxide	Epoxy resin coating	Atlas Minerals & Chemicals Div., ESB
Nevidene	Coumarone-indene resin	Neville Chemical Co.

Trade or brand name	Product	Manufacturer
Nevillac	Modified coumarone-indene resin	Neville Chemical Co.
Niax	Polyol polyesters	Union Carbide Corp.
Nimbus	Polyurethane foam	General Tire & Rubber Co.
Nipeon	Polyvinyl chloride	Japanese Geon Co.
Nipoflex	Ethylene-vinyl acetate copolymer	Toyo Soda Mfg. Co.
Nipolon	Polyethylene	Toyo Soda Mfg. Co.
Noan	Styrene-methyl methacrylate copolymer	Richardson Corp.
Nomex	Nylon	E.I. du Pont de Nemours & Co., Inc.
Nopcofoam	Polyurethane foams	Nopco Chemical Co.
Nordel	Ethylene-propylene	E.I. du Pont de Nemours & Co., Inc.
Noryl	Polyphenylene oxide	General Electric Co.
Novacite	Altered novaculite	Malvern Minerals Co.
Novodur	ABS polymers	Farbenfabriken Bayer AG
Nuba	Modified coumarone	Neville Chemical Co.
Nuclon	Polycarbonate	Pittsburgh Plate Glass Co.
Nukem	Acid-resistant resin cements	Amercoat Corp.
Numa	Spandex fibers	American Cyanamid Corp.
Nylafil	Reinforced nylon	Rexall Chemical Co.
Nylasint	Sintered nylon parts	The Polymer Corp.
Nylon	Polyamides	E.I. du Pont de Nemours & Co., Inc.
Olefane	Polypropylene film	Avisun Corp.
Olemer	Propylene copolymer	Avisun Corp.

Trade or brand name	Product	Manufacturer
Opalon	Polyvinyl chloride	Monsanto Chemical Co.
Oppanol	Polyisobutylene	Badische Anilin & Soda-Fabrik AG
Orlon	Acrylic fiber	E.I. du Pont de Nemours & Co., Inc.
Ortix	Poromeric film	Celanese Corp.
Oxiron	Epoxidized polybutadiene	
Panarez	Hydrocarbon resins	Amoco Chemical Corp.
Panelyte	Laminates	Thiokol Chemical Co.
Papi	Polymethylene, poly-phenyl isocyanate	Upjohn Co.
Paracon	Polyester rubber	Bell Telephone Laboratories
Paracryl	Butadiene-acrylonitrile copolymer	U.S. Rubber Co.
Paradene	Coumarone-indene resins	Neville Chemical Co.
Paraplex	Plasticizers	Rohm & Haas Co.
Parfe	Rayon fiber	Beaunit Mills Corp.
Parlon	Chlorinated rubber	Hercules Corp.
Parylene	Polyxylene	Union Carbide Corp.
Pearlon	Polyethylene film	Visking Corp.
Pee Vee Cee	Rigid polyvinyl chloride	ESB Corp.
Pelaspan	Expandable polystyrene	Dow Chemical Co.
Pentalyn	Abietic acid derivative	Hercules Co., Inc.
Penton	Chlorinated polyether resins	Hercules Co., Inc.
Perbunan N	Butadiene-acrylonitrile copolymers	Farbenfabriken Bayer AG
Percadox	Organic peroxides	Cadet Chemical Corp.
Peregal	Antistatic agents	General Aniline & Film Corp.

Trade or brand name	Product	Manufacturer
Perlon	Polyurethane filament	Farbenfabriken Bayer AG
Permutit	Ion-exchange resin	Permutit Co.
Perspex	Acrylic resins	Imperial Chemical Industries, Ltd.
Petrothene	Polyethylene	National Distillers & Chemical Corp.
Pevalon	Polyvinyl alcohol	May and Baker Ltd.
Phenoxy	Polyhydroxy ether of bisphenol A	Union Carbide Corp.
Philprene	Styrene-butadiene rubber	Phillips Petroleum Co.
Phosgard	Phosphorus compounds	Monsanto Co.
Picco	Hydrocarbon resins	Hercules, Inc.
Piccocumaron	Hydrocarbon resins	Hercules, Inc.
Piccolyte	Terpene polymer resins	Hercules, Inc.
Pip Pip	Rubber accelerator	Generic name
Plaskon	Amino resins	Allied Chemical Corp.
Plastacele	Cellulose acetate flake	E.I. du Pont de Nemours & Co., Inc.
Plastanox	Antioxidant	American Cyanamid Corp.
Plastigel	Liquid thickeners	Plasticolors, Inc.
Plastylene	Polyethylene	Pechiney-Saint-Gobain
Plenco	Phenolic resins	Plastics Engineering Co.
Plexiglas	Acrylic sheets	Rohm & Haas Co.
Pliofilm	Rubber hydrochloride	Goodyear Tire & Rubber Co.
Plioflex	Polyvinyl chloride	Goodyear Tire & Rubber Co.
Pliolite	Cyclized rubber	Goodyear Tire & Rubber Co.
Pliovic	Polyvinyl chloride	Goodyear Tire & Rubber Co.
Pluracol	Polyethers	Wyandotte Chemicals Corp.

Trade or brand name	Product	Manufacturer
Plyfoam	PVC foam	
Plyophen	Phenolic resins	Reichhold Chemicals, Inc.
Pluronic	Block polyether diols	Wyandotte Corp.
Polyallomer	Ethylene block copolymers	Eastman Chemical Products
Poly-eth	Polyethylene	Gulf Oil Corp.
Poly-eze	Ethylene copolymers	Gulf Oil Corp.
Polygard	Stabilizer	Goodyear Tire & Rubber Co.
Polylite	Polyester resins	Reichhold Chemicals, Inc.
Polylumy	Polypropylene	Kohjin Co.
Polymin	Polyethyleneimine	Badische Anilin & Soda-Fabrik AG
Poly-pro	Polypropylene	Gulf Oil Corp.
Polyox	Water soluble resins	Union Carbide Corp.
Polysizer	Polyvinyl alcohol	Showa Highpolymer Co.
Polyviol	Polyvinyl alcohol	Wacker Chemie GmbH
Powminco	Asbestos fibers	Powhatan Mining Co.
PPO	Polyphenylene oxide	Hercules, Inc.
Pro-fax	Polypropylene resins	Hercules Powder Co.
Propathene	Polypropylene	Imperial Chemical Industries, Ltd.
Pyralin	Cellulose nitrate	E.I. du Pont de Nemours & Co., Inc.
Q-Cel	Inorganic hollow microspheres	Philadelphia Quartz Co.
Quadrol	Polyhydroxy amine	Wyandotte Chemicals, Inc.
Ravinil	Polyvinyl chloride	ANIC, S.P.A.
Raybrite	Alpha-cellulose filler	Rayonier, Inc.
Resimene	Urea and melamine resins	Monsanto Co.
Resinol	Polyolefins	Allied Resinous Products, Inc.

Trade or brand name	Product	Manufacturer
Resinox	Phenolic resins	Monsanto Co.
Resistoflex	Polyvinyl alcohol	Resistoflex Corp.
Resloom	Melamine resins	Monsanto Co.
Restirolo	Polystyrene	Societa Italiana Resine
Reynolon	Plastic films	Reynolds Metals Co.
Rezimac	Alkyds	Commercial Solvents Corp.
Rezyl	Alkyd varnish	Sinclair-Koppers Co., Inc.
Rhonite	Resins for textile finishes	Rohm & Haas Co.
Rhoplex	Acrylic emulsions	Rohm & Haas Co.
Riblene	Polyethylene	ANIC, S.p.A.
Rigidex	Polyethylene	BP Chemicals (U.K.) Ltd.
Rigolac	Polyester resins	Showa Highpolymer Co.
Rilsan	Nylon 11	Aquitaine-Organico
Royalite	Thermoplastic sheet material	Uniroyal, Inc.
Roylar	Polyurethanes	Uniroyal Inc.
Rucon	Polyvinyl chloride	Hooker Chemical Corp.
Rucothane	Polyurethanes	Hooker Chemical Corp.
Rulan	Flame-retardant plastic	E.I. du Pont de Nemours & Co., Inc.
Rulon	Flame retardant	E.I. du Pont de Nemours & Co., Inc.
Ryton	Polyphenylene sulfide	Phillips Petroleum Co.
Saflex	Polyvinyl butyral	Monsanto Co.
Safom	Polyurethane foam	Monsanto Co.
Santicizer	Plasticizers	Monsanto Co.
Santocel	Silica aerogel fillers	Monsanto Co.
Santocure	Accelerator	Monsanto Co.

Trade or brand name	Product	Manufacturer
Santoflex	Antioxidants	Monsanto Co.
Santolite	Sulfonamide resin	Monsanto Co.
Santonox	Antioxidant	Monsanto Co.
Saran	Polyvinylidene chloride	Dow Chemical Co.
Scotch	Adhesives	Minnesota Mining & Mfg. Co.
Scotchpak	Polyester film	Minnesota Mining & Mfg. Co.
Scotchweld	Adhesives	Minnesota Mining & Mfg. Co.
Seilon	Thermoplastic sheets	Seiberling Rubber Co.
Selectron	Polyester resins	PPG Corp.
Silastic	Silicone materials	Dow Corning Corp.
Silastomer	Silicones	Midland Silicones Ltd.
Silbon	Rayon paper	Kohjin Co.
Silene	Calcium silicate	PPG Corp.
Silvacon	Lignin extenders and	Weyerhauser Co.
Sirfen	Phenol-formaldehyde resins	Societa Italiana Resine
Sir-pel	Poromeric film	Georgia Bonded Fibers
Sirtene	Polyethylene	Societa Italiana Resine
Solithane	Urethane prepolymers	Thiokol Corp.
Solka-Floc	Alpha-cellulose filler	Brown Co.
Solvar	Polyvinyl acetate	Shawinigan Resins Corp.
Solvic	Polyvinyl chloride	Solvay & Cie
Spandex	Polyurethane filaments	E.I. du Pont de Nemours & Co., Inc.
S-polymers	Butadiene-styrene copolymer	Esso Labs
Spraythane	Urethane resin	Thiokol Chemical Corp.
Staflex	Vinyl plasticizers	Reichhold Chemical, Inc.
Standlite	Phenol-formaldehyde resins	Hitachi Chemical Co.

Trade or brand name	Product	Manufacturer
Starex	Polyvinyl acetate	International Latex & Chemical Corp.
Statex	Carbon black	Columbian Carbon Co.
Structo-Foam	Foamed polystyrene slab	Stauffer Chemical Co.
Strux	Cellular cellulose	Aircraft Specialties
Sty-Grade	Degradable additive for polymers	Bio-Degradable Plastics, Inc.
Stymer	Styrene copolymer	Monsanto Co.
Styrafil	Fiber-glass-reinforced polystyrene	Dart Industries, Inc.
Styraglas	Fiber-glass-reinforced polystyrene	Dart Industries, Inc.
Styrex	Resin	Dow Chemical Co.
Styrocel	Polystyrene (expandable)	Styrene Products Ltd.
Styrofoam	Extruded expanded polystyrene	Dow Chemical Co.
Styron	Polystyrene	Dow Chemical Co.
Sullvac	Acrylonitrile-butadiene-styrene copolymer	O'Sullivan Rubber Corp.
Super Dylan	High-density polyethylene	Arco Polymer Co.
Surlyn	Ionomer resins	E.I. du Pont de Nemours & Co., Inc.
Swedcast	Acrylic sheet	Swedlow, Inc.
Sylgard	Silicone casting resins	Dow Corning Corp.
Sylplast	Urea-formaldehyde resins	Sylvan Plastics, Inc.
Synpro	Metallic stearates	Dart Industries, Inc.
Syntex	Alkyd resins	Celanese Corp.
Synthane	Laminated plastic products	Synthane Corp.
TDI	Tolylene diisocyanate	E.I. du Pont de Nemours & Co., Inc.

Trade or brand name	Product	Manufacturer
Tedlar	Polyvinyl fluorocarbon resins	E.I. du Pont de Nemours & Co., Inc.
Teflon	Fluorocarbon resins	E.I. du Pont de Nemours & Co., Inc.
Teflon FEP	TFE copolymer	E.I. du Pont de Nemours & Co., Inc.
Teflon TFE	Polytetrafluoroethylene	E.I. du Pont de Nemours & Co., Inc.
Teglac	Alkyd coatings	American Cyanamid Co.
Tego	Phenolic resins	Rohm & Haas Co.
Tempra	Rayon fiber	American Enka Corp.
Tempreg	Low-pressure laminate	U.S. Plywood Corp.
Tenamene	Antioxidants	Eastman Kodak Co.
Tenite	Cellulose derivatives	Eastman Kodak Co.
Tenox	Antioxidant	Eastman Chemical Products, Inc.
Teracol	Polyoxytetramethylene glycol	E.I. du Pont de Nemours & Co., Inc.
Terluran	ABS polymers	Badische Anilin & Soda-Fabrik AG
Terylene	Polyester fiber	ICI
Tetran	Tetrafluoroethylene	Pennsalt Chemical Corp.
Tetronic	Polyethers	Wyandotte Chemical Corp.
Texicote	Polyvinyl acetate	Scott Bader Co.
Texileather	Pyroxylin-leather cloth	General Tire & Rubber Co.
Texin	Urethane elastomer	Mobay Chemical Co.
Textolite	Laminated plastic	General Electric Co.
Thermaflow	Reinforced polyesters	Atlas Powder Co.
Thermax	Carbon black	Commercial Solvents Corp.
Thiokol	Polyethylene sulfide	Thiokol Corp.

Trade or brand name	Product	Manufacturer
Thornel	Graphite filaments	Union Carbide Corp.
Thurane	Polyurethane foam	Dow Chemical Co.
Tinuvin	Ultraviolet stabilizers	Geigy Industrial Chemicals, Div., Geigy Chemical Corp.
Ti-Pure	Titanium dioxide pigments	E.I. du Pont de Nemours & Co., Inc.
Titanox	Titanium dioxide pigments	Titanium Pigment Corp.
Topel	Rayon fiber	Courtaulds
TPX	Poly-4-methylpentene-1	Imperial Chemical Industries, Ltd.
Trans-4	trans-1,4-Polybutadiene	Phillips Petroleum Co.
Trem	Viscosity depressant	Nopco Chemical Div., Diamond Shamrock Chemical Co.
Trevarno	Resin-impregnated cloth	Coast Mfg. & Supply Corp.
Trithene	Trifluorochloroethylene	Union Carbide Corp.
Trolen	Polyethylene	Dynamit Nobel AG
Trosiplast	Polyvinyl chloride	Dynamit Nobel AG
Trulon	Polyvinyl chloride resin	Olin Corp.
Tuads	Accelerator	R. T. Vanderbilt Co.
Tusson	Rayon fiber	Beaunit Mills Corp.
Tybrene	ABS polymers	Dow Chemical Co.
Tygon	Vinyl copolymer	U.S. Stoneware Co.
Tylose	Cellulose ethers	Farbwerke Hoechst AG
Tynex	Nylon bristles and filaments	E.I. du Pont de Nemours & Co., Inc.
Tyril	Styrene-acrylonitrile copolymer	Dow Chemical Co.
Tyrin	Chlorinated polyethylene	Dow Chemical Co.
Ucon	Lubricants	Union Carbide Corp.

Trade or brand name	Product	Manufacturer
Udel	Plastic film	Union Carbide Corp.
Uformite	Urea resins	Rohm & Haas Co.
Ultramid	Nylons	Badische Anilin & Soda-Fabrik AG
Ultrathene	Finely divided polyolefins	National Distillers & Chemical Corp.
Ultrapas	Melamine-formaldehyde resins	Dynamit Nobel AG
Ultron	Vinyl film	Monsanto Co.
Ultryl	Polyvinyl chloride	Phillips Petroleum Co.
Unitane	Titanium dioxide	American Cyanamid Co.
Unox	Epoxides	Union Carbide Corp.
Updown	Polychloroprene foam	
Urac	Urea-formaldehyde resins	American Cyanamid Co.
Uscolite	ABS copolymer	U.S. Rubber Co.
Uvex	Cellulose acetate butyrate	Eastman Kodak Co.
Uvinul series	Ultraviolet light absorbers	General Aniline & Film Corp.
Valox	Polybutylene terephthalate	General Electric Co.
Vanstay	Stabilizers	R. T. Vanderbilt Co.
Varcum	Phenolic resins	Reichhold Chemicals, Inc.
Varex	Polyester resins	McClosky Varnish Co.
Vazo	Azobisisobutyronitrile	E.I. du Pont de Nemours & Co., Inc.
Velon	Polyvinyl chloride	Firestone Tire & Rubber Co.
Verel	Modacrylic staple fibers	Eastman Chemical Products, Inc.
Versamid	Polyamide resins	General Mills, Inc.
Vespel	Polymellitimide	E.I. du Pont de Nemours & Co., Inc.

Trade or brand name	Product	Manufacturer
Vestamid	Nylon 12	Chemische Werke Huls AG
Vestolit	Polyvinyl chloride	Chemische Werke Huls AG
Vestyron	Polystyrene	Chemische Werke Huls AG
VGB	Acetaldehyde-aniline accelerator	Uniroyal Corp.
Vibrathane	Polyurethane intermediates	Uniroyal Corp.
Vibrin	Polyester resins	Uniroyal Corp.
Vicara	Protein fiber	Virginia-Carolina Chem. Corp.
Viclan	Polyvinylidene chloride	Imperial Chemical Industries, Ltd.
Vicron	Fine calcium carbonate	Pfizer Minerals, Pigments & Metals
Videne	Polyester film	Goodyear Tire & Rubber Co.
Vinac	Polyvinyl acetate emulsions	Air Reduction Co.
Vinapas	Polyvinyl acetate	Wacker Chemie GmbH
Vinoflex	Polyvinyl chloride	BASF Corp.
Vinol	Polyvinyl alcohol	Air Reduction Co.
Vinsil	Rosin derivative	Hercules, Inc.
Vinylite	Polyvinyl chloride co-vinyl acetate	Union Carbide Corp.
Vinyon	Polyvinyl chloride-co-acrylonitrile	Union Carbide Corp.
Vipla	Polyvinyl chloride	Montecatini Edison S.p.A.
Viscalon	Rayon fiber	American Enka Corp.
Viskon	Nonwoven fabrics	Union Carbide Corp.
Vistanex	Polyisobutylene	Enjay Chemical Co.
Vitel	Polyester resins	Goodyear Tire & Rubber Co.

Trade or brand name	Product	Manufacturer
Vithane	Polyurethanes	Goodyear Tire & Rubber Co.
Viton	Copolymer of vinylidene fluoride and hexafluoro-propylene	E.I. du Pont de Nemours & Co., Inc.
Vulcaprene	Polyurethane	Imperial Chemical Industries, Ltd.
Vulkollan	Urethane elastomer	Mobay Chemical Co.
Vybak	Polyvinyl chloride	Bakelite Xylonite Ltd.
Vycron	Polyester fiber	Beaunit Mills Corp.
Vydax	Release agent	E.I. du Pont de Nemours & Co., Inc.
Vydyne	Nylon resins	Monsanto Co.
Vygen	Polyvinyl chloride	General Tire & Rubber Co.
Vynex	Rigid vinyl sheeting	Nixon-Baldwin Chemicals, Inc.
Vyram	Rigid polyvinyl chloride	Monsanto Co.
Vyrene	Spandex fiber	U.S. Rubber Co.
Webril	Nonwoven fabric	The Kendall Co.
Welvic	Polyvinyl chloride	Imperial Chemical Industries, Ltd.
Whirlclad	Plastic coatings	The Polymer Corp.
Whirlsint	Powdered polymers	The Polymer Corp.
Wing-stay	Alkylated phenol antioxidants	Goodyear Tire & Rubber Co.
Wintrol	Retarders	Stepan Chemical Co.
XT Polymer	Acrylics	American Cyanamid Co.
Xylonite	Cellulose nitrate	B.X. Plastics, Ltd.
Zantrel	Rayon fiber	American Enka Corp.
Zee	Polyethylene wrap	Crown Zellerbach Corp.
Zefran	Acrylic fiber	Dow Chemical Co.

Trade or brand name	Product	Manufacturer
Zelan	Water repellent	E.I. du Pont de Nemours & Co., Inc.
Zelec	Lubricant and release agent	E.I. du Pont de Nemours & Co., Inc.
Zendel	Polyethylene	Union Carbide Corp.
Zerok	Protective coatings	Atlas Minerals & Chemicals Div.,
Zetafax	Polyethylene-co-acrylic acid	Dow Chemical Co.
Zetafin	Polyethylene-co-ethyl acrylate	Dow Chemical Co.
Zytel	Nylon	E.I. du Pont de Nemours & Co., Inc.

Appendix C

Sources of Laboratory Exercises

The Education Committees of the Divisions of Polymer Chemistry and Organic Coatings and Plastics Chemistry strongly advise that laboratory experiences illustrating principles presented in the lecture material be included in introductory courses of polymer chemistry. The extent and type of these laboratory experiences will vary from teacher to teacher and from course to course and may include lecture demonstrations, group experiments, and individual laboratory exercises.

There is no single, dominating, polymer laboratory textbook. A listing of recent books written specifically as laboratory manuals follows. This is followed by a list, divided into several categories, of Journal of Chemical Education articles related to polymers. All exercises should emphasize safety-related aspects and should be performed by the instructor before asking the students to perform them, to minimize problems.

Teachers just beginning to master polymer lecture and laboratory are encouraged initially to emphasize the lecture portion by utilizing simple exercises demonstrating solution of polymers, increase in viscosity of dilute polymer solutions, and the synthesis of a condensation and a vinyl polymer. Help should be available from surrounding chemical industry personnel involved with polymers or from a nearby school employing a person experienced with polymers. Such associations can become mutually beneficial.

Again, the safety and toxicological aspects associated with each exercise must be stressed. Some of the monomers may be quite toxic, but it should be emphasized to students that the resulting polymers are not typically toxic.

LABORATORY MANUALS

1. D. Braun, H. Cherdron, and W. Kern, Techniques of Polymer Synthesis and Characterization, Wiley Interscience, New York, 1972.

2. E. A. Collins, J. Bares, and F. W. Billmeyer, Experiments in Polymer Science, Wiley Interscience, New York, 1973.

3. E. M. McCaffery, Laboratory Preparation for Macromolecular Chemistry, McGraw-Hill, New York, 1970.

4. W. R. Sorenson and T. W. Campbell, Preparative Methods of Polymer Chemistry, 2nd ed., Wiley Interscience, New York, 1968.

JOURNAL OF CHEMICAL EDUCATION ARTICLES

General

1. J. Benson, Viscometric determination of the isoelectronic point of a protein, 40:468 (1963).

2. F. Rodriguez, Simple models for polymer stereochemistry, 45:507 (1968).

3. H. Kaye, Disposable models for the demonstration of configuration and conformation of vinyl polymers, 48:201 (1971).

4. I. Nicholson, Disposable macromolecular model kits, 46:671 (1969).

5. P. H. Mazzocchi, Demonstration-ordered polymers, 50:505 (1973).

6. C. E. Carraher, Polymer models, 47:581 (1970).

7. F. Rodriguez, Demonstrating rubber elasticity, 50:764 (1973).

8. D. Napper, Conformation of macromolecules, 67:305 (1969).

9. D. Smith and J. Raymonda, Polymer molecular weight distribution, 49:577 (1972).

10. F. Billmeyer, P. Geil, and K. van der Weg, Growth and observation of spherulites in polyethylene, 37:460 (1960).

11. P. Morgan, Models for linear polymers, 37:206 (1960).

12. H. Hayman, Models illustrating the helix-coil transition in polypeptides, 41:561 (1964).

13. G. Gorin, Models of the polypeptide α-helix and of protein molecules, 41:44 (1964).

14. H. Pollard, Polyethylene and pipecleaner models of biological polymers, 43:327 (1966).

15. W. Van Doorne, J. Kuipers, and W. Hoekstra, A computer program for the distribution of end-to-end distances in polymer molecules, 53:353 (1976).

16. R. Seymour and G. A. Stahl, Plastics, separation of waste. An experiment in solvent fractionation, 53:653 (1976).

17. T. L. Daines and K. W. Morse, The chemistry involved in the preparation of a paint pigment. An experiment for the freshman laboratory, 53:117 (1976).

18. S. S. Taylor and J. E. Dixon, Affinity chromatography of lactate dehydrogenase. A biochemistry experiment, 55:675 (1978).

19. S. Krause, Macromolecular solutions as an integral part of beginning physical chemistry, 55:174 (1978).

20. G. A. Krulik, Electroless plating of plastics, 55:361 (1978).

21. M. Gorodetsky, Electroplating of polyethylene, 55:66 (1978).

22. W. C. Penker, Recycling disposable plastics for laboratory use, 54:245 (1977).

23. S. D. Daubert and S. F. Sontum, Computer simulation of the determination of amino acid sequences in polypeptides, 54:35 (1977).

24. G. E. Dirreen and B. Z. Shakhashiri, The preparation of polyurethane foam: A lecture demonstration, 54:431 (1977).

25. Optical rotation and the DNA helix-to-coil transition. An undergraduate project, 51:591 (1974).

26. A. Factor, The chemistry of polymer burning and flame retardance, 51:453 (1974).

27. M. B. Hocking and G. W. Rayner Canham, Polyurethane foam demonstrations: The unappreciated toxicity of toluene-2,4-diisocyanate, 51:A580 (1974).

28. R. Har-zri and J. T. Wittes, Calculation of the number of cis-trans isomers in a "symmetric" polyene, 52:545 (1975).

29. G. A. Hiegel, A simple model of an α-helix, 52:231 (1975).

30. B. Morelli and L. Lampugnani, Ion-exchange resins—A simple apparatus, 52:572 (1975).

31. M. E. Mrvosh and K. E. Daugherty, The low cost construction of inorganic polymer models using polyurethane, 52:239 (1975).

32. E. J. Barrett, Biopolymer models of nucleic acids, 56:168 (1979).

33. W. D. Wilson and M. W. Davidson, Isolation and characterization of bacterial DNA: A project-oriented laboratory in physical biochemistry, 56:204 (1979).

34. D. E. Powers, W. C. Harris, and V. F. Kalasinsky, Laboratory automation in the undergraduate curriculum: Determination of polyethylene chain branching by computerized IR methods, 56:128 (1979).

35. R. E. Baudreau, A. Heaney, and D. L. Weller, A sedimentation experiment using a preparative ultracentrifuge, 52:128 (1975).

36. M. W. Davidson and W. D. Wilson, Stand polarity: Antiparalleled molecular interactions in nucleic acids, 52:323 (1975).

37. P. Ander, An introduction to polyelectrolytes via the physical chemistry laboratory, 56:481 (1979).

38. C. E. Carraher, Resistivity measurements, 54:576 (1977).

39. C. Arends, Stress-strain behavior of rubber, 37:41 (1960).

40. C. Carraher, Reaction vessel with stirring and atmosphere controls, 46:314 (1969).

Synthesis

1. A. Silkha, M. Albeck, and M. Frankel, Anionic polymerization of vinyl monomers, 35:345 (1958).

2. P. Ander, Dependence of molecular weight of polystyrene on initiator concentration, 47:233 (1970).

3. D. Armitage, M. Hughes, and A. Sindern, Preparation of "bouncing putty," 50:434 (1973).

4. W. Rose, Preparation of terephthaloyl chloride. Prelude to erzatz nylon, 44:283 (1967).

5. S. Wilen, C. Kemer, and I. Waltcher, Polystyrene—A multistep synthesis, 38:304 (1961).

6. E. Senogles and L. Woolf, Polymerization kinetics. Dead-end radical polymerization, 44:157 (1967).

7. J. Bradbury, Polymerization kinetics and viscometric characterization of polystyrene, 40:465 (1963).

8. W. R. Sorenson, Polymer synthesis in the undergraduate organic laboratory, 42:8 (1965).

9. C. E. Carraher, Synthesis of poly(β-alanine), 55:668 (1978).

10. G. Ceska, Emulsion polymerization and film formation of dispersed polymeric particles, 50:767 (1973).

11. E. McCaffery, Kinetics of condensation polymerization, 46:59 (1969).

12. C. Carraher, Synthesis of furfuryl alcohol and furoic acid, 55:269 (1978).

13. P. Morgan and S. Kwolek, The nylon rope trick, 36:182 (1959).

14. C. E. Carraher, Synthesis of caprolactam and nylon 6, 55:51 (1978).

15. G. R. Pettit and G. R. Pettit, III, Preparation of a polysulfide rubber, 55:472 (1978).

16. A. S. Wilson and V. R. Petersen, Bakelite demonstration: A safer procedure, 55:652 (1978).

17. M. Morcellet, J. Morcellet, M. Delporte, and J. Esterez, Synthesis and characterization of vinyl pyridine styrene copolymers, 55:22 (1978); 54:770 (1977).

18. J. Siberman and R. Silberman, Synthesis of stabilized semi-crystalline polymer foam, 55:797 (1978).

19. R. J. Mazza, Free radical polymerization of styrene. A radiotracer experiment, 52:476 (1975).

20. D. E. Kranbuehl, T. V. Harris, A. K. Howe, and D. W. Thompson, Organometallic catalyzed synthesis and characterization of polyethylene. An advanced laboratory experiment, 52:261 (1975).

Reactions of and on Polymers

1. W. F. Berkowitz, Acid hydrolysis of nylon 66, 47:536 (1970).

2. C. E. Carraher, Generation of poly(vinyl alcohol) and arrangement of structural units, 55:473 (1978).

3. J. Vinson, Hydrolysis of latex paint in dimethyl sulfoxide, 46:877 (1969).

4. D. N. Buchanan and R. W. Kleinman, Peptide hydrolysis and amino acid analysis. A first year organic or biochemistry experiment, 53:255 (1976).

5. D. Blackman, Acid-catalyzed hydrolysis of starch, 55:722 (1978).

6. J. H. Ross, Polymer crosslinking and gel formation without heating, 54:110 (1977).

7. K. Rungruangsak and B. Panijpan, The mechanism of action of salivary amylase, 56:423 (1979).

8. N. S. Allen and J. F. McKellar, Polymer photooxidation: An experiment to demonstrate the effect of additives, 56:273 (1979).

Appendix D

Syllabus

Three interrelated questions can be addressed when considering the construction of course syllabi. These questions are (a) topics to be covered, (b) order in which these topics should be covered, and (c) proportion of time spent on each topic. Just as with other areas of chemistry such as general and organic chemistry, there exists a healthy variety of topics, extent of coverage of each topic, and a certain order to follow.

The problem with respect to polymer science is compounded in that there exists a wide variety of introductory polymer courses with respect to duration. Typically the duration of such courses fall within the range of 30 to 90 hours of lecture (1 quarter to 2 semesters—3 hours credit) with 45 hours being the most common length.

One major assumption agreed upon by most academic and industrial polymer scientists and associated education committees is that there should be both a core of material common to introductory courses and a portion of optional material reflecting individual interests of teachers, student bodies, and local preferences and circumstances. (For instance, if a student population within an introductory course is largely premedicine, then topics related to natural polymers might be emphasized, while student populations high in material sciences and engineering might consider greater emphasis of polymer rheology and dynamics.) This assumption was utilized in the generation of the first ACS Standardized Examination in Polymer Chemistry (1978) and is continuing to be utilized in deliberations made by the Joint Committee on Polymer Education.

The Polymer Syllabus Committee developed a proposal listing broad topic areas and general proportion of time to be devoted to each topic area. This listing is given below along with associated chapters present in the present text for ready identification.

Topics	Amount of course time (%)	Chapter
Major topics		
Introduction	5	1
Morphology	10	2
Stereochemistry		
Molecular interactions		
Crystallinity		
Molecular Weights	10	3,4
Average molecular weight		
Fractionation of polydisperse systems		
Characterization techniques		
Testing and Characterization of Polymers	10	5
Structure-property relationships		
Physical tests		
Instrumental characterizations		
Step Reaction Polymerizations	10	7
Kinetics		
Polymers produced by step polymerizations		
Chain Reaction Polymerization	10	8,9
Kinetics of ionic chain reaction polymerization		
Kinetics of free radical chain reaction polymerization		
Polymers produced by chain reaction polymerization		
Copolymerization	10	10
Kinetics		
Types of copolymers		
Polymer blends		
Principal copolymers		
Optional topics	35	
Rheology (Flow Properties-Viscoelasticity)		3
Solubility		3

Topics	Amount of course time (%)	Chapter
Natural and Biomedical Polymers		6
Additives Fillers Plasticizers Stabilizers Flame retardants Colorants		7,13
Reactions of Polymers		14
Synthesis of Polymer Reactants		15
Polymer Technology Plastics Elastomers Fibers Coatings and adhesives		14

Basically, the Syllabus Committee has proposed that all lecture courses should include portions of the first seven topics with the level and extent of coverage guided by such factors as available class time, additional topics covered, interest of instructor, student interests, class composition, etc.

It must be emphasized that the "Optional Topics" listed are not to be considered limiting and that additional topics can be introduced, again dependent on factors such as available time.

The Syllabus Committee, and other committees derived from the Joint Polymer Education Committee, have considered the question of order of topics concluding that almost any order of topics is possible, used and practical in given situations—i.e., the decision was made not to agree on a given order of topic introduction. The present text is written to permit the various chapters to be considered in almost any order without significant loss of teaching and learning effectiveness.

Thus there exists both a freedom in choice of topics, depth of coverage, and order for presentation of topics, as well as some guidelines regarding the important subjects every polymer science teacher must consider.

Index

Underscored numbers give the page on which the complete definition is listed. All other numbers give pages where the entry is mentioned in text.